Fundamentals of
FLUID MECHANICS

Fundamentals of FLUID MECHANICS

ALAN L. PRASUHN

South Dakota State University
Brookings, South Dakota

PRENTICE-HALL, INC., Englewood Cliffs, New Jersey 07632

Library of Congress Cataloging in Publication Data

Prasuhn, Alan L   date
  Fundamentals of fluid mechanics.

  Bibliography: p.
  Includes index.
  1. Fluid mechanics. I. Title.
TA357.P728   620.1'06   79-23205
ISBN 0-13-339507-3

Editorial/production supervision and interior design by
  MARY CARNIS and ALLYSON EVERNGAN
Cover Design: FREDERICK CHARLES LTD.
Manufacturing Buyer: GORDON OSBOURNE

Printed in the United States of America

10 9 8 7 6 5 4 3 2

Prentice-Hall International, Inc., *London*
Prentice-Hall of Australia Pty. Limited, *Sydney*
Prentice-Hall of Canada, Ltd., *Toronto*
Prentice-Hall of India Private Limited, *New Delhi*
Prentice-Hall of Japan, Inc., *Tokyo*
Prentice-Hall of Southeast Asia Pte. Ltd., *Singapore*
Whitehall Books Limited, Wellington, *New Zealand*

Contents

3

Kinematics of Fluid Motion

4

Reynolds' Transport Theorem and Continuity

5

Dynamics of Fluid Motion

9

Flow Past Immersed Bodies : Lift and Drag

283

10

Open-Channel Flow

313

11

Compressible Flow

353

appendix A
Notation, Dimensions, Fluid Properties

appendix B
S.I. Units

appendix C
Geometric Properties

appendix D
Vector Operations

Preface

This book is intended as an introductory textbook for undergraduate students in engineering and the applied sciences. A complete course in calculus including differential equations is assumed. A firm grasp of calculus is necessary for a thorough understanding of a basic mechanics course such as fluid mechanics. The text builds upon this mathematical foundation and every effort has been made to explain the significance of the mathematical equations. However, it is equally important that the student have a clear physical picture of the various types of flow problems under consideration. To this end detailed explanatory material has been included to prevent the mathematics from overshadowing the physical significance of a given flow.

Most undergraduates have had an introduction to vectors by the time they start their third year (and in fact have often used vector approaches in their previous mechanics courses). Thus, vectors have been introduced and used wherever appropriate. However, in most such situations multiple approaches are included and a complete undergraduate course can be structured around the book without any measurable introduction of vectors. An appendix which contains the basic vector definitions and operations is included.

In keeping with the trend toward a complete changeover to S.I. units in the future, the S.I. system is used throughout the book along with the conventional English units. The mix of S.I. and English units is roughly 50/50 in both the illustrative examples and in the problem sets at the end of each chapter. The emphasis in the book is strongly toward developing the ability of the student to work comfortably in either system rather than convert back and forth between the two systems. An appendix has been included to help familiarize the student with the general characteristics of the S.I. system.

The various basic equations formulated for a system which the students have become familiar with in their dynamics courses are transformed to equations appropriate for the control volume approach through the Reynolds transport theorem. These equations—continuity, energy and momentum—are ultimately compared with the similar equations which result from Newtonian Physics. The basic relationships are all followed by a variety of applications illustrated by numerous worked examples.

Approximately two-thirds to three-fourths of the text can be covered during the normal three-unit course. This would include most or all of the first nine chapters plus selected material from the remaining chapters as the instructor sees fit or as is appropriate to the type of engineering students taking the course. It is also possible to alter the order of the material introducing such subjects as compressible flow (Chapter 11) or ideal flow (Chapter 12) earlier in the course. As another alternative, much of the theoretical portion of the first nine chapters can be deleted so that more of the remaining material can be covered leading to a much broader, more practically oriented course.

Generally, problem solving aids, such as the tables to calculate normal depth in an open channel or the compressible flow tables, are not included. It was felt that in the brief encounter the student has with these specialized subjects during an introductory course, the slight amount of extra time required to obtain the solutions is rewarded by a better understanding of what is being calculated.

Fluid mechanics is one of the more difficult undergraduate courses for most students. This thought has been constantly kept in mind during the development of this book. Every attempt has been made to include lucid explanations so that the learning process will be at least fruitful if not altogether pleasant. I would like to take this opportunity to thank the typists who waded through several, not always easy to follow, drafts of the manuscript. I also would like to express my appreciation to my family for their patience and understanding during the writing of the book.

Finally, I would like to acknowledge the immeasurable help of the many engineering students both in California and South Dakota who suffered through some of the early drafts of the book and whose comments and criticisms play a significant role in the final form of the book.

Alan L. Prasuhn
Brookings, South Dakota

Introduction

1–1 INTRODUCTION, DEFINITIONS, AND GENERAL ASSUMPTIONS

The air we breathe, the water we drink, and the blood and other liquids that flow in our bodies demonstrate the close dependence of our lives on various fluids. Not only must these fluids, as well as many others, be present when we need them, but they must be present where we need them with not only satisfactory quality but also sufficient quantity.

Although our many rivers can provide water for agriculture, industry, personal use, navigation, recreation, and power, management and control are required to reap these benefits. Even when managed, rivers can go on a rampage and destroy whole communities built near their banks. It is vital, then, that their flow be understood, controlled where possible, and the damaging effects minimized. Our atmosphere, which supports life on the earth in another sense, supports aircraft in flight and conceivably will support land craft separated from the earth by a cushion of air.

It is these types of considerations involving such a wide range of applications—from the field of medicine to the design of a submarine, from the blowing of wheat through a pipeline to the pouring of molten iron ore—that makes the study of fluid mechanics so important today. Some of the aforementioned subjects are relatively new, others have been around since the dawn of man. In particular, problems involving the maintenance of a water supply have always beset mankind. As man started settling in concentrated areas, the problems started taking on an engineering nature. Historical records are full of early hydraulic works dating back thousands of years in China, Egypt, Greece, and Rome, to mention a few examples. The ruins of many ancient dams, irrigation canals, and aqueducts are still in existence; and a few are still in use!

The development of engineering through the centuries has more often than not been on a trial-and-error basis, and the design relationships that resulted were largely empirical in nature. It has only been during the last century that fluid mechanics developed as an engineering science with a theoretical formulation that could be applied to practical problems. For a thorough presentation of the history leading up to modern fluid mechanics, the reader is referred to the references by Rouse listed at the end of the chapter.

The paragraphs above were designed to give you an idea of the breadth and depth of the subject of fluid mechanics. However, a more rigorous definition is now in order. *Fluid mechanics* is the study of the motion and stresses that result when a fluid has a given set of forces and boundary conditions imposed upon it. A *fluid* is often described as a substance that takes the shape of its container, a gas completely filling the container while a liquid fills only that lower portion which is consistent with its nearly constant volume. As a somewhat more sophisticated definition, we will also take a fluid to be a substance that will begin to deform when a shear force is applied to it and continue to deform as long as force is applied. By way of contrast, a solid will deform a fixed amount under an applied stress and rebound part or all of the way when the force is removed, depending on whether or not the elastic limit was exceeded. A few general assumptions and restrictions need to be made at the beginning. Forces imposed on a fluid may be either *surface forces* (i.e., applied at a particular point, or distributed over a particular surface) or *body forces* (considered to act throughout the body of fluid). Of the latter type only gravity will be considered in this text.

Flow relationships developed in this book will be obtained using the assumption that the fluid is a continuum. Although certain fluid properties will be explained on the basis of molecular considerations, the formulation of the basic relationships is based on a hypothetical continuous fluid, a fluid that can be continually subdivided without thought of a molecular structure. This approach avoids the difficulty of dealing with the complexity of molecular motion itself. Provided that the boundary dimensions of interest in a problem are large relative to the mean free path of the molecules, as is usually the case, the assumption is amply justified.[1]

---

[1] For air at atmospheric pressure, this requires that all open spaces be in excess of approximately 10^{-3} mm.

A final assumption that requires brief mention is that no slip can occur either between the fluid and a boundary or internally in the fluid itself. In other words, the velocity of a fluid at a boundary must be identical to the velocity of the boundary and there may be no velocity discontinuities within the fluid. This is a companion assumption to the continuum model and like the foregoing is amply justified by experience.

1-2 FUNDAMENTAL DIMENSIONS AND BASIC UNITS

The fundamental dimension of length (L) is perhaps the best understood of the various dimensions. The distance between two points in space, whether it is the shortest distance, via a straight line, or is one of a large number of curvilinear or irregular routes, is measured in units of length. Commonly, in English units we will use inches, feet, or miles, while SI units of length will include millimeters, centimeters, and meters.[2] The concepts of area and volume involving units of square inches, square feet, or square miles, and cubic inches, cubic feet, or even cubic miles, respectively, in English units, are simply the same fundamental dimension of length to the second and third powers. Although physically hard to visualize, we will involve the length dimension to noninteger powers as in Fig. 1-1, where the liquid velocity discharging from an orifice a distance H below the water surface is proportional to $H^{1/2}$ (or the length dimension of depth to the one-half power).

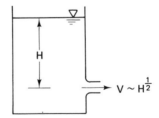

Fig. 1-1. Discharge from an orifice.

As equations are developed throughout the text, they will usually be general and therefore applicable to more than one fluid. This requires that the equations be dimensionally homogeneous; that is, all terms in a given equation must have identical dimensions. In the problem illustrated by Fig. 1-1, we will find that the appropriate equation is

$$H = \frac{V^2}{2g}$$

[2]A discussion of the SI (Système International d'Unités) system is given in Appendix B, as are conversion factors between English and SI units. See also Example 1-2.

The dimensions of the velocity V and the acceleration of gravity g must occur in a combination which results in the same dimensions for the term as that for the depth H. Upon solving for the velocity, its dependence on the square root of H should now be apparent.

The dimensions of time (T), generally expressed in seconds, may be combined with the length scale to give different kinematic[3] quantities. The various velocities and velocity components all have the dimension of length per unit time (L/T), or in usual English units, ft/s, while accelerations are expressed by length/time squared (L/T^2), or, for example, m/s² in SI units. The volume rate of flow, or discharge, is also kinematic and is expressed by volume per unit time (L^3/T). The most common English unit for discharge is the cubic foot per second (cfs). Other terms occurring in the literature equivalent to cfs are the second-foot and the cusec. On occasion other units, such as gallons per minute (gpm), will be employed. The most common SI units for discharge will be cubic meters per second (m³/s), although for low flow rates, liters per unit time may be more convenient. In addition, kinematic mixing coefficients[4] on both the very small or molecular scale and the large or eddy scale will be introduced. These have the dimensions L^2/T, usually ft²/s or m²/s.

The remaining fundamental dimensions are force and mass. The units generally employed here will be the pound or newton as the unit of force, and the slug or kilogram as the unit of mass. The four dimensions of length, time, force, and mass are sufficient to describe the mechanics of fluid behavior. However, if thermodynamic effects are coupled with the fluid flow, then temperature would also have to be included as a fundamental dimension. The four dimensions do not exist independently but are related through Newton's second law; consequently, only three dimensions can be considered to be independent. This may be seen by writing Newton's second law,

$$F = Ma \tag{1-1}$$

in the fundamental dimensions

$$F \sim M\frac{L}{T^2}$$

If the proportional symbol is replaced by an equality sign and the mass, length, and time units specified, this becomes the defining equation for the force. Specifically, if the slug, foot, and second are selected, we have immediately

$$1\ lb = 1\ slug\text{-}ft/s^2$$

Alternatively, if the pound, foot, and second are specified, the companion

---

[3] *Kinematics* refers to the description of motion irrespective of force and mass.
[4] The kinematic viscosity v (defined in Section 1-3) and the kinematic eddy viscosity ϵ (which is not defined until Section 7-3) are quantities that measure not only the intensity of mixing but also the resistance to flow.

equation,

$$M = \frac{FT^2}{L}$$

becomes the defining equation for mass:

$$1 \text{ slug} = 1\frac{\text{lb-s}^2}{\text{ft}}$$

Similarly, if as basic units, the kilogram, meter, and second are chosen,

$$1 \text{ newton} = 1 \text{ kilogram meter/second}^2$$

As a result of these considerations, the dynamic variables of mechanics may be expressed in alternative dimensions. Consider either the fluid pressure or a shear stress. Both are usually expressed as a force per unit area (F/L^2) or pounds per square foot in English units. They can also be obtained in mass, length, and time units through the equality of dimensions given above. The resulting dimensions are M/LT^2, or slugs/ft-s^2 in English units. Other quantities, such as the dynamic viscosity, to be introduced later, can be expressed equally well with either set of dimensions. In the F, L, and T system the English viscosity units are pound-seconds/square foot, while in the M, L, and T system the viscosity units become slugs/foot-second. The fundamental dimensions in both systems, the most common units, and the appropriate symbol for most variables used in the text are given in Table A-I of Appendix A.

EXAMPLE 1-1

A relatively famous relation which will be developed in a later chapter is the *Bernoulli equation*. The equation states that the sum of three terms must remain constant. This may be written as

$$y + \frac{p}{\gamma} + \frac{V^2}{2g} = C$$

where y is the elevation, p the pressure, γ the specific weight, V the velocity, g the acceleration of gravity, and C the Bernoulli constant. With reference to Table A-1, show that the equation is dimensionally homogeneous and determine the dimensions of the constant C.

SOLUTION:

Using FLT dimensions from Table A-1, we find that the symbols have the following dimensions:

y	L (length)
p	F/L^2 (force/length^2)
γ	F/L^3
V	L/T
g	L/T^2

Hence, the relationship may be written

$$y + \frac{p}{\gamma} + \frac{V^2}{2g} = C$$

$$L \quad \frac{F}{L^2}\frac{L^3}{F} \quad \left(\frac{L}{T}\right)^2\frac{T^2}{L}$$

and upon simplifying, each term has as dimensions length only. The equation is thereby dimensionally homogeneous, and the C must have the dimension length as well.

EXAMPLE 1-2

Convert the following quantities, given in English and SI units, into respective SI and English units: (a) $\rho = 1.94$ slugs/ft^3; (b) $\gamma = 9800$ N/m^3; (c) $\nu = 1.2 \times 10^{-4}$ ft^2/s; (d) 100 kN/m^2.

SOLUTION:

Using the conversion factors from Appendix B:

(a) $\rho = 1.94$ slugs/ft$^3 = (1.94)(515.38) = 999.8$ kg/m^3.

(b) $\gamma = 9800$ N/m$^3 = (9800)\left(\frac{1}{157.09}\right) = 62.38$ lb/ft^3.

(c) $\nu = 1.2 \times 10^{-4}$ ft^2/s $= (1.2 \times 10^{-4})(0.0929) = 1.11 \times 10^{-5}$ m^2/s.

(d) 100 kN/m$^2 = 100{,}000$ N/m$^2 = (100{,}000)\left(\frac{1}{6894.8}\right) = 14.50$ psi.

1–3 FLUID PROPERTIES

Fluid properties are those characteristics common to all fluids, which make it possible for general kinematic and dynamic relationships to be developed for an unspecified fluid and then applied directly to any given fluid. Although the magnitude of these properties, and consequently the resulting flows, differ greatly from fluid to fluid, the necessity of developing separate analyses for each fluid is thus eliminated. In each case, the properties will also be seen to vary to a greater or lesser degree with temperature and pressure. The fluid properties to be considered here are density, specific weight, viscosity, vapor pressure, surface tension, and elasticity. In the remainder of this section, each of these properties will be examined and their general effect on fluid flow discussed.

Density

The characteristic of a fluid most directly related to Newton's law (Eq. 1-1) is its mass. The mass of a quantity of any substance is a constant proportional to the number of molecules contained in the volume and the molecular weight of the molecules. This is true whether the substance is a solid, a liquid, or a gas. However, the relationship is simplified for a gas because the almost complete absence of attractive force between molecules results in Avogadro's law. This principle from physics states that for an identical pressure and temperature all gases have the same number of molecules per unit volume. Thus, the mass of different gases depends entirely on the molecular weight.

In dealing with the analysis of fluid motion, a fixed (in space) arbitrary volume is often defined and the flow studied as it passes through this particular region. Thus, it is not a fixed volume of fluid that is identified and followed. Consequently, it will be more convenient to consider the mass per unit volume of fluid rather than the mass itself. The mass per unit volume is defined as the mass density or more simply the density. The usual notation is the Greek lowercase letter rho, ρ. Its fundamental dimensions as well as typical units are given in Table A-I of Appendix A. The density of various fluids is given in Tables A-II through A-V. The density of liquids is only slightly dependent on either temperature or pressure and the variation can generally be ignored. The density of water, for example, will be used almost exclusively throughout the books as 1.94 slugs/ft³ or 1000 kg/m³. Exceptions to the assumption of constant density in a liquid are the very rapid stopping of liquid flow in a pipe where the compressive waves, referred to as *water hammer*, are rapidly transmitted through the liquid; and the variation in density that must be considered if great depths of liquid, such as occurs in the ocean, are involved. The density of a gas, on the other hand, varies significantly with both temperature and pressure. The density of air as it varies with temperature is tabulated in Table A-IV for conditions at atmospheric pressure. The effect of pressure on the density of a gas will be discussed later in this section.

The density, with its obvious relationship to mass, may be expected to be of importance, referring again to Eq. 1-1, in flows that involve acceleration of the fluid. In other words, the inertia of the fluid, which is proportional to its density, will directly affect the magnitude of the forces required to accelerate the fluid. In addition, since the basic momentum principle of dynamics also stems from Newton's law, it can be anticipated that flows involving momentum exchange will be dependent on the density as well.

Specific Weight

The specific weight, γ (Greek lowercase gamma), similarly to the density, is defined on a unit volume basis. Thus, the specific weight is the fluid weight per unit volume. Whereas the mass measures the quantity of fluid, the weight is a measure of the earth's attraction for the fluid. Consequently, for flows in the vicinity of the surface of the earth the mass and weight are related by the nearly constant gravitational acceleration g, which may be taken as 32.2 ft/s² or 9.81 m/s² for most practical problems. Since the weight of a body equals its mass times the acceleration of gravity, it follows directly that on a unit weight basis

$$\gamma = \rho g \tag{1-2}$$

The term *specific gravity*, often used in conjunction with fluids, is the ratio of the specific weight of a fluid to that of water. In the strictest sense the density of water must be taken at some specified temperature. The usual reference temperature is 4°C, at which temperature water has its greatest density. In many applications, however, this degree of accuracy is unnecessary. From the foregoing it follows that

$$\text{sp. gr.}_{\text{fluid}} = \frac{\gamma_{\text{fluid}}}{\gamma_{\text{water}}} = \frac{\rho_{\text{fluid}}}{\rho_{\text{water}}} \tag{1-3}$$

As with density, the specific weight of liquids may quite often be considered constant. The specific weight of gases, on the other hand, is very susceptible to changes in temperature or pressure. These changes can be evaluated using the *perfect gas law* (or *equation of state*) of thermodynamics,

$$p = \gamma RT \tag{1-4}$$

where p = absolute pressure
T = absolute temperature
R = gas constant of the particular gas

For many problems involving real gases this expression is sufficiently accurate, although it is not exact except at the asymptotic conditions of zero pressure or infinite temperature. If p, γ, and T are specified in lb/ft², lb/ft³, and degrees Rankine, respectively, the gas constant has dimensions of ft/°R. The Rankine temperature scale is essentially an absolute Fahrenheit scale with 0°R corresponding to approximately -460°F. If R is multiplied by the molecular weight of the gas, the product is the *universal gas constant* of thermodynamics. In SI units the absolute temperature scale is the Kelvin scale, wherein 0°K is approximately equal to -273°C (Celsius).[5] The gas constant R then has dimensions of m/°K. Selected values of the gas constant R are tabulated with the other properties of gases in Table A-III.

Specific weight, although present as a fluid property at all times, is only important as a factor influencing the flow when the flow is directly affected by gravity. A liquid flowing down an incline, for example, is a direct result of the component of the weight of the liquid parallel to the slope. Surface waves are a second example of flows affected by gravity. Completely contained conduit flow, on the other hand, will be found not to depend on gravitational attraction; the flow inside a pipe flowing full is not dependent on the orientation of the pipe.

---

[5]More accurately, 0°R = -459.6°F and 0°K = -273.15°C.

EXAMPLE 1-3

If a fluid has a specific weight of 9200 N/m³ and the acceleration of gravity is 9.81 m/s², what is the density of the fluid? If the same fluid (at constant temperature) is moved to an elevation where the gravitational acceleration is only 9.805 m/s², what is the effect on the specific weight and density?

SOLUTION:

From Eq. 1-2,

$$\rho = \frac{\gamma}{g} = \frac{9200 \text{ N/m}^3}{9.81 \text{ m/s}^2} = 937.8 \frac{\text{N s}^2}{\text{m}^4}$$

or 937.8 kg/m³ the equivalent dimensions for mass. Since the mass and hence the density are constant, only the specific weight will change with change in gravitational acceleration. Hence,

$$\gamma = \rho g = (937.8)(9.805) = 9195 \text{ N/m}^3$$

EXAMPLE 1-4

If a tank of air is heated from 100°F to 400°F, what will be the effect on its specific weight and pressure? Assume that the volume of the tank does not change with temperature.

SOLUTION:

Since a constant quantity of a fluid is contained in a fixed volume, the specific weight γ must remain unchanged. Therefore, the pressure change can be determined directly from Eq. 1-4, which for constant γR may be written

$$\frac{p_1}{T_1} = \frac{p_2}{T_2}$$

or

$$\frac{p_2}{p_1} = \frac{T_2}{T_1} = \frac{400 + 460}{100 + 460} = 1.54$$

Thus, in this case a fourfold increase in temperature (Fahrenheit scale) results in a 54% increase in pressure.

Viscosity

Viscosity is another property possessed by all fluids to a greater or lesser degree. This property is essentially a measure of the fluid's ability to transmit shear stresses. Although all fluids do not behave similarly in this respect, the following model, involving what is known as simple shear, has been found to represent the behavior of many fluids. The upper of the two parallel boundaries in Fig. 1-2 is moved to the right with a constant velocity V. The plates are separated a distance B by a given fluid, and as the fluid offers a frictional resistance to the motion a force F is required to move the plate. Since no slipping can occur either at a fluid boundary or internally in the fluid, the fluid must remain stationary at the lower plate and move with

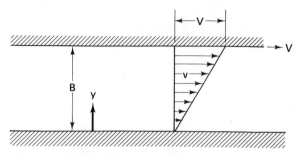

Fig. 1-2. Velocity distribution due to moving boundary.

velocity V at the contact with the upper plate. Between the boundaries the velocity must therefore vary in a continuous fashion. By experiment the velocity distribution is found to be linear, with

$$v = \frac{yV}{B}$$

or

$$\frac{dv}{dy} = \frac{V}{B}$$

Furthermore, it is also found that

$$F \sim \frac{AV}{B}$$

where A is the surface area of the upper boundary. The shear force F per unit area may be defined as a shearing stress τ (Greek lowercase tau), so that

$$\tau = \frac{F}{A}$$

and

$$\tau \sim \frac{dv}{dy}$$

The constant of proportionality in the expression above is defined as the *dynamic* (or sometimes *absolute*) *viscosity* μ (Greek lowercase mu). Consequently,

$$\mu = \frac{\tau}{dv/dy} \qquad \left(\frac{F/L^2}{L/TL} = \frac{FT}{L^2}\right) \tag{1-5}$$

Equation 1-5 is taken as the definition of dynamic viscosity. The dimensions for dynamic viscosity may be obtained directly from Eq. 1-5 as FT/L^2, for which the English units are lb-s/ft², while SI units are N·s/m². Additional SI units are the poise, which is equal to 0.1 N·s/m², and the centipoise, which is 10^{-2} poise.[6] Those fluids that fit into the model above, and thus

---

[6]For conversion between systems, 1 lb-s/ft² = 47.88 N·s/m² = 478.8 poise = 47,880 centipoise.

have a viscosity μ = constant as per Eq. 1-5, are referred to as *Newtonian fluids*. This relationship is shown in Fig. 1-3, which includes Newtonian fluids as well as a possible non-Newtonian fluid (as the other curve is labeled).

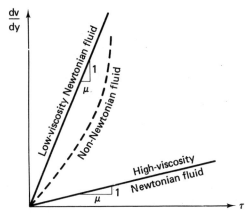

Fig. 1-3.   Shear-deformation relationship for different viscosity fluids.

Most of the fluids frequently encountered in engineering problems (water, oil, and air as three examples) are Newtonian, fortunately; while such substances as blood, paint, and sewage sludge are non-Newtonian. Only Newtonian fluids will be considered further in this text; however, references to non-Newtonian fluid mechanics are given at the end of the chapter. Values of dynamic viscosity are given as a function of temperature for various gases and liquids in Fig. A-1 in Appendix A. Except for extreme pressures, the dynamic viscosity of Newtonian fluids has been found to be independent of the pressure.

An inspection of Fig. A-1 indicates that as the temperature increases the viscosity of gases increases, whereas the viscosity of liquids decreases. This is significant because it is consistent with the explanation of viscosity on a molecular basis. In liquids the molecules are packed relatively close together and the molecular attraction is high between the molecules (but not as high as it is in solids). Therefore, the magnitude of the viscosity depends to a large extent on the cohesive attraction between the molecules of the liquid in question. Thus, increasing the temperature weakens the cohesive bonds and the viscosity drops. Gas molecules, on the other hand, are much farther apart and cohesive forces are correspondingly low. Therefore, as indicated on Fig. A-1, the dynamic viscosity of gases is far less than that of liquids. This relatively low viscosity is primarily due to the random motion of the individual molecules. The collisions that result from this random motion tend to retard the flow. Thus, as the temperature increases, the molecular activity, which also increases, results in a higher viscosity.

In the formulation of the equations of fluid dynamics, the ratio of dynamic viscosity to density frequently occurs. This combination, because it involves only length and time dimensions, is defined as the *kinematic viscosity* v (Greek lowercase nu).

$$v = \frac{\mu}{\rho} \tag{1-6}$$

The fundamental dimensions for kinematic viscosity are L^2/T, and hence English units are ft²/s while SI units are m²/s. The stoke, which equals 10^{-4} m²/s, and the centistoke, equivalent to 10^{-2} stoke, are also used.[7] Although the dynamic viscosity of gases is much less than that of liquids, the kinematic viscosity of gases is (perhaps surprisingly) higher than that of many liquids. This is, of course, due to the relatively low density associated with gases. For convenience the kinematic viscosities of common gases and liquids are also given in Appendix A (Fig. A-2). Since the density of gases varies with pressure, the Appendix values of kinematic viscosity of gases are only valid for atmospheric pressure, however.

EXAMPLE 1-5

A thin, 1-mm-thick plate is pulled between two stationary plates which are separated by a gap of 2 mm. The moving plate has an area of 0.2 m by 2.0 m and is equidistant between the nonmoving plates. The gap is filled with SAE 30 oil at 90°C. What force is required to pull the plate at 1 m/s?

SOLUTION:

A temperature of 90°C corresponds to $(90)(1.8) + 32 = 194$°F and from Fig. A-1, $\mu = 3.1 \times 10^{-4}$ lb-s/ft². From the conversion factor at the bottom of Fig. A-1,

$$\mu = (3.1 \times 10^{-4} \text{ lb-s/ft}^2)\left(47.88 \ \frac{\text{N·s/m}^2}{\text{lb-s/ft}^2}\right) = 1.48 \times 10^{-2} \text{ N·s/m}^2$$

The gap between the moving plate and either side is 0.5 mm. Also note that shear develops on both sides of the moving plate and hence an area of

$$(2)(0.2 \text{ m})(2.0 \text{ m}) = 0.8 \text{ m}^2$$

must be used. Then from Eq. 1-5, with τ replaced by F/A and the velocity gradient replaced by V/B, where B equals the thickness of the gap, we get

$$F = \frac{\mu A V}{B}$$

$$= \frac{(1.48 \times 10^{-2} \text{ N·s/m}^2)(0.8 \text{ m}^2)(1 \text{ m/s})}{0.0005 \text{ m}}$$

$$= 23.68 \text{ N}$$

---

[7]English to SI conversion is given by 1 ft²/s $= 9.29 \times 10^{-2}$ m²/s $= 929$ stokes $= 92,900$ centistokes.

Vapor Pressure

The *vapor pressure p_v* of a liquid is the (generally small) pressure at which the liquid vaporizes or boils as it changes from the liquid to the gaseous or vapor state. The vapor pressure is strongly dependent on temperature, and although water boils at atmospheric pressure (about 14.7 psi absolute) when the temperature is 212°F, at more normal temperatures water will not boil until its pressure is reduced to a fraction of 1 psi. The vapor pressure of water is given in Table A-V of Appendix A. This property usually has no effect on a fluid flow; however, if a flowing liquid experiences a pressure reduction at any point which lowers the pressure locally to the vapor pressure for that temperature, then this vaporization will take place. In problems involving siphoning, the result of pressure reduction to the vapor point will be to break the siphon and interrupt the flow. In other cases the flow will continue, altered in form, as the phenomenon of cavitation occurs. *Cavitation* is the rapid formation and collapse of small vapor bubbles which are not only disruptive, but are also frequently destructive as well. This subject will be treated more fully in subsequent chapters.

Surface Tension

Another property which only occasionally affects the behavior of a fluid is that called *surface tension σ* (Greek lowercase sigma). An unbalance in molecular attraction, due to a difference in the magnitudes of cohesion and adhesion, occurs at the contact between a liquid and a solid boundary or at the interface between two liquids or a liquid and a gas. The molecules near the interface (or surface) are attracted with a different force by the molecules on the opposite side of the interface than the attractive force between the molecules in the same fluid. This is demonstrated schematically in Fig. 1-4 for the example of water with a *free surface*. (It is, in fact, a water/air interface.) The force imbalance on the surface molecules is indicated by nonsymmetrical force-direction arrows. Although the unbalance of molecular

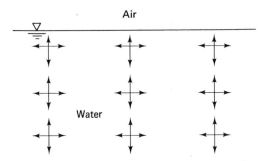

Fig. 1-4. Surface tension due to molecular attraction.

forces will always exist, it is particularly significant when the surface is curved, in which case the imbalance will tend to pull in the surface, thereby increasing the pressure, as will be seen when Fig. 1-5 is considered.

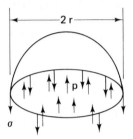

Fig. 1-5. Pressure in a sphere due to surface tension.

The strength of the imbalance is referred to by the not altogether descriptive term "surface tension." It is a function of temperature and is expressed as a force per unit length of the surface (typically lb/ft or N/m). Values of this property are tabulated for common liquids in Tables A-II and A-V.

For the case of a spherical drop of liquid of radius r the pressure inside, p (relative to the ambient outside pressure), can be determined from the force diagram of Fig. 1-5. Summing forces in the vertical direction, the pressure exerts an upward force $p\pi r^2$ over the circular cross-sectional area which is in equilibrium with the downward force around the circumference, $\sigma\pi 2r$ so that when they are equated,

$$p = \frac{2\sigma}{r} \tag{1-7}$$

As a second example, consider the rise of a liquid between the two closely spaced flat plates in Fig. 1-6. The distance h, referred to as the height of capillary rise, results from the equilibrium between the upward force due to the surface tension and the weight of water which has been lifted,

$$\sigma \cos \theta (2L) = hBL\gamma$$

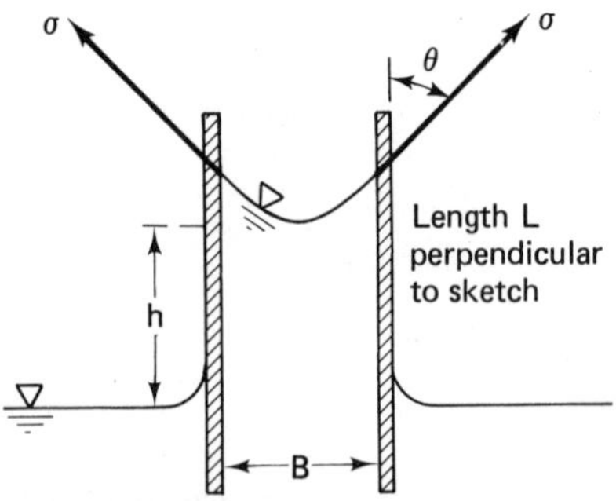

Fig. 1-6. Definition sketch for capillary rise.

This becomes

$$h = \frac{2\sigma \cos \theta}{\gamma B} \tag{1-8}$$

since the surface length L perpendicular to the figure drops out. Capillary rise in a glass tube of radius r results in the similar equation,

$$h = \frac{2\sigma \cos \theta}{\gamma r} \tag{1-9}$$

The angle θ is usually taken as zero for water and $180°$ for mercury. The latter results in a depression of the liquid surface in the confined region. It should be noted that any impurities in the liquid can appreciably alter the value of both θ and σ.

EXAMPLE 1-6

What diameter circular tube would be required to raise water at $70°F$ to a height of 100 ft?

SOLUTION:

Using Eq. 1-9 with $\theta = 0°$ and $\sigma = 0.005$ lb/ft (from Table A-V) gives

$$r = \frac{2\sigma \cos \theta}{\gamma h} = \frac{(2)(0.005)(1)}{(62.3)(100)} = 1.61 \times 10^{-6} \text{ ft}$$

or

$$d = 2r = 3.21 \times 10^{-6} \text{ ft.}$$

Compressibility

The compressibility of a fluid is defined as the ratio of an incremental compressive stress dp to the relative change in volume that results from the incremental stress. This is known as the *modulus of compressibility*. Since a relative reduction in volume must be directly proportional to the relative increase in density, the modulus of compressibility may be written

$$E = \frac{dp}{dp/\rho} \tag{1-10}$$

From Eq. 1-10 the modulus of compressibility must have dimensions of force per area. This will usually be expressed in psi or N/m^2. Values of E for water are tabulated as a function of temperature in Table A-V. It is of particular importance to note that although gases are thousands of times as compressible as liquids, the compressibility of neither has any effect on fluid flow if the flow velocity is far enough below the speed of sound in the fluid in question.[8] Since the speed of sound in air and water is approximately 1100 and 4800 ft/s, respectively, a wide range of air flows and most water flows

---

[8]See Chapter 11 for proof of this statement.

may be assumed incompressible. In particular, compressibility effects become important in air flows with speeds over about three-tenths the speed of sound in air. Compressibility effects only become important in liquid flows in problems involving water hammer and more advanced subjects, such as those dealing with sonar.

When dealing with compressibility effects we will have cause to consider two situations. The first is the change in pressure during a process wherein the temperature is held, or otherwise remains, constant. This may occur when the temperature distribution is so controlled externally, perhaps by cooling, that the flow temperature remains constant. This is known as an *isothermal process*. Directly from the perfect gas law (Eq. 1-4),

$$\frac{p}{\gamma} = RT = \text{constant} \qquad (1\text{-}11)$$

If we now substitute this relationship (*Boyle's law*) into our definition equation for compressibility (Eq. 1-10), we have

$$E = \rho \frac{d(\gamma RT)}{d\rho} = \rho \frac{d(\rho g RT)}{d\rho}$$

and since g, R, and T are all constant,

$$E = \rho g RT = \gamma RT$$

Finally, this gives

$$E = p \qquad (1\text{-}12)$$

as the modulus of compressibility of a perfect gas during an isothermal process. The second situation occurs if the pressure changes without heat transfer to or from the gas. This may be due to the insulation of the region of flow or to changes in the flow which occur so rapidly that there is insufficient time for a significant amount of heat transfer. During this type of process, which is known as *adiabatic*,[9] the relationship for a perfect gas is

$$\frac{p}{\gamma^k} = \text{constant} \qquad (1\text{-}13)$$

where k, the adiabatic constant, is the ratio of specific heat at constant pressure to the specific heat at constant volume. For air and diatomic gases $k = 1.4$. Other values are listed in Table A-III. If Eq. 1-13 is, in turn, substituted into Eq. 1-10, there results

$$E = kp \qquad (1\text{-}14)$$

which gives the modulus of compressibility of a perfect gas undergoing an adiabatic process.

---

[9]For Eq. 1-13 to be exactly true the process or flow must be both adiabatic and frictionless.

EXAMPLE 1-7

Air at 20°C with a pressure of 10^6 N/m²(abs) undergoes an adiabatic pressure increase to 3×10^6 N/m²(abs). What will be the resulting temperature of the air?

SOLUTION:

First the initial specific weight of the air may be calculated from Eq. 1-4 as follows:

$$\gamma_1 = \frac{p_1}{RT_1} = \frac{10^6 \text{ N/m}^2}{(29.2 \text{ m/°K})(20 + 273°\text{K})} = 116.88 \text{ N/m}^3$$

Since the pressure change is adiabatic, we have, from Eq. 1-13,

$$\frac{p_2}{\gamma_2^k} = \frac{p_1}{\gamma_1^k}$$

where $k = 1.4$ for air. Hence,

$$\gamma_2 = \gamma_1 \left(\frac{p_2}{p_1}\right)^{1/1.4}$$

$$= (116.9 \text{ N/m}^3)\left(\frac{3 \times 10^6 \text{ N/m}^2}{10^6 \text{ N/m}^2}\right)^{1/1.4} = 256.2 \text{ N/m}^2$$

Reverting again to Eq. 1-4, the final temperature is given by

$$T_2 = \frac{p_2}{\gamma_2 R} = \frac{3 \times 10^6}{(256.2)(29.2)} = 401°\text{K} = 128°\text{C}$$

PROBLEMS

Sec. 1-2

Refer to the list of symbols in Table A-1 for Problems 1-1 through 1-8.

1-1. Determine the dimensions of each of the following terms in both the *FLT* and *MLT* systems:
  (a) $V^2/2g$ (b) p/γ (c) $\rho V^2/2$ (d) γy

1-2. Determine the dimensions of each of the following terms in both the *FLT* and *MLT* systems:
  (a) dp/dx (b) $\partial\tau/\partial y$ (c) $\rho Q V$ (d) $\rho V^2 Q$

1-3. Determine the dimensions of each of the following terms in both the *FLT* and *MLT* systems:
  (a) $\Delta p/\rho V^2$ (b) $V/\sqrt{gy}$ (c) $V y \rho/\mu$ (d) $V/\sqrt{\sigma/\rho y}$

1-4. Determine the dimensions of each of the following:
  (a) V^2/gy (b) $V/\sqrt{E/\rho}$
  (c) $\rho V^2 y/\sigma$ (d) $(V y \rho/\mu)(V/\sqrt{gy})^2$

1-5. What are the dimensions of the constant C in the open-channel equation where V is the velocity, R the hydraulic radius, and S the slope?

$$V = C\sqrt{RS}$$

1-6. What are the dimensions of the constant f in the resistance equation where h_ℓ is the head loss over a length, L, D is the pipe diameter, V is the average velocity, and g is the acceleration of gravity?

$$h_\ell = f\frac{L}{D}\frac{V^2}{2g}$$

1-7. Assuming dimensionless constants (C, f) and numerical values, which of the following equations are dimensionally homogeneous? (R is the hydraulic radius.)

(a) $V = CH^{1/2}$

(b) $V = \dfrac{1.49}{n}R^{2/3}S^{1/2}$

(c) $V = C\sqrt{RS}$

(d) $h_\ell = f\dfrac{L}{D}\dfrac{V^2}{2g}$

(e) $\dfrac{\partial \tau}{\partial y} = \dfrac{\partial p}{\partial x}$

(f) $\tau = \mu\dfrac{\partial V}{\partial y}$

1-8. Which of the following equations are dimensionally homogeneous? The constant C is dimensionless and R is the hydraulic radius.

(a) $F = \rho Q(V_2 - V_1)$

(b) $F = CA\rho V^2/2$

(c) $\tau = \gamma RS$

(d) $V = 1.32CR^{0.63}S^{0.54}$

Sec. 1-3

1-9. Determine the density of a fluid with a specific weight of 60.5 lb/ft³.

1-10. If the density of a gas is 0.0024 slug/ft³, what is its specific weight?

1-11. Determine the density of a fluid with a specific weight of 9500 N/m³.

1-12. Convert the specific weight of water at 50°F from Table A-V to SI units of N/m³.

1-13. Convert the density of air at 70°F from Table A-IV to SI units, kg/m³ and g/cm³.

1-14. Air is compressed in a 10-ft³ tank to a pressure of 114.7 psi absolute. What will be the specific weight of the air if the temperature is 100°F?

1-15. If the tank of Prob. 1-14 is subsequently heated to 500°F, what will be the resultant air pressure in the tank?

1-16. Air is compressed in a 5-m³ tank to a pressure of 6.5×10^5 Pa (absolute). What will be the specific weight of the air if the temperature is 40°C?

1-17. If a liquid with specific gravity of 0.85 has a dynamic viscosity of 6×10^{-5} lb-s/ft², what is its kinematic viscosity?

1-18. If a liquid with specific gravity of 0.85 has a dynamic viscosity of 2.87×10^{-3} N·s/m², what is the kinematic viscosity?

1-19. What is the kinematic viscosity ν of a fluid having a dynamic viscosity of 2.25×10^{-5} lb-s/ft² and a density of 1.69 slugs/ft³? Express the answer in both SI and English units.

1-20. From the dimensions for μ and ρ in Eq. 1-6, show that ν has dimensions L^2/T.

1-21. If the moving plate of Fig. 1-2 has a surface area of 2 ft², what viscosity μ is indicated by a velocity $V = 10$ ft/s if the gap $B = 0.1$ in., and the required force is 1.2 lb? If the fluid is SAE 10 oil, what is its temperature?

1-22. If the moving plate of Fig. 1-2 has a surface area of 2 m², what viscosity μ is indicated by a velocity $V = 10$ m/s if the gap $B = 0.25$ cm and the required force is 5.3 N?

1-23. Determine the force required to pull a 1-mm-thick plate between two stationary parallel plates separated by a gap of 4 mm. The moving plate is 2 m by 3 m and is located $\frac{1}{2}$ mm from one of the plates. The plate has a velocity of 1.2 m/s and the fluid is glycerin at 25°C.

1-24. What torque is required to rotate a circular disk 1 ft in diameter at 200 rpm when the 1/16-in. gap is filled with 90°F SAE 30 oil?

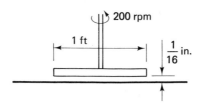

1-25. A circular rod 10 cm in diameter rotates at the rate of 100 rpm inside a 20-cm-long sleeve with a clearance all around of 0.5 mm. What torque is required if the fluid within the gap is (a) air at 20°C; (b) water at 20°C; (c) SAE 30 oil at 20°C?

1-26. What is the atmospheric pressure if water boils (a) at 180°F; (b) at 150°F?

1-27. What is the atmospheric pressure in SI units if water boils (a) at 80°C; (b) at 60°C?

1-28. What is the pressure inside a spherical 60°F water drop if the diameter is (a) 2 mm; (b) 0.2 mm?

1-29. What is the diameter of a spherical water drop at 15°C if the inside pressure is 15.0 N/m²?

1-30. To what height will water at 10°C rise in a glass tube if its diameter is (a) $\frac{1}{2}$ in.; (b) 1 mm; (c) 0.1 mm?

1-31. Derive Eq. 1-9 for the capillary rise in a glass tube of radius r.

1-32. If the density of a liquid is increased 0.02% by a pressure increase of 250 psi, what is its modulus of compressibility?

1-33. What pressure increase is required to increase the density of a liquid by 0.05% if its modulus of compressibility is 1.40×10^{10} N/m²?

1-34. Derive Eq. 1-14.

REFERENCES

BURDON, R., *Surface Tension and the Spreading of Liquids*, 2nd ed. Cambridge: Cambridge University Press, 1949.

Handbook of Chemistry and Physics, 54th ed., Cleveland, Ohio: CRC Press, 1973.

KNAPP, R., J. DAILY, and F. HAMMITT, *Cavitation*. New York: McGraw-Hill, 1970.

METZNER, A., "Flow of Non-Newtonian Fluids," Chapter 7 in *Handbook of Fluid Dynamics*, V. L. Streeter (ed.). New York: McGraw-Hill, 1961.

ROUSE, H., *Hydraulics in the United States, 1776–1976*. Iowa City, Iowa: Iowa Institute of Hydraulic Research, 1976.

ROUSE, H., and S. INCE, *History of Hydraulics*. New York: Dover Publications, 1963.

SHAPIRO, A. H., *Compressible Fluid Flow* (2 vols.). New York: Ronald Press, 1953.

TOKATY, G., *A History and Philosophy of Fluid Mechanics*. London: G. T. Foulis, 1971.

WILKINSON, W. L., *Non-Newtonian Fluids*. New York: Pergamon Press, 1960.

2

Hydrostatics

In this chapter the principles of hydrostatics (fluids at rest) will be developed. It will be shown in Chapters 5 and 7 that the concepts of hydrostatics are a natural outcome of the equations of motion. For the present, however, we will proceed directly from Newton's second law. The first section will discuss fluid pressure and the basic laws of fluids at rest. This will be followed by sections applying these principles to manometers, forces on plane surfaces, forces on curved surfaces, and finally buoyancy and stability of floating bodies. It should be noted that shear stresses (and for that matter shear forces) are not present since they, by Eq. 1-5, must immediately result in a velocity gradient and fluid deformation. This follows, in fact, by the very definition of a fluid in Section 1-1.

2–1 PRINCIPLES OF HYDROSTATICS

Pressure at a Point

It will first be shown that for fluids at rest the pressure at a point is independent of its orientation and therefore a scalar quantity. Consider the finite but small element shown in Fig. 2-1. The z direction, not shown, is normal to the x–y plane. Since the fluid is at rest, only normal stresses and the fluid weight are present and act as shown. Since pressures, and shearing stresses

21

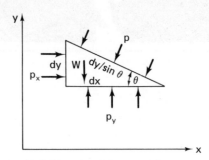

Fig. 2-1. Definition sketch for normal stress at a point.

when they occur, act on the surface, the forces that they give rise to are referred to as *surface forces*. The weight, shown acting vertically downward in Fig. 2-1, acts throughout the volume and consequently is referred to as a *body force*. The differential length of each side is appropriately labeled. The corresponding areas over which the pressures act are obtained by multiplying the appropriate side length shown, by dz the differential length in the z direction.

Applying Eq. 1-1 in the x direction gives

$$p_x \, dy \, dz - \left(p \frac{dy}{\sin \theta} \, dz \right) \sin \theta = 0$$

and immediately $p_x = p$. Selecting a similar element in the y–z plane and summing forces in the z direction would lead directly to $p_z = p$. The equation for the vertical direction, which must also include the weight, is

$$p_y \, dx \, dz - \left(p \frac{dx}{\cos \theta} \, dz \right) \cos \theta - \frac{\gamma \, dx \, dy \, dz}{2} = 0$$

or

$$p_y - p - \frac{\gamma \, dy}{2} = 0$$

If we now let the element shrink to a point, dy becomes infinitesimal and the last term vanishes. Thus, we have established that at a point

$$p = p_x = p_y = p_z$$

or, that the pressure is independent of its orientation.

Pressure Distribution

The pressure variation throughout a fluid at rest can be obtained by again applying Newton's second law to a differential element such as shown in Fig. 2-2. Note that the pressures shown are all compressive. This, by convention, is defined as positive pressure, since tensile stresses in fluids are relatively rare. The pressure on the left-hand face is taken as p. If the rate

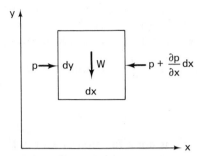

Fig. 2-2. Definition sketch for horizontal pressure variation.

of change of pressure (or pressure gradient) in the x direction is $\partial p/\partial x$, then the total change in pressure between the left face and the right face is the rate of change of pressure times the distance between the two faces, or $(\partial p/\partial x)\,dx$.

Summing forces in the x direction gives

$$p\,dy\,dz - \left(p + \frac{\partial p}{\partial x}\,dx\right) dy\,dz = 0$$

or, upon simplifying,

$$\frac{\partial p}{\partial x} = 0$$

Summing forces in the z direction would give, in a similar manner,

$$\frac{\partial p}{\partial z} = 0$$

The preceding two equations show, respectively, that the pressure does not change in the x and z directions. Thus, the pressure is constant throughout a horizontal plane.

With reference to Fig. 2-3 the vertical direction will now be examined.

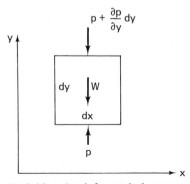

Fig. 2-3. Definition sketch for vertical pressure variation.

Similar to the foregoing procedure, if the pressure on the bottom face is taken as p, the pressure on the top face becomes $p + (\partial p/\partial y)\, dy$. Summing vertical forces and including the weight of the element yields

$$p\, dx\, dz - \left(p + \frac{\partial p}{\partial y}\, dy\right) dx\, dz - \gamma\, dx\, dy\, dz = 0$$

Simplifying,

$$\frac{\partial p}{\partial y} = -\gamma$$

It has been shown that p is not a function of x or z. If it is further assumed that the pressure does not change with time, the relationship may be replaced by the total differential equation,

$$\frac{dp}{dy} = -\gamma \tag{2-1}$$

This equation can now be integrated to give the actual pressure variation in the vertical direction. This will first be done for incompressible fluids, where γ can be treated as constant. This will subsequently be followed by consideration of a variable specific weight as it occurs in the atmosphere.

Incompressible Pressure Variation

If the fluid can be assumed incompressible so that $\gamma = $ constant, this can be integrated to give

$$p + \gamma y = \text{constant} \tag{2-2}$$

This expression defines what is often referred to as the *hydrostatic pressure variation*, in which the pressure increases linearly with decreasing elevation. The constant of integration can be absorbed by integrating Eq. 2-2 between two elevations y_1 and y_2 with corresponding pressures p_1 and p_2 to give

$$p_1 + \gamma y_1 = p_2 + \gamma y_2 \tag{2-3}$$

which again demonstrates the linear decrease in pressure with increasing elevation.

Consider a liquid with a free surface such as that shown in Fig. 2-4. Here point 1 is at an arbitrary depth while point 2 has been located on the surface.

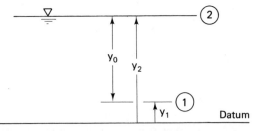

Fig. 2-4. Pressure relative to the surface of a liquid.

At this latter point the pressure must be atmospheric, or zero, as will be discussed shortly. Thus, Eq. 2-3 becomes

$$p_1 = \gamma(y_2 - y_1) = \gamma y_0 \qquad (2\text{-}4)$$

and the pressure is proportional to the depth below the free surface. In other words, the pressure at a point in a stationary liquid is the product of the depth of the point and the specific weight of the fluid. If a free surface does not exist, for example in a closed container completely filled with liquid, Eq. 2-4 can be applied in reverse to determine the position of a line of zero pressure, provided that the actual pressure is known at some point in the container.

The hydrostatic relationships have been derived by assuming a stationary fluid. It will be found, when considering the equations of motion in Chapter 5, that these relationships may also apply, at least as a good approximation in a direction perpendicular to the general flow direction. The only requirement will be that there is no acceleration in the direction perpendicular to the flow.

EXAMPLE 2-1

Calculate the pressure at the bottom of a tank that contains 10 ft of gasoline floating over 1 ft of water.

SOLUTION:

The pressure will increase linearly through the gasoline at a rate based on the specific weight of gasoline. The pressure will continue to increase linearly through the water but at a somewhat greater rate because of the greater specific weight of the water. Thus, the pressure at the bottom of the gasoline, from Eq. 2-4, is

$$p = \gamma_{\text{gas}} y = (42.4 \text{ lb/ft}^3)(10 \text{ ft}) = 424 \text{ lb/ft}^2$$

The pressure at the bottom of the tank is the sum of the pressure at the bottom of the gasoline plus the pressure due to 1 ft of water:

$$p = 424 \text{ lb/ft}^2 + (62.4 \text{ lb/ft}^3)(1 \text{ ft}) = 486 \text{ lb/ft}^2$$

Pressure Scales

The notion of zero pressure introduced with regard to Fig. 2-4 requires some explanation as we commonly define two different zero pressures. Figure 2-5 shows schematically the measurements of various pressures relative to the two "zeros." The first "zero" is absolute zero, the pressure that would be achieved in a perfect vacuum. The second "zero" is the atmospheric pressure. Although the pressure of the atmosphere is variable, the sea-level value at standard conditions of approximately 14.7 psia or 101.3×10^3 N/m^2(abs) [or 101.3 kN/m^2(abs)] may be assumed here.[1] Pressures in pounds

---

[1]The designation of pressures in N/m^2 leads to such large numbers that for convenience the unit "bar" is often used. One bar equals 10^5 N/m^2.

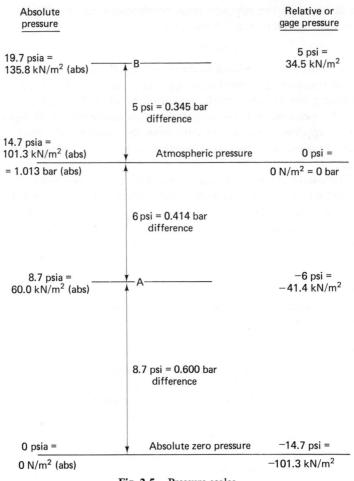

Fig. 2-5.   Pressure scales.

per square inch will be written psia to indicate absolute pressure and simply psi to indicate the more commonly used relative or gage pressure. The notation "abs" will follow the SI units when absolute pressures are intended. Pressures below atmospheric represent a partial vacuum. Point A on Fig. 2-5, for example, has a positive pressure of 8.7 psia, but its gage pressure is -6.0 psi. Point B, on the other hand, has a pressure greater than atmospheric, and consequently both absolute and gage pressures are positive. The term "*gage pressure*" derives from the fact that most pressure-measuring devices, or gages, measure the pressure relative to the local atmospheric pressure.

   Only if the pressure drops below absolute zero pressure is the fluid in tension. This rarely occurs in engineering practice, as the liquid must be exceptionally pure. In nature, however, the capillary force that raises water to heights of 200 to 300 ft in tall trees does create large tensile stresses.

Atmospheric Pressure Variations

The variable specific weight of a gas can usually be ignored when dealing with small, even up to several hundred foot, elevation changes, since the low specific weight results in almost negligible pressure differences. The most notable exception to this is the atmosphere and we can again return to Eq. 2-1:

$$\frac{dp}{dy} = -\gamma \qquad (2\text{-}1)$$

As before, this equation must be integrated in order to obtain the pressure at a specific elevation. However, the specific weight cannot be taken as constant when large differences in atmospheric elevation are involved.

We may make several more or less accurate assumptions to approximate the manner in which the specific weight changes with elevation. It will be assumed first that the temperature does not change with elevation.[2] Then from Eq. 1-11 we have

$$\frac{p}{\gamma} = \frac{p_0}{\gamma_0} = \text{constant}$$

The quantities p_0, γ_0, and T_0 will indicate known quantities at the elevation y_0, the latter frequently taken as sea level. Then from Eq. 2-1,

$$\frac{dp}{dy} = -\gamma = \frac{-p}{p_0/\gamma_0}$$

Separating variables,

$$\frac{dp}{p} = \frac{-dy}{p_0/\gamma_0}$$

and integrating from y_0 to y, we get

$$\frac{p}{p_0} = \exp\left(-\frac{y - y_0}{p_0/\gamma_0}\right) \qquad (2\text{-}5\text{a})$$

or from the perfect gas law (Eq. 1-4),

$$\frac{p}{p_0} = \exp\left(-\frac{y - y_0}{RT_0}\right) \qquad (2\text{-}5\text{b})$$

These equations are most applicable to problems involving limited thicknesses of the atmosphere since a constant temperature was assumed. Remember also in the application of these equations that absolute units of pressure and temperature must be used.

When considering large differences in elevation a more realistic assumption of the temperature variation is required. A nearly linear decrease in

---

[2]Here and in the following, the gravitational acceleration will still be assumed constant.

temperature with elevation gives a good approximation of the temperature in the troposphere, which extends up to about 36,000 ft or 11,000 m. The rate of decrease, or lapse rate, is 3.57°F/1000 ft or 6.51°C/1000 m. Thus, in English units,

$$T = T_0 - 0.00357y \tag{2-6}$$

where T_0 is the temperature in degrees Rankine at sea level ($y = 0$). This time Eq. 2-1 becomes

$$\frac{dp}{dy} = -\gamma = -\frac{p}{RT}$$

and

$$\frac{dp}{p} = \frac{-dy}{R(T_0 - 0.00357y)}$$

When integrated from sea level to the elevation y, the equation becomes

$$\ln\left(\frac{p}{p_0}\right) = \left[\ln\left(\frac{T_0 - 0.00357y}{T_0}\right)\right]\frac{1}{0.00357R}$$

whereupon

$$\frac{p}{p_0} = \left(1 - \frac{0.00357y}{T_0}\right)^{1/0.00357R} \tag{2-7}$$

If we assume what is known as the *standard atmosphere*, where

$$T_0 = 59°F = 519°R$$

and

$$p_0 = 14.7 \text{ psia}$$

then Eq. 2-7 further reduces to

$$\frac{p}{p_0} = (1 - 0.00000688y)^{5.25} \tag{2-8}$$

At the upper limit of the troposphere ($y = 36,000$ ft) the pressure becomes

$$\frac{p}{14.7} = [1 - (0.00000688)(36,000)]^{5.25}$$

or

$$p = 3.30 \text{ psia}$$

The stratosphere, which extends from 36,000 ft to 100,000 ft, has a nearly constant temperature of $-70°F$ or $390°R$. In this region Eqs. 2-5 can be applied directly. Taking the reference conditions as those previously obtained at 36,000 ft, Eq. 2-5b becomes

$$\frac{p}{3.30} = \exp\left[-\frac{y - 36,000}{(53.3)(390)}\right] \tag{2-9}$$

The pressure distribution based on the standard atmosphere (Eqs. 2-8 and 2-9) is plotted on Fig. 2-6 along with curves based on the assumptions of constant specific weight and constant temperature. It should be noted that the standard atmosphere as described herein, is highly idealized. No account

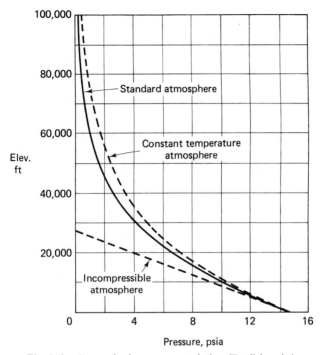

Fig. 2-6. Atmospheric pressure variation (English units).

has been made of naturally varying conditions, and questions concerning atmospheric stability and temperature inversions have not been addressed. Corresponding relationships in SI units are left as an exercise.

EXAMPLE 2-2

Calculate the pressure and density at an elevation of 3000 m. Assume a constant-temperature atmosphere for which sea-level conditions are $T = 20°C$ and $p = 97$ kN/m²(abs).

SOLUTION:

For isothermal conditions, Eq. 2-5b may be applied. For $R = 29.2$ m/°K,

$$\frac{p}{p_0} = \exp\left(-\frac{y - y_0}{RT}\right)$$

becomes

$$\frac{p}{97 \times 10^3 \text{ N/m}^2} = \exp\left[-\frac{3000 \text{ m}}{(29.2 \text{ m/°K})(20 + 273 \text{ °K})}\right]$$

Solving, we obtain $p = 68.3$ kN/m²(abs) at 3000 m. From Eq. 1-4, the density is

$$\rho = \frac{p}{gRT} = \frac{68.3 \times 10^3 \text{ N/m}^2}{(9.81 \text{ m/s}^2)(29.2 \text{ m/°K})(293°K)}$$

$$= 0.814 \text{ kg/m}^3$$

EXAMPLE 2-3

Relative to the standard atmosphere, what is the error in pressure that would result at an elevation of 10,000 ft if a constant specific weight was assumed? If a constant temperature was assumed? Take $T_0 = 59°F$ and $p_0 = 14.7$ psia.

SOLUTION:

In the troposphere we can use Eq. 2-8, which is valid for the standard atmosphere and the temperature and pressure specified. Solving yields

$$p = (14.7)[1 - (0.00000688)(10,000)]^{5.25} = 10.1 \text{ psia}$$

(This may also be read directly from Fig. 2-6.) Assuming a constant specific weight,

$$\gamma = \frac{p}{RT}$$

$$= \frac{(14.7)(144)}{(53.3)(59 + 460)} = 0.0765 \text{ lb/ft}^3$$

(or Table A-IV may be used). From hydrostatics and the assumption of a constant value of γ,

$$p = 14.7 - \frac{(0.0765)(10,000)}{144} = 9.4 \text{ psia}$$

Hence the error in assuming a constant value of γ is

$$\frac{10.1 - 9.4}{10.1}(100) = 6.9\%$$

If a constant temperature (59°F) is assumed, then from Eq. 2-5b,

$$p = (14.7) \exp\left[-\frac{10,000}{(53.3)(59 + 460)}\right] = 10.2 \text{ psia}$$

and the error is

$$\frac{10.2 - 10.1}{10.1}(100) = 1.0\%$$

2–2 PRESSURE MEASUREMENT: MANOMETERS

A number of pressure-measuring devices will be discussed in this section; however, special emphasis will be placed on manometers since they best illustrate the principles developed in the preceding section. Manometers consist of one or more vertical or inclined tubes, usually of glass, which are connected to a pipe or tank in which the pressure is to be measured. By measuring the liquid level or levels in these columns and applying the hydrostatic equations, the desired pressures may be obtained. The procedure may be applied to both liquids and gases (if enclosed) either at rest or in motion, as for example flow in a pipe or channel. The validity of these latter applications will be discussed further after the equations of motion are introduced.

For the present it may be justified physically, since the flow along a pipe has no velocity components and therefore no dynamic effects in the plane perpendicular to the flow. The application of hydrostatic equations to the measurement of pressures will be illustrated by a series of worked examples. In these examples, and in fact throughout the book, fluid properties will be identified by subscripts when more than one fluid is involved. The properties will not be subscripted if there is no ambiguity.

In working manometer problems it is not advisable to identify specific equations with the different manometers. It is better to apply the hydrostatic principles anew in each case. With the equations of Section 2-1 in mind, the basic rules may be stated as follows:

1. Work through the system considering only one fluid at a time.
2. Add pressure differences as you proceed down through a fluid from the starting point (or subtract them when working upward).
3. Move horizontally through a fluid without change in the pressure.

EXAMPLE 2-4

It is desired to determine the pressure at point A for each case in Fig. 2-7.

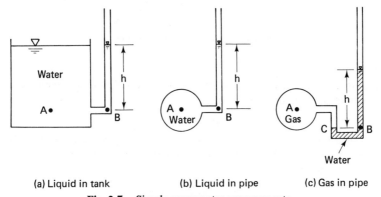

(a) Liquid in tank   (b) Liquid in pipe   (c) Gas in pipe

Fig. 2-7.   Simple manometer arrangements.

SOLUTION:

Note that in each case the manometer column is open to the atmosphere and that the free surface therein is consequently at atmospheric pressure ($p = 0$ psi). Note also that in each case the pressure at point B must be due to the depth of water above it, or

$$p_B = \gamma h$$

by Eq. 2-4. In Fig. 2-7a and b, points A and B lie in the same fluid (water) and at the same elevation. Thus, $P_A = P_B$ and the desired results for these two cases is

$$p_A = \gamma h$$

In Fig. 2-7c, points B and C lie in the same fluid and also are at the same elevation, so that $P_C = P_B$. The specific weight of a gas is so small that although points A and C lie at different elevations, the pressure difference will generally be very small so that $p_A = p_C$, and finally

$$p_A = \gamma h$$

EXAMPLE 2-5

Consider the U-tube manometer of Fig. 2-8. Although it is the water pressure at point A which is to be determined, mercury is used as the manometer fluid. This arrangement might be convenient if the water pressure in the pipe (at A) were very high so that an excessively long column would be required if only water were used as in Fig. 2-7b.

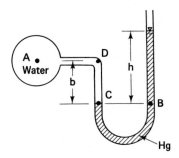

Fig. 2-8.   Two-liquid manometer.

SOLUTION:

Proceeding as before from the free surface in the open column (where again the pressure is zero) to point B, we have

$$p_B = \gamma_{Hg} h$$

which is also the pressure at point C. The pressure at point D, which is also the pressure at point A, will be less than that at point C by the difference in water pressure over a height b. Thus,

$$p_A = \gamma_{Hg} h - \gamma_w b$$

EXAMPLE 2-6

As a final example, determine the difference in pressure between points A and B in separate pipes connected to a differential manometer as shown in Fig. 2-9. The basic manometer fluid is mercury, while a number of different combinations of fluids will be considered in the two pipes.

SOLUTION:

(a) Consider first the situation where both pipes contain a gas. For ease of bookkeeping we will start at point B and work point by point to point A. Assuming that the distance $a + b$ is small, we have $p_C = p_B$. Thus, at D (and E) we have the higher

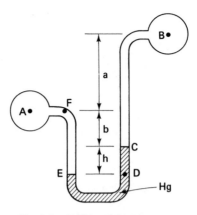

Fig. 2-9. Differential manometer.

pressure

$$p_D = p_B + \gamma_{Hg}h$$

Again, assuming A and E to be at almost the same pressure, we have the result

$$p_A = p_B + \gamma_{Hg}h$$

or as a pressure difference

$$p_A - p_B = \gamma_{Hg}h$$

(b) If both A and B contain water (which also extends in both columns to the interface with the mercury), then in the same way

$$p_C = p_B + \gamma_w(a + b)$$
$$p_D = p_E = p_C + \gamma_{Hg}h$$
$$p_F = p_A = p_E - \gamma_w(h + b)$$

Combining the equations above yields the pressure difference

$$p_A - p_B = \gamma_w a + (\gamma_{Hg} - \gamma_w)h$$

The distance b has dropped from the equation since it represents a balanced column of water on both sides.

(c) Finally, if A is oil (specific weight, γ_{oil}) and B is water, we may again work through the system. This time the reasoning is arranged in a more continuous and compact manner.

$$p_B + \gamma_w(a + b) + \gamma_{Hg}h - \gamma_{oil}(h + b) = p_A$$

or

$$p_A - p_B = \gamma_w a + (\gamma_w - \gamma_{oil})b + (\gamma_{Hg} - \gamma_{oil})h$$

Note that the b dimension now becomes important since it represents unbalanced legs of oil and water.

On occasion one leg of a manometer is replaced by a large reservoir, as shown in Fig. 2-10a. The pressure line, or the high-pressure side if a difference in pressure is to be measured, is then connected to the reservoir. If the reser-

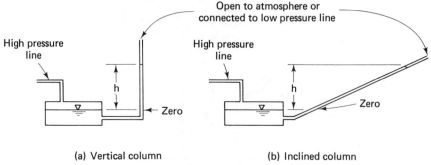

(a) Vertical column   (b) Inclined column

Fig. 2-10. Manometers with reservoirs.

voir is sufficiently large, its deflection can be ignored and the desired pressure
or pressure difference obtained directly from the remaining leg. In any case,
knowing the respective diameters of reservoir and manometer tube, the
depression of the liquid in the reservoir can be considered for higher accuracy.

Often the column of this type of manometer is inclined at an angle (see
Fig. 2-10b) so that relatively small pressures or pressure differences will
give larger deflections. Frequently, in commercial units the graduated scales
not only take into account the effect of the angle of the tube but also com-
pensate for the deflection in the reservoir as well. Rarely are the inclined
columns placed on a slope less than 1 on 12, as it becomes increasingly difficult to read the miniscus.

An additional problem common to all manometers is that capillary action
is present at all free surfaces and interfaces in the manometer. For tubes
with diameters less than $\frac{1}{2}$ in., this effect can become appreciable. When
pressure differences are measured with multiple columns, the capillary effects
usually cancel out, while in other cases the relatively large diameters or large
pressure differences involved make the capillary effects minor. The user must
ensure that one of these situations does occur, or else he must allow for the
resulting errors.

Another pressure-measuring device is the barometer. Since it measures
the atmospheric pressure in absolute units, it is one of the few "absolute"
pressure gages. The mercury barometer consists of a slender tube sealed at
one end, completely filled with mercury, and then inverted in a reservoir of
mercury as shown in Fig. 2-11. The mercury will drop down until the height
of the mercury column above the reservoir surface just balances the atmospheric pressure on that same surface. Since the vapor pressure of mercury
(which is all that remains above the mercury) is exceedingly low (see Table
A-II), a nearly perfect vacuum exists above the mercury column. Thus, the
vapor pressure above the mercury can be ignored and the barometer is
reasonably insensitive to temperature changes.

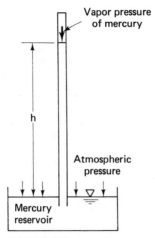

Fig. 2-11. Mercury barometer.

If we equate the height of the mercury column h in inches to the standard atmospheric pressure of 14.7 psia,

$$14.7 = \frac{\gamma_{Hg} h}{(144)(12)}$$

$$h = \frac{(14.7(144)(12)}{845.5} = 30.0 \text{ in.}$$

we get standard atmospheric pressure corresponding to 30.0 in. of mercury.[3] By graduating the tube in inches or millimeters, the atmospheric pressure may be read directly in inches or millimeters of mercury.

In practice, the tube is adjusted vertically until the zero graduation is at the level of the reservoir surface. For precise measurements, corrections must also be made to correct for the different expansion rates of the mercury and glass with temperature.

One type of mechanical pressure gage is the *Bourdon gage*, shown schematically in Fig. 2-12. It is connected to a pipe or tank so that the inside of the curved tube in the gage is at the same pressure level as that which is to be measured. Since the outside of the tube is exposed to the atmosphere, the pressure difference between the inside and the outside of the curved tube is the gage pressure introduced in Section 2-1. As this pressure difference increases, the curved tube tends to straighten, and this is in turn linked to the rotating pointer by a gear mechanism.

The dial is usually calibrated so that positive pressures are read in psi or

---

[3]The standard atmospheric pressure may also be expressed as 33.9 ft of water, 101.3 kN/m² or 763 mm of mercury. These values all correspond to a temperature of 60 to 70°F.

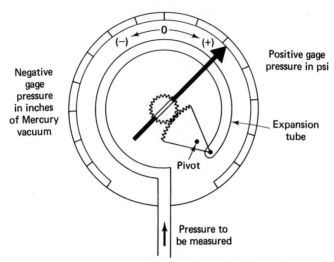

Negative gage pressure in inches of Mercury vacuum

Positive gage pressure in psi

Expansion tube

Pivot

Pressure to be measured

Fig. 2-12.   Bourdon gage (reading in English units).

N/m^2, and negative pressures (i.e., below atmospheric) are read in inches or mm of mercury vacuum. Not all gages will read both positive and negative pressures, however.

A second common type of mechanical pressure gage consists of a *bellows* apparatus. It is provided with tubing connections so that the inside of the bellows connects to one pressure tap and the outside is either open to the atmosphere or connects to a second tap. As the pressure (or difference in pressure) changes, the bellows will expand or contract. A mechanical linkage may be used to convert the bellows movement to a dial reading. Alternatively, electrical transducers are available which will provide an electronic readout of the pressure.

2–3 FORCES ON PLANE SURFACES

In Section 2-1 the variation of pressure throughout a fluid at rest was determined. It is now desired to evaluate the effect of this pressure distribution on areas exposed to the fluid. For the present we shall discuss surfaces in contact with or submerged in liquids; however, in application these may be the walls of a tank, a submerged gate, a ship hull, or any of a large number of engineering structures.

In theory, since the pressure is by definition the normal force per unit area, we can always obtain the force on a surface by integrating the pressure distribution over the surface area. This, on occasion, may be instructive, but it is usually tedious and time consuming. Thus, general procedures will be developed in the next two sections to shortcut the calculations. In this section we will study forces on plane surfaces, and in the next section we will expand the procedures to include forces on curved surfaces. We will concentrate on forces due to liquids, since the nearly constant pressure throughout a gas which is at rest immediately gives

$$F = \int_A p \, dA = pA$$

Forces on horizontal surfaces may also be determined with ease. Since the surface in question is everywhere at the same depth, it is everywhere at constant pressure as well. Thus, we have, once again,

$$F = \int_A p \, dA = pA$$

or

$$F = \gamma h A$$

where h is the distance from the free surface or plane of zero pressure down to the horizontal surface. Although the derivations generally assume that the zero (i.e., atmospheric) pressure surface is a free surface, this is not always the case. If the liquid is completely contained and under sufficient pressure, then there is no plane of zero pressure within the liquid. However, by assuming that liquid of the same specific weight replaces the top of the container to a depth consistent with the pressure against the top, an imaginary free surface can be created. Specifically, if the pressure against the top of the container is p, the imaginary depth given by

$$h = \frac{p}{\gamma}$$

would be required. For purposes of calculation this surface may be treated as the free surface. If a reduced pressure is applied to the closed container, the zero pressure surface will lie in or below the container. This line may still be treated as a free surface; however, liquid above the line will now be at negative (i.e., below atmospheric) pressure.

In order to determine a more general expression for the force on a plane surface, consider the arbitrarily shaped surface of area A shown in Fig. 2-13. This surface is inclined at an angle θ to the free surface. The projection shown is the true shape, that is, the shape seen by an observer looking directly at the face of the surface. Distances measured from the free surface along the incline are indicated by y and vertical distances by h. Distances to the centroid of the area are indicated by an overbar, and the subscript p indicates the distance to the center of pressure, or point of application of the resultant force.

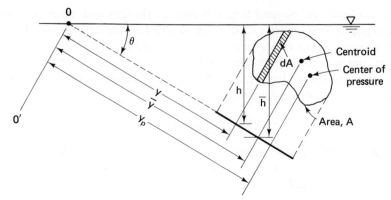

Fig. 2-13. Definition sketch for forces on a plane surface.

The force on the differential area is

$$dF = p \, dA = \gamma h \, dA$$

and the integration over the area gives the total force,

$$F = \int_A \gamma h \, dA = \gamma \sin \theta \int_A y \, dA$$

The quantity $\int_A y \, dA$ represents the first moment of the area about the $O\text{-}O'$ axis, or $\bar{y}A$. Thus,

$$F = \gamma \sin \theta \, \bar{y}A = \gamma \bar{h}A = p_c A \qquad (2\text{-}10)$$

where p_c is the pressure at the centroid.

Since the pressure increases linearly with depth, this resultant force does not act at the centroid of the area, but rather at some point below the centroid defined as the center of pressure. This distance along the incline shown as y_p can be obtained by taking the moment of the force F about the $O\text{-}O'$ axis. Since the moment of the differential force dF about the $O\text{-}O'$ axis is

$$dM = yp \, dA$$

this may be integrated over the area and set equal to $y_p F$.

$$y_p F = \int_A yp \, dA = \gamma \int_A yh \, dA = \gamma \sin \theta \int_A y^2 \, dA$$

The quantity $\int_A y^2 \, dA$ will be recognized as the second moment of the area about the axis $O\text{-}O'$, often referred to as the moment of inertia, I_0. Substituting for the force using Eq. 2-10 and simplifying,

$$y_p = \frac{\gamma \sin \theta \, I_0}{\gamma \sin \theta \, \bar{y}A} = \frac{I_0}{\bar{y}A} \qquad (2\text{-}11)$$

Applying the parallel-axis theorem, which converts the moment of inertia about the centroidal axis to an arbitrary axis, and vice versa, gives

$$y_p = \frac{I_0}{\bar{y}A} = \frac{\bar{I}}{\bar{y}A} + \frac{\bar{y}^2 A}{\bar{y}A} = \frac{\bar{I}}{\bar{y}A} + \bar{y} \qquad (2\text{-}12)$$

where $\bar{I}$ is the moment of inertia about the centroidal axis of the surface.

Summing up, the force on a plane surface submerged in a liquid at rest is equal to the pressure at the centroid of that surface times the surface area. This force acts perpendicular to the surface and can be considered to act below the centroid a distance, measured in the plane of the surface, equal to the ratio of the moment of inertia of the area about its centroidal axis to the first moment of the area about the axis at the intersection of the plane of the surface and the liquid surface. Although the foregoing expressions have all been developed with respect to the free surface of a liquid, they apply equally well to a completely enclosed liquid if the distances are referred to the plane of zero pressure. Obviously, the pressure must be known at some point in the closed container; otherwise, the problem is indeterminate.

EXAMPLE 2-7

Determine the force and point of application of the force on the circular plate covering the hole in the water tank of Fig. 2-14. The depth to the top of the 4-ft-diameter plate is 5 ft.

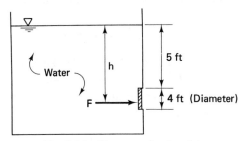

Fig. 2-14. Force on circular plate.

SOLUTION:

The force by Eq. 2-10 is

$$F = \gamma \bar{h} A = (62.4)(5 + 2)(\pi/4)(4^2) = 5489 \text{ lb}$$

Since the moment of inertia of a circle about its diameter is $\pi D^4/64$, the location of the force is given by

$$h = \frac{\bar{I}}{\bar{y}A} + \bar{y}$$

$$= \frac{\pi D^4}{(64)(7)} \frac{4}{\pi D^2} + 7 = 7.14 \text{ ft}$$

EXAMPLE 2-8

Determine the magnitude of the force on the inclined gate shown in Fig. 2-15. The tank of water is completely closed and the pressure gage at the lower corner reads 88,000 N/m².

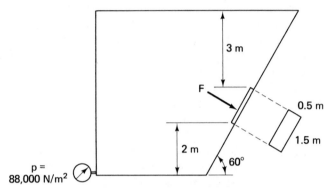

Fig. 2-15. Force in a pressure tank.

SOLUTION:

A pressure of 88,000 N/m² is equivalent to that due to a depth of water of

$$h = \frac{p}{\gamma} = \frac{88,000 \text{ N/m}^2}{9800 \text{ N/m}^3} = 8.98 \text{ m}$$

The line of zero pressure is 8.98 m above the bottom of the tank. Since the centroid of the gate is

$$2 + \frac{(1.5) \sin 60°}{2} = 2.65 \text{ m}$$

above the tank bottom it also lies $8.98 - 2.65 = 6.33$ m below the line of zero pressure. The force on the gate can now be calculated by Eq. 2-10:

$$F = \gamma \bar{h} A = (9800 \text{ N/m}^3)(6.33 \text{ m})(1.5 \text{ m})(0.5 \text{ m})$$
$$= 46,500 \text{ N}$$

Pressure Prisms

The procedures developed thus far for forces on plane surfaces can be supplemented by a simplified approach based on direct integration of the pressure diagram. The linear pressure distribution on the plane surface OA is shown in Fig. 2-16, and the pressure at depth h is identified. The force on surface OA is the integration of the pressure distribution over the area. The differential force acting on dA can be considered as the shaded volume under the pressure diagram or pressure prism. The total force F is therefore the total volume under the pressure diagram. The calculation of this force is readily accomplished when the surface under consideration is rectangular and extends to the free surface. For surfaces of other shapes, the superposi-

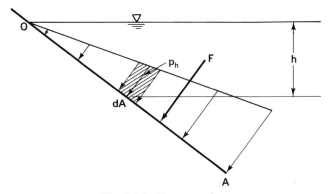

Fig. 2-16. Pressure prism.

tion of the triangular pressure on the more complicated geometric shape of the surface becomes complicated, and the use of Eq. 2-10 is the more attractive approach. The resultant force can be considered to act through the centroid of this same pressure prism. This is easily located at two-thirds of the depth when the surface is rectangular and intersects the free surface, but more generally it is easier to apply Eq. 2-12.

EXAMPLE 2-9

A vertical wall 5 ft wide backs up water to a depth of 8 ft (Fig. 2-17). Determine the force and point of application using the pressure prism and verify the results using Eqs. 2-10 and 2-12.

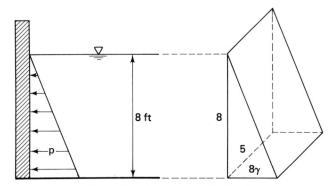

Fig. 2-17. Force on a vertical wall.

SOLUTION:

The surface in question is a 5-ft by 8-ft rectangle. Thus, the pressure prism has dimensions of 8, 5, and 8γ, as shown. The total force is therefore

$$F = (\tfrac{1}{2})(8)(5)(8)(62.4) = 9980 \text{ lb}$$

Since the prism is triangular, its centroid and the point of application of the force must lie one-third of the way up from the base, or at a depth of

$$y_p = (\tfrac{2}{3})(8) = 5.33 \text{ ft}$$

Repeating, we get from Eq. 2-10,

$$F = \gamma \bar{h} A$$

$$= (62.4)(\tfrac{8}{2})(8)(5) = 9980 \text{ lb}$$

and from Eq. 2-12,

$$y_p = \bar{y} + \frac{\bar{I}}{\bar{y}A}$$

$$= 4 + \frac{(5)(8)^3}{(12)(4)(8)(5)} = 5.33 \text{ ft}$$

In summary, if the surface is a rectangle extending to the surface, the pressure prism is triangular and the force and its point of application easily obtained. If the rectangular surface does not extend to the surface as shown in Fig. 2-18, the pressure prism will be trapezoidal in form. The force may still be easily calculated by addition of the rectangular and triangular portions of the prism; however, obtaining the point of application is now a little more difficult, as it requires combining of the separate centroids. In other cases, direct application of the pressure prism is not recommended.

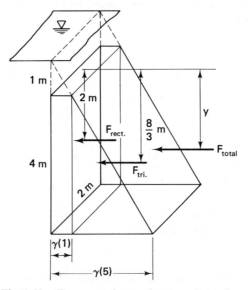

Fig. 2-18. Force on submerged rectangular surface.

EXAMPLE 2-10

Determine the magnitude and location of the force on the vertical 2-m by 4-m rectangular surface shown in Fig. 2-18. Water extends to a height of 1 m above the top of the surface.

SOLUTION:

The pressure prism may be broken into rectangular and triangular portions. Assuming a specific weight for water of 9800 N/m³, the total force, which is the sum of the respective volumes, is

$$F = (4)(2)(9800)(1) + (\tfrac{1}{2})(4)(2)(9800)(4)$$

$$= 78,400 + 156,800 = 235,200 \text{ N}$$

The centroid of the rectangular portion of the prism is halfway, or 2 m, from the top of the vertical surface, while the centroid of the triangular portion is two-thirds of the way from the top, or $\tfrac{8}{3}$ m. Thus, the resultant force is located a distance y below the top of the rectangular surface given by

$$y = \frac{(78,400)(2) + (156,800)(\tfrac{8}{3})}{235,200}$$

$$= 2.44 \text{ m}$$

Therefore, relative to the water surface, the resultant force acts at a depth of 3.44 m.

2-4 FORCES ON CURVED SURFACES

It is possible, as with plane surfaces, to determine forces on curved surfaces by integration of the pressure distribution over the surface. However, it is again advantageous to develop general procedures. This time, however, the horizontal and vertical components of the resultant force will be evaluated separately, rather than simply the resultant force.

Horizontal Force on a Curved Surface

With the aid of Fig. 2-19 the horizontal force F_H on the curved surface AB may be determined. To do this, consider the volume ABC, which consists of the surface AB on one end, and AC the vertical projection of the actual surface AB on the other end. The force on AC is called F'_H. Note that an observer looking in the direction of F'_H will, in fact, see the vertical projection of AB. Since this body must be in equilibrium and F'_H and F_H are the only horizontal forces present, they must be of equal magnitude with an identical line of action. Thus, the horizontal component of the force on a curved surface is equal to the force on the vertical projection of that surface, and may be calculated accordingly. Likewise, calculating the point of application of

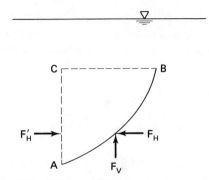

Fig. 2-19. Horizontal force on a curved surface.

the force on the vertical projection also locates the line of action of the horizontal component of the force on the actual surface.

Vertical Force on a Curved Surface

The determination of the vertical force on a curved surface is equally straightforward but is perhaps sometimes harder to visualize. Refer to the series of sketches in Fig. 2-20. In each case it is desired to determine the vertical force on the curved surface AB. Case (a) represents a container filled with liquid as shown. Since there can be no shear force, the side walls can offer no support to the liquid, and equilibrium can exist only if the force AB exerts on the liquid (which is, in turn, equal to the force the liquid exerts on AB) is exactly equal to the weight of the liquid. Because the vertical force is due purely to the weight of liquid above AB, the line of action of the

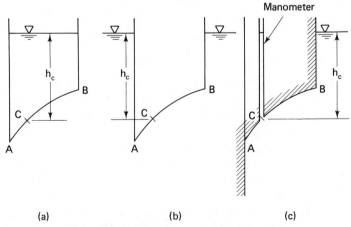

Fig. 2-20. Vertical force on a curved surface.

force must act through the centroid of the liquid volume (i.e., through its center of gravity).

Consider now case (b) of Fig. 2-20, where a similar container, now empty, is submerged to a corresponding depth in the same liquid. If the surface AB is assumed to be of negligible thickness, the pressure distribution on AB will be identical to the pressure distribution on AB of Fig. 2-20(a). This follows since for any arbitrary point C between A and B, the depth of liquid h_c causing the pressure is the same in each case. Thus, the vertical force, which is the integration of the vertical component of the pressure over AB, will be the same in both Fig. 2-20(a) and (b). Since this reasoning must apply to a similar surface AB with liquid both above and below it, equilibrium requires that the vertical force in each case be on a common line of action.

It has been shown that the vertical force on a curved surface is equal to the weight of liquid above it or to the weight of liquid displaced as the case may be. Regardless, the point of application of the force is identical. To further reinforce the concept of a displaced fluid, refer finally to Fig. 2-20(c). Here the surface AB forms part of the outside boundary of the liquid. It is perhaps more difficult to identify the displaced fluid in this type of situation, but again note that the point C is under the same pressure as in the foregoing two situations. We can immediately conclude that the surface AB is exposed to the same vertical force as were the previous two cases and the displaced volume must also be the same. This may also be readily visualized if a manometer column is imagined at the arbitrary point C. Since it is usually easy to identify the height to which the liquid would rise in the column, this device can be used to trace out the displaced volume.

Buoyancy

The foregoing analysis of vertical forces leads directly to the explanation of buoyancy, the famous discovery of Archimedes: the net vertical force on a submerged body is equal to the weight of liquid displaced. Consider Fig. 2-21 and the arbitrary submerged body $ABCD$. The points A and C define the lateral extremities of the body and $ABCFE$ defines the volume of liquid above the body.

Note first that the downward vertical force on ABC must equal the weight of liquid above it, that is, the weight of $ABCFE$. Likewise, the upward vertical force on ADC must be identical to the vertical force on a body defined by the limits $AEFCD$, since in both cases the pressure distribution on the surface ADC must be identical. Thus, the vertical force on ADC is equal to the weight of liquid required to fill the volume $AEFCD$.

The volume $AEFCD$ equals the sum of $AEFCB$ plus $ABCD$. Therefore, the net vertical force on the body due to the liquid, which is the difference between vertical forces on ADC and ABC, is equal to the weight of liquid

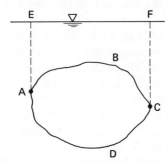

Fig. 2-21. Buoyancy, the principle of Archimedes.

required to fill *ABCD*. Finally, the vertical force on a submerged body is equal to the weight of liquid displaced and is independent of the depth of submergence (provided that the increased pressures at greater depths do not change the volume). In other words, a body submerged in a liquid will lose weight at the rate equal to the weight of liquid displaced.

EXAMPLE 2-11

In Fig. 2-22, determine:
(a) The horizontal force on surface *ABC*.
(b) The location of the horizontal force on *ABC*.
(c) The vertical force on surface *AB*.
(d) The vertical force on surface *BC*.
(e) The net vertical force on the projecting body *ABC*.

   Assume that the container and boundary projection *ABC* are two-dimensional in form and work with a unit length of 1 ft in the direction normal to the sketch.

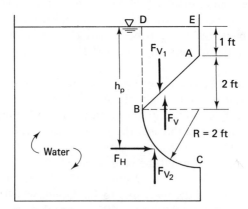

Fig. 2-22. Forces on curved and plane surfaces.

SOLUTION:

(a) The horizontal component of the force on the surface ABC, F_H, is equal to the force on the vertical projection of ABC, a rectangle 4 ft by 1 ft. Using Eq. 2-10,

$$F_H = (62.4)(1 + 2)(4)(1) = 748.8 \text{ lb}$$

(b) Since the moment of inertia of the projected area equals $(1)(4)^3/12$ (ft^4), Eq. 2-12 gives

$$h_p = \frac{(4)^3(1)}{(12)(2 + 1)(4)(1)} + (2 + 1) = 3.44 \text{ ft}$$

(c) The downward vertical force on AB, F_{v_1}, is the weight of the volume of water above AB:

$$F_{V_1} = (62.4)[(1)(2)(1) + (\tfrac{1}{2})(2)(2)(1)] = 249.6 \text{ lb}$$

(d) The upward force on the surface BC, F_{v_2}, will equal the weight of water, which could be contained in the volume $BDEAC$, or

$$F_{V_2} = (62.4)\left[(3)(2)(1) + \left(\frac{\pi}{4}\right)(2)^2(1)\right] = 570.4 \text{ lb}$$

(e) The net force on the volume ABC is equal to the weight of water displaced:

$$F_V = (62.4)\left[(2)(2)(1)(\tfrac{1}{2}) + \left(\frac{\pi}{4}\right)(2)^2(1)\right] = 320.8 \text{ lb}$$

This may also be obtained by taking the difference in vertical forces in parts (c) and (d).

EXAMPLE 2-12

Determine the specific weight of a body consisting of a 30-cm-diameter hemisphere and a 50-cm-long by 30-cm-diameter cylinder which floats, as shown in Fig. 2-23, at an oil (sp. gr. = 0.87)/water interface.

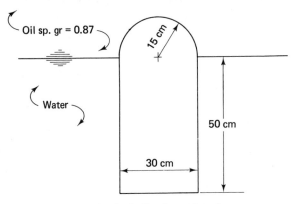

Fig. 2-23. Body floating at interface.

SOLUTION:

The weight of the body must exactly equal the weight of the displaced oil and water. Hence,

$$\left[\frac{\pi}{4}(0.30)^2(0.50) + \frac{\pi}{12}(0.30)^3\right]\gamma_{\text{body}} = \frac{\pi}{4}(0.30)^2(0.50)\gamma_{\text{water}} + \frac{\pi}{12}(0.30)^3\gamma_{\text{oil}}$$

With $\gamma_{\text{water}} = 9800$ N/m^3 and $\gamma_{\text{oil}} = (0.87)(9800) = 8526$ N/m^3, this expression reduces to

$$\gamma_{\text{body}} = 9588 \text{ N/m}^3$$

Stability of Floating Bodies

In addition to the more-or-less straightforward analysis of vertical forces which explain buoyancy, the stability of an object against overturning must frequently be considered. A stable object is one that will either remain in a specified position or, if displaced, return to its initial position. This stability depends upon the relative positions of the center of gravity of the mass of the body and the center of gravity of the displaced fluid, hereafter referred to as the *center of buoyancy*. They need not coincide. Further, since the center of buoyancy depends on the displaced fluid, its location will vary with a floating body depending on its orientation but remain constant for a completely submerged object.

The center of gravity of the mass, on the other hand, depends solely on the arrangement of the mass for a particular body. In the case of a barge, for example, the positioning of cargo would have to be included. Only if the object were completely submerged and of constant density throughout would the centers of gravity and buoyancy always coincide.

Figure 2-24 shows a completely submerged object with buoyant force F_B and weight F_G acting, respectively, at the center of buoyancy (B) and center of gravity (G). The object can only be stable if point B lies directly above

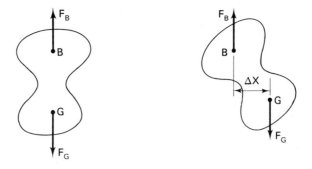

(a) Stable position.   (b) Displaced position.

Fig. 2-24. Stability sketch for a completely submerged object.

point G, in which case an angular displacement such as shown in Fig. 2-24b causes a righting moment proportional to the forces and the offset distance ΔX. The object will return to the stable configuration of Fig. 2-24a once the disturbing force is removed.

Clearly, if G is above B in Fig. 2-24a, the slightest displacement would cause an overturning moment and the object would rotate to its stable position. As a limiting case, an object would be stable in any position if points B and G coincide. A disturbing force would cause rotation to a new position, which would be equally stable, as neither a righting nor an overturning moment is created. Finally, it should be apparent that the more removed are the points B and G in the submerged body of Fig. 2-24a, the greater will be its inherent stability. In summary, if an object is fully submerged, whether it be a balloon in air or a submarine in water, it must be so designed or weighted that the center of buoyancy lies some distance above the center of gravity.

For relatively simple shapes such as cylinders and other bodies of revolution, stability analysis of floating bodies proceeds in much the same way as fully submerged bodies. That is, the body will be stable in a desired position only if its mass is so arranged that the center of gravity lies below the centroid of the displaced volume of liquid as shown on Fig. 2-25. The higher the object floats in the liquid, the more weighting or ballast will be required to maintain stability.

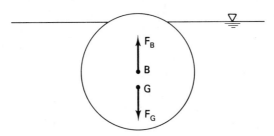

Fig. 2-25.   Stability of an axisymmetric floating body.

If the body is not axisymmetric, an angular displacement may result in a significant change in the geometry of the displaced volume, even to an extent that permits the center of gravity to lie above the center of buoyancy. The stability analysis, which now becomes more complicated, will bear this out. This will be illustrated for the barge of Fig. 2-26, which has an assumed rectangular cross section. If the center of buoyancy lies above the center of gravity, as may be the case when the barge is unloaded, the vessel is stable and need not be considered further. As the barge is loaded, raising the center of gravity to a point above the center of buoyancy, the situation depicted in Fig. 2-26a may occur.

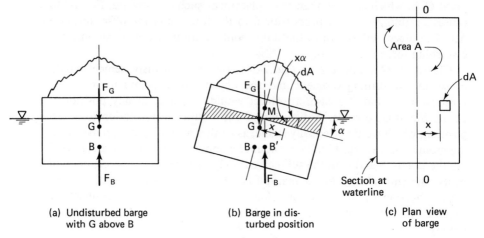

(a) Undisturbed barge   (b) Barge in dis-   (c) Plan view
    with G above B   turbed position   of barge

Fig. 2-26.   Stability of floating body.

When the barge is displaced through an angle α known as the *angle of heel*, as shown in Fig. 2-26b, there is a shift in the center of buoyancy from B to B'. Thus, the forces give rise to a counterclockwise couple or righting moment. The shift in location of the buoyant force occurs because the volume of the left-hand shaded area no longer can contribute to the buoyancy, whereas an additional volume, the right-hand shaded area, is now submerged, the effect of which moves the centroid of the submerged volume to the right. The intersection of the original line of action containing points B and G with the new line of action of the buoyancy force through B' locates the *metacenter M*. As long as the point M remains above point G, the body will be stable. If the angle α is further increased, the metacenter will eventually drop below point G and the body will heel over or capsize.

Defining the displaced volume (which remains constant regardless of α) as V and the horizontal area of the barge at the water line as A, the distance BB' may be determined for small angles of α as follows. The moment of the displaced volume V about point B must equal the moment of the shaded triangular portions. Thus, as determined from Fig. 2-26b and c,

$$(V)(BB') = \int_A x(x\alpha \, dA) = \alpha \int_A x^2 \, dA$$

The latter integral is the second moment, or moment of inertial $\bar{I}$, of the area A about the longitudinal axis O (which is the centroidal axis of the area). Therefore,

$$BB' = \frac{\bar{I}\alpha}{V} \tag{2-13}$$

Also, for small angles of heel,

$$BB' = (MB)(\alpha)$$

and therefore

$$MG = MB - GB = \frac{\bar{I}}{V} - GB \qquad (2\text{-}14)$$

Equation 2-14 locates the metacenter for small angles of α. Clearly, the greater the distance MG, the greater the stability. Since a barge or other floating body becomes unstable as M falls below G, Eq. 2-14 becomes a direct indicator of this condition. In particular,

$$\frac{\bar{I}}{V} > GB \qquad \text{stable body}$$

$$\frac{\bar{I}}{V} < GB \qquad \text{unstable body}$$

EXAMPLE 2-13

A barge such as that shown in Fig. 2-26 is 10 m wide by 30 m long. When loaded, the barge displaces 5 MN, and its center of gravity is 0.5 m above the waterline. Determine the metacenter height above the center of gravity and the righting moment for a roll angle of 10°.

SOLUTION:

For a specific weight of 9800 N/m³, the depth of water displaced, y, is calculated by

$$(y \text{ m})(10 \text{ m})(30 \text{ m})(9800 \text{ N/m}^3) = 5 \times 10^6 \text{ N}$$

or

$$y = 1.7 \text{ m}$$

and the center of buoyancy is normally 0.85 m below the waterline. Therefore, the center of gravity is $0.5 + 0.85 = 1.35$ m above the center of buoyancy. Using the notation of Eq. 2-14,

$$MG = \frac{\bar{I}}{V} - GB$$

$$= \frac{(30 \text{ m})(10 \text{ m})^3/12}{(1.7 \text{ m})(10 \text{ m})(30 \text{ m})} - 1.35 \text{ m}$$

$$= 4.90 - 1.35 = 3.55 \text{ m}$$

Hence, the metacenter is 3.55 m above the center of gravity. From Eq. 2-13, the distance BB' is

$$BB' = \frac{\bar{I}\alpha}{V}$$

where $\bar{I}/V = 4.90$ m and $\alpha = 10° = 0.175$ rad, yielding

$$BB' = (4.90)(0.175) = 0.858 \text{ m}$$

Therefore, the righting moment is

$$(F_G)(BB') = (5 \times 10^6 \text{ N})(0.858 \text{ m}) = 4.29 \times 10^6 \text{ N·m}$$

or 4.29 MN·m.

EXAMPLE 2-14

For a ship with a water-line cross section as shown in Fig. 2-27 and a displacement of 600 tons, determine the maximum distance GB that the center of gravity may lie above the center of buoyancy if the ship is to remain stable.

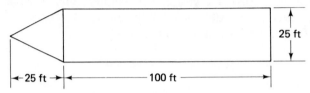

Fig. 2-27. Stability of a ship.

SOLUTION:

At the point of incipient instability, $GB = \bar{I}/V$, where

$$\bar{I} = \frac{(100)(25)^3}{12} + \frac{(2)(25)(12.5)^3}{12} = 1.383 \times 10^5 \text{ ft}^4$$

and

$$V = \frac{(600 \text{ tons})(2000 \text{ lb/ton})}{62.4 \text{ lb/ft}^3} = 1.923 \times 10^4 \text{ ft}^3$$

Finally,

$$GB = \frac{1.383 \times 10^5}{1.923 \times 10^4} = 7.19 \text{ ft}$$

PROBLEMS

Sec. 2-1

2-1. Through use of Newton's law and the free body diagram shown, prove that the pressure at depth y_0 is equal to γy_0 (Eq. 2-4).

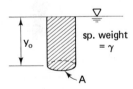

2-2. If the atmospheric pressure is 14.1 psia, determine the following:
(a) The absolute pressure when a gage reads 100 psi.
(b) The absolute pressure when a gage reads -7 psi.
(c) The gage pressure corresponding to absolute zero.
(d) The gage pressure corresponding to 14.7 psia.

2-3. If the atmospheric pressure is 100 kN/m²(abs), determine the following:
(a) Absolute pressure when a gage reads 1.59 MN/m² (1.59×10^6 N/m²).
(b) Gage pressure corresponding to absolute zero.
(c) Gage pressure corresponding to 50 kN/m²(abs).
(d) The atmospheric pressure, in bars.

2-4. If wet concrete weighs 150 lb/ft³, what is the pressure at the bottom of a tank containing 6 ft of concrete?

2-5. What is the pressure at the bottom of a tank containing:
(a) 2 ft of water?
(b) 2 ft of mercury?

2-6. A tank is filled with wet concrete weighing 23.5 kN/m³. If the pressure at the bottom of the tank is 35.25 kN/m², what is the depth of the concrete?

2-7. Determine the depth of a tube filled with mercury if the pressure at the bottom is 202.4 kN/m².

2-8. What is the pressure at point A for both of the following tanks of water?

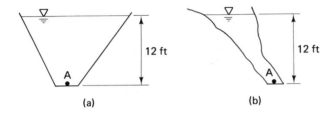

(a)   (b)

2-9. Determine and plot the vertical pressure distribution if 4 ft of oil (sp. gr. = 0.85) floats above 6 ft of water.

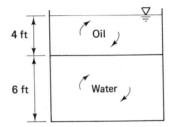

2-10. If the pressure gage shown indicates a pressure of 80 psi, what are the pressures at points A, B, and C?

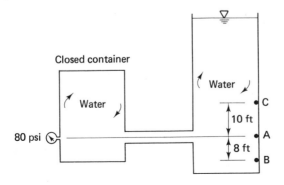

2-11. If the pressure gage shown indicates a pressure of 6.5×10^5 N/m², what are the pressures at points A, B, and C? Express in SI and English units.

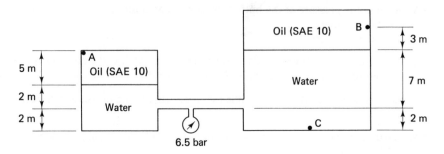

2-12. If a spherical air bubble has a diameter of 1 cm at a depth of 10 m, what would be its diameter as it rises to 5 m below the surface? What would be its diameter just below the surface? Ignore surface tension and assume that the overlying air is at standard atmospheric pressure.

2-13. Assuming standard atmospheric conditions at sea level, compare the pressure at 5000 ft calculated first by assuming constant density and second by assuming a lapse rate of 3.57°F/1000 ft.

2-14. Repeat Prob. 2-13 for the case where temperature *increases* at the rate of $\frac{1}{2}$°F/1000 ft. What is the specific weight at 5000 ft?

2-15. Assume a lapse rate of 3.57°F/1000 ft and determine the pressure at 36,000 ft if the temperature at sea level is 80°F and the pressure 14.2 psia.

2-16. Based on a lapse rate of 6.51°C/1000 m, develop the equations in SI units, corresponding to Eqs. 2-8 and 2-9.

2-17. Assume a standard atmosphere and plot the pressure variation up to an elevation of 30,000 m. Assume a lapse rate of 6.51°C/1000 m.

2-18. Determine the pressure at 10,000 m if the sea-level temperature is 10°C and the pressure is 0.99 bar(abs). Assume a lapse rate of 6.51°C/1000 m.

Sec. 2-2

2-19 through 2-22. Find the pressure in psi at point A for each of the following:

2-19.

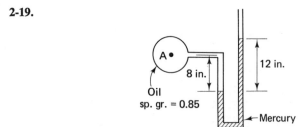

2-20.

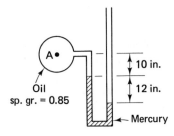

2-21.

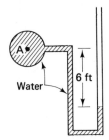

2-22.

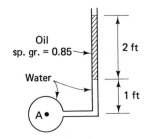

2-23. Determine the pressure at point A of Fig. 2-7b, if $h = 10$ in. and the liquid is (a) water; (b) kerosene.

2-24. Determine the pressure at point A of Fig. 2-7b if $h = 0.34$ m and the liquid is (a) water at 20°C; (b) kerosene. Express the answers in pascals and bars.

2-25. Determine the pressure at point A of Fig. 2-8 if the liquid at A is water, and the manometer fluid is mercury, when:
(a) $h = b = 13$ in.
(b) $h = 1$ in., $b = 16$ in.

2-26. Determine the pressure at point A of Fig. 2-8 if the liquid at A is water and the manometer fluid has a sp. gr. $= 1.92$, when:
(a) $h = 0.53b = 0.25$ m.
(b) $h = 2b = 0.5$ m.

2-27. Determine the pressure at point A of Fig. 2-8 if the liquid at A is water and the manometer fluid has a sp. gr. $= 1.92$, when:
(a) $h = b = 13$ in.
(b) $h = 1$ in., $b = 16$ in.

2-28. How high will mercury rise in the manometer of Fig. 2-8 ($h = $?) if the water pressure at point A is 6.0 psi and $b = 48$ in.?

2-29. What is the difference in water pressure between points A and B if the fluid at the top of the manometer is (a) oil (sp. gr. $= 0.92$), (b) air?

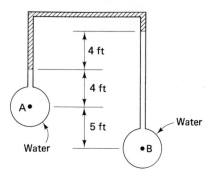

2-30. If the water pressure at point B is 25 psi, what is the water pressure at point A?

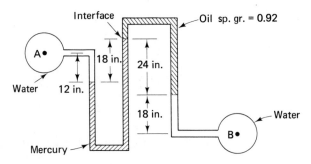

2-31 through 2-33 all refer to the following figure.

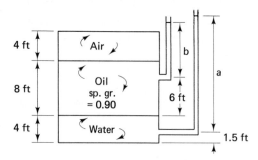

2-31. If $a = 20$ ft, what is the air pressure in the closed container above the oil?

2-32. If $a = 20$ ft, to what height will the oil rise in the oil column ($b =$?)?

2-33. If the air pressure above the oil is 12 psi, determine the height to which the liquids will rise in the two columns (i.e., $a =$? and $b =$?).

2-34. Compute the atmospheric pressure on a day when the height of the mercury barometer is 760 mm.

2-35. If the barometer of Fig. 2-11 used water rather than mercury, calculate the height of the water column on a day when the atmospheric pressure was 13.8 psia and the temperature was 60°F. (Include the effects of vapor pressure.)

Sec. 2-3

2-36. What is the force on the bottom of a circular tank of water if the diameter of the tank is 3 ft and the depth is 7 ft?

2-37. The bottom of a circular water tank will support a maximum load of 20,000 N. If the height of the tank is 10 times the diameter, what are the dimensions of the tank when filled with water?

2-38. What is the hydrostatic force on a vertical seawall if the depth is 20 ft and the length is 2000 ft? Where is the center of pressure?

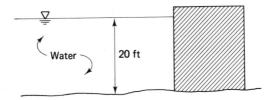

2-39. Determine the force on the vertical wall of Prob. 2-38 if the depth is 10 m and the length of the wall is 500 m.

2-40. Determine the magnitude and point of application of the force on a vertical lift gate 6 ft wide by 10 ft high if the water surface is 12 ft above the top of the gate.

2-41. If the water level behind the gate of Prob. 2-40 is raised 3 ft, what increase in force must the gate withstand?

2-42. If a circular gate is pivoted as shown, what moment must be applied to the axis to keep the gate closed?

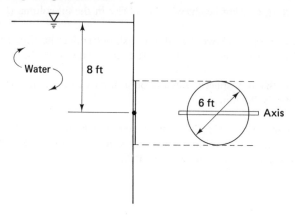

2-43. Determine the diameter of a vertical circular gate similar to that of Prob. 2-42 if a torque about the pivot of 100 kN·m is required to keep it closed and its axis is 3 m below the water surface.

2-44. Determine the net force and its point of application on a vertical circular gate connecting two reservoirs of different depths as shown.

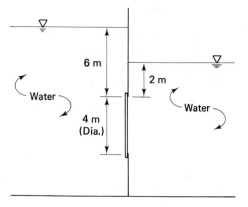

2-45. Determine the magnitude and location of the hydrostatic force on the inclined wall when the water depth is 10 m and length of the structure is 50 m.

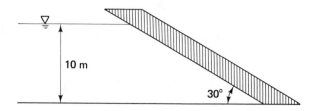

2-46. A circular gate such as that in Prob 2-42 is placed in the side wall of a completely closed tank filled with water. The gate has a diameter of 2 m and the pressure within the tank has been adjusted so that the line of zero pressure passes through the horizontal axis of the gate. Determine the force of the water on the gate and the moment required to keep the gate closed.

2-47. What depth of oil (sp. gr. = 0.9) must be maintained behind the plate (hinged at the bottom) if the plate is to remain vertical?

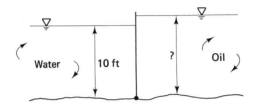

2-48. If the water to the left of the hinged gate of Prob. 2-47 has a depth of 5 m and the oil to the right has a depth of 6 m, what must be the reaction force and moment at the hinge in order for the gate to remain vertical?

2-49. Determine the magnitude and location of the hydrostatic force per foot of length on the levee when the water has a depth of 15 ft.

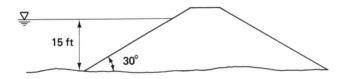

2-50. Repeat Prob. 2-49 if the depth of water is 10 m.

2-51. What force R is required to open the gate? The gate is 6 ft wide.

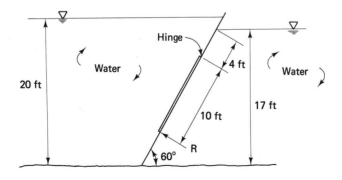

2-52. Repeat Prob. 2-51 if the gate is circular with a diameter of 10 ft.

Sec. 2-4

2-53. Determine the net vertical and horizontal forces on the roller gate. Where do the forces act?

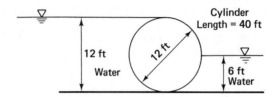

2-54. If the roller gate of Prob. 2-53 is 3 m in diameter and 10 m long, determine the magnitude and location of the force due to water backed up to a depth of 3 m on one side.

2-55. Determine the horizontal force on the surface BC, the vertical forces on the surfaces AB and BC, and the net vertical force on the volume ABC. Note that ABC represents the cross section of one-fourth of a circular cylinder which extends 20 ft perpendicular to the plane of the sketch.

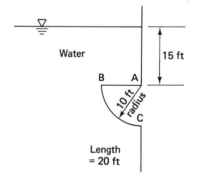

2-56. If the spherical plug weighs 900 lb, what head of water, h, is required to lift the plug?

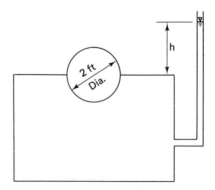

2-57. If the head *h* of Prob. 2-56 is 2 m, determine the necessary weight for a spherical plug with diameter 0.5 m.

2-58. The 2-ft-diameter by 10-ft-long cylinder is positioned as shown. What are the net horizontal and vertical forces on the cylinder due to the water? Where do they act?

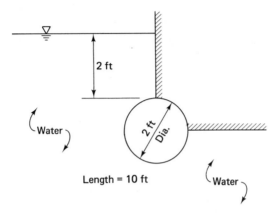

2-59. When the pressure gage reads 70,000 N/m², what is the upward force on the hemispherical dome?

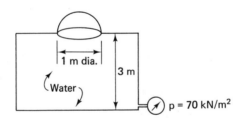

2-60. The large tank shown weighs 3000 lb. How many pounds of a substance with sp. gr. = 1.5 may be placed inside before the tank will sink?

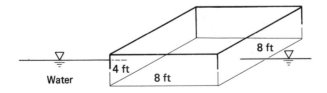

2-61. A dirigible weighs 10,000 lb. If filled with helium at 68°F at standard atmospheric pressure, what volume of helium would be required in order for the dirigible to rise from the ground?

2-62. Assuming standard atmospheric pressure at sea level and 20°C, what diameter spherical balloon filled with hydrogen would be required to lift a combined balloon and basket weight of 7000 N? How many newtons of hydrogen would be required?

2-63. How many cubic meters of coal weighing 17 kN/m³ may be placed in a wooden barge which may be approximated as a prism 25 m long, 8 m wide, and 3 m deep? Assume that the timber has an average thickness of 20 cm and sp. gr. of 0.85. Allow 0.5 m for free board.

2-64. A 2-ft-diameter sphere sits on the bottom of a tank as shown. If the sphere weighs 500 lb in air, what is the supportive force *F* if the liquid is water? If the liquid is oil? (Sp. gr. = 0.89.)

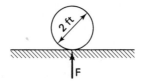

2-65. If a sphere (diameter 50 cm) with sp. gr. = 1.8 sits on the bottom of a tank as shown in Prob. 2-64, what force is required to support it if the liquid is water? What force is required to hold it down if the liquid is mercury?

2-66. The two spheres each have a sp. gr. = 1.4. Ignore friction and the weight of the support system. If the system is balanced, what must be the diameter of the sphere that is submerged in water?

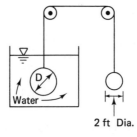

2 ft Dia.

2-67. If the spheres of Prob. 2-66 both have a diameter of 40 cm, what force will be required to hold the left sphere down in the tank of water?

2-68. If the cubic crate (1 m on each side) floats exactly half submerged in water, how far will it sink into salt water (sp. gr. = 1.05)? Assume that the crate is stable in either liquid.

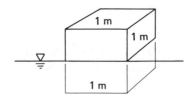

2-69. If a uniform-density cone, base diameter 2 ft and altitude 3 ft, floats in water as shown, how far will it sink into a liquid with a specific weight of 85 lb/ft³ ? Assume that the cone is stable in either liquid.

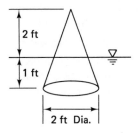

2-70. A pail of water weighing 18 N rests on scale *B*. A uniform density block having a volume of 35 cm³ and a specific gravity of 2.5 is hung from scale *A* and submerged in the water as shown. Assume that no water spills. What will be the reading of scales *A* and *B*? What will the scales read if the block is exactly half submerged?

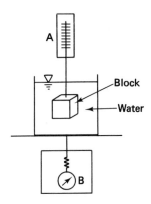

2-71. Repeat Prob. 2-70 if the pail is initially full so that all the displaced water is spilled.

2-72. A rectangular barge 12 m long by 5 m wide and 3 m deep is found to draw 2 m of water when fully loaded (i.e., the waterline will be 2 m above the bottom of the barge). Assume that the center of gravity is located at the geometric center of the cross section. Is the barge stable? Locate the metacenter.

2-73. A rectangular barge 30 ft long by 12 ft wide and 6 ft deep weighs 120,000 lb when fully loaded. If the center of gravity is exactly at the top surface of the barge when fully loaded, will the barge be stable?

2-74. A solid 1-m cube of wood floats on water. Determine whether it will be stable with one side horizontal if its specific gravity is (a) 0.85; (b) 0.70.

2-75. A buoy consists of a circular cylinder 1 m in diameter and 10 m in length, weighted so as to float in a vertical position. The cylinder weighs 30,000 N and its center of gravity is located 0.8 m from the lower end. What maximum weight of additional equipment may be placed at the upper end if the buoy is to remain stable? Assume that the additional load will have its center of gravity 0.4 m above the top of the cylinder.

2-76. Is the cube of Prob. 2-68 stable in fresh water? In salt water?

2-77. Consider the cone of Prob. 2-69 when it floats in water as shown, and locate the metacenter M. Is the cone stable? (Note that the centroid of a cone lies three-fourths of the distance from the vortex.)

3

Kinematics of Fluid Motion

As we now start to consider fluid motion we will begin with an analysis of the kinematic, as opposed to dynamic, characteristics of fluid flow. At no time in this chapter will the causes of fluid motion be discussed. Rather, only ways of describing the motion will be investigated. Particular emphasis will be placed on the understanding of velocities, discharge (or rate of flow), accelerations, and the relationship among them. Through concepts involving relative motion, velocities will be considered in both moving and fixed reference planes.

A very brief introduction to the subject of turbulence and the differences between laminar and turbulent flow will also be presented at this point. This introduction will permit the reader to understand the distinction between the two conditions, better appreciate the differences between real and idealized fluids, and finally better estimate the accuracy of some of the simplified relationships that follow. Beginning in Chapter 7, the latter subjects will be covered in considerably more detail.

3–1 VELOCITY FIELD

Our primary goal in this chapter is to be able to describe the flow pattern or flow field; to be able to quantify what the fluid is doing. One of the best ways of achieving this is through the ability to determine the velocity at particular points, or for that matter, every point in the flow field. The velocity at a point could be determined, as in dynamics, by examining a particle of fluid passing a point and taking its derivative with time. We will find that this is rarely convenient. This concept does lead, however, in a differential sense to one means of visualizing a laboratory free surface flow. By sprinkling confetti or similar substances on a liquid surface and taking a short time exposure, the image of each piece of confetti can be interpreted as a velocity. This is, each particle will appear as a short line, the direction of which is the direction of the flow at that "point," and the length of which, when divided by the time of the exposure, yields the magnitude of the velocity.

The foregoing procedure points out the vector nature of velocity. Velocity is indeed a vector and we will in general have to specify both the magnitude and direction of the velocity or else its components in the coordinate system in which we are working. As the various principles are developed, alternative derivations applying vector mechanics will also be encountered. However, most of the principles will be developed at least once in a scalar, or component form, to ensure a firm grasp of the physical significance.

Continuing, if we have a velocity $\mathbf{V}$ in a rectangular Cartesian coordinate system as indicated in Fig. 3-1, we can express the velocity components in terms of the cosines of the angles as follows:

$$u = |\mathbf{V}| \cos \alpha \qquad\qquad (3\text{-}1a)$$

$$v = |\mathbf{V}| \cos \beta \qquad\qquad (3\text{-}1b)$$

$$w = |\mathbf{V}| \cos \gamma \qquad\qquad (3\text{-}1c)$$

where u, v, and w are the x, y, and z components of the velocity, respectively. If we have unit vectors $\mathbf{i}, \mathbf{j}$, and $\mathbf{k}$ in the same respective directions, we may

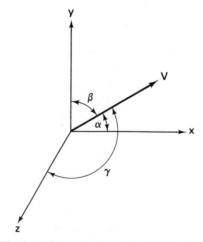

Fig. 3-1. Rectangular Cartesian coordinates.

also write the vector equation

$$\mathbf{V} = u\mathbf{i} + v\mathbf{j} + w\mathbf{k} \tag{3-2}$$

and finally

$$|\mathbf{V}| = \sqrt{u^2 + v^2 + w^2} = V \tag{3-3}$$

The absolute value of the velocity, which is of course the magnitude of the velocity vector, will be written henceforth as simply V. In a two-dimensional flow with appropriate coordinates shown in Fig. 3-2, the velocity components become

$$u = V \cos \alpha \tag{3-4a}$$

$$v = V \sin \alpha \tag{3-4b}$$

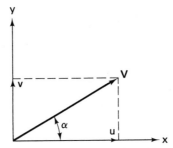

Fig. 3-2. Rectangular Cartesian coordinates in two dimensions.

EXAMPLE 3-1

A three-dimensional velocity field is specified by the equations

$$u = 2x + 2y \quad \text{(m/s)}$$

$$v = -y + z \quad \text{(m/s)}$$

$$w = x - z \quad \text{(m/s)}$$

Determine the magnitude and direction of the velocity at the point $x = 2, y = 4, z = 2$.

SOLUTION:

At the specific point

$$u = (2)(2) + (2)(4) = 12 \text{ m/s}$$

$$v = -4 + 2 = -2 \text{ m/s}$$

$$w = 2 - 2 = 0$$

and the required velocity from Eq. 3-3 is

$$V = \sqrt{(12)^2 + (-2)^2 + (0)^2} = 12.17 \text{ m/s}$$

The velocity at the point in question lies entirely in the x–y plane, and at an angle below the x axis given by either

$$\alpha = \cos^{-1}\left(\frac{u}{V}\right)$$

or

$$\alpha = \sin^{-1}\left(\frac{v}{V}\right)$$

From the former

$$\alpha = \cos^{-1}\left(\frac{12}{12.17}\right) = 9.5°$$

which is sketched on Fig. 3-3.

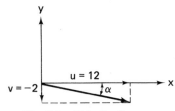

Fig. 3-3.   Velocity diagram.

Relative Motion

On occasion it will be advantageous to approach a problem from the concept of relative motion. This is because a flow may be time-dependent (unsteady) to one observer (or, more technically, reference system), while to another the flow is quite independent of time. Solving the problem from the latter point of view will generally be less cumbersome. As an example, the waves generated by a passing boat present a transient or unsteady appearance to a person standing on the shore, but these same waves form a steady, unchanging pattern to a passenger on the boat.

The relative motion problem can readily be formulated by vector addition of the corresponding velocities according to the following rule: The actual velocity of the fluid is equal to the velocity of the fluid relative to a moving reference point plus (the vector sum of) the velocity of the reference point:

$$\mathbf{V}_{\text{actual}} = \mathbf{V}_{\text{fluid/body}} + \mathbf{V}_{\text{body}} \tag{3-5}$$

EXAMPLE 3-2

A passenger on the ship shown in Fig. 3-4 estimates that the velocity at point A near the bow is 21 ft/s relative to the boat and at an angle of 20°. What is the actual velocity of the water at that point if the ship is passing through otherwise calm water with a speed of 20 ft/s?

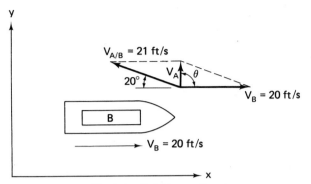

Fig. 3-4. Relative motion.

SOLUTION:

Let V_B be the velocity of the boat and $V_{A/B}$ be the velocity of the water at point A relative to the boat; then the actual velocity at point A is

$$\mathbf{V}_A = \mathbf{V}_{A/B} + \mathbf{V}_B$$

as shown on the vector diagram of Fig. 3-4. Using u and v for the x and y coordinates shown, we have the component equations

$$u_A = -u_{A/B} + u_B$$
$$= -21 \cos 20° + 20 = 0.27 \text{ ft/s} \quad \text{(to the right)}$$
$$v_A = v_{A/B} + v_B$$
$$= 21 \sin 20° + 0 = 7.18 \text{ ft/s} \quad \text{(in the } +y \text{ direction)}$$

Thus, the actual velocity is

$$V_A = (u_A^2 + v_A^2)^{1/2}$$
$$= [(0.27)^2 + (7.18)^2]^{1/2} = 7.19 \text{ ft/s}$$

at an angle to the x axis of

$$\theta = \tan^{-1}\left(\frac{v_A}{u_A}\right)$$
$$= \tan^{-1}\left(\frac{7.18}{0.27}\right)$$
$$= 87.9°$$

Streamlines and Path Lines

The aforementioned sprinkling of confetti on the flow surface is one way to obtain a visualization of an entire flow field. Another technique is the sketching of *streamlines*. If the confetti streaks were connected by a series of smooth lines, these would form streamlines. As a formal definition, a streamline is a line everywhere tangent to the velocity vectors at any instant.

Conversely, it also follows that if the streamlines for a flow are given, at least the direction of the velocity is known at every point (see Fig. 3-5). The time constraint is necessary to include situations when the flow pattern itself is changing with time.

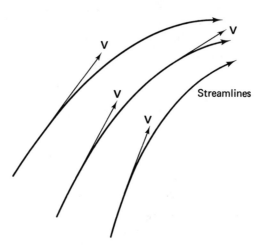

Fig. 3-5. Streamlines.

A second useful definition is that of a path line. A *path line* is the locus of points occupied by a particular fluid particle as the flow takes place. If the flow pattern is not changing with the time, the path lines and streamlines will be identical. A particle starting, for instance, on the center streamline of Fig. 3-5 will move along that streamline, always occupying points on the streamline and thus tracing out a path line identical with the streamline.

In an unsteady flow such as in Example 3-2, the streamline pattern will be continuously changed with time as the boat passes. The streamline passing through point A of Fig. 3-4 is shown in Fig. 3-6. The curved path indicates that as fluid gets pushed out of the way by the bow it must also flow back past the ship and in toward the stern filling the region that the ship is vacating. This streamline only exists instantaneously at any given position, however, since it moves forward with the ship.[1] On the other hand, a particle that is at point A at the instant shown will trace out a small loop, at each instant following a completely different streamline for each short increment of time. This is the path line shown on Fig. 3-6. The sketching of streamlines

---

[1]To put the concept of relative motion another way, the unsteady flow streamline of Fig. 3-6 which is seen by a fixed observer (or stationary coordinate system) can be switched to a steady flow streamline by the simple expedient of changing the observation point to one astride the body (i.e., by adopting a coordinate system which moves with the body).

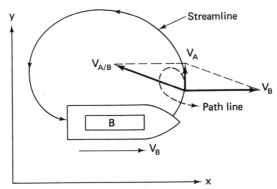

Fig. 3-6. Streamline and path line for Fig. 3-4.

and the relationship between the streamlines and the velocity field are considered in Example 3-3. In Chapter 12 the actual equations of the streamlines will be determined.

EXAMPLE 3-3

Sketch the streamlines in the first quadrant for the two-dimensional flow field specified by

$$u = x + 2y \quad \text{(m/s)}$$

$$v = 2x - y \quad \text{(m/s)}$$

SOLUTION:

Velocity components at representative points may be calculated:

x (m)	y (m)	u (m/s)	v (m/s)
0	0	0	0
0	1	2	−1
0	2	4	−2
0	4	8	−4
1	0	1	2
2	0	2	4
4	0	4	8
1	1	3	1
1	2	5	0
1	4	9	−2
2	1	4	3
2	2	6	2
2	4	10	0
4	1	6	7
4	2	8	6
4	4	12	4

These components, along with others, have been plotted to scale in Fig. 3-7. The respective velocity vectors are shown by the dashed arrows and the streamlines sketched from them.

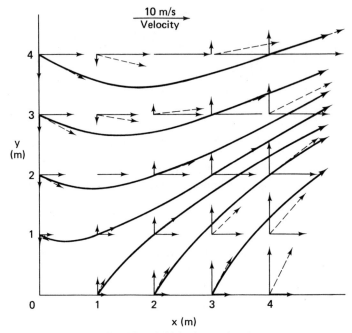

Fig. 3-7.   Flow field for Example 3-3.

3–2 RATE OF FLOW AND AVERAGE VELOCITY

Having considered the velocity of a fluid in some detail, we will proceed to a second equally important kinematic property of the flow, the rate of flow or discharge. This will be followed by the determination of average velocities, which will in turn be related to both the velocity distribution and the discharge.

Rate of Flow

The *rate of flow* passing a given cross section may be determined from the velocity distribution across the section, as shown in Fig. 3-8. The section is bounded by a ring of streamlines, which may or may not be a solid boundary. If they represent a solid boundary, the velocity must be zero at the perimeter of the cross section, as shown on the figure.

With reference now to Fig. 3-8, the differential area dA has been chosen as a sufficiently small portion of the cross-sectional area A, so that the fluid passing through dA may be treated as having a constant velocity v.

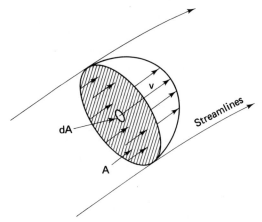

Fig. 3-8. Relationship between velocity and discharge.

In a time interval, dt, the fluid will travel a distance $ds = v\,dt$. Therefore, the volume passing through dA during time dt will be $v\,dt\,dA$, and the corresponding fluid mass must be $\rho v\,dt\,dA$. Consequently, the rate of flow of mass (or mass per unit time) dG passing dA is $\rho v\,dt\,dA/dt$, or

$$dG = \rho v\,dA$$

while the volume rate of flow is

$$dQ = v\,dA$$

Integration of these quantities over the cross-sectional area A gives the mass discharge

$$G = \int_A \rho v\,dA \tag{3-6}$$

and the volumetric discharge

$$Q = \int_A v\,dA \tag{3-7}$$

respectively. When no confusion can result, the terms discharge and flow rate will be used interchangeably to represent either of the above.

The foregoing has assumed that the cross section has been chosen perpendicular to the streamlines. If this is not done, then the component of the velocity normal to the section must be used in Eqs. 3-6 and 3-7. If the angle between the velocity and the normal to the cross section is designated by θ, the mass discharge becomes

$$G = \int_A \rho v \cos \theta\,dA \tag{3-8}$$

and the volumetric discharge is

$$Q = \int_A v \cos \theta\,dA \tag{3-9}$$

The discharge question may be readily formulated in vector notation as well. A generalized surface of area A and representative velocity vector $\mathbf{V}$ are shown in Fig. 3-9. The small differential area dA may be represented by the vector $\mathbf{dA}$, which has magnitude equal to dA and direction normal to the surface. The rate of flow through the differential area is[2]

$$\mathbf{V} \cdot \mathbf{dA} = v \, dA \cos \theta$$

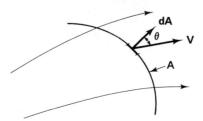

Fig. 3-9. Vector formations for determination of discharge.

This may be integrated over the surface A to get the discharge passing through the surface. By inclusion of the density the mass rate of flow becomes

$$G = \int_A \rho \mathbf{V} \cdot \mathbf{dA} \tag{3-10}$$

while the volumetric discharge is

$$Q = \int_A \mathbf{V} \cdot \mathbf{dA} \tag{3-11}$$

Average Velocity

The *average velocity V* passing the section of Fig. 3-8 may also be obtained by integration of the velocity distribution according to the following averaging process:

$$V = \frac{1}{A} \int_A v \, dA \tag{3-12}$$

By comparison with Eq. 3-7,

$$AV = \int_A v \, dA = Q \tag{3-13}[3]$$

The various integrations expressed in this section may usually be performed in closed form if the velocity (and density, if also variable) variation is

[2]Refer to Appendix D for an explanation of vector operations.

[3]Letting ρ_{AV} be the average density across the section of a variable density flow, the corresponding equation for evaluating the average velocity becomes

$$\rho_{AV} AV = \int_A \rho v \, dA = G$$

expressed mathematically (see Example 3-4). If the velocity distribution is obtained experimentally as in a laboratory experiment, graphic integration will be necessary, as in Example 3-5.

EXAMPLE 3-4

Determine the discharge and average velocity past a circular section in which a velocity distribution similar to Fig. 3-8 is given by

$$v = v_{\max}\left[1 - \left(\frac{r}{r_0}\right)^2\right]$$

The distribution is symmetrical with respect to the axis $r = 0$, the outer radius is r_0, and $v_{\max}$ is the velocity along the axis.

SOLUTION:

The discharge is given by Eq. 3-7, where dA is the incremental ring of Fig. 3-10. It is located a distance r from the origin and has an area

$$dA = 2\pi r\, dr$$

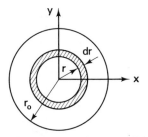

Fig. 3-10. Definition sketch for Examples 3-4 and 3-5.

Thus, the discharge is

$$Q = \int_A v\, dA = \int_0^{r_0} v(2\pi r\, dr)$$

$$= 2\pi v_{\max} \int_0^{r_0} r\left[1 - \left(\frac{r}{r_0}\right)^2\right] dr$$

$$= 2\pi v_{\max}\left(\frac{r_0^2}{2} - \frac{r_0^2}{4}\right)$$

and finally

$$Q = \frac{\pi r_0^2 v_{\max}}{2}$$

The average velocity as given by Eqs. 3-12 or 3-13 is

$$V = \frac{\pi r_0^2 v_{\max}}{2\pi r_0^2} = \frac{v_{\max}}{2}$$

showing that the average value of a paraboloid of revolution is one-half its maximum value.

EXAMPLE 3-5

Determine the discharge and average velocity in a 1-m-diameter circular pipe. Velocity measurements are tabulated below and plotted on Fig. 3-11a.

r (m)	v (m/s)	rv (m²/s)
0	7.8	0
0.1	7.6	0.76
0.2	7.3	1.46
0.3	7.0	2.10
0.4	6.5	2.60
0.45	5.8	2.61
0.5	—	0

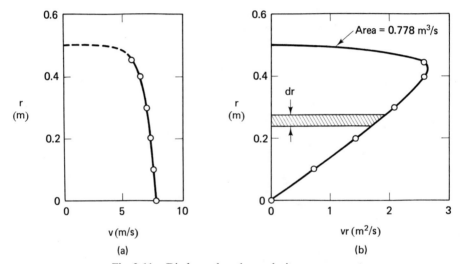

Fig. 3-11. Discharge based on velocity measurements.

SOLUTION:

In addition to the data points shown in Fig. 3-11a, the velocity at $r = 0.5$ m must equal zero. With respect to Fig. 3-10, the graphic integration of the velocity profile must again follow from

$$Q = \int_A v \, dA = \int_0^{r_0} v(2\pi r) \, dr$$

This can be obtained from the data if we plot vr as a function of r as in Fig. 3-11b. The shaded area is $vr \, dr$ and the total area under the curve is $\int_0^{r_0} vr \, dr$. Thus, the discharge is

$$Q = (2\pi) \times \text{(area under curve)}$$
$$= (2\pi)(0.778 \text{ m}^3/\text{s}) = 4.89 \text{ m}^3/\text{s}$$

and the average velocity

$$V = \frac{Q}{A} = \frac{4.89 \text{ m}^3/\text{s}}{(\pi/4)(1)^2 \text{ m}^2} = 6.22 \text{ m/s}$$

3–3   ACCELERATIONS: DEFINITIONS
OF STEADINESS AND UNIFORMITY

In dealing with a particle or body in dynamics, velocities and accelerations were obtained by taking, respectively, the first and second derivatives of the displacement with time. In fluid mechanics we generally start with the velocities rather than displacements, although this is not the only point of view that can be adopted. Before attempting to determine accelerations from the velocity field, consider a flow such as that in the contracting pipe of Fig. 3-12. As the valve is opened or closed over a period of time the flow

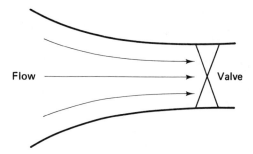

Flow   Valve

Fig. 3-12.   Example of accelerating flow.

experiences accelerations due to the changes in the magnitude of the velocities at various points with time. Note also that at any given valve opening the streamlines are contracting and therefore the flow is speeding up as it moves from the left to the right. This also is an acceleration; however, this acceleration results from changes in velocity due to changes in position rather than changes with time per se. Finally, all but the centerline streamline are curved in this figure, hence there is generally an additional acceleration due to change in the direction of the velocity vector. Both of these latter types of accelerations must also be incorporated in the expressions for acceleration that follow.

Acceleration in Cartesian Coordinates

Acceleration will first be considered in the conventional, three-dimensional, rectangular Cartesian coordinate system shown in the definition sketch of Fig. 3-13. The velocity at a point on one of the streamlines is shown along with the velocity components u, v, w, in the x, y, z directions, respec-

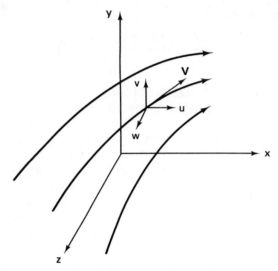

Fig. 3-13.   Acceleration in rectangular Cartesian coordinates.

tively. The corresponding accelerations in the three directions will be denoted by a_x, a_y, and a_z.

As in dynamics, an acceleration can be expressed as the derivative of the velocity with time. Considering first a_x, we have

$$a_x = \frac{du}{dt} \qquad (3\text{-}14)$$

but

$$u = u(t, x, y, z)$$

Therefore, changes in u (i.e., du) must reflect changes with respect to all the variables. We may express this as follows:

$$du = \frac{\partial u}{\partial t}\, dt + \frac{\partial u}{\partial x}\, dx + \frac{\partial u}{\partial y}\, dy + \frac{\partial u}{\partial z}\, dz$$

where the quantity $(\partial u/\partial t)\, dt$ represents that part of the change in velocity due to time, and so on for the other terms. As indicated, summing the changes in velocity due to each of the four independent variables gives the total change in velocity, du. The acceleration, a_x, can be obtained directly from Eq. 3-14 by dividing the value above of du by dt, the time interval during which the change in velocity occurs. Then

$$a_x = \frac{du}{dt} = \frac{\partial u}{\partial t} + \frac{\partial u}{\partial x}\frac{dx}{dt} + \frac{\partial u}{\partial y}\frac{dy}{dt} + \frac{\partial u}{\partial z}\frac{dz}{dt}$$

But, dx/dt, dy/dt, and dz/dt are simply the velocities, u, v, and w, respectively. Thus, the x component of the acceleration is given as

$$a_x = \frac{\partial u}{\partial t} + u\frac{\partial u}{\partial x} + v\frac{\partial u}{\partial y} + w\frac{\partial u}{\partial z} \tag{3-15a}$$

In like fashion we can also obtain

$$a_y = \frac{\partial v}{\partial t} + u\frac{\partial v}{\partial x} + v\frac{\partial v}{\partial y} + w\frac{\partial v}{\partial z} \tag{3-15b}$$

and

$$a_z = \frac{\partial w}{\partial t} + u\frac{\partial w}{\partial x} + v\frac{\partial w}{\partial y} + w\frac{\partial w}{\partial z} \tag{3-15c}$$

The first term on the right-hand side of each of the preceding equations, the partial derivatives with respect to time, are a measure of that part of the acceleration in each direction which is due to changes in velocity, at a point, with time. Because they reflect changes at a point, they are known as the local acceleration terms. If all three vanish, the flow is defined as a steady flow; if one or more are present, the flow is unsteady. Physical examples are more readily related to streamline coordinates which follow later in the section; however, these local accelerations would be the result of opening or closing the valve of Fig. 3-12. The remaining three terms on the right-hand side of each equation are called the *convective acceleration terms*. These terms measure that part of the acceleration which is due to changes in the velocity as the flow moves (or is convected) from one point to another. If all nine of these terms vanish, the flow is referred to as *uniform*, whereas if any one or more of the nine is nonvanishing, the flow is *nonuniform*. Note that there are four possibilities: the flow may be steady uniform (the easiest to analyze), unsteady nonuniform (generally the most difficult case), steady nonuniform, or unsteady uniform.

Considering only the uniformity of the flows in Fig. 3-14, part (a) is clearly uniform, since the only velocity component present is u and it is a constant. Part (b) definitely shows that the velocity is changing as the flow moves from left to right—it is therefore nonuniform. In order to determine the actual acceleration from point to point, the velocity field would have to be given. In the flow in sketch (c) we may note that although the velocities are not changing in magnitude as the flow proceeds along the streamlines, the curvature must cause a radial acceleration, thereby making the flow non-uniform. This type of acceleration is more easily described in either the polar-cylindrical or streamline coordinate systems which follow. Part (d) is similar to (a) except that a different velocity distribution is given with $u = f(y)$. Since $v = w = 0$, all the convective terms in Eqs. 3-15 will vanish, even though $\partial u/\partial y$ is not itself equal to zero, and this flow must also be uniform. We can conclude from this that a velocity variation perpendicular to the flow

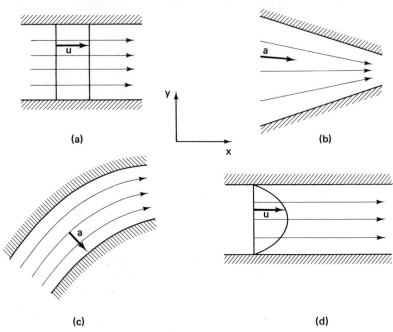

Fig. 3-14. Types of accelerations.

direction can exist in a uniform flow, provided that the velocity distribution is the same at each cross section.

The acceleration equations for a two-dimensional flow in the x–y plane can be obtained directly from Eqs. 3-15, which simplify to

$$a_x = \frac{\partial u}{\partial t} + u\frac{\partial u}{\partial x} + v\frac{\partial u}{\partial y} \qquad (3\text{-}16a)$$

and

$$a_y = \frac{\partial v}{\partial t} + u\frac{\partial v}{\partial x} + v\frac{\partial v}{\partial y} \qquad (3\text{-}16b)$$

EXAMPLE 3-6

Determine the acceleration at the point $x = 2$ ft, $y = 2$ ft, and $z = 1$ ft after 3 s if the velocity field is specified as follows:

$$u = 2t + 2x + 2y \qquad (\text{ft/s})$$

$$v = t - y + z \qquad (\text{ft/s})$$

$$w = t + x - z \qquad (\text{ft/s})$$

SOLUTION:

Taking the derivatives necessary for Eqs. 3-15, we have

$$\frac{\partial u}{\partial t} = 2 \qquad \frac{\partial v}{\partial t} = 1 \qquad \frac{\partial w}{\partial t} = 1$$

Also,

$$\frac{\partial u}{\partial x} = 2 \qquad \frac{\partial u}{\partial y} = 2 \qquad \frac{\partial u}{\partial z} = 0$$

$$\frac{\partial v}{\partial x} = 0 \qquad \frac{\partial v}{\partial y} = -1 \qquad \frac{\partial v}{\partial z} = 1$$

$$\frac{\partial w}{\partial x} = 1 \qquad \frac{\partial w}{\partial y} = 0 \qquad \frac{\partial w}{\partial z} = -1$$

Inserting the values $x = 2$, $y = 2$, $z = 1$, and $t = 3$ into the equations specifying the velocity field gives

$$u = (2)(3) + (2)(2) + (2)(2) = 14 \text{ ft/s}$$
$$v = 3 - 2 + 1 = 2 \text{ ft/s}$$
$$w = 3 + 2 - 1 = 4 \text{ ft/s}$$

which is the velocity at the required point and time. Now, substituting all of the above into Eqs. 3-15,

$$a_x = 2 + (14)(2) + (2)(2) + (4)(0) = 34 \text{ ft/s}^2$$
$$a_y = 1 + (14)(0) + (2)(-1) + (4)(1) = 3 \text{ ft/s}^2$$
$$a_z = 1 + (14)(1) + (2)(0) + (4)(-1) = 11 \text{ ft/s}^2$$

which are the accelerations requested. The only caution required is that the various derivatives be taken before specific values of location or time are introduced into the equations.

Acceleration in Polar-Cylindrical Coordinates

Equations that have been developed in one coordinate system often need to be applied to other coordinate systems. They could be rederived in the new coordinate system, but from the educational viewpoint this is redundant. Alternatively, the equations themselves can be transformed from one coordinate system to another, but this is a long and tedious process. As an expediency, once equations are derived in one coordinate system they will usually be presented without derivation in alternative coordinate systems as needed throughout the text.

It is frequently convenient to work in *polar-cylindrical coordinates*, as defined in Fig. 3-15, where the x, y, and z dimensions are replaced by r, θ, and z, as shown. The three components of the velocity, $\mathbf{V}$, will here be defined as v_r, v_θ, and v_z in the r, θ, and z directions, respectively. The acceleration

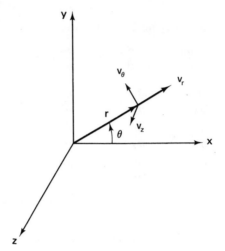

Fig. 3-15. Polar-cylindrical coordinates.

equations in this system become

$$a_r = \frac{dv}{dt} = \frac{\partial v_r}{\partial t} + v_r \frac{\partial v_r}{\partial r} + \frac{v_\theta}{r} \frac{\partial v_r}{\partial \theta} + v_z \frac{\partial v_r}{\partial z} - \frac{v_\theta^2}{r} \qquad (3\text{-}17a)$$

$$a_\theta = \frac{dv_\theta}{dt} = \frac{\partial v_\theta}{\partial t} + v_r \frac{\partial v_\theta}{\partial r} + \frac{v_\theta}{r} \frac{\partial v_\theta}{\partial \theta} + v_z \frac{\partial v_\theta}{\partial z} + \frac{v_r v_\theta}{r} \qquad (3\text{-}17b)$$

and

$$a_z = \frac{dv_z}{dt} = \frac{\partial v_z}{\partial t} + v_r \frac{\partial v_z}{\partial r} + \frac{v_\theta}{r} \frac{\partial v_z}{\partial \theta} + v_z \frac{\partial v_z}{\partial z} \qquad (3\text{-}17c)$$

The last term of Eq. 3-17a is the *radial* (or *centrifugal*) *acceleration* such as in Fig. 3-14c and the last term in Eq. 3-17b is the *Coriolis acceleration*.

The notation used above is necessary for denoting the velocity components under very general conditions. As more simplified specific cases are examined (e.g., flow taking place in a single direction in a pipe), a more convenient notation with fewer subscripts will be used. This should not cause any confusion, however.

EXAMPLE 3-7

An example of an unsteady circular flow (or vortex) is defined by

$$v_\theta = \frac{C}{r} e^{-kt} \qquad v_r = v_z = 0$$

where C and k are constants. Determine the acceleration components.

SOLUTION:

The three components may be obtained from Eqs. 3-17, which will have the following nonvanishing terms:

$$a_r = -\frac{v_\theta^2}{r} = -\frac{C^2}{r^3}e^{-2kt}$$

$$a_\theta = \frac{\partial v_\theta}{\partial t} = -\frac{kC}{r}e^{-kt}$$

$$a_z = 0$$

Streamline Coordinates

Another coordinate system, usually confined to flows that can be specified by two coordinate directions, will find a great deal of application. Referred to as *streamline* (or sometimes *natural*) *coordinates*, they are defined by Fig. 3-16. The coordinate direction s is along a streamline and is taken as positive

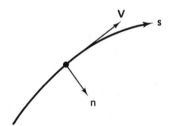

Fig. 3-16.   Streamline coordinates.

in the direction of flow. The normal direction n is positive inward. A principal advantage of this system is that the velocity can have no component in the n direction since, by definition, the velocity must be tangent to the streamline. The velocity along the streamline will be denoted by v. This should cause no confusion with the notation of Eqs. 3-1, since the appropriate coordinate system will always be known. It is also necessary to define components of v in the s and n directions. These will be noted as v_s and v_n, respectively. It is apparent that

$$v_s = v \quad \text{and} \quad v_n = 0$$

However, the subscript notation will be temporarily retained for clarity, since the derivatives of v_n do not necessarily vanish. This is demonstrated in Fig. 3-17, where the change in direction of the velocity introduces the normal component dv_n.

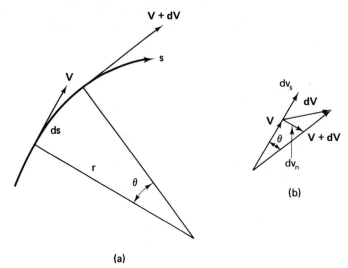

Fig. 3-17.   Geometry of velocity changes.

Expressing the velocities as functions of s, n, and t, acceleration equations similar to Eqs. 3-16 will be obtained.

$$a_s = \frac{dv_s}{dt} = \frac{\partial v_s}{\partial t} + v_s \frac{\partial v_s}{\partial s} + v_n \frac{\partial v_s}{\partial n}$$

$$a_n = \frac{dv_n}{dt} = \frac{\partial v_n}{\partial t} + v_s \frac{\partial v_n}{\partial s} + v_n \frac{\partial v_n}{\partial n}$$

Now since $v_n = 0$, these reduce to

$$a_s = \frac{\partial v_s}{\partial t} + v_s \frac{\partial v_s}{\partial s} \qquad\qquad (3\text{-}18\text{a})$$

$$a_n = \frac{\partial v_n}{\partial t} + v_s \frac{\partial v_n}{\partial s} \qquad\qquad (3\text{-}18\text{b})$$

The convective portion of dv_s/dt, that is, $v_s \, \partial v_s/\partial s$, gives the change in magnitude of the velocity as the flow proceeds along the streamline. It is this portion of the change in velocity, dv_s, during a time interval dt, which is attributable to changes in the streamline spacing. As the distance ds is traversed along a curved streamline, the velocity undergoes a change in direction. This gives rise to a normal component whose change with time dv_n/dt leads to the convective acceleration term in Eq. 3-18b. The normal acceleration is therefore a consequence of changes in the direction of the velocity rather than in changes in magnitude.

To put these equations into more usable forms, note first that

$$v_s \frac{\partial v_s}{\partial s} = \frac{\partial}{\partial s}\left(\frac{v_s^2}{2}\right) = \frac{\partial}{\partial s}\left(\frac{v^2}{2}\right)$$

The subscript s on the velocity will usually be dropped as has been done in the last portion of the equation, when there is no confusion since in fact $v_n = 0$. Next, to simplify the term $v_s(\partial v_n/\partial s)$, the geometry of the velocity directional changes will be utilized. As the distance ds of Fig. 3-17a is traversed, the velocity changes from $\mathbf{V}$ to $\mathbf{V} + \mathbf{dV}$, the radius of curvature is r, and the included angle is θ. The two velocity vectors are translated in Fig. 3-17b to a common point where the change in velocity, $\mathbf{dV}$, is resolved into its two components, dv_n and dv_s, as shown. Whereupon by similar triangles, we get

$$\frac{ds}{r} = \frac{dv_n}{|\mathbf{V}|} = \frac{dv_n}{v}$$

since the magnitude of $\mathbf{V}$ is v_s (or simply v). Substituting back into Eq. 3-18b, we can rewrite the pair of equations as

$$a_s = \frac{\partial v_s}{\partial t} + \frac{\partial}{\partial s}\left(\frac{v^2}{2}\right) \tag{3-19a}$$

$$a_n = \frac{\partial v_n}{\partial t} + \frac{v^2}{r} \tag{3-19b}$$

With the acceleration equations in this form it is easy to attach physical significance to the various terms. The term $\partial v_s/\partial t$ in Eq. 3-19a is the local acceleration in the direction of flow. The effects of opening or closing a valve in a flow system would be measured by this term. If a valve is used to change the velocity in a section of straight pipe, then, except in the immediate vicinity of the valve, $\partial v_s/\partial t$ would be the only acceleration term. The other local acceleration term, $\partial v_n/\partial t$, will seldom be present. The swinging of a hose nozzle would be an example in which this term would not vanish. Likewise, the change in inclination of a constant velocity flow through a straight pipe must result in a change in velocity direction and the only acceleration term involved is the local acceleration in the normal direction. The convective term of Eq. 3-19a, $\partial(v^2/2)/\partial s$, is due to convergence or divergence of the streamlines, for example in a pipe contraction. The remaining term, v^2/r, is the normal or radial acceleration due to curvature of the streamlines, examples of which would be flow around a channel bend or a pipe elbow. This term has the opposite sign from the similar term in Eq. 3-17a, since the coordinate directions n and r are defined in opposite senses in the two systems. We are now in a position to make a more physical distinction between uniform and nonuniform flows. A flow will be uniform only if the stream-lines are straight and parallel. If the streamlines converge or diverge, or if they are curved, the flow must be nonuniform.

Again, a word on notation. In many instances, relatively simple flow fields may be specified with equal ease by more than one coordinate system. Under these circumstances the most convenient notation will be used. Thus, the notation may vary to some extent; however, no confusion should result.

Vector Analysis of Acceleration

The derivative techniques developed earlier in the section apply to vector quantities as well as scalar quantities. Thus, in rectangular Cartesian coordinates if $\mathbf{V} = \mathbf{V}(t, x, y, z)$, then

$$\mathbf{a} = \frac{d\mathbf{V}}{dt} = \frac{\partial \mathbf{V}}{\partial t} + u \frac{\partial \mathbf{V}}{\partial x} + v \frac{\partial \mathbf{V}}{\partial y} + w \frac{\partial \mathbf{V}}{\partial z} \tag{3-20}$$

Substituting Eq. 3-2 for $\mathbf{V}$ into Eq. (3-20) and separating the three component equations would yield Eqs. 3-15 once more. A more general vector equation exists:

$$\mathbf{a} = \frac{\partial \mathbf{V}}{\partial t} + (\mathbf{V} \cdot \nabla)\mathbf{V} \tag{3-21}$$

where the vector operation inside the parentheses must be carried out first if only vector and scalar quantities are to be considered. Upon specifying the velocity vector as well as the del operator in a given coordinate system, Eq. 3-21 would lead to the corresponding scalar equations for acceleration.

EXAMPLE 3-8

Show that Eq. 3-21 is equivalent to Eq. 3-20.

SOLUTION:

As indicated above the quantity in parentheses must be treated first. Consequently

$$(\mathbf{V} \cdot \nabla) = [u\mathbf{i} + v\mathbf{j} + w\mathbf{k}] \cdot \left[\frac{\partial(\ )}{\partial x}\mathbf{i} + \frac{\partial(\ )}{\partial y}\mathbf{j} + \frac{\partial(\ )}{\partial z}\mathbf{k} \right]$$

$$= u \frac{\partial(\ )}{\partial x} + v \frac{\partial(\ )}{\partial y} + w \frac{\partial(\ )}{\partial z}$$

and therefore

$$(\mathbf{V} \cdot \nabla)\mathbf{V} = u \frac{\partial \mathbf{V}}{\partial x} + v \frac{\partial \mathbf{V}}{\partial y} + w \frac{\partial \mathbf{V}}{\partial z}$$

Upon adding the remaining term from the right-hand side of Eq. 3-21, this immediately yields Eq. 3-20.

3–4 INTRODUCTION TO TURBULENT AND LAMINAR FLOW

It is important that the reader be aware of the distinction between laminar and turbulent flows early in the study of fluid mechanics. A laminar flow is characterized by a complete orderliness of the flow. If laminar flow is steady, the velocity at a point is unchanging in any respect with time. If it is unsteady, although the velocity is changing with time, it is an orderly change resulting from external influences. Oil or antifreeze as they are poured into a car are readily apparent examples of laminar flow. Because of the orderliness and lack of mixing, light diffusion is low so that it is relatively easy to see distinctly through the laminar flow of a clear liquid. Other important examples are groundwater flow, the flow of blood in capillaries, and the flow of liquids in very thin sheets.

On the other hand, a turbulent flow is characterized by a constantly fluctuating velocity due to an inherent unstableness of the flow. Jets of water, for example, are generally turbulent. The mixing due to eddies in the jet diffuses light, making a turbulent jet more translucent than transparent. Other examples of turbulent flow are the large eddies or boils in a river, and the even larger scale movement of air masses as manifested by the ever-changing pattern and shape of clouds. For comparison, the smoke that rises from a just extinguished candle may rise for a few centimeters as a laminar plume, whereupon eddies will begin to form and a turbulent plume continue. We may obtain a graph of the turbulent velocity at a point and its behavior with time. Figure 3-18 is typical. It is possible to resolve the instantaneous velocity u into mean and fluctuating components as shown. Then,

$$u = \bar{u} + u' \qquad (3\text{-}22)$$

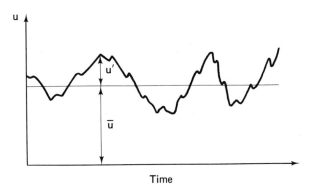

Fig. 3-18. Turbulent fluctuations with time.

87

If the mean component $\bar{u}$ is constant with time, as in the case shown, then this is included in our definition of steady flow. If $\bar{u}$ varies with time at a point, the flow is unsteady. In other words, even though the instantaneous velocity varies with time, a turbulent flow will be defined as steady if the mean component of the velocity at every point does not change with time. The mean component, usually referred to as the *temporal mean velocity*, or *time-averaged velocity*, is obtained by the usual averaging process for a variable with time, namely,

$$\bar{u} = \frac{1}{T} \int_0^T u \, dt \qquad (3\text{-}23)$$

where T is the time over which the average is taken. As two different averaging processes have now been defined, this expression should be contrasted with Eq. 3-12.

Laminar and turbulent flows will be treated in a far more quantitative manner in Chapters 7 and 8. We are not even prepared yet to say under what conditions either type of flow will prevail. The subject of viscosity was, however, introduced in Chapter 1. Let it suffice for now that the higher the viscosity of the fluid, the more likely it is that its flow will be laminar. The lower the viscosity, the greater the chance that the flow will be turbulent. The requirement that there be no slip at a boundary leads to nonconstant-velocity distributions perpendicular to the flow. The profile of Example 3-4, with maximum velocity much greater than the average, is typical of laminar flows. The eddies present in turbulent flow carry fluid with different velocities from region to region. Slippage still does not occur; however, the mixing due to the turbulence reduces the variation in velocity and a profile more similar to that in Example 3-5 results. In those portions of Chapter 5 and elsewhere which ignore the velocity variation across the flow section, a higher accuracy will therefore usually result if the flow is turbulent.

PROBLEMS

Sec. 3-1

3-1. If the velocity in a flow field is specified by

$$\mathbf{V} = (t + 3x)\mathbf{i} + (2t - 2y^2)\mathbf{j} + (4y - 3)z\mathbf{k}$$

determine the magnitude of the velocity after 2 s at the origin and at the point $x = 2, y = 2$, and $z = 1$.

3-2. If a two-dimensional flow is specified by

$$u = 3x^2 + y^2$$
$$v = x^2 - 6xy$$

what is the magnitude of the velocity at the point $x = 6, y = 4$?

3-3. If a boat with an actual velocity of 20 ft/s moves through water with a velocity of 5 ft/s as shown, determine the magnitude and direction of the water as it appears to a passenger on the boat.

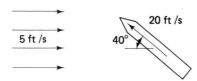

3-4. If water passes out of the moving vane with magnitude and direction relative to the vane as shown, what is the actual velocity of the water as it leaves the vane?

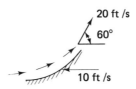

3-5. If the boat in Prob. 3-3 has a velocity of 8.10 m/s and an angle to the stream flow of 10°, what is the resultant magnitude and direction of water as it appears to the passengers? The undisturbed stream velocity is 1.5 m/s.

3-6. The vane of Prob. 3-4 moves to the left with a velocity of 5 m/s. What is the actual magnitude and direction of the water as it leaves the vane if its velocity relative to the vane is 6 m/s at 60°?

Sec. 3-2

3-7. Determine the volumetric discharge and average velocity of water past a cross section of 2 ft² if the mass discharge is 65 slugs/s.

3-8. Air at atmospheric pressure with a temperature of 20°C is blown through a 0.5-m-diameter duct with an average velocity of 30 m/s. Determine the flow rate in m³/s, kg/s, and N/s.

3-9. Determine the pipe size required to carry 1.5 m³/s of water if the average velocity is not to exceed 5 m/s.

3-10. A reservoir needs to be filled to capacity of 100,000,000 gal. The inlet pipe is 6 ft in diameter and the water is pumped at 30 ft/s. How long will it take to fill the reservoir?

3-11. Determine the discharge per unit length between parallel flat plates if the velocity distribution is given by

$$u = u_{max}\left[1 - \left(\frac{y}{B}\right)^2\right]$$

where $y = 0$ at the centerline, and $y = \pm B$ at the plates.

3-12. Show that if the velocity distribution between parallel plates is parabolic, the average velocity will equal two-thirds of the centerline or maximum velocity.

Sec. 3-3

3-13. Determine the x, y, and z components of the acceleration at the origin for Example 3-6. What is the resultant acceleration?

3-14. A velocity field is specified as follows:

$$u = t^2(y + z)$$
$$v = t^2(1 + y^2)$$
$$w = t^2(1 - 2yz)$$

(a) What is the acceleration at the origin when $t = 0$ s, when $t = 2$ s?
(b) What is the acceleration at the point (2, 3, 1) when $t = 2$ s?
(c) Is the flow steady or unsteady?
(d) Is the flow uniform or nonuniform?

3-15. Determine the acceleration at point $x = 5$ mm, $y = 3$ mm, $z = 1$ mm after 10 s if the velocity field is specified as

$$u = 2tx + xy + 3yz \quad \text{(mm/s)}$$
$$v = 5tz - 3yz + 2yt \quad \text{(mm/s)}$$
$$w = 3t + 5xyt - 3y \quad \text{(mm/s)}$$

3-16. A three-dimensional flow is described by the following equations:

$$u = 2(2 + t) \quad \text{(m/s)}$$
$$v = 2t \quad \text{(m/s)}$$
$$w = 2(1 + t) \quad \text{(m/s)}$$

What is the velocity and acceleration at the point (2, 3, 1) after 2 s? After 4 s? Is the flow steady or unsteady? Uniform or nonuniform?

3-17. A flow is specified in polar-cylindrical coordinates as

$$v_r = \frac{4}{r^2}$$
$$v_\theta = 4r$$
$$v_z = \frac{4z}{r^3}$$

What are the three components of acceleration at the point $r = 2$ ft, $z = 0$?

3-18. The velocity is given by

$$v_\theta = \frac{C}{r} \qquad v_r = v_z = 0$$

where C = constant. The velocity v_θ equals 1 ft/s, where the radius $r = 10$ ft.
(a) What is the velocity 2 ft from the axis (i.e., at $r = 2$ ft)?
(b) Sketch the flow field.
(c) What is the acceleration at any radial distance r?

3-19. A fluid flows with a velocity of 1.5 m/s along a circular streamline with a radius of 2 m. If the flow is steady, what are the tangential and normal components of acceleration?

3-20. If the water at the bottom of the spillway has a radius of curvature of 15 ft, what is the acceleration if the average velocity is 75 ft/s?

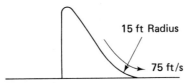

15 ft Radius

75 ft/s

3-21. If the water at the toe of the spillway of Prob. 3-20 has a radius of curvature of 5 m, what is the velocity if the acceleration is 120 m/s² ?

3-22. If the velocity in a straight pipe increases linearly with time from 0 to 2 m/s in 4 s, what is the acceleration?

3-23. By expansion in rectangular Cartesian coordinates, show that Eq. 3-21 leads to Eqs. 3-15.

Sec. 3-4

3-24. Show or explain why the mean of the fluctuation $(\overline{u'})$ must equal zero.

3-25. Instantaneous velocity measurements at a point in a flume were obtained at 1-s intervals as follows:

Time (s)	Velocity (m/s)	Time (s)	Velocity (m/s)
1	1.51	21	1.59
2	1.40	22	1.54
3	1.36	23	1.49
4	1.56	24	1.55
5	1.48	25	1.64
6	1.59	26	1.57
7	1.61	27	1.53
8	1.50	28	1.56
9	1.39	29	1.65
10	1.46	30	1.61
11	1.62	31	1.54
12	1.54	32	1.58
13	1.48	33	1.55
14	1.59	34	1.51
15	1.54	35	1.49
16	1.41	36	1.57
17	1.48	37	1.67
18	1.54	38	1.63
19	1.63	39	1.62
20	1.59	40	1.59

Assuming that the flow is steady, determine the time-averaged mean velocity, the mean of the fluctuations, and the root-mean-square value of the fluctuations.

3-26. Is the flow of Prob. 3-25 probably steady or unsteady? Why?

REFERENCES

CURRIE, I. G., *Fundamental Mechanics of Fluids*. New York: McGraw-Hill, 1974.

ROUSE, H. *Advanced Mechanics of Fluids*. New York: Wiley, 1959.

TENNEKES, H., and J. L. LUMLEY, *A First Course in Turbulence*. Cambridge, Mass.:
    MIT Press, 1972.

4

Reynolds' Transport Theorem and Continuity

This chapter will be devoted to the development of two basic concepts. The first, Reynolds' transport theorem, is a comprehensive relationship which will be useful in the derivation and understanding of the basic relationships that follow, including the continuity equation. This second concept of continuity is simply a restatement of the conservation of mass. It will be seen to apply to fluids at all times. Depending on its use, it will be expressed alternately in both differential and integral form.

4–1 REYNOLDS' TRANSPORT THEOREM

The necessity for the relationship that follows lies in the inherent difference between solid and fluid mechanics. In solid mechanics it is readily possible to identify either a particle or finite body, and starting from a prescribed point, follow its motion. Thus, its location and behavior may be described relative to the fixed starting or initial point. A description of the motion based on the approach of following a particular particle or particles is often referred to as the *Lagrangian approach* and the relevant equations as *Lagrangian equations*. Although this approach is sometimes used in fluid mechanics, it is usually more satisfactory to select a particular point, or a particular volume in space, and describe the behavior of the fluid as it passes past this point or through this volume. This point of view, referred to as the *Eulerian approach*, is taken because of the complexity that ensues when the fluid not only rotates and translates but also deforms. Under these conditions it is no longer easy to keep track of and describe the path of specific particles.

In the course of this discussion, and in fact, frequently hereafter, it will be convenient to use the descriptive terms "system" and "control volume." A *system* is defined as an identified amount or quantity of fluid. The system therefore contains a prescribed mass of fluid. Equations that treat a system directly must follow and describe the movement of this mass as it translates, rotates, and deforms. It follows that such equations must be Lagrangian. A *control volume*, on the other hand, is simply a prescribed volume in space through which the fluid passes. Its size and shape may be arbitrarily selected to suit the requirements of the problem, but must then be held constant. The bounding surface of the control volume will be called the *control surface*. We will generally refer to equations that describe the motion of the fluid as it passes through the control volume as Eulerian.

Strictly speaking, the equations we will use are a blend of the two concepts, since we will attempt to express what happens to the fluid at the instant the system passes through and coincides with the control volume. Although a subtlety of some formal importance, we need to be able from a practical standpoint to formulate and use equations appropriate to a convenient control volume. However, the basic principles of physics are stated for a system (e.g., Newton's second law permits calculation of the force which must be applied to a system or fixed mass to give it a specified acceleration). The Reynolds transport theorem, which will now be derived, provides this necessary relationship between the system and control volume approach.

Reynolds' transport theorem will be derived in terms of a general property which in due course will be taken as the mass, energy, and finally momentum of the fluid. This property will be defined on a per unit mass basis as n. It is assumed that n varies throughout the system both in position and time. The total amount of n within the system, which will be designated as N, may be determined from

$$N = \int_{\text{system}} n\rho \, d\mathcal{V} \tag{4-1}$$

where $d\mathcal{V}$ is a differential volumetric element. We wish now to develop an expression that will permit evaluation of the rate at which the quantity of N within the system changes with time (i.e., dN/dt). However, we want the expression to be in terms of the control volume itself. To achieve this end, consider Fig. 4-1, in which the system, moving with the flow, is depicted as S_1 and S_2 at times t and $t + \Delta t$. The stationary control volume, shown with dashed lines, is chosen to coincide with the system at time t. The regions contained in S_1 are $\mathcal{V}_1$ and $\mathcal{V}_2$, whereas S_2 contains $\mathcal{V}_2$ and $\mathcal{V}_3$. Note that as

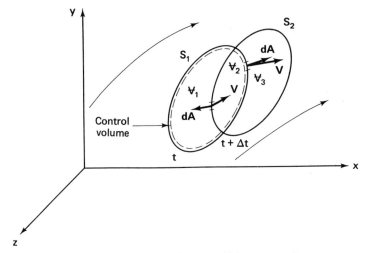

Fig. 4-1. Definition sketch for Reynolds' transport theorem.

$\Delta t \rightarrow 0$, V_2 becomes the control volume and V_1, $V_3 \rightarrow 0$. Corresponding in form to Eq. 4-1, the amount of N at any time in any of the regions of Fig. 4-1 (i.e., N_1, N_2, and N_3) may be obtained by a similar integration of the quantity ρn over the appropriate volume. Hence, during the time interval Δt, the increase in the amount of N within the system may be written as

$$\Delta N = N_{t+\Delta t} - N_t = (N_2 + N_3)_{t+\Delta t} - (N_1 + N_2)_t$$

$$= \left[\int_{V_2} n\rho \, dV + \int_{V_3} n\rho \, dV \right]_{t+\Delta t} - \left[\int_{V_1} n\rho \, dV + \int_{V_2} n\rho \, dV \right]_t$$

or

$$\Delta N = \left[\int_{V_2} n\rho \, dV + \int_{V_1} n\rho \, dV \right]_{t+\Delta t} - \left[\int_{V_1} n\rho \, dV + \int_{V_2} n\rho \, dV \right]_t$$

$$+ \left[\int_{V_3} n\rho \, dV - \int_{V_1} n\rho \, dV \right]_{t+\Delta t}$$

where the quantity $\left[\int_{V_1} n\rho \, dV \right]_{t+\Delta t}$ has been arbitrarily added and subtracted. Upon dividing through by the time interval Δt, we get the rate at which the amount of N in the system increases with time:

$$\frac{\Delta N}{\Delta t} = \frac{\left[\int_{V_2} n\rho \, dV + \int_{V_1} n\rho \, dV \right]_{t+\Delta t} - \left[\int_{V_1} n\rho \, dV + \int_{V_2} n\rho \, dV \right]_t}{\Delta t}$$

$$+ \frac{\left[\int_{V_3} n\rho \, dV - \int_{V_1} n\rho \, dV \right]_{t+\Delta t}}{\Delta t}$$

Considering now the limit as $\Delta t \rightarrow 0$, the left-hand side becomes dN/dt and represents the total rate at which N increases within the system. The first term on the right-hand side is the increase with time of the amount of N within the control volume itself. Since the volume is held constant, this represents a change with respect to time only, and at the limit above may be written

$$\frac{\partial}{\partial t} \int_{\substack{\text{control} \\ \text{volume}}} n\rho \, d\mathcal{V}$$

The two integrals included in the last term require a bit more discussion. The first,

$$\int_{\mathcal{V}_3} n\rho \, d\mathcal{V}$$

is of course the amount of N in the region $\mathcal{V}_3$. As Δt increases, the amount of N increases accordingly. Hence, division by Δt represents the rate of increase of N contained in $\mathcal{V}_3$ or, as can be seen from Fig. 4-1, the rate at which N is leaving the control volume. But, the quantity $\mathbf{V} \cdot \mathbf{dA}$[1] (on the right side of region $\mathcal{V}_2$, Fig. 4-1) is the volume rate of flow through the unit area dA as developed in Section 3-2. Hence, the quantity $\rho n \mathbf{V} \cdot \mathbf{dA}$ is the rate of flow of N through the same unit area. If this quantity is integrated over the portion of the surface of the control volume for which N is leaving, it must equal

$$\lim_{\Delta t \to 0} \frac{\int_{\mathcal{V}_3} n\rho \, d\mathcal{V}}{\Delta t}$$

In like fashion, as Δt increases and the system is seen to move away from the control volume, the fluid moving into the control volume to replace that of the system brings in N at the rate of

$$\frac{\int_{\mathcal{V}_1} n\rho \, d\mathcal{V}}{\Delta t}$$

Again, showing $\mathbf{dA}$ as an outward (from the control volume) area vector and the velocity in the sense of the flow direction, we may equate the integral above, at the limit as $\Delta t \to 0$, to the integral of $-\rho n \mathbf{V} \cdot \mathbf{dA}$ over the inflow area of the control volume. Finally, at any portion of the boundary of the control volume where fluid is neither leaving nor entering, the velocity and area vectors are orthogonal and

$$\mathbf{V} \cdot \mathbf{dA} = 0$$

Therefore, as $\Delta t \to 0$, the last term becomes

$$\lim_{\Delta t \to 0} \frac{\int_{\mathcal{V}_3} n\rho \, d\mathcal{V} - \int_{\mathcal{V}_1} n\rho \, d\mathcal{V}}{\Delta t} = \int_{\substack{\text{control} \\ \text{surface}}} n\rho \mathbf{V} \cdot \mathbf{dA}$$

[1]For an explanation of vector operations, see Appendix D.

Putting all of the foregoing together, Reynolds' transport theorem becomes

$$\frac{dN}{dt} = \frac{\partial}{\partial t} \int_{\substack{\text{control} \\ \text{volume}}} n\rho \, d\mathcal{V} + \int_{\substack{\text{control} \\ \text{surface}}} n\rho \mathbf{V} \cdot d\mathbf{A} \qquad (4\text{-}2)$$

In effect, the rate at which the property N increases with time within the system is equal to the time rate of increase of N in the control volume plus the net rate of flow of N through the control surface. Subsequently in this chapter we will use Eq. 4-2 to transform the expression for conservation of mass as formulated for a system to a form readily applicable to a control volume. In Chapter 5 energy and momentum principles will be similarly treated.

4–2   CONTINUITY EQUATION

One constraint that the natural laws impose on a fluid flow is an equation on continuity. This is an expression resulting from the principle of conservation of mass. As applied to a system, this principle states that the mass of a given quantity of fluid remains constant. As applied to a control volume it states that as flow passes through a fixed volume in space, if the rate at which mass flows out of the volume is greater than that entering the volume, there must be a corresponding decrease in mass inside the volume. Furthermore, if the fluid is incompressible, so that the mass per unit volume cannot change, the mass rate in must equal the mass rate out. More simply, under these circumstances the volume rate of flow in must equal the volume rate of flow out. In the course of this section these concepts will be formalized and applied in both differential and integral forms.

Differential Form of Continuity Equation

The differential form of continuity equation may be obtained by keeping track of the mass rate of flow[2] in and out of the differential rectangular parallelepiped of Fig. 4-2. A differential element such as shown here may be arbitrarily shrunk in size, consistent with the continuum assumption, until it is infinitesimally small. A small lack of mathematical rigor is present in this formulation since the velocities shown represent averages over the respective faces. A more precise accounting, based on specifying velocities at the corner points in much the same way they are expressed on the opposite faces of Fig. 4-2, would allow for possible variations in the velocity over the faces. However, as the element shrinks to a point the average velocity on a face becomes a point velocity and either procedure leads to the same result (see Prob. 4-9). The mass rates of flow per unit area are shown entering and

---

[2]For example, the quantity ρu with dimensions $(M/L^3)(L/T)$ may be treated as the mass rate of flow (M/T) per unit area (L^2). See Section 3-2.

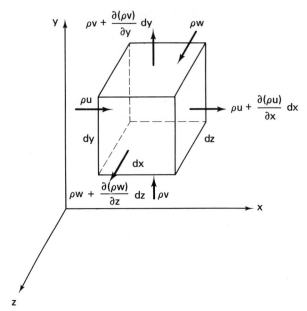

Fig. 4-2. Continuity in rectangular Cartesian coordinates.

leaving through the various faces. The amount out in the x direction is increased over that entering in the x direction by the change in the quantity ρu [i.e., the rate at which ρu is changing with the x distance, $\partial(\rho u)/\partial x$, times the distance over which the change is occurring, dx]. The other directions follow accordingly.

Since the mass inside the volume $dx\,dy\,dz$ is $\rho\,dx\,dy\,dz$, we can equate the net rate of mass flow out with the rate at which the mass is decreasing inside the element:

$$\left[\rho u + \frac{\partial(\rho u)}{\partial x}\,dx\right][dy\,dz] - [\rho u\,dy\,dz] + \left[\rho v + \frac{\partial(\rho v)}{\partial y}\,dy\right][dx\,dz]$$

$$- [\rho v\,dx\,dz] + \left[\rho w + \frac{\partial(\rho w)}{\partial z}\,dz\right][dx\,dy] - [\rho w\,dx\,dy] = -\frac{\partial}{\partial t}[\rho\,dx\,dy\,dz]$$

Since the volume is not changing with time, $dx\,dy\,dz$ may be pulled out of the final derivative. Then by canceling and rearranging,

$$\left[\frac{\partial(\rho u)}{\partial x} + \frac{\partial(\rho v)}{\partial y} + \frac{\partial(\rho w)}{\partial z} + \frac{\partial\rho}{\partial t}\right][dx\,dy\,dz] = 0$$

The volume is arbitary and not necessarily zero; therefore, the quantity within the first brackets must itself equal zero, giving one form of the continuity equation:

$$\frac{\partial\rho}{\partial t} + \frac{\partial(\rho u)}{\partial x} + \frac{\partial(\rho v)}{\partial y} + \frac{\partial(\rho w)}{\partial z} = 0 \qquad (4\text{-}3)$$

This equation must be satisfied at every point in the flow field. If the flow is incompressible so that the density is a constant, the equation further simplifies to

$$\frac{\partial u}{\partial x} + \frac{\partial v}{\partial y} + \frac{\partial w}{\partial z} = 0 \qquad (4\text{-}4)$$

which is the continuity equation for three-dimensional incompressible flow in Cartesian coordinates.

Other arrangements of Eq. 4-3 are sometimes useful. If each of the derivatives with distance is taken by parts,

$$\frac{\partial \rho}{\partial t} + u\frac{\partial \rho}{\partial x} + v\frac{\partial \rho}{\partial y} + w\frac{\partial \rho}{\partial z} + \rho\frac{\partial u}{\partial x} + \rho\frac{\partial v}{\partial y} + \rho\frac{\partial w}{\partial z} = 0$$

For $\rho = \rho(t, x, y, z)$, the first four terms are the total derivative of the density, $d\rho/dt$,[3] and therefore the equation becomes

$$\frac{d\rho}{dt} + \rho\left(\frac{\partial u}{\partial x} + \frac{\partial v}{\partial y} + \frac{\partial w}{\partial z}\right) = 0$$

As a constraint on the flow field, the differential form of the continuity equation performs two major functions. On the one hand, it may be combined with other partial differential equations describing a flow so that a mathematical solution may be obtained for a specific set of boundary conditions. This technique is generally beyond the scope of this book. On the other hand, if a velocity field is specified, the differential form of the continuity equation may be easily used to determine whether or not it is a physically possible flow field as in Example 4-1.

The continuity equation may be obtained in other coordinate systems by starting with the appropriate element. In polar-cylindrical coordinates the element shown in Fig. 4-3 (with the side perpendicular to the x–y plane, dz, not shown) leads to a corresponding continuity equation, Eq. 4-5.

$$\frac{1}{r}\frac{\partial(\rho v_r r)}{\partial r} + \frac{1}{r}\frac{\partial(\rho v_\theta)}{\partial \theta} + \frac{\partial(\rho v_z)}{\partial z} + \frac{\partial \rho}{\partial t} = 0 \qquad (4\text{-}5)$$

For incompressible flow, this reduces to

$$\frac{1}{r}\frac{\partial(v_r r)}{\partial r} + \frac{1}{r}\frac{\partial v_\theta}{\partial \theta} + \frac{\partial v_z}{\partial z} = 0 \qquad (4\text{-}6)$$

the continuity equation for an incompressible flow in polar-cylindrical coordinates.

---

[3]Compare with the differentiation of velocity to obtain the acceleration equations (Eqs. 3-15) in Section 3-3.

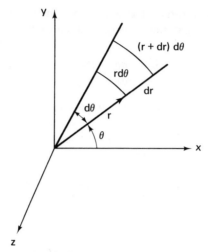

Fig. 4-3.   Continuity in polar-cylindrical coordinates.

EXAMPLE 4-1

Show that the flow of Example 3-6 is a possible flow; that is, that it satisfies the continuity equation.

The velocities were given as follows:

$$u = 2t + 2x + 2y$$

$$v = t - y - z$$

$$w = t + x - z$$

SOLUTION:

We must show that continuity is satisfied everywhere, not just at the point $(2, 2, 1)$. Since the density is not specified, we can assume that the flow is incompressible and substitute directly into Eq. 4-4.

$$\frac{\partial u}{\partial x} = 2 \qquad \frac{\partial v}{\partial y} = -1 \qquad \frac{\partial w}{\partial z} = -1$$

$$\frac{\partial u}{\partial x} + \frac{\partial v}{\partial y} + \frac{\partial w}{\partial z} = 2 - 1 - 1 = 0$$

Hence, continuity is satisfied throughout the flow field.

Integral Form of Continuity Equation

The differential form of the continuity equation clearly owes its name to the fact that it was developed on the basis of a differential element and expresses the continuity of mass in the form of a differential equation. Similarly, the integral form will address the same continuity relationship, this time, however, on the basis of an integration process as applied to a finite control volume.

The integral form will first be obtained directly from the Reynolds' transport theorem (Eq. 4-2). An arbitrary control volume V, with surface area A, is shown in Fig. 4-4. By the previous definition of a control volume, this is a

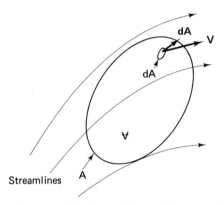

Fig. 4-4. Development of the integral form of the continuity equation.

fixed (but arbitrary) volume in space through which the flow occurs. The velocity at any point is $\mathbf{V}$ and in Eqs. 4-1 and 4-2 we will let the indefinite flow property N be the mass. Then n is the mass per unit mass. The latter is, of course, unity; hence, Eq. 4-1 gives the mass in the system as follows:

$$M_{\text{system}} = \int_{\text{system}} (1)\rho \, dV \tag{4-7}$$

The mass in the control volume at any instant is correspondingly given by

$$M_{\substack{\text{control} \\ \text{volume}}} = \int_{\substack{\text{control} \\ \text{volume}}} \rho \, dV \tag{4-8}$$

and Eq. 4-2 becomes

$$\frac{dM}{dt}_{\text{system}} = \frac{\partial}{\partial t} \int_{\substack{\text{control} \\ \text{volume}}} \rho \, dV + \int_{\substack{\text{control} \\ \text{surface}}} \rho \mathbf{V} \cdot \mathbf{dA}$$

The *law of conservation of mass* says that the mass within a system (Eq. 4-7) cannot change with time (excluding Einstein's relativity effects). Hence, $dM/dt = 0$ in the above and the conservation of mass, as applied to a control volume, becomes

$$\frac{\partial}{\partial t} \int_{\substack{\text{control} \\ \text{volume}}} \rho \, dV + \int_{\substack{\text{control} \\ \text{surface}}} \rho \mathbf{V} \cdot \mathbf{dA} = 0$$

Exchanging the order of integration and differentiation, this becomes

$$\int_{\substack{\text{control} \\ \text{volume}}} \frac{\partial \rho}{\partial t} \, dV + \int_{\substack{\text{control} \\ \text{surface}}} \rho \mathbf{V} \cdot \mathbf{dA} = 0 \tag{4-9}$$

The application of this equation will be considered shortly. First note that Eq. (4-9) may also be formulated directly from Fig. 4-4. The velocity $\mathbf{V}$ is shown passing through the differential area dA, which is given vector representation, as in Fig. 4-1, by the vector $d\mathbf{A}$ equal in magnitude to the area dA with direction normal to the surface at that point. The mass rate of flow through dA will be the component of $\rho\mathbf{V}$ perpendicular to the surface times the area, or $\rho\mathbf{V}\cdot d\mathbf{A}$. The integral of this term over the entire control surface area will be the net rate of mass flow out. From conservation of mass, this in turn must equal the rate of decrease of mass in the element; thus,

$$\int_A \rho\mathbf{V}\cdot d\mathbf{A} = -\frac{\partial}{\partial t}\int_\mathcal{V} \rho\,d\mathcal{V} \tag{4-10}$$

Here, $d\mathcal{V}$ represents a differential volume of mass $\rho\,d\mathcal{V}$, the integral over the control volume $\mathcal{V}$ gives the total mass, and the partial derivative consequently gives the rate of change of this mass with time. With minimal rearranging this immediately becomes Eq. 4-9.

Gauss's theorem, which converts a surface integral to a volume integral, may be applied to the left-hand side of Eq. 4-10 (or the second term of Eq. 4-9) to simplify the expression. If $\mathbf{B}$ is an arbitrary vector, then according to Gauss's theorem,

$$\int_A \mathbf{B}\cdot d\mathbf{A} = \int_\mathcal{V} \nabla\cdot\mathbf{B}\,d\mathcal{V} \tag{4-11}$$

where $\nabla\cdot\mathbf{B}$ is referred to as the divergence of $\mathbf{B}$, and ∇ is the del operator.[4] In rectangular Cartesian coordinates the del operator may be written

$$\nabla(\ ) = \mathbf{i}\frac{\partial(\ )}{\partial x} + \mathbf{j}\frac{\partial(\ )}{\partial y} + \mathbf{k}\frac{\partial(\ )}{\partial z} \tag{4-12}$$

Changing the area integral in Eq. 4-10 to a volume integral according to Gauss's theorem and changing the order of integration and differentiation on the right-hand side yields

$$\int_\mathcal{V} \nabla\cdot(\rho\mathbf{V})\,d\mathcal{V} = -\int_\mathcal{V} \frac{\partial\rho}{\partial t}\,d\mathcal{V}$$

Placing both terms under the same integral,

$$\int_\mathcal{V} \left[\frac{\partial\rho}{\partial t} + \nabla\cdot(\rho\mathbf{V})\right]d\mathcal{V} = 0$$

This expression can equal zero only if the integrand is itself equal to zero, since the volume is arbitrary. Thus, we have obtained the differential form of the continuity equation,

$$\frac{\partial\rho}{\partial t} + \nabla\cdot(\rho\mathbf{V}) = 0 \tag{4-13}$$

[4]Vector operation and theorems are further summarized in Appendix D.

Expanding Eq. 4-13 in rectangular Cartesian coordinates using Eq. 4-12 gives the previously derived Eq. 4-3. Using the del operator in polar-cylindrical coordinates, which is defined by

$$\nabla(\ ) = e_r\left[\frac{\partial(\ )}{\partial r} + \frac{(\ )}{r}\right] + e_\theta\frac{1}{r}\frac{\partial(\ )}{\partial\theta} + e_z\frac{\partial(\ )}{\partial z} \qquad (4\text{-}14)$$

to expand Eq. 4-13 would give the corresponding continuity equation in polar-cylindrical coordinates, Eq. 4-5. Here unit vectors in the r, θ, and z directions are indicated by e_r, e_θ, and e_z, respectively.

To relate the foregoing arbitrary control volume to a more practical or flow-oriented geometry, consider a series of streamlines which surround a region of flow as in Fig. 4-5. This circumferential group of streamlines is

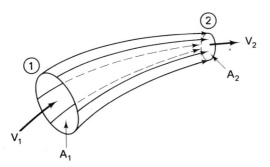

Fig. 4-5. Continuity applied to a streamtube.

called a *streamtube*. Since the velocity must be everywhere tangent to the streamlines, there can be no flow in or out of the region except at the end sections 1 and 2. Thus, a streamtube may just as well represent confined flow through a pipe or other flow passage.

We will let V and ρ represent the average values of velocity and density over a cross section of area A and the appropriate subscripts indicate the particular section. The product of VA is the discharge Q, which upon multiplication by the average density over A gives the mass discharge $\rho Q = G$. The conservation of mass may now be applied to a compressible steady flow through a streamtube. Since the flow is steady, the mass rate of flow in must equal the mass rate out, or

$$\rho_1 V_1 A_1 = \rho_2 V_2 A_2 \qquad (4\text{-}15)$$

Continuing, for an incompressible flow $\rho_1 = \rho_2$, and immediately

$$V_1 A_1 = V_2 A_2 = Q \qquad (4\text{-}16)$$

Although Eq. 4-15 applies only to steady flow, Eq. 4-16 is valid for unsteady flows as well, as long as the volume of the streamtube is assumed not to change with time. These expressions can easily be generalized for flows entering and leaving from more than one point.

Returning to Eq. 4-10, if the density is constant, the right-hand side will vanish, leaving the integral form of the continuity equation for an incompressible fluid,

$$\int_A \mathbf{V} \cdot \mathbf{dA} = 0 \qquad (4\text{-}17)$$

It will now be shown that this also leads directly to Eq. 4-16. Figure 4-6 is a repeat of Fig. 4-5, with average velocities and area vectors shown. The

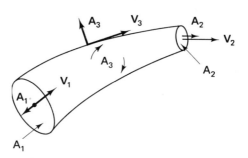

Fig. 4-6. Vector approach to continuity in a streamtube.

area vectors are shown as positive outward. There are no contributions to Eq. 4-17 except at the two ends, since elsewhere the velocity $\mathbf{V}_3$ is tangential to the surface while the area vector $\mathbf{A}_3$ is perpendicular to the surface, resulting in a dot product $\mathbf{V}_3 \cdot \mathbf{A}_3$, which vanishes. At the left end the two vectors are collinear but in opposite directions; thus,

$$\mathbf{V}_1 \cdot \mathbf{A}_1 = -V_1 A_1$$

At the right end the area vector and the velocity vector are not only collinear, but also in the same direction,

$$\mathbf{V}_2 \cdot \mathbf{A}_2 = V_2 A_2$$

Thus, Eq. 4-17 gives

$$-V_1 A_1 + V_2 A_2 = 0$$

which is the identical continuity equation given in Eq. 4-16.

EXAMPLE 4-2

A liquid flows into the 2-cm-diameter manifold of Fig. 4-7 and out through the eight 1-mm-diameter orifices. The design is such that each orifice has 2% less flow through it than the one on its left. If the incoming flow has an average velocity of 0.15 m/s, determine the velocities in the extreme left and right orifices.

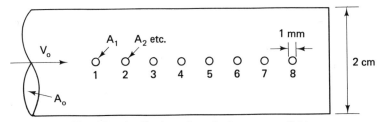

Fig. 4-7. Application of continuity to a manifold.

SOLUTION:

The manifold section shown in Fig. 4-7 may be taken as the control volume. The continuity equation may then be applied to this control volume in a generalized form of Eq. 4-15, namely,

$$V_0 A_0 = V_1 A_1 + V_2 A_2 + \ldots + V_8 A_8$$
$$= (V_1 + V_2 + \ldots + V_8) A_1$$

since the area of each orifice is the same. The decrease in velocity from orifice to orifice may be expressed as follows:

$$V_2 = 0.98 V_1$$
$$V_3 = 0.98 V_2 = (0.98)^2 V_1$$
$$\cdot$$
$$\cdot$$
$$\cdot$$
$$V_8 = (0.98)^7 V_1$$

Hence,

$$V_0 A_0 = [1 + 0.98 + (0.98)^2 + \ldots + (0.98)^7] V_1 A_1$$

or

$$(0.15 \text{ m/s}) \left[\left(\frac{\pi}{4} \right)(0.02)^2 \text{ m}^2 \right] = [1 + 0.98 + (0.98)^2 +$$

$$\ldots + (0.98)^7][V_1 \text{ m/s}] \left[\left(\frac{\pi}{4} \right)(0.001)^2 \text{ m}^2 \right]$$

Solving,

$$V_1 = 8.04 \text{ m/s} \quad \text{and} \quad V_8 = (0.98)^7(8.04) = 6.98 \text{ m/s}$$

PROBLEMS

Sec. 4-2

4-1. Show that the following flow satisfies continuity:

$$u = y^2 - x^2$$
$$v = 2xy$$
$$w = C \quad (C = \text{constant})$$

4-2. Does the flow of Prob. 3-1 satisfy the continuity equation?

4-3. Does the flow of Prob. 3-2 satisfy the continuity equation?

4-4. Does the flow of Prob. 3-13 satisfy the continuity equation?

4-5. Does the flow of Prob. 3-17 satisfy the continuity equation?

4-6. Using the element of Fig. 4-3, derive Eq. 4-5.

4-7. Using the element of Fig. 4-3, derive Eq. 4-6 for an incompressible flow.

4-8. Does the following flow satisfy continuity?

$$\rho = t^2$$

$$u = \frac{1}{\rho}(y^2 - x^2)$$

$$v = \frac{1}{\rho}(2xy)$$

$$w = \frac{-2tz}{\rho}$$

4-9. With reference to Fig. 4-2, select the velocity components at the lower rear corner nearest the origin, as u, v, w. Express the velocities at the other seven corners appropriately [e.g., the lower front left has velocity components $\left(u + \frac{\partial u}{\partial z} dz\right)$, $\left(v + \frac{\partial v}{\partial z} dz\right)$, and $\left(w + \frac{\partial w}{\partial z} dz\right)$ and the x component only at the upper front right is $\left(u + \frac{\partial u}{\partial x} dx + \frac{\partial u}{\partial y} dy + \frac{\partial u}{\partial z} dz\right)$]. Then average the velocity over each face and develop the differential form of the continuity equation accordingly.

4-10. If the average velocity in a 12-in. pipe is 8 ft/s, what will be the corresponding velocity at a section that has been reduced to 6-in. diameter?

4-11. If the velocity in the 6-in. pipe is one-half the velocity in the 8-in. pipe, what must be the ratio of their discharge?

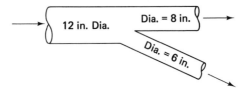

4-12. Water from a 6-in. vertical pipe strikes a flat surface and spreads radially as shown. The flow rate is 8 cfs. If at a distance $R = 3$ ft the velocity is exactly that in the pipe itself, what is the depth y of the flow at this point?

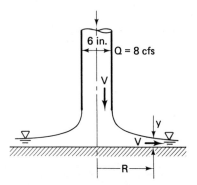

4-13. Calculate the average velocity of the water at the orifice and in the jet exiting from the orifice, if the average velocity in the 0.6-m-diameter pipe is 6 m/s.

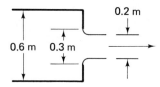

4-14. A hose with an inside diameter of 0.8 in. supplies water to a nonrotating sprinkler head consisting of 22 holes, each hole being 0.06 in. in diameter. The water leaves the sprinkler holes at 25 ft/s. What is the flow rate and the velocity of water in the hose?

4-15. Develop the continuity equation in rectangular Cartesian coordinates (Eq. 4-3), by expanding Eq. 4-13.

4-16. Use the del operator in polar-cylindrical coordinates to expand Eq. 4-13 to get Eq. 4-5.

4-17. Assuming that the velocities out of the orifices of Example 4-2 remain unchanged, determine the diameter of orifice 8 on the manifold of Fig. 4-7, so that the discharge through orifice 8 is identical to the discharge through orifice 1, which has a diameter of 1 mm.

REFERENCES

CURRIE, I. G., *Fundamental Mechanics of Fluids.* New York: McGraw-Hill, 1974.

ROUSE, H. (ed.), *Advanced Mechanics of Fluids.* New York: Wiley, 1959.

5

Dynamics of Fluid Motion

The dynamics of fluid motion will now be treated. Building upon the basic relationships of Chapters 3 and 4, the cause-and-effect relationships will now be investigated for the first time. The chapter will begin with the development and subsequent application of basic equations of motion for steady frictionless flow.[1] These will, in turn, lead to the Bernoulli equation, which we will apply to steady, incompressible frictionless flows. Basic relationships for both energy and momentum will also be derived. These derivations will initially be quite general. However, the applications in the course of this chapter will usually be restricted to steady, incompressible frictionless flow. Even though the modifying effects of friction are not included until later chapters, the results of many of the problems which will be considered in Chapter 5 are reasonably accurate. In this regard bear in mind also the differences between laminar and turbulent flow discussed at the end of Chapter 3.

Although the significance of the various equations and, in fact, the interdependence of the equations will be stressed during their development, the final emphasis will be placed on the application of the equations to engineering problems. A broad variety of applications will be covered during the course of Chapter 5, both in the illustrative examples and in the problem lists. The reader should be particularly alert to those problems which are

---

[1] The more general equations of motion will be discussed in Chapter 7.

unsteady as stated but may be made steady by the relative motion concept of Section 3-1.

5–1 EQUATIONS OF MOTION: THE EULER EQUATIONS

Previously, we have examined the pressure variation in fluids at rest. The pressure distribution which was developed, known as the hydrostatic pressure variation, implied that a pressure gradient was necessary to counteract gravity, or elevation effects. Specifically, a pressure drop was required in the direction of increasing elevation. In this section the fluid is still assumed to be frictionless, and consequently shear stresses will still not be included in the formulation. In Chapter 7, however, we will see that a pressure drop is also required to overcome friction losses. In this section we will find that an additional pressure drop is necessary if the flow is to be accelerated. This acceleration may be a local acceleration, a convective acceleration, or both. In order to obtain this relationship between pressure differences and accelerations, Newton's second law will once again be applied, first in rectangular Cartesian coordinates, then in alternative systems.

Euler Equations in Rectangular Cartesian Coordinates

At the risk of some loss of generality, the following derivation will assume that the y axis is in the vertical direction and opposite in sense to the effective direction of the acceleration of gravity. A more general approach will also be taken in this section for both streamline coordinates and rectangular Cartesian coordinates. Although the element is shown three-dimensionally in Fig. 5-1, for clarity only the forces due to pressure acting in the x direction are labeled. As has been done with other quantities previously, the forces over the various faces will be represented by the average pressure over a particular face, times the area of the face. (The force on the left face is $p \, dy \, dz$, for example). This once again is less precise mathematically than is specifying a variable pressure over the face, but it leads to the same results when the element is reduced to a point. The forces due to the varying pressure in the x direction may now be summed and set equal to the acceleration in the x direction. Subsequently, the y and z directions will be treated in a similar fashion.

Since the weight has no component in the x direction and there are still no shearing stresses, application of Newton's second law in the x direction gives

$$p \, dy \, dz - \left(p + \frac{\partial p}{\partial x} dx \right) dy \, dz = \rho \, dx \, dy \, dz \, a_x$$

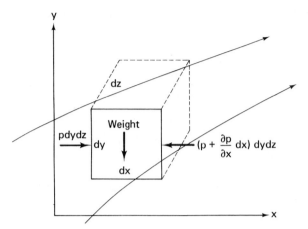

Fig. 5-1. Definition sketch for Euler equations in rectangular Cartesian coordinates.

Simplifying the algebra, dividing through by the mass $\rho\ dx\ dy\ dz$ and expressing a_x by Eq. 3-15a yields

$$\frac{\partial u}{\partial t} + u\frac{\partial u}{\partial x} + v\frac{\partial u}{\partial y} + w\frac{\partial u}{\partial z} = -\frac{1}{\rho}\frac{\partial p}{\partial x} \qquad (5\text{-}1a)$$

This equation relates the acceleration in a given direction to the pressure gradient in that direction. The z direction, which is written out as Eq. (5-1c), is identical except for the interchange of z and x. The vertical direction, which is to be considered next, must also include the effect of gravity.

Formulating Newton's law in the vertical direction, with the weight of the fluid in the element included as the additional term gives

$$p\ dx\ dz - \left(p + \frac{\partial p}{\partial y}\ dy\right)dx\ dz - \gamma\ dx\ dy\ dz = \rho\ dx\ dy\ dz\ a_y$$

and simplifying as before,

$$\frac{\partial v}{\partial t} + u\frac{\partial v}{\partial x} + v\frac{\partial v}{\partial y} + w\frac{\partial v}{\partial z} = -\frac{1}{\rho}\frac{\partial p}{\partial y} - g \qquad (5\text{-}1b)$$

Finally, in the z direction,

$$\frac{\partial w}{\partial t} + u\frac{\partial w}{\partial x} + v\frac{\partial w}{\partial y} + w\frac{\partial w}{\partial z} = -\frac{1}{\rho}\frac{\partial p}{\partial z} \qquad (5\text{-}1c)$$

Like the continuity equation, these equations must apply at every point throughout the fluid. The Euler equations[2] as derived here are more restrictive than the continuity equation, however, since they are valid only for a

[2]This set of equations is named after the Swiss mathematician Leonhard Euler, who similarly applied Newton's second law in 1750.

frictionless flow. However, they are applicable to both compressible and incompressible flows, since no constraint has been placed on either the specific weight or the density. The modification that results when the direction of gravitational acceleration and a coordinate axis are not collinear will be discussed shortly.

Euler Equation in Streamline Coordinates

We will often find it advantageous in solving flow problems to revert to the previously discussed streamline coordinates. Thus, it becomes necessary to establish the form of the Euler equations appropriate to this coordinate system as well. Using the same techniques developed earlier in the section, we will first sum forces in the arbitrary s direction of Fig. 5-2 and set the result equal to the mass times the acceleration in the s direction. This acceleration will be noted for the present as a_s, as the s direction is at present an arbitrary direction. The differential element chosen here is the cylindrical

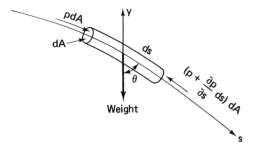

Fig. 5-2. Definition sketch for Euler equations in streamline coordinates.

tube of cross-sectional area dA and length ds. The weight acts vertically in the direction opposite to the positive y direction of Fig. 5-2, with a magnitude equal to $\gamma \, ds \, dA$. We therefore have in this s direction,

$$p \, dA - \left(p + \frac{\partial p}{\partial s} \, ds \right) dA + \gamma \, ds \, dA \cos \theta = \rho \, ds \, dA \, a_s$$

As before, the first two terms cancel each other. In addition, note from Fig. 5-3 the relationship between the vertical and the s directions. A change in vertical distance of $-\Delta y$ corresponds to a positive change of Δs, and vice versa. Consequently, at the limit as Δs approaches zero,

$$\cos \theta = -\frac{\partial y}{\partial s}$$

Substituting this into the previous expression and simplifying,

$$-\frac{\partial p}{\partial s} - \gamma \frac{\partial y}{\partial s} = \rho a_s \tag{5-2}$$

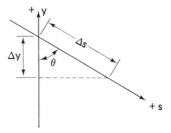

Fig. 5-3. Relationship between coordinate directions.

Up to this point, the s direction has not been restricted and could be any general direction. If we now pick the s direction as the streamline direction, then, with a_s from Eq. 3-19a, the expression becomes the Euler equation along a streamline:

$$-\frac{\partial p}{\partial s} - \gamma\frac{\partial y}{\partial s} = \rho\left[\frac{\partial v}{\partial t} + \frac{\partial}{\partial s}\left(\frac{v^2}{2}\right)\right] \qquad (5\text{-}3a)$$

Letting the arbitrary s direction of Eq. 5-2 be the normal or n direction of streamline coordinates, we get, by replacing s by n, the Euler equation in the direction perpendicular to a streamline,

$$-\frac{\partial p}{\partial n} - \gamma\frac{\partial y}{\partial n} = \rho a_n = \frac{\rho v^2}{r} \qquad (5\text{-}3b)$$

where a_n (with $\partial v_n/\partial t$ assumed zero) is given by Eq. 3-19b. If the fluid is incompressible, so that γ may be treated as a constant, the equations become

$$-\frac{1}{\rho}\frac{\partial}{\partial s}(p + \gamma y) = \frac{\partial v}{\partial t} + \frac{\partial}{\partial s}\left(\frac{v^2}{2}\right) \qquad (5\text{-}4a)$$

and

$$-\frac{1}{\rho}\frac{\partial}{\partial n}(p + \gamma y) = \frac{v^2}{r} \qquad (5\text{-}4b)$$

the Euler equations for an incompressible flow.

Consideration of Eqs. 5-4 shows that if flow occurs in a horizontal plane, or if the fluid is a gas, the γy term drops out or becomes negligible. Under these circumstances the acceleration will occur in the direction of decreasing pressure. Along a line of constant pressure (a line where $dp = 0$) the pressure gradient $\partial p/\partial s$ must vanish and there can be no acceleration. Therefore, an acceleration, if present, must be perpendicular to a line of constant pressure under these circumstances.

In the more general case where the γy term does not vanish, the foregoing remarks still apply but to the quantity $(p + \gamma y)$ rather than just to the pressure. Equations 5-4 are often divided by γ and rearranged to give

$$\frac{\partial}{\partial s}\left(\frac{p}{\gamma} + y\right) = -\frac{1}{g}\left[\frac{\partial v}{\partial t} + \frac{\partial}{\partial s}\left(\frac{v^2}{2}\right)\right] \qquad (5\text{-}5a)$$

and

$$\frac{\partial}{\partial n}\left(\frac{p}{\gamma} + y\right) = -\frac{1}{g}\frac{v^2}{r} \qquad (5\text{-}5b)$$

The quantity in the parentheses on the left-hand side of both equations is often defined as the *piezometric head, h*; thus,

$$h = \frac{p}{\gamma} + y \qquad (5\text{-}6)$$

We may immediately note that there can be no acceleration along a line of constant piezometric head. The acceleration in general must be perpendicular to lines of constant piezometric head and in the direction of decreasing values of h.

EXAMPLE 5-1

Use Eqs. 5-5 to show how pressure must vary in a direction in which there is no acceleration.

SOLUTION:

For the case of zero acceleration, the right-hand side of both Eq. 5-5a and Eq. 5-5b must equal zero. Consequently, the quantity $(p/\gamma + y)$ can change with neither the s nor the n direction. In other words, $(p/\gamma + y)$ is constant everywhere, and this is identically the hydrostatic pressure distribution, since y is in the vertical direction. If y is constant (i.e., on a horizontal plane), p/γ is constant. As y increases, p/γ drops accordingly.

General Rectangular Cartesian and Vector Forms of the Euler Equations

A form of the Euler equations for Cartesian coordinates in which none of the axes is in the vertical direction may be formulated similar to that for streamline coordinates. Define η as the vertical direction relative to arbitrary xyz coordinates as in Fig. 5-4. Then the changes of η with respect to $x, y,$

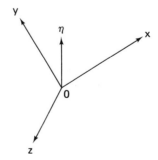

Fig. 5-4. Arbitrary rectangular Cartesian coordinates.

and z can be formulated essentially as was $\partial y/\partial s$ using Fig. 5-3 previously. This leads to the only difference from Eqs. 5-1, and the more general Euler equations in rectangular Cartesian coordinates for compressible or incompressible flow therefore become

$$\frac{\partial u}{\partial t} + u\frac{\partial u}{\partial x} + v\frac{\partial u}{\partial y} + w\frac{\partial u}{\partial z} = -\frac{1}{\rho}\frac{\partial p}{\partial x} - g\frac{\partial \eta}{\partial x} \qquad (5\text{-}7a)$$

$$\frac{\partial v}{\partial t} + u\frac{\partial v}{\partial x} + v\frac{\partial v}{\partial y} + w\frac{\partial v}{\partial z} = -\frac{1}{\rho}\frac{\partial p}{\partial y} - g\frac{\partial \eta}{\partial y} \qquad (5\text{-}7b)$$

$$\frac{\partial w}{\partial t} + u\frac{\partial w}{\partial x} + v\frac{\partial w}{\partial y} + w\frac{\partial w}{\partial z} = -\frac{1}{\rho}\frac{\partial p}{\partial z} - g\frac{\partial \eta}{\partial z} \qquad (5\text{-}7c)$$

Note that as the y axis becomes vertical, these equations immediately revert back to Eqs. 5-1.

The Euler equations will not be derived by vector procedures; however, the Eqs. 5-7 may easily be put into vector notation. The left-hand sides of the equations are, as we have seen before, the components of the acceleration $\mathbf{a}$. The derivatives with respect to x, y, and z of the pressure and elevation are the x, y, and z components of the respective gradients of pressure and elevation. That is,

$$\nabla p = \mathbf{i}\frac{\partial p}{\partial x} + \mathbf{j}\frac{\partial p}{\partial y} + \mathbf{k}\frac{\partial p}{\partial z}$$

and

$$\nabla \eta = \mathbf{i}\frac{\partial \eta}{\partial x} + \mathbf{j}\frac{\partial \eta}{\partial y} + \mathbf{k}\frac{\partial \eta}{\partial z}$$

Thus, the vector equation is immediately,

$$\mathbf{a} = \frac{\partial \mathbf{V}}{\partial t} + (\mathbf{V}\cdot\nabla)\mathbf{V} = -\frac{1}{\rho}\nabla p - g\,\nabla \eta \qquad (5\text{-}8)$$

5–2 SOLID BODY MOTION

The Euler equations of the preceding section will be applied in a variety of ways in this and succeeding chapters. In most cases there will be a degree of approximation involved in their usage. There are cases, however, when the Euler equation can be applied quite exactly. One type is that of Example 5-1, which requested that the Euler equations be used to develop the laws of hydrostatics. A couple of other examples form the essence of this section. The common feature of the following examples is that the fluid acts as if it were a solid body, that is, without any relative motion from one point to the next. These cases all involve accelerating fluids, although the acceleration will be of different forms.

Constant Linear Acceleration

In the last section it was established that the acceleration must be perpendicular to lines of constant piezometric head. Note also the following two points. First, a free surface must be a surface (or line if the problem is two-dimensional) of constant pressure. If the surface is in contact with the atmosphere, and we take the atmospheric pressure as zero, it will be a surface of zero pressure. Referring back to Eq. 5-6, the quantity p/γ has the same dimensions as the piezometric head h, namely, length; it is therefore customarily referred to as the *pressure head*. Thus, the free surface must also be at a constant value of pressure head. Second, the remaining term of Eq. 5-6, y, is for similar reasons referred to as the *elevation head*. Accordingly, a horizontal surface must be a surface of constant elevation head.

With this in mind, consider the open tank of fluid accelerated to the right with acceleration a_s in Fig. 5-5. If the acceleration a_s is a constant, the surface will, after an initial period of adjustment, align itself as shown by the dashed line. The value θ must now be determined. Bear in mind that after the period of adjustment there is no relative motion and that all of the fluid is exposed to the identical acceleration. The lines of constant piezometric head will be vertical lines decreasing in value in the direction of the acceleration, which is toward the right end of the tank. Consider two such lines shown on Fig. 5-5. If the datum is taken at the bottom of the tank, then, at the

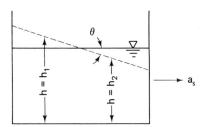

Fig. 5-5. Linear horizontal acceleration of a liquid.

free surface where the pressure is zero, the piezometric head, by Eq. 5-6, must be the elevation head or simply the depth. Thus, the piezometric heads h_1 and h_2 are the depths at the respective sections. Now, apply the Euler equation in a form that combines Eqs. 5-5a and 5-6, so as to give

$$\frac{\partial h}{\partial s} = -\frac{a_s}{g} \tag{5-9}$$

We have seen that h is the elevation of the free surface; thus, $\partial h/\partial s$ is the slope of that surface and further

$$\frac{\partial h}{\partial s} = \tan \theta = -\frac{a_s}{g}$$

yielding

$$|\theta| = \tan^{-1}\left(\frac{a_s}{g}\right) \tag{5-10}$$

Since the piezometric head is a constant in the vertical direction, the pressure variation in the vertical is identical to that of hydrostatics; this is also referred to as a *hydrostatic pressure distribution*. Lines of constant pressure can be determined throughout the tank. Since the entire tank is exposed to the same constant acceleration, they will all be inclined at the same angle as the free surface. The pressure variation in the horizontal is not hydrostatic (i.e., a zero gradient); however, it is easily determined either from the free surface or directly from integration of Eq. 5-9 in the horizontal direction.

If a tank similar to Fig. 5-5 is closed and completely filled with liquid, the problem becomes indeterminate unless some reference pressure is available. This could be in the form of either a pressure gage or a direct connection to the atmosphere at some point. In either case, there is no adjustment of the fluid as in the open tank. However, a line of zero pressure can be identified which can then be treated exactly as if it were a free surface, and all of the foregoing considerations will still apply. Liquid below this line will be at a positive pressure, while the pressure of that above will be negative or below atmospheric.

If a tank is accelerated vertically, lines of constant piezometric head must be horizontal. An open tank is considered in Fig. 5-6; however, if the line

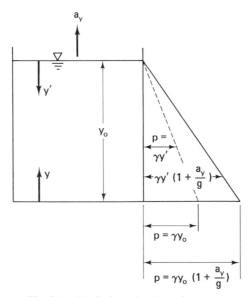

Fig. 5-6. Vertical acceleration of a liquid.

of zero pressure may be determined, a closed tank could be considered as well.

Since lines of both constant piezometric head and constant elevation head are horizontal, lines of constant pressure, including the free surface, must also remain horizontal. The vertical pressure distribution, which is no longer hydrostatic, can be obtained by integrating Eq. 5-9. Using the usual vertical notation, Eq. 5-9 becomes

$$\frac{\partial}{\partial y}\left(\frac{p}{\gamma} + y\right) = -\frac{a_y}{g}$$

or

$$\frac{\partial}{\partial y}\left(\frac{p}{\gamma}\right) = -1 - \frac{a_y}{g}$$

Thus, the pressure decreases in the vertical direction at a rate given by

$$\Delta p = -\gamma\,\Delta y\left(1 + \frac{a_y}{g}\right)$$

Measuring vertically downward from the surface, the pressure increases with the depth y' according to

$$p = \gamma y'\left(1 + \frac{a_y}{g}\right) \qquad (5\text{-}11)$$

The pressure variation is still linear in the vertical but increases with depth at a rate that is greater or less than the hydrostatic rate, depending on whether the acceleration is upward or downward.

EXAMPLE 5-2

The tank of Fig. 5-5 contains oil with sp. gr. = 0.88. If the tank is 10 m long, the initial depth of oil is 2 m, and the tank accelerates to the right at 2.45 m/s², determine the slope of the surface and the minimum and maximum pressures at the bottom of the tank. Assume that the tank walls are sufficiently high so that there is no spillage.

SOLUTION:

Since the slope of the free surface must equal the gradient of the piezometric head, Eq. 5-10 gives

$$\theta = \tan^{-1}\left(\frac{a_s}{g}\right)$$

$$= \tan^{-1}\left(\frac{2.45 \text{ m/s}^2}{9.80 \text{ m/s}^2}\right) = 14.04°$$

Since there is no spillage, the oil surface will rotate about the midpoint and rise and drop equal amounts:

$$\Delta y = (5 \text{ m})(\tan 14.04°) = 1.25 \text{ m}$$

At the front end of the tank, the pressure is due to a depth of $2.0 - 1.25 = 0.75$ m, while at the rear the depth is 3.25 m. The corresponding pressures are

$$p_{\text{front}} = \gamma y_{\text{front}}$$
$$= (9800 \times 0.88 \text{ N/m}^3)(0.75 \text{ m}) = 6470 \text{ N/m}^2$$

and

$$p_{\text{rear}} = \gamma y_{\text{rear}}$$
$$= (9800 \times 0.88 \text{ N/m}^3)(3.25 \text{ m}) = 28{,}000 \text{ N/m}^2$$

respectively. Note that the pressures are affected by the specific gravity of the liquid but that the slope of the surface is not.

Constant Angular Velocity

A second type of solid body motion is that of a liquid rotating at a constant angular velocity. The container shown in Fig. 5-7 is an example. The assumed

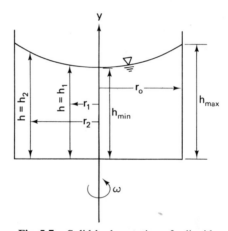

Fig. 5-7. Solid body rotation of a liquid.

shape of the free surface will be justified below. We know from solid body dynamics that the streamlines are concentric circles and that the velocity at any distance r from the axis is a constant equal to $r\omega$. Here ω (Greek lower-case omega) is the angular velocity in radians per second. The acceleration by Eq. 3-19b must be radially inward and of magnitude

$$a_n = \frac{v^2}{r} = r\omega^2$$

Since the acceleration is horizontal and radially inward, lines of constant piezometric head will again be vertical lines (actually, vertical concentric cylinders) with decreasing magnitude toward the axis and with magnitude equal to the height of the free surface above the datum conveniently taken again at the tank bottom.

Proceeding much as in the previous example, the Euler equation combining Eqs. 5-5b and 5-6 may be written as

$$\frac{\partial h}{\partial n} = -\frac{v^2}{gr} = -\frac{r\omega^2}{g}$$

Since the direction n is radially inward while r is measured positive outward, this may be changed to

$$\frac{\partial h}{\partial r} = \frac{r\omega^2}{g}$$

and subsequently integrated from r_1 to r_2 to give

$$h_2 - h_1 = \frac{\omega^2}{2g}(r_2^2 - r_1^2) \qquad (5\text{-}12)$$

Letting r_1 equal the rotational axis where the piezometric head is h_{min}, this equation becomes

$$h_2 - h_{min} = \frac{\omega^2 r_2^2}{2g} \qquad (5\text{-}13)$$

Thus, the difference in liquid level between any two points r_1 and r_2 measured from the axis is given by Eq. 5-12. The vertical distance between outer and innermost points is, accordingly,

$$h_{max} - h_{min} = \frac{\omega^2 r_0^2}{2g}$$

The free surface, by Eq. 5-13, is a paraboloid of revolution.[3] Other surfaces of constant pressure will have a similar form. If the pressure variation on the bottom of the tank, or on any other horizontal plane, is desired, substitution of Eq. 5-6 into Eq. 5-12 and noting that $y_1 = y_2$ gives

$$p_2 - p_1 = \frac{\rho\omega^2}{2}(r_2^2 - r_1^2)$$

If the rotated container is filled and closed at the top, no displacement of liquid can take place. The surfaces of constant pressure will nevertheless be similar to the foregoing. However, unless the pressure is known at some point, the actual value of the pressure is indeterminate. As a final comment, although a circular container has been assumed in Fig. 5-7, the relationships all hold regardless of container shape.

EXAMPLE 5-3

A closed tank 2 ft in diameter and 3 ft high is filled with water and rotates about its axis at 100 rpm (Fig. 5-8). A pressure gage at the center of the top reads 4 psi during the rotation. Determine the pressure at the outer perimeter at the bottom of the tank.

[3]Since the average value of a paraboloid of revolution is one-half the peak value (see Example 3-4), the liquid displacements above and below the initial level will be equal provided that no liquid spills.

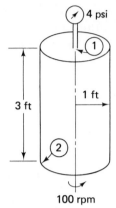

Fig. 5-8. Closed rotating tank.

SOLUTION:

Applying Eq. 5-12 between points 1 and 2 as shown in Fig. 5-8 and replacing the piezometric heads by the sum of the pressure and elevation heads gives

$$\left(\frac{p_2}{\gamma} + y_2\right) - \left(\frac{p_1}{\gamma} + y_1\right) = \frac{\omega^2}{2g}(r_2^2 - r_1^2)$$

whence

$$\left(\frac{p_2 \text{ lb/ft}^2}{62.4 \text{ lb/ft}^3} + 0 \text{ ft}\right) - \left[\frac{(4)(144)}{62.4} + 3\right] = \frac{(100 \text{ rpm})^2(2\pi \text{ rad/rev})^2(1^2 - 0^2 \text{ ft}^2)}{(60 \text{ s/min})^2(2)(32.2 \text{ ft/s}^2)}$$

Solving, we obtain

$$p_2 = 869.5 \text{ psf} = 6.04 \text{ psi}$$

5–3 BERNOULLI'S EQUATION

In the preceding section we were able to apply the Euler equations directly to special cases in which the acceleration imposed on the fluid permitted easy evaluation and integration. Let us now attempt to integrate the Euler equations in a somewhat more general situation. Continue to assume that the flow is frictionless and incompressible, and refer back to Eq. 5-5a. This equation may be rewritten as

$$\frac{\partial}{\partial s}\left(\frac{p}{\gamma} + y + \frac{v^2}{2g}\right) = -\frac{1}{g}\frac{\partial v}{\partial t}$$

If we knew how the locals acceleration $\partial v/\partial t$ varied along the streamline, this could theoretically be integrated as is, although usually with great difficulty. For our present purposes we will consider only steady flows for which the right-hand side goes to zero and the quantity within the parentheses must be a constant. Thus,

$$\frac{p}{\gamma} + y + \frac{v^2}{2g} = C \tag{5-14}$$

This represents integration of the Euler equations along a streamline for steady, incompressible, frictionless flow. Just as the first two terms have been previously defined as pressure and elevation heads, the third term is usually called the *velocity head* and the sum of the three, the *total head*. In general, we can say that the total head at any point is the sum of the pressure, elevation, and velocity heads. Equation 5-14 then says that the total head (the usual symbol will be H) is a constant along a streamline in steady, incompressible, frictionless flows. Between any two points, we may further write

$$H_1 = H_2$$

or

$$\frac{p_1}{\gamma} + y_1 + \frac{v_1^2}{2g} = \frac{p_2}{\gamma} + y_2 + \frac{v_2^2}{2g} \tag{5-15}$$

If the velocity variation along a streamline is known or can be determined using the continuity equation, then Eq. 5-15 permits calculation of the corresponding pressure distribution. Conversely, Eq. 5-15 may be used in conjunction with the continuity equation to determine the velocities if pressures are given. Equation 5-15 is referred to as the *Bernoulli equation*, after the Swiss scientist Daniel Bernoulli.[4] Later, we will see that the effect of friction will cause the total head to decrease in the direction of flow. Attempts to integrate the Euler equation in a direction normal to the stream lines will wait until Chapter 12, which deals with ideal fluid flow. It will be seen that even then, only under certain conditions, can we easily integrate the Euler equation perpendicular to the flow direction.

When dealing with the flow of air or other gases, elevation head differences become insignificant, and the Bernoulli equation is usually written in the form

$$p_1 + \frac{\rho v_1^2}{2} = p_2 + \frac{\rho v_2^2}{2} \tag{5-16}$$

The term $\rho v^2/2$ is known as the *dynamic pressure*, so called because it is equal in magnitude to the pressure increase which results at a point where the velocity is brought to zero (see Fig. 5-9). Any point in the flow field where this occurs is known as a *stagnation point*. For example, see point 2 in Fig. 5-9.

A measuring device based directly on the application of the foregoing

[4]Daniel Bernoulli (1700–1782) was a contemporary of Euler.

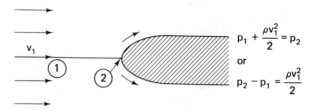

Fig. 5-9. Pressure at a stagnation point.

principle is the Pitot-static tube, credited to Henri Pitot.[5] Although shown schematically in Fig. 5-10, it is carefully proportioned so as to minimize flow disturbances. To analyze this device, the Bernoulli equation can first be written between point 1 and the stagnation point 2,

$$p_1 + \frac{\rho v_1^2}{2} = p_2$$

and second between points 1 and 3,

$$p_1 + \frac{\rho v_1^2}{2} = p_3 + \frac{\rho v_3^2}{2}$$

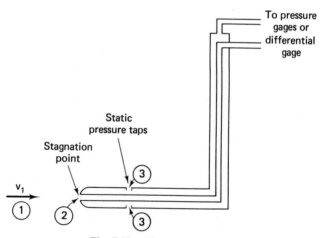

Fig. 5-10. Pitot-static tube.

The static pressure taps 3 are so located that $v_3 = v_1$ and $p_1 = p_3$. Thus, the two equations may be combined to yield

$$p_2 - p_3 = \frac{\rho v_1^2}{2}$$

or

$$v_1 = \sqrt{2(p_2 - p_3/\rho} = \sqrt{2\,\Delta p/\rho} \qquad (5\text{-}17)$$

[5]Henri Pitot, French scientist, developed the Pitot-static tube in 1732.

Pressure gages connected as shown will measure the necessary pressure difference. The Pitot-static tube may be used in both gas and liquid flows. In actual application the pressure difference must frequently be calculated from a manometer differential using the hydrostatic principles of Chapter 2.

EXAMPLE 5-4

Both tanks of Fig. 5-11 have a liquid depth z. Tank (a) discharges a jet of diameter D through the rounded orifice from whence it falls freely, whereas tank (b) has a pipe with rounded entrance connected to it, and after a length L, it discharges a jet also of diameter D.

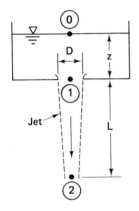
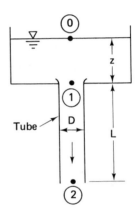

(a) Discharge through an orifice.   (b) Discharge through a tube.

Fig. 5-11.   Application of the Bernoulli equation.

Which of the systems has the greater discharge through it? In answering this question first compare the velocities and discharges at points 1 and 2 in system (a) with the corresponding points in system (b).

SOLUTION:

In solving problems involving Bernoulli's equation along a streamline, a suitable streamline must be justified. In this problem it is easy to accept that a streamline can be found in both tanks that passes from the free surface through points 1 and 2. The elevation of the points 2 is taken as the datum. We will label the surface points as 0, where, for a sufficiently large tank, it is possible to ignore the velocity and velocity head. The Bernoulli equation will be applied from 0 to 2 (i.e., from point 0 to point 2) in both tanks: In (a) the total head at the surface relative to the datum through point 2 is

$$H_0 = \frac{p_0}{\gamma} + y_0 + \frac{v_0^2}{2g} = 0 + (z + L) + 0$$

This follows since the pressure at the free surface is atmospheric, the height of point 0 is $(z + L)$ above the datum and, as previously mentioned, $v_0 = 0$. Similarly, the total head at point 2 is

$$H_2 = \frac{p_2}{\gamma} + y_2 + \frac{v_2^2}{2g} = 0 + 0 + \frac{v_2^2}{2g}$$

This time the pressure head is zero, since the jet is discharging into the atmosphere, which is at zero pressure, and the elevation head is zero since point 2 is on the datum. Thus, the Bernoulli equation gives

$$0 + (z + L) + 0 = 0 + 0 + \frac{v_2^2}{2g}$$

or

$$v_2 = \sqrt{2g(z + L)} \qquad \text{for (a)}$$

Similarly, in tank (b), also from 0 to 2,

$$0 + (z + L) + 0 = 0 + 0 + \frac{v_2^2}{2g}$$

$$v_2 = \sqrt{2g(z + L)} \qquad \text{for (b)}$$

The velocity v_2 is seen to be identical in each case. Now writing the equation between 0 and 1 for tank (a) only,

$$0 + (z + L) + 0 = 0 + L + \frac{v_1^2}{2g}$$

and

$$v_1 = \sqrt{2gz} \qquad \text{for (a)}$$

The velocity in tank (b) at point 1 will not be the same, since the pressure will not equal zero as it does in tank (a). Rather, note by continuity that

$$v_1 = v_2 \qquad \text{in (b)}$$

Summing up, the following information is obtained:

		Tank (a)	Tank (b)
Velocity	Point 1	$\sqrt{2gz}$	$\sqrt{2g(z + L)}$
	Point 2	$\sqrt{2g(z + L)}$	$\sqrt{2g(z + L)}$
Discharge $(= AV)$		$\sqrt{2gz}\dfrac{\pi}{4}D^2$	$\sqrt{2g(z + L)}\dfrac{\pi}{4}D^2$

In conclusion, it is apparent that the discharge will be greater through (b).

EXAMPLE 5-5

Assume the pipe contraction of Fig. 5-12 to be frictionless. Determine the liquid flow rate associated with the manometer differential of 1 ft.

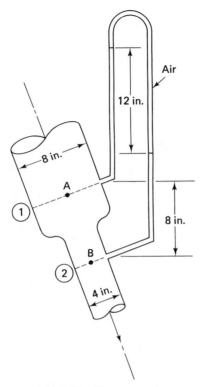

Fig. 5-12.   Pipe contraction.

SOLUTION:

It must be assumed that the flow is essentially uniform at both sections 1 and 2 and that the velocity is constant across the two sections. This guarantees that the velocity along any streamline between sections 1 and 2 will change between the same limits and we can proceed without identifying a particular streamline. These are reasonable assumptions, and they put little restriction on the flow behavior between sections 1 and 2.

Since the pipe inclination is not given, it will be impossible to separate pressure and elevation heads. Rather, we must substitute the piezometric head into Eq. 5-15, giving

$$h_1 + \frac{v_1^2}{2g} = h_2 + \frac{v_2^2}{2g}$$

The manometer measures the difference in piezometric head; thus,

$$h_1 - h_2 = \frac{v_2^2}{2g} - \frac{v_1^2}{2g} = 1 \text{ ft}$$

From continuity,

$$v_1 \frac{\pi}{4} \frac{(8)^2}{(12)^2} = v_2 \frac{\pi}{4} \frac{(4)^2}{(12)^2}$$

or

$$v_2 = 4v_1$$

Combining,

$$\frac{15v_1^2}{2g} = 1$$

giving

$$v_1 = 2.07 \text{ ft/s} \quad \text{and} \quad Q = 0.723 \text{ cfs}$$

If the pipe were rotated toward the vertical position (with the manometer tubes remaining vertical), the constant discharge would be reflected by a constant differential on the manometer. If pressure gages were placed at points A and B, the pressure difference would decrease during the rotation, exactly compensating for the increase in elevation head of point A relative to point B.

Cavitation

Cavitation was described in Chapter 1, in conjunction with vapor pressure of liquids. When applying the Bernoulli equation it must always be borne in mind that the pressure of a flowing liquid cannot fall below the vapor pressure of that liquid. Even in problems where the calculation of pressures is not otherwise required, the pressure must be checked if there is any possibility of low pressures and cavitation occurring. If the pressure as calculated by the Bernoulli equation drops below the vapor pressure at any point, the flow is not going to behave in accordance with the basis relationships.

The extent and intensity of cavitation depends on several factors. Since cavitation is the very rapid formation and collapse (as they move into regions of higher pressure) of vapor pockets, it is most intense when air is excluded from the flow. The presence of even dissolved air, which will come out of solution as the pressure drops, will cushion the collapsing vapor bubbles. Other factors being equal, cavitation will therefore be less severe in free surface flows. The extent of cavitation depends primarily on the portion of the flow that has dropped to the vapor pressure. Cavitation damage depends on the proximity of the cavitating zone to the boundaries, as well as the geometric shape and curvature of the boundary.

None of the foregoing factors can be evaluated from the basic relationships of fluid mechanics, with the exception of the onset of cavitation, which can be determined from the Bernoulli equation. Generally, the operation, if not the design, of a system must be such that cavitation is avoided.[6]

---

[6]There are exceptions; for example, propellers for some high-speed boats are designed to operate in what is called the supercavitating range.

EXAMPLE 5-6

If the depth z in the tank of Fig. 5-11b is 5 m, determine the maximum length L of connecting pipe which may be used without the occurrence of cavitation if the liquid is water at (a) 20°C; (b) 70°C. What is the discharge in each case if the pipe diameter is 20 cm?

SOLUTION:

It will be assumed that the inlet from the tank to the pipe is so designed that the local velocity at any point along the curvature does not exceed the average in the pipe. Further, an atmospheric pressure of 1.013×10^5 N/m² will be used. Then from Table A-5, $p_v = 2340$ N/m²(abs) at 20°C and 31,160 N/m² at 70°C. Since the velocities are identical at sections 1 and 2 of Fig. 5-11b, the Bernoulli equation for any streamline between the two sections is

$$\frac{p_1}{\gamma} + L = \frac{p_2}{\gamma} + 0$$

if the datum is taken at the outlet. Noting that $p_1 = p_v$, $p_2 = p_{atmos}$ and using $\gamma_{20°C} = 9790$ N/m³ and $\gamma_{70°C} = 9590$ N/m³,

$$L = \frac{p_2 - p_v}{\gamma}$$

$$= \frac{101,300 - 2340}{9790} = 10.11 \text{ m at } 20°C$$

while at 70°C,

$$L = \frac{101,300 - 31,160}{9590} = 7.31 \text{ m}$$

From Example 5-5, the discharge is

$$Q = \sqrt{2g(z + L)} \frac{\pi}{4} D^2$$

Therefore, the flow rates associated with the maximum noncavitating pipe lengths are at 20°C,

$$Q = \sqrt{(2)(9.81)(5 + 10.11)} \frac{\pi}{4} (0.2)^2 = 0.541 \text{ m}^3/\text{s}$$

and at 70°C,

$$Q = \sqrt{(2)(9.81)(5 + 7.31)} \frac{\pi}{4} (0.2)^2 = 0.488 \text{ m}^3/\text{s}$$

Although cavitation was not mentioned in conjunction with Example 5-5, it should be clear that it may be an extremely important factor in that type of system. Obviously, if the pipe length exceeds that calculated above for a given temperature, the flow is not going to stop. Rather, cavitation will occur in the vicinity of the inlet, and the resulting discharge will depend on the shape of the cavitating region, which cannot in general be calculated.

5–4 LIQUID JETS

The liquid jets considered in this section are an example of steady, incompressible flow characterized by zero pressure at all points. Jet flow falls into this category since the entire outer surface and consequently the interior portions as well are at atmospheric pressure.[7] Ignoring the effect of friction, which is due primarily to the relatively low air drag on the passing jet, will usually result in only a slight overestimation of the jet trajectory. A jet discharging from a poorly designed nozzle may break up rather rapidly, in which case the results of this section may be considerably in error.

With these limitations in mind the Bernoulli equation may be written for the jet of Fig. 5-13, which has an initial velocity V_0 at an inclination and datum as shown. It must be assumed at this point that either each streamline

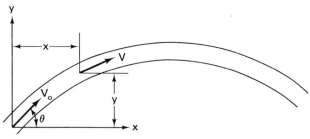

Fig. 5-13. Liquid jet.

in the jet has identical characteristics or else the equations are written for the "average" streamline, which adequately represents all streamlines in the jet. Between the origin and the point (x, y), we have

$$\frac{V_0^2}{2g} = y + \frac{V^2}{2g} \tag{5-18}$$

The initial velocity can be broken up into its x and y components, which are

$$u_0 = V_0 \cos \theta \quad \text{and} \quad v_0 = V_0 \sin \theta$$

Then

$$u_0^2 + v_0^2 = V_0^2$$

or

$$\frac{V_0^2}{2g} = \frac{u_0^2}{2g} + \frac{v_0^2}{2g} \tag{5-19}$$

in terms of velocity heads. Likewise, at any point along the trajectory the

---

[7] Actually, surface tension, streamline convergence, and other factors create a very small pressure within the jet, but this may safely be ignored in most engineering applications.

velocity V can be related to its x and y components u and v such that

$$\frac{V^2}{2g} = \frac{u^2}{2g} + \frac{v^2}{2g} \tag{5-20}$$

In addition, the acceleration in the x and y directions can be specified from particle dynamics as

$$a_x = \frac{du}{dt} = 0 \tag{5-21a}$$

and

$$a_y = \frac{dv}{dt} = -g \tag{5-21b}$$

Integrating Eq. 5-21a,

$$u = C_1$$

and C_1 is evidently u_0, since the x component of velocity is constant. From Eq. 5-21b,

$$v = -gt + C_2$$

But at $t = 0$, $v = v_0$ and therefore $C_2 = v_0$. If x and y are the distances traveled in the two coordinate directions during time t, we can integrate

$$u = \frac{dx}{dt} \tag{5-22a}$$

and

$$v = \frac{dy}{dt} \tag{5-22b}$$

to get

$$x = u_0 t + C_3$$

where C_3 must be zero, and

$$y = -\frac{gt^2}{2} + v_0 t + C_4$$

in which C_4 must vanish. Finally, the traiectory, in terms of the initial velocity and time, is given as

$$x = u_0 t \tag{5-23a}$$

and

$$y = -\tfrac{1}{2}gt^2 + v_0 t \tag{5-23b}$$

Eliminating time between these two equations, the trajectory becomes simply

$$y = \left(\frac{v_0}{u_0}\right)x - \left(\frac{g}{2u_0^2}\right)x^2 \tag{5-24}$$

This equation gives a curve similar to Fig. 5-13 or 5-14. In Fig. 5-14 the total head line and the maximum elevation of the jet are also shown. At the top of the rise, $v = 0$ and thus the velocity is $u = u_0$. The velocity head at the peak must therefore be $u_0^2/2g$, the velocity head of the horizontal component of the initial velocity, and since the total head by Eq. 5-18 is $V_0^2/2g$, we get

$$y_{max} = \frac{v_0^2}{2g} \tag{5-25}$$

which is the velocity head of the vertical component of the initial velocity.

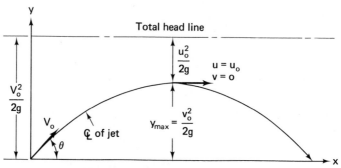

Fig. 5-14.   Trajectory of a liquid jet.

EXAMPLE 5-7

For an initial velocity V_0 determine the angle θ for which the jet will have the greatest throw (i.e., maximum horizontal distance x in Fig. 5-14). What will be the distance to the point where the jet returns to its initial height ($y = 0$)?

SOLUTION:

Note that $\tan \theta = v_0/u_0$ and $\cos \theta = u_0/V_0$. Thus, Eq. 5-24 may be rewritten as

$$y = x \tan \theta - \frac{gx^2}{2 V_0^2 \cos^2 \theta}$$

At $y = 0$ this may be arranged to yield

$$\sin \theta = \frac{gx}{2 V_0^2 \cos \theta}$$

and hence

$$x = \frac{2V_0^2}{g} \sin \theta \cos \theta$$

or

$$x = \frac{V_0^2}{g} \sin 2\theta$$

By inspection of this equation, or by setting $dx/d\theta = 0$ and solving for θ, it is apparent that the maximum throw will be achieved by an initial angle of 45°. The distance traversed will equal V_0^2/g, twice the initial velocity head. Note also that there are two values of θ which will cause the jet to strike the initial plane at any intermediate value of x.

EXAMPLE 5-8

Determine the minimum jet velocity V_0 for which a jet will strike the window shown in Fig. 5-15. What will be the corresponding angle θ?

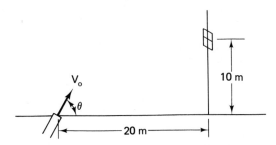

Fig. 5-15. Trajectory for Example 5-8.

SOLUTION:

Using Eq. 5-24 as in Example 5-7, the trajectory may be written as

$$y = x \tan \theta - \frac{gx^2}{2V_0^2 \cos^2 \theta}$$

which for the given conditions becomes

$$10 = 20 \tan \theta - \frac{400g}{2V_0^2 \cos^2 \theta}$$

Rearranging,

$$V_0^2 \cos^2 \theta (20 \tan \theta - 10) = 200g$$

or

$$V_0^2 = \frac{200g}{20 \sin \theta \cos \theta - 10 \cos^2 \theta}$$

The velocity V_0 may now be minimized by setting the derivative $dV_0/d\theta = 0$. Differentiating eventually leads to

$$\frac{dV_0}{d\theta} = -\frac{V_0^3}{400g}(20 \cos 2\theta + 10 \sin 2\theta) = 0$$

whereupon

$$\theta = 58.3°$$

Therefore, the minimum jet velocity is

$$V_0 = \left[\frac{(200)(9.81)}{(20)(\sin 58.3°)(\cos 58.3°) - (10)(\cos^2 58.3°)} \right]^{1/2}$$
$$= 17.82 \text{ m/s}$$

5–5 ENERGY EQUATION

During the course of this section the energy equation will be developed from both the conservation of energy principle and the differential Euler equations. The first approach, which will involve combining the conservation of energy and the Reynolds transport theorem, is general and therefore applicable to both compressible and incompressible flows. However, applications and subsequent derivations will be primarily restricted to incompressible flows, reserving the study of the more general case for Chapter 11. In all cases, the control volume approach will be emphasized.

Conservation of Energy and Reynolds' Transport Theorem

The *conservation of energy* states that energy can be neither created nor destroyed, ignoring the energy–matter exchange accompanying a nuclear reaction. This is formally expressed for a system by the *first law of thermodynamics*, as follows:

$$\Delta Q_H = \Delta E + \Delta W \tag{5-26}$$

where ΔQ_H is the net heat added to the system and ΔE and ΔW are the resulting change in energy and work done by the system, respectively. In other words, the net heat added to a system is equal to the energy added to the system plus the work done by the system on its surroundings. If there is no heat transfer into or out of the system, the left-hand side of Eq. 5-26 equals zero and the equation becomes the familiar *work–energy principle*—the work done by the system equals the decrease of energy of the system.

The work-energy principle refers only to a system and it remains to employ the Reynolds' transport theorem, Eq. 4-2, in order to have a usable equation for a control volume. Considering each term of Eq. 5-26 in sequence, the net heat added during a time interval dt is dQ_H. Hence, heat enters at the rate of dQ_H/dt. Likewise, work is done by the system at the rate of dW/dt. But the work done by the system consists of three parts. That part contributed by the effect of pressure p can be expressed as the product of the force due to the pressure, $p\,dA$, and the distance over which the pressure does work during time interval dt. For a differential area this may be expressed as $p\mathbf{V}\cdot\mathbf{dA}\,dt$. Since the pressure must be normal to dA, the velocity component normal to dA must be collinear with p, and this velocity component times dt is the distance over which p does work. When integrated over the surface of a control volume and expressed on a per unit time basis, this term becomes

$$\int_{\substack{\text{control} \\ \text{surface}}} p\mathbf{V}\cdot\mathbf{dA}$$

A second part of the work term is due to the shear stresses acting on the control surface. This term will be deleted from the formulation, since both this chapter and most of Chapter 11 on compressible flow will assume a frictionless fluid. The third part of the work term reflects the relationship between the system and a turbine or pump. This component is frequently called the *shaft work term*. The rate at which shaft work is done by the system is dW_{shaft}/dt, which will be positive when the system does work on a turbine and negative when a pump does work on the system.

Thus, the conservation of energy takes the form

$$\frac{dQ_H}{dt} - \frac{dW_{shaft}}{dt} = \frac{dE}{dt} + \int_{\substack{\text{control} \\ \text{surface}}} p\mathbf{V} \cdot d\mathbf{A} \qquad (5\text{-}27)$$

Letting e equal the amount of energy E per unit of mass, Reynolds' transport theorem will express the rate of increase of energy within the system as

$$\frac{dE}{dt} = \frac{\partial}{\partial t} \int_{\substack{\text{control} \\ \text{volume}}} e\rho \, dV + \int_{\substack{\text{control} \\ \text{surface}}} e\rho\mathbf{V} \cdot d\mathbf{A} \qquad (5\text{-}28)$$

where n has been replaced by e in Eq. 4-2. If Eq. 5-28 is now substituted into Eq. 5-27, a general equation for the conservation of energy results,

$$\frac{dQ_H}{dt} - \frac{dW_{shaft}}{dt} = \frac{\partial}{\partial t} \int_{\substack{\text{control} \\ \text{volume}}} e\rho \, dV + \int_{\substack{\text{control} \\ \text{surface}}} (p + e\rho)\mathbf{V} \cdot d\mathbf{A} \qquad (5\text{-}29)$$

As written, the equation relates the rates at which heat is added, and shaft work done, to the increase of energy within the control volume, the work done by the pressure, and the rate of flow of energy across the control surface.

The energy per unit mass e is composed of the various types of energy possessed by the fluid and will generally include kinetic, potential, and internal energy. The *kinetic energy* is the product of mass times $v^2/2$ and hence on a per unit mass basis will be simply $v^2/2$. The *potential energy* is the energy the fluid possesses because of elevation differences. It is expressed as the product of the elevation of the fluid relative to an arbitrary datum and the fluid weight, $(wt)y$. On a per unit mass basis this becomes gy. Finally, the *internal energy* is the energy of the individual atoms or molecules, which for a perfect gas is a function of temperature only. We will have cause later to deal with the internal energy per unit weight u. The internal energy per unit mass will therefore be written gu. Combining the above, the energy per unit mass e in Eq. 5-29 may be expanded as

$$e = \frac{v^2}{2} + gy + gu \qquad (5\text{-}30)$$

Usually, Eq. 5-29 will be applied within the context of one or more simplifications. If there is no net heat transfer, the first term will disappear. Similarly, if no shaft work is done, the second term will equal zero. If the flow is completely steady, the first term to the right of the equality sign will be zero. Under conditions where all three of the preceding terms vanish, the last term must equal zero as well. This last condition will be pursued in some detail as one of the important cases for this chapter.

One-Dimensional Analysis of Energy
from Bernoulli's Equation

Before pursuing Eq. 5-29 further, or attempting application of the equation to engineering problems, the concept of energy will be considered directly from the Bernoulli equation. Rather than a general approach, such as the foregoing, several constraints will be placed on the flow and we will concentrate on the very practical one-dimensional approach which will be found quite useful in the solution of very complex and definitely not one-dimensional flows. The term "one-dimensional" refers here not to a straight line necessarily but to a coordinate direction, most frequently, the streamline coordinate. Consequently, the one-dimensional method of analysis takes into account only changes in the direction of flow. Changes of quantities (pressure, velocity, etc.) in directions perpendicular to the direction in which the one-dimensional analysis is applied must therefore be handled by an averaging process. The degree to which this can be done, that is, the extent to which an average quantity or single value will reflect actual conditions for the entire flow cross section, will determine the accuracy of the procedure.

To apply the one-dimensional approach to the Bernoulli equation, consider the control volume of Fig. 5-16. The boundary streamlines have again

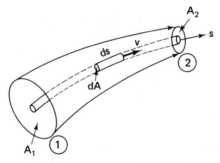

Fig. 5-16. Control volume for development of the one-dimensional energy equation.

been chosen to form a streamtube. In addition, a differential streamtube is shown. At any cross section this differential streamtube has a cross section area dA and velocity v. Note that although neither v nor dA is constant along the differential streamtube, the continuity equation has shown that their product $v\,dA$ is constant for incompressible flow.

Returning now to the Bernoulli equation (Eq. 5-14 or 5-15), we know that the total head ($p/\gamma + y + v^2/2g$) is constant along a streamline in steady, incompressible, frictionless flow. The total head can be taken (for the foregoing conditions) to be constant along the differential streamtube as well, for very small dA. We wish to integrate the head terms over the cross-sectional area; however, if the head is multiplied by dA, the product will no longer be constant along the stream tube. To circumvent this difficulty the total head will be multiplied by the differential discharge $v\,dA$.[8] The resulting product,

$$\left(\frac{p}{\gamma} + y + \frac{v^2}{2g}\right)v\,dA$$

is still constant along the streamtube. If we used an alternative form obtained by multiplication of the equation above by γ, the result is still a constant but each term in

$$\left(p + \gamma y + \frac{\rho v^2}{2}\right)v\,dA = \text{constant}$$

is now seen to have dimensions of FL/T. That is, each term represents a rate of flow of energy (or energy flux), and the sum, being the total energy flux, is conserved from section to section in steady, incompressible, frictionless flow. If we integrate the energy flux over the entire cross-sectional area (less formally, all the differential streamtubes making up the total are summed), we get

$$\int_A (p + \gamma y)v\,dA + \int_A \frac{\rho v^3}{2}\,dA = \text{constant} \qquad (5\text{-}31)$$

Now, with reference to the Euler equations (Eq. 5-5), recall that the piezometric head is constant in a direction of zero acceleration. Thus, if a region of the flow has nearly straight parallel streamlines, the piezometric head $(p/\gamma + y)$ will be a constant across the section and accordingly so will be the quantity $(p + \gamma y)$. Thus, we need to make the additional restriction that the end sections (e.g., sections 1 and 2 in Fig. 5-16) be located in regions of nearly uniform flow. This will still permit considerable nonuniformity within the control volume (i.e., between end sections). With this restriction the first integral of Eq. 5-31 can be evaluated as

$$\int_A (p + \gamma y)v\,dA = (p + \gamma y)\int_A v\,dA = (p + \gamma y)VA \qquad (5\text{-}32)$$

The second integral may be written as

$$\int_A \frac{\rho v^3}{2}\,dA = \frac{\alpha \rho V^3 A}{2} = \frac{\alpha \rho V^2 Q}{2} \qquad (5\text{-}33)$$

whence

$$\alpha = \frac{1}{AV^3}\int_A v^3\,dA \qquad (5\text{-}34)$$

---

[8]The assumption herein is that the area of the differential streamtube dA changes in the s-direction just as the cross-sectional area A does, whereas continuity requires that the discharge $v\,dA$ remain constant in the s-direction regardless of changes in dA.

Inspection shows that the introduction of α is no improvement without further amplification. To proceed we must evaluate α, which requires knowledge and manipulation of the velocity distribution contrary to the goal of one-dimensional analysis. Further, α will not equal unity, since the equations, unlike the earlier integration of the velocity profile in Eq. 3-12 to obtain the average velocity, involve higher powers of the velocity. In other words, although the average velocity is equal to the average of the point velocities, the average velocity squared, or in this case cubed, is not equal to the average of the square or cube of the point velocities. In fact, if the velocity profile is parabolic, such as is the case in laminar flow through a pipe, α will equal 2.0. If the pipe flow is turbulent, α will approach unity, usually lying below 1.1. Consequently, in solving problems, some knowledge of the flow may permit a satisfactory approximation of α. In the analysis of most turbulent flows it will be sufficiently accurate to take α as equal to 1.0.

With these limitations in mind, Eqs. 5-32 and 5-33 may be substituted into Eq. 5-31, giving

$$(p + \gamma y)VA + \alpha\frac{\rho V^3 A}{2} = \text{constant}$$

Dividing through by the constant weight discharge $\gamma A V$ and applying the result between sections 1 and 2 of Fig. 5-16 now gives the one-dimensional energy equation for steady, incompressible, frictionless flow:

$$\frac{p_1}{\gamma} + y_1 + \alpha_1\frac{V_1^2}{2g} = \frac{p_2}{\gamma} + y_2 + \alpha_2\frac{V_2^2}{2g} \tag{5-35}$$

This equation, although similar in appearance to the Bernoulli equation, Eq. 5-15, particularly when α is taken as unity, has two important differences. First, it applies to the entire flow entering or leaving through a cross section of a control volume, rather than just to points along a single streamline. Second, it must be applied between sections of reasonably uniform flow and even then becomes less accurate as the velocity profile across the section deviates from a constant value. For clarity, the term "Bernoulli equation" will be reserved for Eq. 5-15, the equation applied to points along a single streamline. The term "energy equation" will refer to application to a control volume. It is appropriate to refer to Eq. 5-35 as an energy equation, since specific terms have been shown to represent energy flux, and the dimensions of the various terms of Eq. 5-35 may be related to energy, namely, energy per unit weight of fluid. Specifically, the elevation head is the potential energy of the fluid on a per unit weight basis, while the velocity head, similarly, is the kinetic energy. However, the derivation came from the Euler equation, which is usually considered an equation of motion rather than a statement of conservation of energy. For completeness it will now be shown that the preceding energy equation may be directly obtained from the basic work–energy principle of physics. This principle states that the work done on an incompressible fluid (i.e., the applied forces times the distance through which they act) equals the change in the energy (kinetic plus potential) of the fluid.

As the differential fluid element of Fig. 5-16 experiences a displacement ds along the streamline, work is done due to the pressure gradient $\partial p/\partial s$. The net force on the element is

$$p \, dA - \left(p + \frac{\partial p}{\partial s} \, ds\right) dA = -\frac{\partial p}{\partial s} \, ds \, dA$$

and the work done thereby is

$$\left(-\frac{\partial p}{\partial s} \, ds \, dA\right) ds$$

The change in energy during the displacement over the distance ds is the change in the sum of the kinetic and potential energy. Since the kinetic energy is $(v^2/2g)\gamma \, dA \, ds$ and the potential energy is $(y)\gamma \, dA \, ds$, the total change is therefore

$$\frac{\partial}{\partial s}\left[\left(\frac{v^2}{2g} + y\right)\gamma \, dA \, ds\right] ds$$

Equating this change in energy to the work done and simplifying gives

$$-\frac{\partial p}{\partial s} = \gamma \frac{\partial}{\partial s}\left(\frac{v^2}{2g} + y\right)$$

As this rearranges to

$$\frac{\partial}{\partial s}\left(\frac{p}{\gamma} + y + \frac{v^2}{2g}\right) = 0$$

which was the starting point for this section, similar treatment from this point on will yield Eq. 5-35. In retrospect, the pressure head is not an energy term and in itself cannot do any work. Only when a pressure difference or a pressure gradient exists is it capable of accomplishing work.

EXAMPLE 5-9

Determine the pressure in the pipe of Fig. 5-17 at section A just upstream of the contracting nozzle if the discharge is 1 cfs. As shown in Fig. 5-17, the pipe is 4 in. in diameter and the nozzle discharges a 2-in.-diameter jet of water.
(a) Assume that $\alpha = 1$ at both sections A and B.
(b) Assume that $\alpha = 1.1$ at section A and 1.02 at section B.

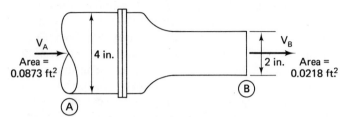

Fig. 5-17. Contracting nozzle.

SOLUTION:

The average velocities at the two sections are:
Section A:

$$V = \frac{Q}{A} = \frac{1}{0.0873} = 11.45 \text{ ft/s}$$

Section B:

$$V = \frac{1}{0.0218} = 45.87 \text{ ft/s}$$

Part (a) The one-dimensional Bernoulli equation,

$$\frac{p_A}{\gamma} + y_A + \alpha_A \frac{V_A^2}{2g} = \frac{p_B}{\gamma} + y_B + \alpha_B \frac{V_B^2}{2g}$$

becomes

$$\frac{p_A}{62.4} + \frac{(1)(11.45)^2}{64.4} = \frac{(1)(45.87)^2}{64.4}$$

since the elevation heads cancel each other and the pressure in the jet at section B equals zero. Solving for p_A gives

$$p_A = 1905 \text{ lb/ft}^2 = 13.23 \text{ psi}$$

Part (b) In this case $\alpha_A = 1.1$ and $\alpha_B = 1.02$; thus, the Bernoulli equation becomes

$$\frac{p_A}{62.4} + \frac{(1.1)(11.45)^2}{64.4} = \frac{(1.02)(45.87)^2}{64.4}$$

and hence

$$p_A = 1933 \text{ lb/ft}^2 = 13.42 \text{ psi}$$

These α values, typical of turbulent flow, do not greatly influence the result.

EXAMPLE 5-10

A turbulent velocity distribution between parallel flat plates (Fig. 5-18) can be approximated by

$$\frac{u}{u_{\max}} = \left(\frac{B/2 - y}{B/2}\right)^{1/7}$$

Calculate the energy correction factor α.

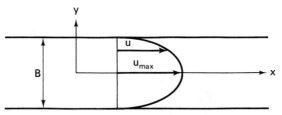

Fig. 5-18. Turbulent velocity distribution.

SOLUTION:

For the two-dimensional flow, α (Eq. 5-34) may be determined from the upper half of the flow field as follows:

$$\alpha = \frac{1}{(B/2)V^3} \int_0^{B/2} u^3 \, dy$$

$$= \frac{2u_{max}^3}{BV^3} \int_0^{B/2} \left(\frac{B/2 - y}{B/2}\right)^{3/7} dy$$

$$= \frac{2u_{max}^3}{V^3 B^{10/7}} \int_0^{B/2} (B - 2y)^{3/7} \, dy$$

$$= \frac{2u_{max}^3}{V^3 B^{10/7}} \frac{(B - 2y)^{10/7}}{(\frac{10}{7})(-2)} \Big|_0^{B/2} = \frac{7}{10}\left(\frac{u_{max}}{V}\right)^3$$

But

$$V = \frac{1}{B/2} \int_0^{B/2} u \, dy$$

$$= \frac{1}{B/2} \int_0^{B/2} u_{max}\left(\frac{B/2 - y}{B/2}\right)^{1/7} dy$$

$$= \frac{2u_{max}}{B^{8/7}} \int_0^{B/2} (B - 2y)^{1/7} \, dy$$

$$= \frac{2u_{max}}{B^{8/7}} \frac{(B - 2y)^{8/7}}{(\frac{8}{7})(-2)} \Big|_0^{B/2} = (\frac{7}{8}) u_{max}$$

Therefore,

$$\alpha = (\tfrac{7}{10})(\tfrac{8}{7})^3 = 1.045$$

Relationship Between Approaches to the Energy Equation

We have now developed the energy equation, first in a very general way from the conservation of energy principle, and second for steady, incompressible, frictionless flow by direct integration of the Bernoulli equation. The latter, it should be recalled, was obtained by integration of the equations of motion (or Euler equations). In both cases the equation refers specifically to fluid passing through a control volume. There remains now to compare further the results of the two approaches and then apply them to specific problems.

In the event of steady, incompressible, frictionless flow, without any net heat transfer and with no shaft work, Eq. 5-29 may be written as

$$\int_{\substack{\text{control} \\ \text{surface}}} (p + e\rho)\mathbf{V} \cdot \mathbf{dA} = 0 \tag{5-36}$$

Substituting e from Eq. 5-30 gives

$$\int_{\substack{\text{control} \\ \text{surface}}} \left(p + \frac{\rho v^2}{2} + \gamma y + \gamma u \right) \mathbf{V} \cdot \mathbf{dA} = 0 \tag{5-37}$$

Since there is no temperature change, the internal energy u must be constant. Integration of the last term gives

$$\int_{\substack{\text{control} \\ \text{surface}}} \gamma u \mathbf{V} \cdot \mathbf{dA} = \gamma u \int_{\substack{\text{control} \\ \text{surface}}} \mathbf{V} \cdot \mathbf{dA} = 0$$

to satisfy continuity. Thus, the internal energy term may be dropped. When applied to a control volume such as in Fig. 5-16 (see also Fig. 4-6), the velocity and area vectors will be perpendicular to each other except in regions where flow is entering the control volume. Whereupon Eq. 5-37 becomes

$$-\int_{A_1} \left(p_1 + \gamma y_1 + \frac{\rho v_1^2}{2} \right) v_1 \, dA + \int_{A_2} \left(p_2 + \gamma y_2 + \frac{\rho v_2^2}{2} \right) v_2 \, dA = 0$$

For reasons detailed previously in the section, the first two terms under each integral can be readily integrated only when the sum $(p + \gamma y)$ is a constant, a condition that is met at a cross section where uniform flow prevails. Also, as previously discussed, the integral of $v^3 \, dA$ may be replaced by $\alpha V^3 A = \alpha V^2 Q$, where α is often taken as unity. Thus, within the preceding limitations, we have

$$\left(p_1 + \gamma y_1 + \frac{\alpha_1 \rho V_1^2}{2} \right) V_1 A_1 = \left(p_2 + \gamma y_2 + \frac{\alpha_2 \rho V_2^2}{2} \right) V_2 A_2$$

Noting that by continuity $V_1 A_1 = V_2 A_2$, and finally dividing through by $\gamma V A$ gives

$$\frac{p_1}{\gamma} + y_1 + \alpha_1 \frac{V_1^2}{2g} = \frac{p_2}{\gamma} + y_2 + \alpha_2 \frac{V_2^2}{2g} \tag{5-38}$$

which is obviously Eq. 5-35.

During the foregoing consideration of Eq. 5-29, friction or energy loss has been ignored. We will continue to consider a steady, incompressible flow with no shaft work, but for the present we will include the effect of fluid friction as it passes through the control volume. Because of friction the fluid is subject to a change in temperature and hence internal energy. As a further consequence, heat transfer is now likely across the control surface due to the change in temperature. When evaluated with respect to Fig. 5-16, the first term of Eq. 5-29, dQ_H/dt, will be the rate at which heat (energy) leaves the control volume due to the temperature rise resulting from friction. When divided by the weight discharge, γVA as above, this becomes

$$\frac{dQ_H/dt}{\gamma VA} = -q_H$$

the heat energy leaving per unit weight of fluid. The negative sign indicates a loss of energy across the boundary. Assuming that the internal energy of the fluid entering and leaving the section can be represented by average quantities u_1 and u_2, respectively, during the integration process, we get a companion equation to Eq. 5-38 or Eq. 5-35:

$$\frac{p_1}{\gamma} + y_1 + \alpha_1 \frac{V_1^2}{2g} = \frac{p_2}{\gamma} + y_2 + \alpha_2 \frac{V_2^2}{2g} + q_H + u_2 - u_1 \qquad (5\text{-}39)$$

Also, because of friction $u_2 > u_1$, hence the quantity $q_H + u_2 - u_1$ represents unavailable energy. The temperature change in a liquid is, in fact, normally very small and the terms are usually lumped together as $h_\ell = q_H + u_2 - u_1$. The quantity h_ℓ becomes the energy loss or head loss experienced as the fluid passes from section 1 to 2. Thus,

$$\frac{p_1}{\gamma} + y_1 + \alpha_1 \frac{V_1^2}{2g} = \frac{p_2}{\gamma} + y_2 + \alpha_2 \frac{V_2^2}{2g} + h_\ell \qquad (5\text{-}40)$$

Using the previous definition of total head, we see that if friction occurs, the total head must decrease in the flow direction. This point will not be pursued further in this chapter but will become very important in due course.

Returning to steady, incompressible, frictionless flow, it is generally advisable first to select a convenient control volume. It should be bounded by surfaces through which either no flow passes or surfaces through which the flow enters and leaves, normal to the surface, if possible. If the simplified one-dimensional approach is to be used, the latter surfaces must be in regions of uniform (or nearly uniform) flow. The energy equation can then be applied to the control volume. If the one-dimensional approach is appropriate, this consists essentially of equating the total head between the inflow and outflow sections. One general type of problem that may be analyzed by this approach is conduit flow.

Steady, Incompressible, Frictionless Conduit Flow

The assumption of a frictionless conduit flow may be highly erroneous if the conduit is very long. It is included at this time partly to introduce proper problem-solving techniques, but more important, because of the excellent opportunity it affords for a thorough examination of the energy equation

(Eq. 5-35) and its components. Later in the text (Chapter 8), frictional effects will be added according to Eq. 5-40. The development that follows will refer primarily to liquids. When applied to incompressible flow of gases, the equation simplifies by the deletion of elevation terms.

The one-dimensional energy equation (Eq. 5-35) can be applied to conduit problems to study the consequences of changes in conduit size and elevation on the various energy terms. Generally, α will be taken as unity and the equation becomes

$$\frac{p_1}{\gamma} + y_1 + \frac{V_1^2}{2g} = \frac{p_2}{\gamma} + y_2 + \frac{V_2^2}{2g} \tag{5-41}$$

Recall that the distance y above the datum gives the elevation head, which, for a conduit or pipe is the centerline, the sum of $p/\gamma + y$ is the piezometric head, and the sum of all three terms yields the total head. It is very instructive to plot these three quantities on a sketch of the conduit or pipe system. In addition to the centerline, the other quantities give rise to the piezometric head line and the total head line. Flow out of a reservoir and through a pipe system is shown in Fig. 5-19, and piezometric and total head lines have been

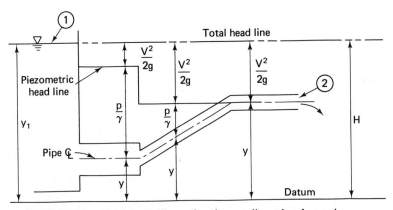

Fig. 5-19.   Pipe system illustrating the one-dimensional equation.

included. Further, the relative pipe diameters are indicated so that the effects of the continuity equation may be incorporated as well. The sketch shows the total head and its three head components at every section. At the surface of the reservoir the total head is the elevation of the surface above the datum, since both the pressure and velocity head must equal zero. This water surface also determines the elevation of the total head line for the entire system, since there are no energy losses.

The rate of flow is dependent only on the height of the reservoir surface above the pipe efflux section. This is seen by writing the Bernoulli equation between sections 1 and 2:

$$y_1 = \frac{V_2^2}{2g} + y_2$$

or

$$V_2 = \sqrt{2g(y_1 - y_2)}$$

Whereupon, the flow rate may be determined by multiplying the velocity by the exit area, the velocity can be found at any point along a pipe system by use of the continuity equation, and the pressure by a second application of the Bernoulli equation. With regard to Fig. 5-19, note that for frictionless flow the zero pressure as the jet discharges into the atmosphere prevails back through the horizontal pipe. In the sloping section of pipe there is no change in velocity, by continuity, and the pressure and elevation heads merely change in inverse proportion, with no change in their sum. The larger pipe shows correspondingly higher pressure and lower velocity than the adjoining pipe. The pressure drop through the contraction is required to provide the necessary acceleration.

Recall from Sections 1-3 and 5-3 that at no point can the pressure in a flowing liquid drop below the vapor pressure of that liquid. This must be checked at points of low pressure to ensure that cavitation or disruption of the flow does not result. This situation will be investigated in the following example.

EXAMPLE 5-11

A siphon is used to draw water from the tank of Fig. 5-20. If the siphon line has a diameter of 6 cm and must rise 1 m above the water level in the tank, what is the maximum discharge that can be obtained without cavitation?

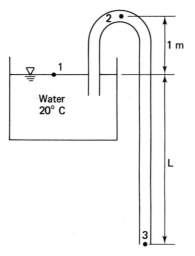

Fig. 5-20. Application of a siphon.

SOLUTION:

Consideration of the energy equation shows that the velocity at the outlet, and hence the flow rate, is dependent on only the vertical distance between the water level in the tank and the outlet below, as long as the pressure does not drop to the vapor pressure at any point. Since the velocity at the high point must equal the velocity at the outlet, we may write Eq. 5-41 between points 2 and 3 as follows:

$$\frac{p_2}{\gamma} + (1 + L) = \frac{p_3}{\gamma} + 0$$

At 20°C the vapor pressure of water is 2.34 kN/m²(abs), and the atmospheric pressure is 101.3 kN/m²(abs). Using gage pressures,

$$p_2 = p_v = 2340 - 101{,}300 = -98{,}960 \text{ N/m}^2 \quad \text{and} \quad p_3 = 0$$

Hence,

$$\frac{-98{,}960 \text{ N/m}^2}{9789 \text{ N/m}^3} + (1 + L \text{ m}) = 0$$

or

$$L = 9.11 \text{ m}$$

This is the maximum length without cavitation and will therefore yield the greatest flow. Between points 1 and 3 we have

$$L = \frac{V_3^2}{2g}$$

whereupon

$$V_3 = \sqrt{2gL}$$
$$= \sqrt{(2)(9.81)(9.11)} = 13.37 \text{ m/s}$$

and

$$Q = (13.37)\left(\frac{\pi}{4}\right)(0.06)^2 = 0.0378 \text{ m}^3\text{/s}$$

Note in this case that cavitation would occur in the low-pressure region if the outlet were further lowered.

Changes in Total Head Due to Pumps or Turbines

A pump or turbine placed in a pipeline will cause changes in the total head; a pump adding energy and therefore raising the total head, and a turbine, lowering the total head as it draws energy from the flow. The increase in total head due to a pump will be indicated by H_P and the decrease due to a turbine will be denoted by H_T. Hence, Eq. 5-41 becomes

$$\frac{p_1}{\gamma} + y_1 + \frac{V_1^2}{2g} + H_P = \frac{p_2}{\gamma} + y_2 + \frac{V_2^2}{2g} \tag{5-42a}$$

or

$$\frac{p_1}{\gamma} + y_1 + \frac{V_1^2}{2g} - H_T = \frac{p_2}{\gamma} + y_2 + \frac{V_2^2}{2g} \tag{5-42b}$$

accordingly. Since the change H_P (or H_T) represents energy per unit weight of fluid, for example ft-lb/lb or N·m/N, the change in power will equal the change in head times the flow rate in units of weight per second. Therefore, if a pump is on the line, the power supplied by the pump is

$$P_P = Q\gamma H_P \qquad (5\text{-}43)$$

If $Q\gamma$ is the weight discharge in lb/s and the head added is in feet, the necessary power is in units of ft-lb/s. Dividing by the 550 ft-lb/s equivalent to 1 horsepower, the expression

$$P_P = \frac{Q\gamma H_P}{550} \qquad (5\text{-}44)$$

gives the power supplied by the pump in horsepower. In SI units, $Q\gamma$ would be in N/s, the head H in meters, and the power given by Eq. 5-43 in N·m/s.[9] For a turbine, the corresponding equation for power removed P_T is obtained by replacing H_P by H_T in Eqs. 5-43 and 5-44.

In the general energy equation (Eq. 5-29) the shaft work term dW_{shaft}/dt represents the rate at which energy is transferred from or to the system by a turbine or pump, respectively. A positive value of dW_{shaft}/dt in Eq. 5-29 represents the rate at which work is done on a turbine by the system and hence results in a removal of energy from the system. Conversely, a pump adds energy at the rate $(-dW_{\text{shaft}}/dt)$, the negative sign necessitated by the original formulation of Eq. 5-29. Each term in this equation, and hence the term dW_{shaft}/dt, as well, is expressed in terms of power. Therefore, in going through a development similar to that starting with Eq. 5-29 and proceeding from Eq. 5-36 to Eq. 5-38, the counterpart to Eq. 5-36 is

$$\int_{\substack{\text{control} \\ \text{surface}}} (p + e\rho)\mathbf{V} \cdot d\mathbf{A} = -\frac{dW_{\text{shaft}}}{dt} = -P_T \quad (\text{or } + P_P) \qquad (5\text{-}45)$$

When each term, including the power P, is divided by $\gamma A V = \gamma Q$, the counterpart of Eq. 5-38 may be obtained, which for $\alpha = 1$ is immediately Eq. 5-42.

The changes that result in Fig. 5-19 if a pump is placed at the pipe contractions are shown in Fig. 5-21. The velocities are now everywhere higher than before, with a resulting increase in flow rate. The pressure distribution is also affected. The pressure drop between the larger and smaller pipes is usually more than offset by the increase in pressure at the pump. In fact, the pressure on the upstream or suction side of the pump frequently becomes negative, and the possibility of cavitation must be considered. In practice, the diameter of the suction pipe is often larger than that of the discharge

[9]In SI units 1 N·m/s = 1 joule/s = 1 watt (see Appendix B).

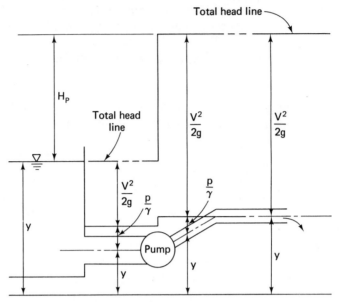

Fig. 5-21. Pipe system with pump.

pipes, to minimize this problem. If H_P is known, the solution would proceed, however, in the same way as that discussed in conjunction with Fig. 5-19.

EXAMPLE 5-12

A turbine is used to recover energy from the simplified system shown in Fig. 5-22. When the flow rate is 19 m³/s, how much power is being developed?

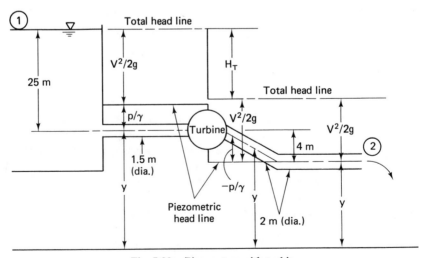

Fig. 5-22. Pipe system with turbine.

SOLUTION:

Piezometric and total head lines have already been drawn. The drop in the total head line is the head removed by the turbine and is unknown at the outset. Although not shown to scale, a larger velocity head is shown in the 1.5-m-diameter section. Note also that a negative pressure prevails in a portion of the discharge section (or draft tube). Finally, the oversimplified system does not represent an efficient design, nor does it include ever-present frictional losses.

The solution requires that H_T be determined first. By Eq. 5-42b,

$$\frac{p_1}{\gamma} + y_1 + \frac{V_1^2}{2g} - H_T = \frac{p_2}{\gamma} + y_2 + \frac{V_2^2}{2g}$$

or

$$29 - H_T = \frac{V_2^2}{2g}$$

but

$$V_2 = \frac{Q}{A_2} = \frac{19}{(\pi/4)(2)^2} = 6.05 \text{ m/s}$$

and hence

$$H_T = 29 - \frac{(6.05)^2}{(2)(9.81)} = 27.13 \text{ m}$$

By Eq. 5-43, as it applies to a turbine, the power developed becomes

$$P = Q\gamma H_T = (19 \text{ m}^3)(9800 \text{ N/m}^3)(27.13 \text{ m})$$
$$= 5.05 \times 10^6 \text{ N·m/s} = 5.05 \text{ MW}$$

5–6 MOMENTUM EQUATION

The momentum equation will not be derived from a conservation principle, as were both continuity and energy, but, rather, directly from Newton's second law. As applied to a system, this law states that the net force in any direction acting on the system equals the rate of increase of momentum of the system in that same direction. In terms of vectors, this may be expressed by

$$\sum \mathbf{F} = \frac{d}{dt}(M\mathbf{V}) \tag{5-46}$$

where the net force is expressed by the vector sum of the forces. Reynolds' transport equation will again be used, this time to transform Eq. 5-46 to a form appropriate to a control volume. In this general form the equation will be applicable to flow with or without friction, steady or unsteady and compressible or incompressible. The equation will also be derived for steady flow using the "one-dimensional" approach similar to that used for the energy equation. The forces involved are those due to gravity (i.e., fluid weight), those due to pressure, and those due to tangential or shear stress. With the emphasis of the chapter placed on steady, frictionless, incompressible flow, the tangential forces will generally be assumed negligible.

Momentum Equation Using Reynolds' Transport Theorem

Reynolds' transport theorem (Eq. 4-2) may be applied directly to the right-hand side of Eq. 5-46. We will let N in Eq. 4-2 equal the momentum of the fluid $M\mathbf{V}$. The momentum is the product of mass times velocity; therefore, n, which will here be the momentum per unit mass, becomes simply the velocity $\mathbf{V}$. In Eq. 5-46 the indicated forces are external forces acting on the fluid. Since Reynolds' transport theorem relates the system to the control volume at the instant the system passes through the control volume, the forces on the system are identically those on the control volume. Hence,

$$\sum \mathbf{F} = \frac{d}{dt}(M\mathbf{V}) = \frac{\partial}{\partial t}\int_{\substack{\text{control}\\\text{volume}}} \rho\mathbf{V}\,d\mathcal{V} + \int_{\substack{\text{control}\\\text{surface}}} \rho\mathbf{V}(\mathbf{V}\cdot\mathbf{dA}) \qquad (5\text{-}47)$$

As applied to the control volume, the general momentum equation states that the net force is equal to the sum of the time rate of increase of momentum in the control volume and the net rate of flow of momentum across the control surface. Note that this is a vector equation and on occasion may require up to three independent equations to express the total effect of the applied forces in each of the coordinate directions.

The forces involved are always those acting on the fluid contained in the control volume. When a force due to the fluid is specified or required, it will be equal to, but in the opposite direction to that acting on the fluid. This is an extremely important point due to the vector nature of the equation. When the flow is steady, the first term on the right-hand side will equal zero, leaving

$$\sum \mathbf{F} = \int_{\substack{\text{control}\\\text{volume}}} \rho\mathbf{V}(\mathbf{V}\cdot\mathbf{dA}) \qquad (5\text{-}48)$$

We will return to these last two equations after first considering the development of the momentum equation from the one-dimensional approach.

One-Dimensional Approach to Steady Momentum Equation

The one-dimensional momentum equation, like the previously considered energy equation, may be developed from Newton's second law. Whereas the energy equation resulted from the application of Newton's law to fluid pressures on a differential element in the flow, the momentum equation considers the results of applying external forces. Since additional information is included, the momentum equation is not redundant and can be used along with the energy equation in the solution of many problems, particularly those involving external forces. As stated before, momentum is a vector quantity and as many as three additional useful equations may result. The derivation that follows, however, will be a scalar derivation based on a single representative direction x.

Figure 5-23 is a repeat of control volume Fig. 5-16 used for the energy equation, except that the vector force $\mathbf{F}$ acting on the differential element is included and the rectangular Cartesian coordinates are identified. Con-

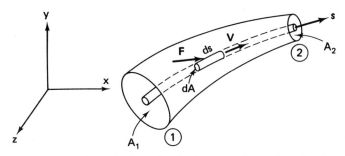

Fig. 5-23.   Control volume for development of one-dimensional momentum equation.

sidering the x direction, the momentum relationship may be written for the differential element shown; in terms of the x component of the force (F_x) that is applied to it,

$$F_x = \frac{d}{dt}(Mv)_x$$

$$= M\frac{dv_x}{dt} + v_x\frac{dM}{dt}$$

Provided that the flow is steady, so that the mass rates of flow in and out of the volumetric element are equal, the continuity equation developed in Chapter 4 requires that $dM/dt = 0$. Thus,

$$F_x = M\frac{dv_x}{dt} \tag{5-49}$$

Since the momentum equation will frequently be applied to problems posed in streamline coordinates, the notation introduced in conjunction with Fig. 3-16 will be adopted. The component of any quantity, be it force or velocity, will then be denoted by the appropriate subscript. The mass M on which F_x acts is $\rho\, dA\, ds$ and thus for steady flow, Eq. 5-49 becomes

$$F_x = \rho\, dA\, ds\, \frac{dv_x}{dt}$$

Although steady flow has been assumed, this does not·preclude variation of the density from point to point, and consequently the derivation will be valid for compressible as well as incompressible flows. Continuing, the quantity dv_x/dt is the acceleration in the x direction. This may be expressed for steady flow in streamline coordinates as

$$\frac{dv_x}{dt} = \frac{\partial v_x}{\partial s}\frac{ds}{dt} + \frac{\partial v_x}{\partial n}\frac{dn}{dt}$$

$$= v\frac{\partial v_x}{\partial s}$$

since $dn/dt = v_n = 0$. This form will be convenient since it is desired to integrate the momentum equation along the streamtube (i.e., in the s direction), as was done previously with the energy equation. Upon rearranging,

$$F_x = (pv\,dA)\frac{\partial v_x}{\partial s}\,ds$$

The quantity $(pv\,dA)$ is the mass rate of flow through the differential streamtube. Since it is constant along the streamtube, the equation may be integrated along the differential streamtube between sections 1 and 2, with the result that

$$F'_x = p\,dQ(v_{x_2} - v_{x_1}) \tag{5-50}$$

Here the prime on the left-hand side is added to distinguish this force from that in Eq. 5-49. The integration process in effect sums all the incremental elements along the streamtube, and therefore the force F'_x is the net force in the x direction on the entire differential streamtube. The internal (to the differential streamtube) forces at the contact surfaces between each pair of differential elements along this streamtube cancel each other. The terms v_{x_2} and v_{x_1} are the x components of the velocity at the two end sections.

It now remains to integrate Eq. 5-50 over the cross section so that the resulting equation will apply to the entire streamtube or control volume between sections 1 and 2. Upon integrating over the cross section, the left-hand side will become the net force on the entire streamtube. Again, the internal forces between adjoining differential stream tubes will neutralize each other during the summing process. The net force will be written as $\sum F_x$, since the computational procedure will require algebraic summation of the x component of all forces on the entire control volume. The right-hand side requires the integration of

$$pv_x\,dQ = pv_x v\,dA$$

In keeping with the spirit of the one-dimensional analysis, this integral will generally be taken as

$$\int_A pv_x v\,dA = \beta p V_x V A = \beta p V_x Q \tag{5-51}$$

where β is defined as

$$\beta = \frac{1}{A}\int_A \frac{v_x}{V_x}\frac{v}{V}\,dA \tag{5-52}$$

In addition, V is the average velocity over the cross section and V_x is the x component of that average velocity. If the x direction is, in fact, the direction of flow at a given section, these two equations become

$$\int_A \rho v^2 \, dA = \beta \rho V^2 A = \beta \rho V Q \tag{5-53}$$

and

$$\beta = \int_A \left(\frac{v}{V}\right)^2 dA \tag{5-54}$$

The value of β like that of α depends upon the velocity distribution; however, β will always be closer to unity than α. For the parabolic profile of laminar flow in a circular tube, β will equal $\frac{4}{3}$, as opposed to the value of 2 for α. For turbulent flow β will be quite close to unity, usually 1.03 to 1.07 for pipe flow. In such cases its value will be taken as unity for all but the most precise work.

Returning to the integration of Eq. 5-50, we now have

$$\sum F_x = (\beta \rho Q V_x)_2 - (\beta \rho Q V_x)_1 \tag{5-55}$$

or if $\beta = 1$ at both sections,

$$\sum F_x = (\rho Q V_x)_2 - (\rho Q V_x)_1 \tag{5-56}$$

The x direction was arbitrary here, and the other directions will follow accordingly. The only difference is that in the y or vertical direction the fluid weight becomes one of the forces. Its effect is usually small relative to the other terms and can frequently be ignored.

Summing up, in the one-dimensional use of the momentum equation, β can be taken as unity for most problems and Eq. 5-56 applied directly. Specifically, the equation says that the net force in any direction applied to fluid flowing through a control volume causes a corresponding change in the rate of flow of momentum (or momentum flux) in that direction. The terms $(\rho Q V_x)_2$ and $(\rho Q V_x)_1$ are, respectively, the momentum flux out of and into the control volume in the x direction. Each of the terms may require the algebraic adding up of momentum flux from two or more entrance or exit areas.

In solving problems it is advisable to sketch the control volume, indicating the entrance and exit portions and the appropriate forces. Whenever possible, show the forces acting on the fluid in their proper direction. In certain cases the one-dimensional approach cannot be used directly, and the momentum flux over a region must be determined by direct integration. Likewise, the magnitude of a given force may require mathematical or graphical integration of the pressure distribution.

Relationship Between Approaches
to Momentum Equation

The general momentum equation (Eq. 5-47) was shown to reduce to Eq. 5-48 when restricted to steady flow. The latter equation,

$$\sum \mathbf{F} = \int_{\substack{\text{control} \\ \text{surface}}} \rho \mathbf{V}(\mathbf{V} \cdot \mathbf{dA}) \qquad (5\text{-}48)$$

needs to be compared with the one-dimensional result, Eq. 5-55, or Eq. 5-56. To this end, the x component of Eq. 5-48 may be considered. Since the product $\mathbf{V} \cdot \mathbf{dA}$ is in itself a scalar quantity, the x component may be written

$$\sum F_x = \int_{\substack{\text{control} \\ \text{surface}}} \rho v_x(\mathbf{V} \cdot \mathbf{dA}) \qquad (5\text{-}57)$$

When applied to a control volume such as Fig. 5-23, we have previously found that the only surfaces where $\mathbf{V} \cdot \mathbf{dA}$ does not immediately vanish are the entrance and exit sections. Further, the vectors $\mathbf{V}$ and $\mathbf{dA}$ are collinear at these sections, differing only in that they act in the same direction at exit sections and in the opposite direction at entrance sections. With reference to the control volume of Fig. 5-23, Eq. 5-57 becomes

$$\sum F_x = \int_{A_2} \rho v_x v \, dA - \int_{A_1} \rho v_x v \, dA$$

Introducing the momentum correction factor β as before, this becomes

$$\sum F_x = (\rho \beta V_x V A)_2 - (\rho \beta V_x V A)_1$$

or, in other words, Eq. 5-55. Examples illustrating the application of the momentum equation are reserved for Section 5-7.

Moment of Momentum Equation

If the moment of each term of Eq. 5-47 is taken about a point O, there results an additional equation:

$$\sum (\mathbf{r} \times \mathbf{F}) = \frac{\partial}{\partial t} \int_{\substack{\text{control} \\ \text{volume}}} \mathbf{r} \times \rho \mathbf{V} \, d\mathcal{V} + \int_{\substack{\text{control} \\ \text{surface}}} (\mathbf{r} \times \rho \mathbf{V})(\mathbf{V} \cdot \mathbf{dA}) \qquad (5\text{-}58)$$

the general moment of momentum equation. The vector operations are explained more fully in Appendix D, but essentially the vector $\mathbf{r}$ is the position vector relative to point O for the respective forces and velocity vectors. The cross product $\mathbf{r} \times \mathbf{F}$ is the moment of the force F about point O and $\mathbf{r} \times \rho \mathbf{V}$ is the moment of the momentum flux (per unit volume), also about point O. Equation 5-58 therefore states that, relative to a common point, the algebraic sum of the moment of the forces (i.e., the torques) acting on the fluid equals the sum of the time rate of increase of angular momentum within the control volume and the net rate of flow of angular momentum from the control volume.

For steady flow the first term on the right-hand side of Eq. 5-58 will equal zero, leaving a relationship between the net torque and the resulting change in angular momentum between incoming and outgoing fluids. Since two directions must be considered, it is somewhat cumbersome to write a general scalar equation; rather, the torque/angular momentum relationship will be illustrated by Examples 5-20 and 5-21 in the next section. Needless to say, care must be taken to associate the proper algebraic sign with the different directions.

5–7 APPLICATION OF THE ENERGY AND MOMENTUM PRINCIPLES

This final section of the chapter is devoted entirely to the application of the energy and momentum principles to the solving of fluid mechanics problems. A few introductory comments will be followed by a series of example problems.

In addition to the use of the momentum equation in a given problem to determine a force due to the flow, frequently the energy and continuity equations will also be required. In such situations the proper sequence of equations should be considered in order to minimize the computations. In some cases, nevertheless, simultaneous equations will have to be solved. To repeat the advice of the previous section, a careful sketch of the flow and the control volume should be made. This should be based on flow entry and exit areas, which are nearly uniform flow regions. The known and desired forces should then be identified and shown in their proper direction, if possible. Note that the derivation of the momentum equation dealt with the forces acting on the fluid. This condition must be carried through the solution. Although a given or desired force is the fluid force on a body, the sketch should show the corresponding, (but opposite in direction) force of the body on the fluid.

EXAMPLE 5-13

Perhaps the least complicated problem involving a change in momentum is that of a liquid jet striking a curved plate as in Fig. 5-24a.
(a) If the 3-in.-diameter jet with a velocity of 50 ft/s is deflected through an angle of 70° when it hits the stationary vane, determine the horizontal and vertical components of the force of the water on the vane.

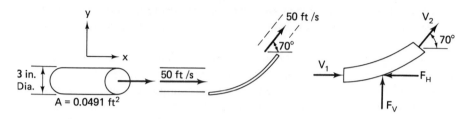

(a) Jet-vane diagram.   (b) Control volume

Fig. 5-24. Jet striking a stationary vane.

SOLUTION:

It is customary in problems of this type to neglect both the weight component of the water and the effect of height changes even if the jet is thrown vertically. The approaching jet is at atmospheric pressure, as must be the jet once it leaves the vane. Since there is neither a change in the elevation head nor the pressure head between sections 1 and 2, the velocity heads must also be equal. Thus, the exiting jet must have a velocity of 50 ft/s, although the direction of the flow and the cross-section shape (but not the cross-sectional area) are changed.

The force diagram indicating the forces acting on the water is shown in Fig. 5-24b. Equation 5-56 may be written in the horizontal direction as follows:

$$-F_H = \rho Q(V_2 \cos \theta - V_1)$$

Therefore,

$$F_H = (1.94)(0.0491)(50)(50 - 50 \cos 70°) = 156.7 \text{ lb}$$

Repeating Eq. 5-56 in the vertical direction,

$$F_V = \rho Q(V_2 \sin \theta - 0)$$

and

$$F_V = (1.94)(0.0491)(50)(50 \sin 70°) = 223.8 \text{ lb}$$

The calculated forces act on the water as shown in Fig. 5-24b. The forces of the water on the vane must be in the opposite direction and therefore act to the right and downward, respectively. Note also that the velocity gives the momentum flux its vector character and that the discharge, which is a scalar quantity, is the same at both sections.

(b) Repeat part (a) with the one change that the vane no longer remains stationary but rather moves to the right at 15 ft/s. Also determine the actual velocity of the water leaving the vane.

SOLUTION:

This has now become a relative motion problem which may be simplified if the reference frames are changed to one moving with the vane. This is accomplished by bringing the plate to rest, that is, by adding everywhere to the flow field a velocity equal but opposite to that of the vane. This is indicated in Fig. 5-25a. The steady flow pattern that results is given in Fig. 5-25b.

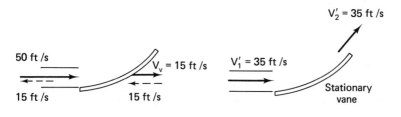

(a) Unsteady diagram   (b) Steady diagram

Fig. 5-25. Relative motion due to a jet striking a moving vane.

The discharge that actually reaches the plate is now based on the 35-ft/s velocity, and the momentum equation in the x direction becomes

$$-F_H = (1.94)(0.0491)(35)(35 \cos 70° - 35)$$

or

$$F_H = 76.8 \text{ lb}$$

Similarly, the vertical force

$$F_V = (1.94)(0.0491)(35)(35 \sin 70°) = 109.6 \text{ lb}$$

Since the magnitude of the force is not dependent on the reference plane, these are the required answers. To get the actual magnitude and direction of the exit velocity, V_2' must be converted back to the original coordinate system. Referring to Fig. 5-26 the two components of V_2 are

$$V_{2_x} = 15 + 35 \cos 70° = 26.97 \text{ ft/s}$$

$$V_{2_y} = 35 \sin 70° = 32.89 \text{ ft/s}$$

Thus

$$V_2 = \sqrt{V_{2_x}^2 + V_{2_y}^2} = 42.53 \text{ ft/s}$$

and

$$\alpha = \tan^{-1}\left(\frac{V_{2_y}}{V_{2_x}}\right) = \tan^{-1}\left(\frac{32.89}{26.97}\right) = 50.66°$$

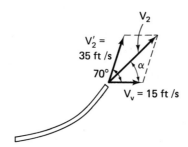

Fig. 5-26. Velocity diagram.

The unsteady condition established for this problem could, of course, prevail for only a short time interval. During this time the lower discharge of part (b) is physically justified, since the deficit in discharge has gone into storage in the ever-lengthening jet.

EXAMPLE 5-14

Determine the force on the joint (at section A) of the contracting nozzle of Fig. 5-17 of Example 5-9.

SOLUTION:

The forces acting on the fluid in the control volume for the nozzle of Fig. 5-17 are shown in Fig. 5-27. With reference to the results of Example 5-9, the velocities

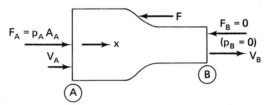

Fig. 5-27. Control volume for contracting nozzle.

were found to be $V_A = 11.45$ ft/s and $V_B = 45.87$ ft/s and the pressure at section A was evaluated as $p_A = 1905$ psf. The force F_A is based on the previously determined pressure (1905 psf) at section A. It is assumed that both α and β are equal to unity. The remaining force shown, F, is the force that the contracted section exerts on the liquid. This, in turn, for equilibrium of the nozzle, is equal to the tensile stress in the joint and is therefore the required answer. Summing forces in the x direction, the momentum equation gives

$$p_A A_A - F = \rho Q(V_B - V_A)$$

Substituting, we obtain

$$(1905)(0.0873) - F = (1.94)(1)(45.87 - 11.45)$$

yielding

$$F = 99.53 \text{ lb}$$

Drawing a free body diagram would quickly reveal that this force is, in fact, equal to the tensile stress in the joint. If the joint consists of flanges bolted together, this is the total tensile stress in the ring of bolts. Note in this problem that the energy equation had to be applied before using the momentum equation.

EXAMPLE 5-15

In many problems the energy loss is desired and the solution requires that the momentum equation be applied first. Although we have given very little consideration to energy losses thus far, it should be clear that if we evaluate the energy or total head at two sections along the flow, the difference will be the energy loss. Consider the sudden expansion of Fig. 5-28. For an air flow of 7200 cubic feet per minute (cfm) at 80°F, evaluate the energy loss due to the expansion.

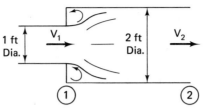

Fig. 5-28. Abrupt expansion.

SOLUTION:

The control volume between sections 1 and 2 is shown in Fig. 5-29. The assumed velocity distributions are also shown, since at section 1 it is not constant across the entire section. This is due to the zone of separation that occurs at the expansion. Like a jet discharging into the atmosphere, the jet at section 1 must have the same pressure as the surrounding air. Thus, the pressure p_1 will be constant across the entire section. The eddies shown in Fig. 5-28 at the contraction carry no momentum into or out of the section. They are, however, the primary cause of the energy loss. Writing the momentum equation,

$$p_1 A_2 - p_2 A_2 = (\rho Q V)_2 - (\rho Q V)_1$$

$$p_1 - p_2 = \frac{\rho Q}{A_2}(V_2 - V_1)$$

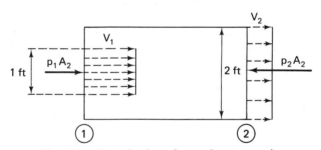

Fig. 5-29. Control volume for an abrupt expansion.

But

$$Q = 7200 \text{ cfm} = 120 \text{ cfs}$$

$$\rho = 0.00228 \text{ slugs/ft}^3$$

$$V_1 = \frac{120}{\pi(1)^2/4} = 152.79 \text{ ft/s}$$

and

$$V_2 = \frac{120}{\pi(2)^2/4} = 38.20 \text{ ft/s}$$

Therefore,

$$p_2 - p_1 = \frac{(0.00228)(120)(152.79 - 38.20)}{\pi(1)^2} = 9.98 \text{ psf}$$

The pressure at section 1 is lower than at 2 due to its higher velocity. Since heads are hard to visualize in gas flows, the total head and its components will be multiplied by γ, so that

$$H\gamma = p + \gamma y + \frac{\rho V^2}{2}$$

Whereas the head terms represented the energy per pound of fluid (ft-lb/lb), each term now is the energy per cubic foot of fluid (ft-lb/ft^3). The energy loss between the two sections is

$$\Delta(H\gamma) = \left(p_1 + \gamma y_1 + \frac{\rho V_1^2}{2}\right) - \left(p_2 + \gamma y_2 + \frac{\rho V_2^2}{2}\right)$$

Dropping the elevation terms,

$$\Delta(H\gamma) = (p_1 - p_2) + \frac{\rho}{2}(V_1^2 - V_2^2)$$

Therefore,

$$\Delta(H\gamma) = -9.98 + \left(\frac{0.00228}{2}\right)(152.79^2 - 38.20^2) = 14.93 \text{ ft-lb/ft}^3$$

The corresponding power loss is

$$\Delta P = \Delta(H\gamma) \cdot Q = (14.93)(120)$$
$$= 1791 \text{ ft-lb/s} = 3.26 \text{ horsepower}$$

Although pressure differences were computed throughout, the actual pressure at a given section is indeterminate for the given information. Also, the additional loss due to pipe friction is not included. It would be very small over the short contraction length as compared with the expansion less that was evaluated here.

EXAMPLE 5-16

Another example involving energy loss and requiring an initial solution of the momentum equation is the *hydraulic jump*. This phenomenon occurs frequently in open channel flows when a high-velocity flow is suddenly retarded to become a much slower, deeper flow. The foot of a spillway below a dam is one location where the hydraulic jump is frequently encountered. The hydraulic jump, in a rectangular channel of width b, is shown on Fig. 5-30a, and the corresponding control volume and force diagram are given in Fig. 5-30b.

The region between sections 1 and 2 is highly nonuniform with a considerable roller formed, as shown. The mechanism here is quite similar to the expansion of Example 5-15, and the large amount of energy loss makes the jump a good energy dissipator. Since sections 1 and 2 are in regions of uniform flow, the pressure distribution is hydrostatic at both sections, as shown on the force diagram. The momentum equation is, accordingly,

$$\tfrac{1}{2}\gamma y_1^2 b - \tfrac{1}{2}\gamma y_2^2 b = \rho Q(V_2 - V_1)$$

From continuity,

$$Q = V_1 y_1 b = V_2 y_2 b$$

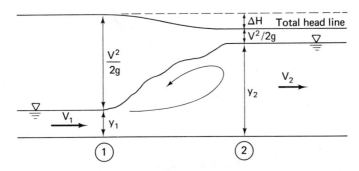

(a) Two-dimensional hydraulic jump.

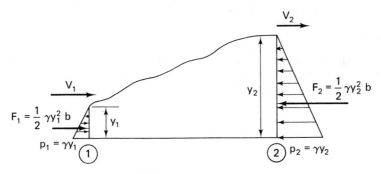

(b) Control volume.

Fig. 5-30. Hydraulic jump.

Combining the two equations,

$$y_1^2 - y_2^2 = \frac{2y_1 V_1^2}{g}\left(\frac{y_1}{y_2} - 1\right)$$

$$y_1 + y_2 = 2\frac{y_1}{y_2}\frac{V_1^2}{g}$$

$$\frac{y_2}{y_1}\left(\frac{y_2}{y_1} + 1\right) = \frac{2V_1^2}{gy_1}$$

and finally, by solution of the preceding quadratic equation in y_2/y_1, we get

$$\frac{y_2}{y_1} = \frac{1}{2}\left(\sqrt{1 + \frac{8V_1^2}{gy_1}} - 1\right)$$

Thus, the downstream depth, more particularly the downstream/upstream depth ratio, is given by upstream (and assumed known) conditions alone.

The energy loss, this time on a head (or LF/F) basis, is immediately

$$\Delta H = \left(\frac{p_1}{\gamma} + y_1 + \frac{V_1^2}{2g}\right) - \left(\frac{p_2}{\gamma} + y_2 + \frac{V_2^2}{2g}\right)$$

At sections 1 and 2, due to the uniform flow in the region, the piezometric head must be a constant throughout the vertical section, and for a datum at the channel bottom, the piezometric head must equal the depth. Consequently,

$$\Delta H = \left(y_1 + \frac{V_1^2}{2g}\right) - \left(y_2 + \frac{V_2^2}{2g}\right)$$

Combining with continuity and dividing through by y_1,

$$\frac{\Delta H}{y_1} = 1 + \frac{V_1^2}{2gy_1} - \frac{y_2}{y_1} - \left(\frac{y_1}{y_2}\right)^2 \frac{V_1^2}{2gy_1}$$

Substituting for y_2/y_1 from the momentum equation gives a cumbersome equation, but it again involves only known upstream conditions. In fact, the solution for ΔH in a numerical problem proceeds quite simply from this point. The hydraulic jump will be considered in more detail in Chapter 10.

EXAMPLE 5-17

Ignore the change in head h in the tank of Fig. 5-31 and compare the thrust developed by the discharging jet of water when the tank is (a) stationary and when it (b) moves to the left at velocity V_1. The area of the jet is A_0.

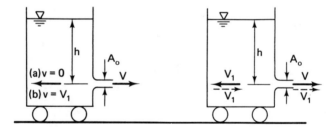

(a) Tank and jet.   (b) Steady solution to moving tank.

Fig. 5-31.   Thrust developed by a jet.

SOLUTION:

When stationary, the energy equation gives

$$V = \sqrt{2gh}$$

From momentum, the force on the water is

$$F_a = \rho Q(V - 0) = \rho V^2 A_0 = \rho(2gh)A_0$$

When the tank moves to the left with velocity V_1, the problem is unsteady, but may be made steady, as shown in Fig. 5-31b, by the addition at all points of the velocity V_1 acting to the right. Then the exit velocity becomes $V + V_1$ and the energy equation now gives

$$V + V_1 = \sqrt{2gh}$$

The momentum equation may be written as

$$F_b = \rho Q[(V + V_1) - 0]$$

where

$$Q = (V + V_1)A_0$$

Thus,

$$F_b = \rho A_0(V + V_1)^2 = \rho(2gh)A_0$$

In other words, the thrust developed by the jet is the same whether the tank is stationary or moving. The reader should determine that the actual velocity of water leaving the tank is less when the tank is moving.

EXAMPLE 5-18

A two-dimensional body is placed equidistant between parallel plates. The two-dimensional flow ahead of the body is approximately constant while downstream it is approximately triangular, as shown in Fig. 5-32. Determine the drag force on the body.

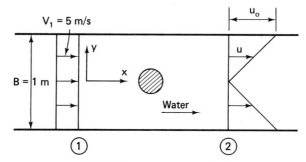

Fig. 5-32. Force on a body.

SOLUTION:

Before using the momentum principle to establish the drag force, the value of u_0 must be determined by continuity. Thus,

$$(1 \text{ m})(5 \text{ m/s}) = (u_0 \text{ m/s})(1 \text{ m})(\tfrac{1}{2})$$

$$u_0 = 10 \text{ m/s}.$$

The forces acting on the fluid are shown on the control volume of Fig. 5-33. In order to include the effect of the pressure difference, the energy equation may be

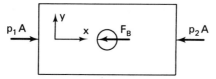

Fig. 5-33. Force diagram from Example 5-18.

applied between sections 1 and 2:

$$\frac{p_1}{\gamma} + \frac{V_1^2}{2g} = \frac{p_2}{\gamma} + \alpha_2 \frac{V_2^2}{2g}$$

where

$$V_1 = V_2 = 5 \text{ m/s}$$

and

$$\alpha_2 = \frac{1}{V^3(B/2)} \int_0^{B/2} u^3 \, dy$$

$$= \frac{2}{BV^3} \int_0^{B/2} \left(\frac{yu_0}{B/2}\right)^3 dy = 2$$

Thus,

$$p_1 - p_2 = \frac{\rho V_1^2}{2}(\alpha_2 - 1)$$

$$= \frac{(998 \text{ kg/m}^3)(5 \text{ m/s})^2}{2} = 12{,}480 \text{ N/m}^2$$

From Fig. 5-33 the momentum equation gives

$$p_1 A - p_2 A - F_B = \rho \beta_2 Q V_2 - \rho Q V_1$$

$$(12{,}480 \text{ N/m}^2)(1 \text{ m}) - F_B = (998 \text{ kg/m}^3)[5 \text{ (m}^3/\text{s)/m}](5 \text{ m/s})(\beta_2 - 1)$$

with

$$\beta_2 = \frac{1}{V^2(B/2)} \int_0^{B/2} u^2 \, dy$$

$$= \frac{2}{BV^2} \int_0^{B/2} \left(\frac{yu_0}{B/2}\right)^2 dy = \frac{4}{3}$$

Substituting this value of β_2 into the proceeding momentum equation gives $F_B = 4160$ N.

EXAMPLE 5-19

Develop an equation for the thrust developed by the jet engine of Fig. 5-34 moving with a constant velocity V_p through air as shown.

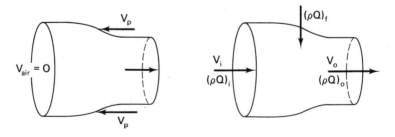

(a) Engine velocity, V_p　　　　　　(b) Steady state relationship

Fig. 5-34.　Jet engine.

SOLUTION:

In this example the problem will be set up directly in terms of the steady-state solution. So as to avoid specific consideration of possible compressibility effects at high speeds, mass flow rates (ρQ) will be considered. The entering velocity V_i will be the velocity of the plane in relation to the air (generally V_p). The mass flow rate of air entering is $(\rho Q)_i$ and, by continuity, the exit flow rate of exhaust gas is

$$(\rho Q)_o = (\rho Q)_i + (\rho Q)_f$$

where $(\rho Q)_f$ is the mass rate of fuel consumption.

Assuming that the exit pressure is equal to the ambient pressure, the momentum equation becomes

$$F = (\rho Q V)_o - (\rho Q V)_i$$
$$= [(\rho Q)_i + (\rho Q)_f]V_o - (\rho Q)_i V_i$$

Generally, the mass rate of fuel consumption is small relative to the mass rate of air flow, in which case the thrust becomes

$$F = (\rho Q)_i (V_o - V_i)$$

Bear in mind that V_i is approximately the plane velocity and that V_o is expressed relative to the plane itself.

EXAMPLE 5-20

Water at the rate of 2.5 ℓ/s enters the hydraulic machine of Fig. 5-35 at the axis. It then flows out through the four rotating arms. Each arm delivers a 1-cm-diameter jet at an angle of 30° as indicated. Determine (a) the torque required to hold the arms stationary; (b) the maximum speed in rpm if mechanical friction is ignored; (c) the power developed if the rotational speed is 120 rpm.

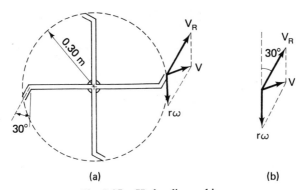

(a)   (b)

Fig. 5-35. Hydraulic machine.

SOLUTION:

(a) Applying the torque/angular momentum relationship of Eq. 5-58, the torque must equal the rate of angular momentum out minus the rate of angular momentum in, since the flow is steady. The total discharge is

$$Q = 2.5 \; \ell/s = 0.0025 \text{ m}^3/s$$

and the relative velocity V_R (the velocity relative to the arms of the machine) is

$$V_R = \frac{0.0025 \text{ m}^3/\text{s}}{(4)(\pi/4)(0.01)^2 \text{ m}^2} = 7.96 \text{ m/s}$$

Note in part (a) of the solution that for no rotation, the relative velocity V_R and the actual velocity V are identical. There is no angular momentum entering; hence, the torque, considering the four arms together, is given by

$$T = r\rho Q V_R \cos 30°$$
$$= (0.30 \text{ m})(1000 \text{ kg/m}^3)(0.0025 \text{ m}^3/\text{s})(7.96 \cos 30° \text{ m/s})$$
$$= 5.17 \text{ N·m}$$

(b) The velocity as calculated by continuity is the water velocity relative to the machine (V_R). If the arms rotate at an angular velocity ω, the tip of the arm advances with velocity $r\omega$ and the actual velocity of the water is the vector sum of the velocity of the water relative to the arm plus the velocity of the tip of the arm (see Fig. 5-36b). The maximum speed will occur when the actual velocity is radial and hence

$$r\omega = V_R \cos 30°$$

or

$$\omega = \frac{7.96 \cos 30° \text{ m/s}}{0.30 \text{ m}} = 22.98 \text{ rad/s}$$

This corresponds to a speed of

$$N = \frac{\omega(60)}{2\pi}$$
$$= \frac{(22.98 \text{ rad/s})(60 \text{ s/min})}{2\pi \text{ rad/rev}} = 219 \text{ rpm}$$

(c) If the actual rotation is at 120 rpm, the advance of the tip of the arms would be

$$r\omega = \frac{(0.3 \text{ m})(2\pi \text{ rad/rev})(120 \text{ rpm})}{60 \text{ s/min}} = 3.77 \text{ m/s}$$

The angular momentum out, which is due to the tangential component of the absolute water velocity, is now ($V_R \cos 30° - r\omega$), hence the torque is

$$T = r\rho Q(V_R \cos 30° - r\omega)$$
$$= (0.30)(1000)(0.0025)(7.96 \cos 30° - 3.77)$$
$$= 2.34 \text{ N·m}$$

The power, given by $T\omega$, is

$$P = T\omega = \frac{(2.34)(2\pi)(120)}{60} = 29.44 \text{ N·m/s} \quad \text{(or joules)}$$

EXAMPLE 5-21

Flows in and out of the water tank of Fig. 5-36a are all in the horizontal plane. Equal discharges of 0.332 m³/s enter through pipes 1 and 2, and the pressure in each of the two pipes is 32 kN/m². Pipes 3, 4, and 5 all discharge into the atmosphere with velocities of 8 m/s. Determine the force and torque on the hinge support at point A.

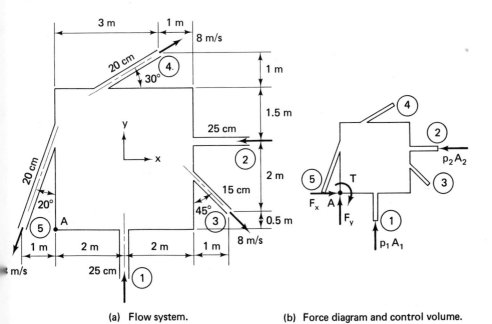

(a) Flow system.   (b) Force diagram and control volume.

Fig. 5-36. Momentum and angular momentum example.

SOLUTION:

Velocities and forces on pipes 1 and 2 are as follows:

$$V_1 = V_2 = \frac{Q}{A} = \frac{0.332}{(\pi/4)(0.25)^2} = 6.56 \text{ m/s}$$

$$F_1 = F_2 = (32{,}000 \text{ N/m}^2)\left[\left(\frac{\pi}{4}\right)(0.25)^2 \text{ m}^2\right] = 1571 \text{ N}$$

while flow rates through pipes 3, 4, and 5 are, respectively,

$$Q_3 = (8)\left(\frac{\pi}{4}\right)(0.15)^2 = 0.141 \text{ m}^3/\text{s}$$

$$Q_4 = Q_5 = (8)\left(\frac{\pi}{4}\right)(0.20)^2 = 0.251 \text{ m}^3/\text{s}$$

In the x direction the momentum equation becomes

$$F_x - F_2 = (\rho Q_3 V_3 \sin 45° + \rho Q_4 V_4 \cos 30°$$
$$- \rho Q_5 V_5 \sin 20°)_{\text{out}} - (-\rho Q_2 V_2)_{\text{in}}$$

Since the actual directions of the force and torque at A are unknown, they have been assumed positive on the control volume of Fig. 5-36b. In order to keep track of the signs of the various terms, the "momentum out" and "momentum in" terms have first been bracketed separately; the proper sign has been associated with each term within the brackets according to its direction. Continuing,

$$F_x - 1571 \text{ N} = [(1000 \text{ kg/m}^3)(0.141 \text{ m}^3\text{/s})(8 \sin 45° \text{ m/s})$$
$$+ (1000)(0.251)(8 \cos 30°) - (1000)(0.251)(8 \sin 20°)$$
$$- [-(1000)(0.332)(6.56)]$$

or

$$F_x = 5599 \text{ N}$$

Similarly, in the y direction,

$$F_y + F_1 = (-\rho Q_3 V_3 \cos 45° + \rho Q_4 V_4 \sin 30°$$
$$- \rho Q_5 V_5 \cos 20°)_{\text{out}} - (\rho Q_1 V_1)_{\text{in}}$$

or

$$F_y + 1571 \text{ N} = [-(1000 \text{ kg/m}^3)(0.141 \text{ m}^3\text{/s})(8 \cos 45° \text{ m/s})$$
$$+ (1000)(0.251)(8 \sin 30°) - (1000)(0.251)(8 \cos 20°)]$$
$$- [(1000)(0.332)(6.56)]$$

yielding

$$F_y = -5429 \text{ N}$$

Since these force components are those acting on the water, the forces of the water on the hinge are as follows:

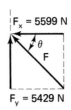

The resultant force $F = \sqrt{F_x^2 + F_y^2} = 7799$ N at an angle given by

$$\theta = \tan^{-1}\left(\frac{5429}{5599}\right) = 44.1°$$

The torque-rate of angular momentum expression may be written next as

$$T - F_1(2.0) - F_2(2.5) = [\rho Q_3 V_3 \sin 45° \ (0.5)$$
$$+ \rho Q_3 V_3 \cos 45° \ (5.0) + \rho Q_4 V_4 \cos 30° \ (5.0)$$
$$- \rho Q_4 V_4 \sin 30° \ (3.0) - \rho Q_5 V_5 \cos 20° \ (1.0)]_{\text{out}}$$
$$- [\rho Q_1 V_1(2.0) - \rho Q_2 V_2(2.5)]_{\text{in}}$$

Thus,

$$T - (1571 \text{ N})(2.0 \text{ m}) - (1571 \text{ N})(2.5 \text{ m})$$
$$= [(1000 \text{ kg/m}^3)(0.141 \text{ m}^3\text{/s})(8 \sin 45° \text{ m/s})(0.5 \text{ m})$$
$$+ (1000)(0.141)(8 \cos 45°)(5.0) + (1000)(0.251)(8 \cos 30°)(5.0)$$
$$- (1000)(0.251)(8 \sin 30°)(3.0) - (1000)(0.251)(8 \cos 20°)(1.0)]$$
$$- [-(1000)(0.332)(6.52)(2.0) - (1000)(0.332)(6.56)(2.5)]$$

Whereupon $T = 25,050$ N·m, with direction as shown in Fig. 5-36b. This is the torque exerted on the water, and hence the torque due to the water will be counterclockwise.

PROBLEMS

Sec. 5-1

5-1. Through use of Eqs. 5-1 or Eqs. 5-7 show that for a fluid at rest, the pressure is constant over a horizontal plane.

5-2. Through use of Eqs. 5-1 or Eqs. 5-7, develop the vertical pressure distribution (Eq. 2-2) for a fluid at rest.

5-3. Show that Eq. 5-7 reduces to Eqs. 5-1 provided that the y axis is vertical.

5-4. Referring to Eqs. 5-5, how does the piezometric head vary throughout a liquid at rest?

5-5. If the datum is chosen as the bottom of a tank containing liquid of depth y_0, what is the magnitude of the piezometric head at the bottom, at the surface, and at middepth?

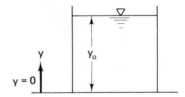

5-6. If the y direction is taken as vertical in Example 3-6, what is the pressure gradient in each direction at the origin?

5-7. Show that Eq. 5-2 will result regardless of the inclination of the s direction by repeating the derivation using the following sketch.

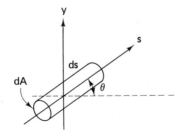

Sec. 5-2

5-8. If a 6-ft-wide tank of oil (sp. gr. = 0.87) is accelerated to the right at 5 ft/s², what will be the slope of the surface of the oil? What will be the pressure at point A? At point B?

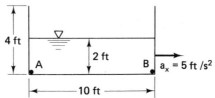

5-9. If the tank of oil in Prob. 5-8 is completely filled to the maximum depth of 4 ft, how many cubic feet will spill under the acceleration of 5 ft/s² shown? What will be the pressure at point A? At point B?

5-10. The tank of the preceding two problems is again completely filled with oil and the top is completely covered. If there is a small air vent open to the atmosphere at corner C, what will be the pressure at points A, B, and D when the acceleration is to the right at 15 ft/s²? If there is a small air vent open to the atmosphere at corner D (but not at C), what will be the pressure at points A, B, and C when the acceleration is to the right at 15 ft/s²?

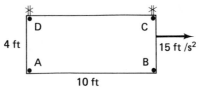

5-11. If the tank of oil in Prob. 5-8 is accelerated so that the oil just touches the top of the tank, how fast has it been accelerated and what will be the pressures at points A and B?

5-12. A truck carries water in an open tank 2 m wide, 10 m long, and 2 m deep. If the water is filled to 0.5 m from the top, what is the greatest horizontal acceleration the truck can have if no water is to spill? What is the maximum pressure due to the liquid? Repeat the problem if the truck contained glycerin to the same depth.

5-13. A rectangular fuel tank in a rapidly accelerating vehicle has an outlet placed as shown. What is the maximum acceleration that will still permit fuel to be fed to the engine?

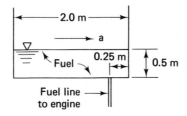

5-14. Repeat Prob. 5-10 if the height of the closed tank is 1 m, the length of the tank is 5 m, and the acceleration to the right is 4 m/s².

5-15. If a 1-m-deep by 1.2-m-diameter tank of concrete ($\gamma = 24$ kN/m³) is given an upward vertical acceleteration of 0.1 g, determine the force on the bottom of the tank.

5-16. Repeat Prob. 5-15 if the acceleration is downward at the rate of 0.25 g.

5-17. A 1-ft-diameter by 2-ft-deep container of water is given a downward acceleration of 0.5 g. What is the pressure on the bottom of the tank? Describe what will happen if the tank is given a downward acceleration of 1.0 g; of 1.5 g.

5-18. A tank of water (Fig. 5-7) is rotated at the rate of 80 rpm. If the radius is 1 ft, the initial depth 2 ft, and the tank depth is sufficient to avoid overtopping, what is the depth at the axis? At the outer radius? What is the water surface slope at the outer radius? Determine the pressure at the bottom of the tank at both the axis and at a 1-ft radius.

5-19. If a 2-m-long slender tube half-filled with water is rotated at an angular velocity of 3 rad/s in the horizontal plane, what is the pressure at the closed end?

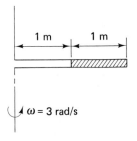

5-20. A bucket of water is rotated at arm's length in the vertical plane. What is the minimum angular velocity in rpm for which no water will spill, if the diameter of the path is 2 m?

5-21. A closed tank such as that in Example 5-3 is 1 m high and has a radius of 0.4 m. It is filled with oil (sp. gr. = 0.89) and closed except for a small vent to the atmosphere at point 1 (see Fig. 5-8). If it is rotated at 200 rpm, what will be the pressure at the bottom of the tank both at the axis and at the outer edge?

Sec. 5-3

5-22. If the blunt body shown is exposed to an airflow (at 70°F) of 100 ft/s, what will be the increase in pressure at point A over the ambient pressure?

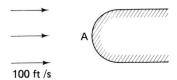

5-23. What is the pressure rise at the front of a wing moving through still air (70°F) at 120 ft/s?

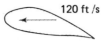

120 ft /s

5-24. If the wing of Prob. 5-23 moves to the left at 30 m/s through otherwise still air at 20°C and pressure of 1.013×10^5 Pa, what is the absolute pressure at the leading edge?

5-25. If the Pitot tube in an airflow at 90°F indicates a pressure difference equivalent to 1 in. of mercury, what is the corresponding velocity?

5-26. Determine the reading in millimeters of mercury of a Pitot tube on an airplane flying at 220 km/hr if the air temperature is 20°C.

5-27. What will be the pressure at the nose of a submarine that is cruising through still water at 20 ft/s at a depth of 40 ft?

5-28. Determine the pressure on the nose of a submarine traveling at 7 m/s against a current of 1 m/s when at a depth of 50 m.

5-29. If the dimension $H = 100$ ft in the tank of Fig. 1-1, what is the velocity through the orifice if the liquid is water? If the liquid is kerosene?

5-30. What head H would correspond to a water velocity of 20 m/s from the orifice of Fig. 1-1?

5-31. If a 4-ft-diameter tank containing SAE 10 oil is rotated about its horizontal axis at 20 rpm, what is the pressure difference between the lower and uppermost points?

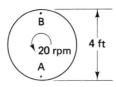

5-32. Water at the rate of 2 cfs passes through the transition shown.
    (a) If flow is downward, what will be the differential in the mercurcy manometer? If the pressure gage at section 1 indicates 100 psi, what will the gage at 2 indicate?
    (b) If the flow is upward, what will be the mercury differential and what will be the pressure at section 2 corresponding to 100 psi at 1?

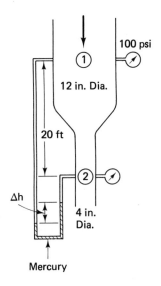

5-33. Oil (sp. gr. = 0.9) flows downward through the contraction of Prob. 5-32. If the manometer indicates a differential $\Delta h = 10$ cm of mercury, what is the flow rate in m³/s?

5-34. Water at 60°F flows past the blunt body of Fig. 5-9. The maximum velocity of the water as it passes the body is 130% of the approach velocity. If the approach flow has a pressure of 10 psi at section 1, what is the greatest approach velocity v_1 that will avoid cavitation?

5-35. A horizontal pipe is reduced by a pipe contraction from a diameter of 0.3 to 0.2 m. If the upstream pressure is 50 kN/m², what is the maximum flow rate of water at 20°C that will avoid cavitation?

5-36. What upstream pressure will cause cavitation in the pipe contraction of Prob. 5-35 if the upstream (of the contraction) velocity is 10 m/s? Assume water at 10°C; at 60°C.

Sec. 5-4

5-37. Water discharges from a 2-in.-diameter pipe at the rate of 1.75 cfs. If the initial inclination is 40°, what will be the maximum height of the jet, its velocity at that point, and the horizontal distance until the jet returns to its original elevation?

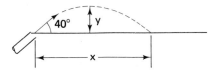

5-38. Water discharges horizontally with a velocity of 40 ft/s. If its height is 20 ft above the horizontal surface, at what distance x will it strike the surface?

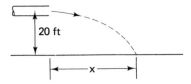

5-39. Oil (sp. gr. $= 0.89$) discharges horizontally with a velocity of 18 m/s similar to Prob. 5-38. If the initial height of the oil jet is 3 m above a horizontal surface, at what distance x will it strike the surface?

5-40. If water discharging from a 5-cm-diameter horizontal pipe strikes a horizontal surface that is 5 m below the pipe elevation at a horizontal distance of 55 m, what is the flow rate?

5-41. If water with a 2-in.-diameter jet directed at an angle of 50° hits a 40-ft distant wall at a height 60 ft above the ground (and jet nozzle), what must be the discharge?

5-42. If a liquid discharges from a 4-in.-diameter orifice at the bottom of a 6-ft-deep tank, what will be the jet diameter 12 ft below the outlet?

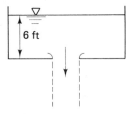

5-43. If water discharges from a 15-cm orifice at the bottom of a 2-m-deep tank similar to Prob. 5-42, what will be the jet velocity and diameter 10 m below the outlet?

5-44. A fire hose discharges water at 2.5 cfs. The nozzle has a diameter of 2 in. What is the horizontal distance water will travel before reaching its initial elevation, if the hose is held at 45° to the horizontal?

5-45. Water discharges from a 6-cm-diameter pipe at the rate of 0.1 m³/s. If the initial inclination is 40° as shown in Prob. 5-37, what will be the maximum height of the jet, the horizontal distance until the jet returns to its original elevation, and the magnitude and direction of the jet at this point?

5-46. With reference to Fig. 5-14, if a jet with an initial velocity of 80 ft/s strikes the horizontal plane $y = 0$ at a distance of 70 ft, what are the two possible angles of inclination, θ?

5-47. What two distances, y_1 and y_2, will cause the jet to strike the horizontal plane 20 m from the tank?

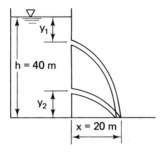

5-48. Determine the two orifice locations, y_1 and y_2, which will cause the jet from a tank of depth h (similar to Prob. 5-47) to strike the plane of the tank bottom a distance x from the tank?

Sec. 5-5

5-49. What is the pressure at A corresponding to a water discharge of 8 cfs through the pipe nozzle shown?

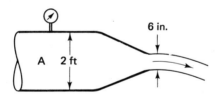

5-50. If the pipe nozzle in Prob. 5-49 reduces from 0.5 m to 0.1 m in diameter, what is the discharge of water corresponding to a pressure at A of 300 kN/m²?

5-51. The pressure inside a 3-in. fire hose is 70 psia. What is the water discharge and velocity through a 1-in. nozzle attached to the end?

5-52. What pressure would be required inside a 8-cm-diameter fire hose with a 3-cm-diameter nozzle if the velocity of the water leaving the nozzle is 25 m/s?

5-53. If the velocity profile in a pipe is parabolic, as given, show that $\alpha = 2.0$.

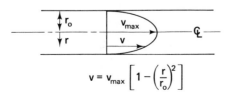

$$v = v_{max}\left[1 - \left(\frac{r}{r_o}\right)^2\right]$$

5-54. For a two-dimensional parabolic velocity distribution between flat plates, determine the value of α.

5-55. Assuming that turbulent flow can be approximated by a "seventh-power" law (as in Example 5-10), such that

$$\frac{v}{v_{max}} = \left(\frac{y}{R}\right)^{1/7}$$

where y is the distance measured from the pipe wall inward, show that $\alpha = 1.058$ for a circular pipe of radius R.

5-56. If depths upstream and downstream of a dam are 100 ft and 4 ft, respectively, what is the flow rate per foot of length (perpendicular to the sketch)?

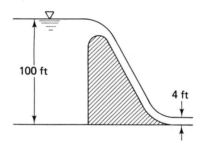

5-57. If the flow over a low weir is 10 m³/s per meter of crest length, and V_2 is twice V_1, what are the upstream and downstream depths and the respective velocities?

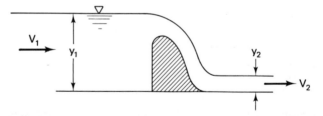

5-58. A square duct, 4 ft by 4 ft in cross section, reduces to a 1-ft by 2-ft rectangular section. Air is blown through the system at the rate of 1000 lb/min. Its temperature is 60°F, the large section has a pressure of 14.7 psia, and density changes are negligible. What will be the pressure in the smaller section?

5-59. Ignoring friction, what is the flow rate and the pressure at point A?

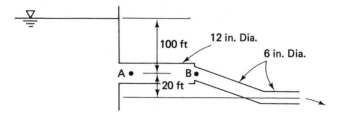

5-60. What is the pressure at point B in Prob. 5-59?

5-61. Ignoring friction, what is the flow rate and the pressure at points A, B, and C?

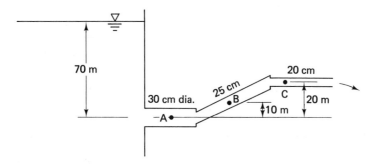

5-62. An elevated water tank has a height of 5 m and a diameter of 6 m. The depth of water in the tank is 3 m and the pipe diameter is 0.25 m. When the discharge is 0.2 m³/s, what are the pressure and average velocity at point A and the pressure at point B? Why is the pressure at B different from that at A? What is the pressure at point C?

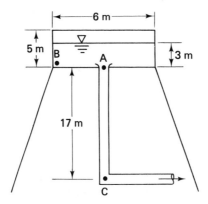

5-63. If the water is pumped from the tank of Prob. 5-62, what flow rate would cause cavitation to occur at point A? Assume a water temperature of 20°C.

5-64. Refer to the figure associated with Prob. 5-59. Keeping the elevation change of 20 ft constant, will continual increasing of the reservoir head above the given value of 100 ft ever lead to cavitation at either point A or point B? If the answer is yes, what head would cause cavitation to occur at point A? At point B? (Assume a water temperature of 60°F.)

5-65. Refer to the figure associated with Prob. 5-59. Keeping the reservoir head of 100 ft constant, will continual decreasing of the outlet elevation below the given value of 20 ft ever lead to cavitation at either point A or point B? If the answer is yes, what dimension, replacing the 20 ft, would cause cavitation to occur at point A? At point B? (Assume a water temperature of 60°F.)

5-66. If the flow rate is 60 cfs, how many horsepower are supplied by the pump?

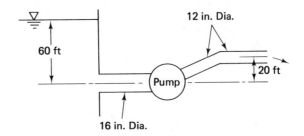

5-67. If the pump of Prob. 5-66 provides 20 hp, what will be the flow rate?

5-68. If the pump shown provides 20 kW, what water discharge will be obtained?

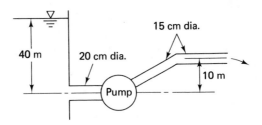

5-69. If the pump shown in Prob. 5-68 is replaced by a turbine, what power would be developed for an exit velocity of 5 m/s? 10 m/s? 15 m/s?

Sec. 5-7

5-70. Determine β for the flow of Prob. 5-53.

5-71. Determine β for the flow of Prob. 5-54.

5-72. A 4-in.-diameter jet of water strikes a stationary vane as shown. If the discharge is 5.5 cfs, what is the force on the vane?

5-73. If the vane of Prob. 5-72 moves to the left at 10 ft/s, determine the force on the vane. What is the magnitude and direction of the velocity leaving the vane?

5-74. If the vane of Prob. 5-72 moves to the right with a velocity of 10 ft/s, what is the force on the vane and the magnitude and direction of the water leaving the vane?

5-75. If a jet with a diameter of 10 cm and velocity of 20 m/s strikes a vane as shown, what is the force on the vane when it is stationary? Moving to the left with a velocity of 5 m/s? What is the magnitude and direction of the exiting velocity in each case?

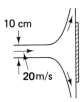

5-76. If a two-dimensional flow from a long slot is deflected as shown, determine the ratio of q_1 to q_2 as a function of θ.

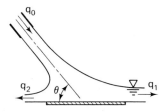

5-77. What is the thrust on the vane of Prob. 5-76?

5-78. A 3-in.-diameter oil jet (sp. gr. = 0.9) with a velocity of 40 ft/s strikes the stationary U-shaped vane shown. What is the force on the vane?

5-79. If the vane of Prob. 5-78 moves to the right at 10 ft/s, what is the force on the vane? What is the actual velocity leaving the vane?

5-80. A 10-cm-diameter jet of water with an actual velocity of 20 m/s encounters a vane, as in Prob. 5-78. Determine the force on the vane if it is stationary. Determine the force on the vane and the actual velocity leaving the vane if the vane moves to the left at 7 m/s.

5-81. If the exiting jet of Prob. 5-78 leaves the U-shaped vane at an elevation 15 ft above the incoming jet, what is the horizontal force on the vane?

5-82. A vertical 6-in.-diameter pipe turns through a 90° bend and discharges water horizontally out through a nozzle which reduces the diameter to 4 in. What are the horizontal and vertical forces on the elbow if the velocity in the jet is 35 ft/s?

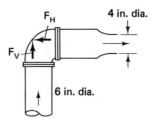

5-83. A vertical 20-cm-diameter pipe turns through a 90° reducing elbow, then through a 15-cm-diameter pipe to a nozzle which further reduces the diameter from 15 cm down to a jet diameter of 12 cm. What are the horizontal and vertical forces on the elbow if the velocity in the jet of water is 20 m/s?

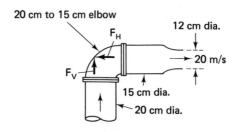

5-84. What force is required to hold the tank stationary? The diameter of the jet of water is 6 in.

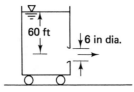

5-85. Water flows over the dam spillway as shown. Determine the magnitude of the horizontal force per foot of length perpendicular to the sketch due to the water.

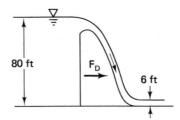

5-86. If a dam similar to that of Prob. 5-85 has an upstream depth of 6 m and a downstream depth of 2 m, what is the force on the dam if it is 30 m long?

5-87. Determine the thrust F on the contraction due to a flow of 2 cfs. The pressure at section 1 is 20 psi. Evaluate F first with the inclusion of the water weight as one of the forces and second by ignoring the force due to the weight. In the first case a rough estimate of volume will suffice.

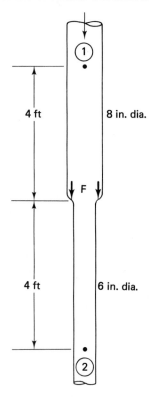

5-88. A hydraulic jump occurs in an 80-ft-wide channel. The flow rate is 7200 cfs and the upstream depth is 3 ft. What is the necessary downstream depth? If a series of 26 blocks, each of which exerts a drag force of 1500 lb is placed in the flow, what downstream depth would be required?

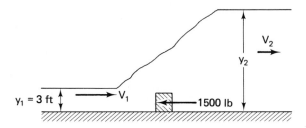

5-89. A hydraulic jump occurs in a rectangular channel of width 1 m and upstream depth 0.2 m. Given a downstream velocity of 1.08 m/s, determine upstream velocity, downstream depth, and flow rate.

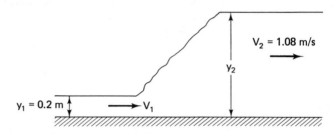

5-90. Determine the force on the body of Example 5-18 (Fig. 5-32), if conditions are identical to that of the example except that the velocity distribution at the downstream section (section 2) is specified by

$$\frac{u}{u_0} = \sin\left|\frac{y\pi}{B}\right|$$

5-91. What discharge of air in N/s is required to develop a thrust of 200 kN in a jet engine? The plane velocity is to be 270 m/s and the exit discharge has an area of 1.5 m² and velocity of 1500 m/s. Ignore the fuel consumption and assume air at $-50°C$ and 35 kN/m²(abs).

5-92. Develop an equation for the thrust of the jet engine in Example 5-19 if the ambient air pressure is p_1 and the pressure of the exhaust gas is p_2.

5-93. Determine the height z at which a weight of 100 N will be supported by a jet of water that leaves a 6-cm-diameter pipe with a velocity of 15 m/s.

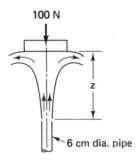

5-94. At what height will the weight of Prob. 5-93 be supported if the jet velocity is doubled?

5-95. A water sprinkler consists of two rotating arms as shown. Each delivers a jet with a diameter of 1 cm. The velocity in the 3-cm-diameter supply pipe is

7 m/s. What torque is required to hold the sprinkler head stationary? What torque would be required to rotate the head counterclockwise at 150 rpm?

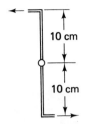

REFERENCES

ROUSE, H., and S. INCE, *History of Hydraulics*. New York: Dover, 1963.

STREETER, V. L. (ed.), *Handbook of Fluid Dynamics*. New York: McGraw-Hill, 1961, Chaps. 3, 4, and 5.

6

Dimensional Analysis and Modeling

At this point many of the basic mechanics principles needed for an understanding of introductory fluid mechanics have been developed. As we now undertake the application of these results to real fluids, the additional complications that will arise require the introduction of new techniques. Frequently, we must resort to the not unrelated results of experiment, modeling, and dimensional analysis. As dimensional analysis provides the guide to profitable experiments and the key to proper modeling, we will consider it first. This will be followed by its application to experimental fluid mechanics in general and modeling in particular.

6–1 DIMENSIONAL ANALYSIS: THE BUCKINGHAM PI THEOREM

Dimensional analysis is the reorganization of the dimensional variables important to a particular problem so as to obtain a lesser number of dimensionless parameters. The advantages that accrue will be discussed subsequently. The starting point is the logical premise that a relationship describing a physical phenomenon operating under natural laws must be dimensionally homogenous. That is, every term in the relationship must have identical dimensions. Any nonhomogenous equation that describes a physical phenomenon cannot be general, but rather can only apply under limited conditions. For example, certain equations describing open-channel flow are applicable only to the flow of water. This premise must be true, whether the relationship is theoretical or experimental, and whether the result is expressed in equation form or graphically.

The procedure that will be introduced here to obtain the dimensionless results was formulated by Buckingham and is referred to as the *Buckingham pi theorem*. It will be presented here without proof. Basically, if a dimensional dependent variable[1] depends on $n - 1$ dimensional independent variables (i.e., there are n variables involved in a problem), and if m independent dimensions are required to define the n variables, then the n dimensional variables can be combined into $n - m$ dimensionless variables. To illustrate the procedure as it is being described, a general but also very instructive problem will be examined. This will involve most of the variables encountered in basic fluid mechanics. Before proceeding further it is useful to divide the typical variables into the three groups described below and summarized in Table 6-1.

Table 6-1 Typical Fluid Mechanics Variables by Group

1. Geometric variables: $D, L, x, y, \ldots, A, V\!\!\!\!/$
2. Flow variables
Kinematic: V, Q, t, a
Dynamic: $\tau, \Delta p, \partial p/\partial x, F, P$
3. Fluid properties: $\rho, \gamma, \mu, \nu, \sigma, E$

The first group is the geometric variables. Generally, length dimensions are used: a diameter, a length in the direction of flow, a depth, a width, and so on, so as to include all relevant characteristics of the geometry. Alternatively, the cross-sectional area or, on occasion, even a volume could be used. Note, for example, that if the diameter of a pipe is chosen, the corresponding area is redundant and cannot be used. The second group consists of kinematic and dynamic variables: velocity, discharge, time, and acceleration are the most common kinematic variables. Again, note that if velocity and pipe diameter are specified, then discharge becomes redundant. The dynamic variables include the shearing stress, pressure difference, pressure gradient, force, and power. The final group contains the fluid properties.

From this list we will take a pressure difference, Δp, as the dependent variable. This could be the pressure difference between selected points on the upstream and downstream sides of a model spillway, or above and below a

---

[1] If more than one dependent variable is involved in a problem, as is often the case, then ensuing procedures must be repeated in turn for each dependent variable. This possibility will not be considered further here.

wing section, for two examples. It must then be determined which independent variables significantly affect Δp. This step frequently involves considerable judgment. If too many independent parameters are chosen, the problem
becomes overcomplicated, whereas too few will give erroneous results. If a
second dependent variable is picked, the procedure will fail again. Let us
assume for this general problem that Δp depends on just three geometric
variables: a diameter D and two additional lengths, x_1 and x_2. Further assume
that the velocity V is important as well as the fluid properties $\rho, \gamma, \mu, \sigma$, and
E. Consequently, a dimensional statement in functional form becomes

$$\Delta p = f(D, x_1, x_2, V, \rho, \gamma, \mu, \sigma, E) \qquad (6\text{-}1)$$

Referring back to the theorem statement, we see that $n = 10$ in Eq. 6-1.
Furthermore, the fundamental dimensions, previously discussed in Section
1-2, consist of either force, length, and time, FLT, or mass, length, and time,
MLT. Either system can be used; here, to continue the example problem the
FLT system is chosen arbitrarily. The four dimensions, force, mass, length,
and time, cannot simultaneously be used in the dimensional analysis procedure, since, as discussed in Section 1-2, only three can be chosen independently. A quick examination of the variables in Eq. 6-1 shows that all three
dimensions are present. To illustrate this, note that the pressure Δp has the
fundamental dimensions of FL^{-2} (or force per unit area), and the velocity V
with dimensions LT^{-1} picks up the third dimension of time. Consequently,
m, the number of fundamental dimensions involved, equals three. Immediately,

$$n - m = 10 - 3 = 7$$

Thus, the variables of Eq. 6-1 can be expected to reduce to seven dimensionless variables by dimensional analysis. These will ultimately be written as

$$\pi_1 = \phi(\pi_2, \pi_3, \pi_4, \pi_5, \pi_6, \pi_7) \qquad (6\text{-}2)$$

These seven *pi terms*[2] will consist of dimensionless combinations of the
m repeating variables with the remaining variables, the latter taken one at
a time. Before explaining this further, some rules for picking the repeating
variables are needed. Although these rules will provide some guidance,
experience plays an equally important role. Further, the different rules will
occasionally be in conflict. In these cases experience and even an anticipation
of the desired results may be required for proper selection of the repeating
variables. These rules, or guidelines, listed in no particular order, are as
follows:

    1. All the fundamental dimensions occurring in the problem must be found
in at least one of the m repeating variables.

---

[2] The use of the *pi* notation is purely by convention and bears no relation to the usual
mathematical significance of *pi*.

2. Pick variables that appear to be important over the range of operating conditions. That is, avoid choosing as repeating variables any that are of doubtful importance. This is suggested since later considerations may indicate that a particular variable is unimportant. If it occurs only once, that particular pi term may be deleted. If the unimportant variable, on the other hand, occurs in most of the terms, the procedure will have to be redone from the beginning.

3. No two repeating variables can have identical dimensions. They would always combine as a dimensionless ratio excluding all the other variables.

4. Choose one repeating variable from each of the three groups. If $m = 2$, variables may be chosen from only two of the groups.

5. Finally, if possible, avoid using the dependent variable as a repeating variable. This is not always possible or desirable, but it is usually advantageous if the dependent variable occurs in only the first pi term.

Continuing with the example problem, D, V, and ρ are taken as repeating variables from Eq. 6-1. The application of certain of the rules is obvious. Note that D is assumed to be the most important of the geometric variables. The choice of ρ is based partly on the suspicion that under certain flow conditions the effects of gravity, viscous effects, surface tension, and compressibility may be unimportant and partly on experience and anticipated results. The seven (in general, $n-m$) pi terms will each consist of one non-repeating variable in combination with the three repeating variables as follows:

$$\pi_1 = f_1(\Delta p, D, V, \rho) \qquad \pi_5 = f_5(\mu, D, V, \rho)$$

$$\pi_2 = f_2(x_1, D, V, \rho) \qquad \pi_6 = f_6(\sigma, D, V, \rho)$$

$$\pi_3 = f_3(x_2, D, V, \rho) \qquad \pi_7 = f_7(E, D, V, \rho)$$

$$\pi_4 = f_4(\gamma, D, V, \rho)$$

It now remains to obtain the appropriate pi term from each of the above. The three fundamental dimensions involved are independent. Therefore, in order for a term such as π_1 to be dimensionless, each of the three dimensions must occur to the zero power. In other words, the pi terms must have dimensions as follows:

$$\pi_1 = F^0 L^0 T^0$$

Assuming π_1 to equal the product of the four variables, each to an unknown power, gives

$$\pi_1 = \Delta p^a D^b V^c \rho^d$$

There is a degree of freedom present, however, since once π_1 is made dimensionless, the result may be raised to any power desired while still remaining dimensionless. Rewriting π_1, with Δp to the first power, which will be seen to place Δp in the numerator of the result, now gives

$$\pi_1 = \Delta p^1 D^a V^b \rho^c \qquad (6\text{-}3)$$

Inserting the fundamental dimensions and appropriate exponents into each term,

$$F^0 L^0 T^0 = (FL^{-2})^1 (L)^a (LT^{-1})^b (FT^2 L^{-4})^c$$

We will start first with the dimension of force. Since the dimensions are independent, the force dimension will disappear from the proceding expressions only if

$$F: \quad F^0 = F^{1+c}$$

This will be satisfied when

$$0 = 1 + c$$

or

$$c = -1$$

Thus, the first pi term, π_1, will be independent of the force dimension only if $C = -1$, or, in other words, if ρ occurs in Eq. 6-3 to the power of -1. Considering the time dimension in the same way,

$$T: \quad 0 = -b + 2c$$

and

$$b = -2$$

Finally, the length dimension gives

$$L: \quad 0 = -2 + a + b - 4c$$

and

$$a = 0$$

Returning to Eq. 6-3,

$$\pi_1 = \Delta p^1 D^0 V^{-2} \rho^{-1} = \frac{\Delta p}{\rho V^2} \qquad (6\text{-}4a)$$

and D drops out of π_1.

Treating π_2 in the same manner,

$$\pi_2 = x_1^1 D^a V^b \rho^c$$

or

$$F^0 L^0 T^0 = (L)^1 (L)^a (LT^{-1})^b (FT^2 L^{-4})^c$$

From the force dimension,

$$F: \quad 0 = c$$

Likewise,

$$T: \quad 0 = -b + 2c$$

giving

$$b = 0$$

and

$$L: \quad 0 = 1 + a + b - 4c$$

$$a = -1$$

Therefore,

$$\pi_2 = x_1 D^{-1} V^0 \rho^0 = \frac{x_1}{D} \qquad (6\text{-}4b)$$

Whenever the nonrepeated variable has identical dimensions to one of the repeating variables, a ratio of the two will result. This is, of course, the reason for rule 3 discussed earlier. In this light, π_3 may be formed by inspection:

$$\pi_3 = \frac{x_2}{D} \qquad (6\text{-}4c)$$

Continuing,

$$\pi_4 = \gamma^1 D^a V^b \rho^c$$
$$F^0 L^0 T^0 = (FL^{-3})^1 (L)^a (LT^{-1})^b (FT^2 L^{-4})^c$$

$$F: \quad 0 = 1 + c$$
$$c = -1$$
$$T: \quad 0 = -b + 2c$$
$$b = -2$$
$$L: \quad 0 = -3 + a + b - 4c$$
$$a = 1$$

Finally,

$$\pi_4 = \frac{\gamma D}{\rho V^2}$$

This term will be used frequently when raised to the negative one-half power:

$$\pi_4 = \frac{V}{\sqrt{D\gamma/\rho}} \qquad (6\text{-}4d)$$

This form would have been obtained directly if in the analysis, π_4 had been formulated thus:

$$\pi_4 = \gamma^{-1/2} D^a V^b \rho^c$$

The next pi term will be derived directly in the most conventional form.

$$\pi_5 = \mu^{-1} D^a V^b \rho^c$$
$$F^0 L^0 T^0 = (FTL^{-2})^{-1} (L)^a (LT^{-1})^b (FT^2 L^{-4})^c$$

$$F: \quad 0 = -1 + c$$
$$c = 1$$
$$T: \quad 0 = -1 - b + 2c$$
$$b = 1$$
$$L: \quad 0 = 2 + a + b - 4c$$
$$a = 1$$

$$\pi_5 = \frac{VD\rho}{\mu} \qquad (6\text{-}4e)$$

For illustrative purposes the formation of this last π term is repeated using the *MLT* system.

$$\pi_5: \quad M^0L^0T^0 = (ML^{-1}T^{-1})^{-1}(L)^a(LT^{-1})^b(ML^{-3})^c$$

$$M: \quad 0 = -1 + c$$

$$T: \quad 0 = 1 - b$$

$$L: \quad 0 = 1 + a + b - 3c$$

and, as before, $a = 1$, $b = 1$, and $c = 1$. Thus, π_5 is the same as before. On occasion, the three dimension equations will have to be solved simultaneously. However, considering them in the proper sequence minimizes the work. The length equation usually has the most terms and is best saved until last. Without including the intermediate details, the final two pi terms are

$$\pi_6 = \frac{V}{\sqrt{\sigma/\rho D}} \tag{6-4f}$$

and

$$\pi_7 = \frac{V}{\sqrt{E/\rho}} \tag{6-4g}$$

Substituting Eqs. 6-4 into Eq. 6-2 gives the resulting dimensionless equation:

$$\frac{\Delta p}{\rho V^2} = \phi\left(\frac{x_1}{D}, \frac{x_2}{D}, \frac{V}{\sqrt{D\gamma/\rho}}, \frac{VD\rho}{\mu}, \frac{V}{\sqrt{\sigma/\rho D}}, \frac{V}{\sqrt{E/\rho}}\right) \tag{6-5}$$

The result is still quite complex, since a total of seven terms remain. It nevertheless served to illustrate the procedure and will be useful in the future.

Before continuing with Eq. 6-5, a few remarks concerning the convenience and advantages of dealing with a reduced number of variables are pertinent. If a variable depends experimentally on three or more variables, it is very difficult to express the results. If a variable x depends on only two variables, y and z, the results can be expressed as in Fig. 6-1, where the variable z is

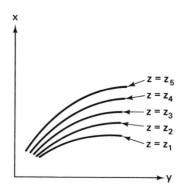

Fig. 6-1. Three variable function.

held constant for each curve. If x depends on only one variable y, the result can be expressed by at the most one curve, as per Fig. 6-2. Finally, if x depends on no other variables, it must be a constant. Thus, if we had had $n = 6$ and $m = 3$ in the previous example, the resulting reduction would have brought the problem into the range of relatively convenient analysis.

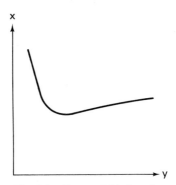

Fig. 6-2.   Two variable function.

The advantages of dimensional analysis hold not just for the presentation of results, but are felt throughout an experimental study. A dimensional analysis of the anticipated variables at the outset of a research project gives a sense of direction to the work. It indicates which dimensionless variables need to be controlled and systematically varied. Certain dimensional variables that are inconvenient to vary (e.g., viscosity) can be held constant, since it is the effect of the dimensionless term rather than the individual variables that is important. In the case of viscosity, the term $VD\rho/\mu$ (from Eq. 6-5) can be varied, perhaps through changes in V, giving the experimenter just as much information as if he actually varied the viscosity itself.

A few comments are also necessary to show how dimensional analysis aids in the direction of the research work. If a four variable problem reduces to one dimensionless pi term, the researcher need perform but one experiment in the laboratory to evaluate the constant that the single pi term must equal. If only two pi terms are involved, the experimental program is then aimed at collecting enough data to generate a curve such as Fig. 6-2. As the problem gets more complicated, the researcher must justify ignoring some of the terms or find some other way of accounting for them.

In this brief introduction, all aspects of dimensional analyses cannot be considered fully. The rules for operating on the various dimensionless pi terms have not been treated. Just as any pi term may be arbitrarily raised to any power, it is also possible to replace any pi term by the product of the given term, to any power, and one or more of the other pi terms, each to any arbitrary power. The only restriction on this type of operation is that the actual number of pi terms does not change. This type of procedure might be undertaken in order to eliminate a given dimensional variable from a particular pi term.

Regardless of the purpose for which a dimensional analysis is being undertaken, it is frequently baffling to the novice, particularly when applied to a completely unfamiliar situation. This can only be overcome by experience, but the difficulties can be minimized if the user can get a good understanding or feeling for the physical situation.

EXAMPLE 6-1

The drag on a submarine is expected to depend on its cross-sectional area A, length L, velocity V and the density ρ_s, and viscosity μ_s, of salt water. Through use of the Buckingham pi method, determine an equation for the drag on the submarine.

SOLUTION:

In dimensional form,

$$F_D = f(A, L, V, \rho_s, \mu_s)$$

Immediately, $n = 6$ and $m = 3$, indicating three pi terms. Choosing A, V, and ρ_s as repeating variables,

$$\pi_1 = f_1(F_D, A, V, \rho_s)$$
$$\pi_2 = f_2(L, A, V, \rho_s)$$
$$\pi_3 = f_3(\mu_s, A, V, \rho_s)$$

In product form,

$$\pi_1 = F_D^1 A^a V^b \rho_s^c$$
$$F^0 L^0 T^0 = (F)^1 (L^2)^a (LT^{-1})^b (FT^2 L^{-4})^c$$
$$F: \quad 0 = 1 + c$$
$$T: \quad 0 = -b + 2c$$
$$L: \quad 0 = 2a + b - 4c$$

Thus,

$$c = -1, \qquad b = -2, \qquad \text{and} \qquad a = -1$$

yielding

$$\pi_1 = \frac{F}{\rho_s V^2 A}$$

Since only length dimensions are involved, we get

$$\pi_2 = \frac{L}{A^{1/2}}$$

Finally, from

$$\pi_3 = \mu_s^{-1} A^a V^b \rho_s^c$$

we get

$$\pi_3 = \frac{V A^{1/2} \rho_s}{\mu_s}$$

and consequently,

$$\frac{F_D}{\rho_s V^2 A} = \phi\left(\frac{L}{A^{1/2}}, \frac{VA^{1/2}\rho_s}{\mu_s}\right)$$

This expression may be written with a drag coefficient C_D as

$$F_D = C_D A \rho_s V^2$$

where

$$C_D = \phi\left(\frac{L}{A^{1/2}}, \frac{VA^{1/2}\rho_s}{\mu_s}\right)$$

Note the similarity of the independent variables derived in this example with π_2 and π_5 of the preceding, more general example.

6–2 MODELING

In the preceding section the concept of dimensional analysis was developed and its applications to experimental work were discussed. As we must refer to the results of experiments frequently in the remainder of the text, we will make considerable use of the techniques developed therein. For the present we will make additional use of dimensional analysis in the study of a particular type of experimental endeavor, modeling. It is relatively simple to make a geometric scale model of a particular flow. To know how to meaningfully operate the model and interpret the experimental results requires more consideration, however. It is these later aspects that will receive our attention in this section.

The various dimensionless terms of Eq. 6-5 have been, by convention and for convenience, assigned particular names. These are as follows:

$$\frac{\Delta p}{\rho V^2/2} = \text{Eu} \qquad (\textit{Euler number}) \qquad (6\text{-}6a)$$

The factor of 2 is added arbitrarily to make the denominator equal to the dynamic pressure of the flow. The Euler number is frequently expressed as the negative one-half power of the above; however, it is more usable in the preceding form.

$$\frac{V}{\sqrt{D\gamma/\rho}} = \text{Fr} \qquad (\textit{Froude number}) \qquad (6\text{-}6b)$$

Note that in most cases the Froude number may be simplified to

$$\text{Fr} = \frac{V}{\sqrt{Dg}}$$

In addition, if the problem involves an interface between two fluids of nearly the same specific weight, the difference in specific weight $\Delta\gamma$ between the two fluids is used rather than γ; hence,

$$\text{Fr} = \frac{V}{\sqrt{D\,\Delta\gamma/\rho}}$$

Also,

$$\frac{VD\rho}{\mu} = \frac{VD}{\nu} = \text{Re} \qquad (\textit{Reynolds number}) \qquad (6\text{-}6c)$$

$$\frac{V}{\sqrt{\sigma/\rho D}} = \text{We} \qquad (\textit{Weber number}) \qquad (6\text{-}6d)$$

$$\frac{V}{\sqrt{E/\rho}} = \text{Ma} \qquad (\textit{Mach number}) \qquad (6\text{-}6e)$$

Thus, Eq. 6-5 may be written in the even more general form

$$\text{Eu} = \phi(\text{geometry, Fr, Re, We, Ma}) \qquad (6\text{-}7)$$

The subject of modeling may be introduced from Eq. 6-7. For simplicity, however, assume that

$$\Delta p = f(\text{various geometric dimensions, } V, \rho, \gamma)$$

so that from Eq. 6-7 there remains only

$$\text{Eu} = \phi(\text{geometry, Fr}) \qquad (6\text{-}8)$$

If a model is to be used to test a prototype flow, similitude must be maintained between the model and the prototype. Achieving geometric similitude is not sufficient. The flow behavior (kinematic similitude) and various forces (dynamic similitude) must also be properly modeled. If the model geometrically resembles the prototype (although the model is usually smaller, it may be larger or even the same size as the prototype) with all dimensions properly scaled, then Eq. 6-8 reduces to

$$\text{Eu} = \phi(\text{Fr})$$

Once again this type of relationship must form some type of graphic curve, such as that sketched in Fig. 6-3. If the geometric model is operated so that the Froude number of both model and prototype is identical, then since both model and prototype enter the curve of Fig. 6-3 at the same point, the Euler

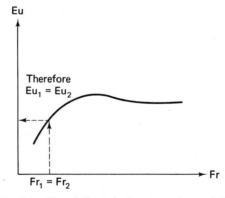

Fig. 6-3. Use of dimensionless terms for modeling.

number of the model and prototype must accordingly be equal. Equality of the Euler number ensures dynamic similiture, since the pressure (with dimensions FL^{-2}) reflects the various forces as well.[3] In addition, the constant Froude number guarantees kinematic similitude, since the only flow variable, the velocity, is included in the Froude number.

To substantiate this argument and also to give further emphasis to the importance of the dimensionless numbers, the various terms of Eqs. 6-5 or 6-7 will be considered again. In a sense there is a degree of sufficiency associated with the proper scaling of the various forces, since only if they are properly modeled can the kinematic similitude also be correct. With this in mind, note that each of the dimensionless terms can be expressed as a ratio of forces. The force causing an acceleration is proportional to the pressure difference times the area, whereas the resulting inertial force from Newton's law, the mass times the acceleration, is

$$M \cdot a \sim (\rho L^3)(LT^{-2}) \sim \rho(LT^{-1})^2(L)^2 \sim \rho V^2 L^2$$

Thus, the Euler number

$$\text{Eu} = \frac{\Delta p}{\rho V^2/2} = \frac{\Delta p L^2}{\rho V^2 L^2/2} \sim \frac{\text{acceleration force}}{\text{inertial force}} \tag{6-9a}$$

is the ratio of accelerative force to inertial force. The Froude number involves the gravity force, weight (γL^3). Thus,

$$\text{Fr}^2 = \frac{V^2}{D\gamma/\rho} \sim \frac{\rho V^2}{\gamma L} = \frac{\rho V^2 L^2}{\gamma L^3} \sim \frac{\text{inertial force}}{\text{gravity force}} \tag{6-9b}$$

and the Froude number is the square root of the ratio of the inertial force to the gravity force. Since the viscous force is proportional to

$$\tau L^2 = \mu \frac{dV}{dy} L^2 \sim \mu \frac{V}{L} L^2 = \mu V L$$

the Reynolds number becomes

$$\text{Re} = \frac{V D \rho}{\mu} \sim \frac{\rho V L}{\mu} = \frac{\rho V^2 L^2}{\mu V L} \sim \frac{\text{inertial force}}{\text{viscous force}} \tag{6-9c}$$

Likewise,

$$\text{We}^2 = \frac{V^2}{\sigma/\rho D} \sim \frac{\rho V^2 L}{\sigma} = \frac{\rho V^2 L^2}{\sigma L} \sim \frac{\text{inertial force}}{\text{surface tension force}} \tag{6-9d}$$

and

$$\text{Ma}^2 = \frac{V^2}{E/\rho} = \frac{\rho V^2}{E} = \frac{\rho V^2 L^2}{E L^2} \sim \frac{\text{inertial force}}{\text{elastic force}} \tag{6-9e}$$

[3]Specifically, if the pressure distribution is properly scaled, point by point, then the forces, which are merely the integration of the pressure distribution over the area, must be properly scaled as well.

If only accelerative and inertial forces are involved in a problem, then, assuming that geometric similitude is already satisfied, since the Euler number must be a constant, the ratio of the two types of forces in the model must equal the same ratio in the prototype. This will generally be written

$$Eu_m = Eu_p$$

where the subscripts m and p stand for model and prototype, respectively. The model in this case may be operated quite independently of the prototype.

If the Euler number depends on only the Froude number, which is to say that only accelerative, inertial, and gravity forces are involved in a certain problem, then operating the model so that the Froude number of the model and prototype are equal,

$$Fr_m = Fr_p$$

ensures that the gravity and inertial forces are properly scaled. Since this guarantees that the Euler numbers are also equal (refer back to dimensional analysis and Eq. 6-8), all relevant forces are proportional.

In the same way, if only inertial, accelerative, and viscous forces are involved, then operation of the model such that the Reynolds numbers are equal guarantees that the Euler numbers are also equal, and consequently all forces are again scaled correctly. Note that when using these different modeling laws, it is not necessary to consider which forces are involved, since the results of dimensional analysis tell which dimensionless parameters need to be considered. This will be illustrated repeatedly in the examples that follow.

If more types of forces are involved, say, the inertial, accelerative, gravity, and viscous force are important, then for the Euler number to be constant, both the Froude number and the Reynolds number must be held constant between model and prototype. This is generally impossible to do; Example 6-4 will illustrate the difficulty, and later Example 9-4 will present one means of circumventing the difficulty. On occasion, a lesser force may be ignored if the magnitude of the error is appreciated. Another procedure, which will be demonstrated in Example 9-4, is to properly model all types of forces except one, and by analytical means calculate the effects of the remaining force. The following examples will illustrate modeling procedures.

EXAMPLE 6-2

The hydraulic jump at the foot of a high dam is to be studied with a scale model. The velocity in the prototype will be 80 ft/s, with a depth of 4 ft. The channel containing the jump is to be 20 ft wide. If the model scale of 1 : 10 is chosen, what must be the velocity and discharge of the model if complete similitude is to be achieved? Also, under proper model flow conditions, if the model force on a baffle block (used in stilling basins to help control the jump) is 2 lb, what is the corresponding force on the prototype?

SOLUTION:

The hydraulic jump (refer to Example 5-16) is primarily a gravity effect; the viscous and other forces can usually be ignored. Thus, from Eq. 6-7, if the geometry is properly scaled, then operating the model so that the Froude numbers are equal means that the Euler numbers are also equal. Since the model scale is $1:10$, the depth in the model y_m must be 0.4 ft and the model channel must be 2 ft wide. To obtain the model velocity V_m, set

$$\text{Fr}_m = \text{Fr}_p$$

or

$$\left(\frac{V}{\sqrt{Lg}}\right)_m = \left(\frac{V}{\sqrt{Lg}}\right)_p$$

Immediately,

$$V_m = V_p\left(\frac{L_m}{L_p}\right)^{1/2}$$
$$= (80)(\tfrac{1}{10})^{1/2} = 25.30 \text{ ft/s}$$

and

$$Q_m = V_m y_m b_m$$
$$= (25.30)(0.4)(2) = 20.\,24 \text{ cfs}$$

The model discharge can also be obtained directly from the Froude modeling law:

$$\left(\frac{V}{\sqrt{Lg}}\right)_m = \left(\frac{V}{\sqrt{Lg}}\right)_p$$

but

$$V \sim QL^{-2}$$

Thus,

$$\left(\frac{Q}{g^{1/2}L^{5/2}}\right)_m = \left(\frac{Q}{g^{1/2}L^{5/2}}\right)_p$$

and for constant gravitational acceleration g,

$$Q_m = Q_p\left(\frac{L_m}{L_p}\right)^{5/2} = [(80)(4)(20)](\tfrac{1}{10})^{5/2} = 20.24 \text{ cfs}$$

To evaluate the force on the prototype, note that

$$\text{Eu}_m = \text{Eu}_p$$

or

$$\left(\frac{\Delta p}{\rho V^2}\right)_m = \left(\frac{\Delta p}{\rho V^2}\right)_p$$

and since

$$\Delta p \sim FL^{-2}$$

The Euler modeling law can be rewritten as

$$\left(\frac{F}{\rho V^2 L^2}\right)_m = \left(\frac{F}{\rho V^2 L^2}\right)_p$$

Since water at approximately the same temperature is anticipated for both model and prototype, we get

$$F_p = F_m\left(\frac{L_p}{L_m}\right)^2\left(\frac{V_p}{V_m}\right)^2$$

Substituting from the Froude law,

$$F_p = F_m\left(\frac{L_p}{L_m}\right)^3 = (2)(10)^3 = 2000 \text{ lb}$$

Note that although the Euler equation written in terms of forces is still general, the final equation was obtained by substitution of the Froude law and is therefore appropriate for Froude law modeling only.

EXAMPLE 6-3

An air flow at 80°F in a 6-in. pipe is to be used to study a water flow at 60°F in a 1-ft-diameter pipe for purposes of evaluating a new type of valve. If the velocity of the water is to be 5 ft/s, what velocity of air flow is required? If the model study under these conditions indicates a power loss of 7 hp, what is the anticipated power loss of the prototype in horsepower?

SOLUTION:

Pipe flow is highly dependent on viscous effects and independent of gravity effects; hence, the Reynolds number becomes the important parameter for modeling purposes. Setting the Reynolds numbers equal,

$$\left(\frac{VL\rho}{\mu}\right)_m = \left(\frac{VL\rho}{\mu}\right)_p$$

Thus,

$$V_m = V_p \frac{L_p}{L_m} \frac{\nu_m}{\nu_p}$$

but

$$\frac{L_p}{L_m} = 2$$

and

$$\nu_m = 1.69 \times 10^{-4} \text{ ft}^2/\text{s} \qquad \text{(air at 80°F)}$$

$$\nu_p = 1.217 \times 10^{-5} \text{ ft}^2/\text{s} \qquad \text{(water at 60°F)}$$

Therefore,

$$V_m = (5)(2)\left(\frac{1.69 \times 10^{-4}}{1.217 \times 10^{-5}}\right) = 138.9 \text{ ft/s}$$

Since the power P is given by

$$P \sim FV \sim \Delta p L^2 V$$

this can be substituted into the Euler equation,

$$\left(\frac{\Delta p}{\rho V^2}\right)_m = \left(\frac{\Delta p}{\rho V^2}\right)_p$$

to give

$$\left(\frac{P}{\rho L^2 V^3}\right)_m = \left(\frac{P}{\rho L^2 V^3}\right)_p$$

or

$$P_p = P_m \frac{\rho_p}{\rho_m}\left(\frac{L_p}{L_m}\right)^2 \left(\frac{V_p}{V_m}\right)^3$$

where
$$\rho_m = 0.00228 \text{ slug/ft}^3 \quad \text{for air}$$
and
$$\rho_p = 1.94 \text{ slugs/ft}^3 \quad \text{for water}$$

Substituting into the relationship for power,

$$P_p = (7)\left(\frac{1.94}{0.00228}\right)(2)^2\left(\frac{5}{138.9}\right)^3 = 1.11 \text{ hp}$$

In this case, the model requires more power to operate than the prototype. This is typical of Reynolds number modeling. Since lengths are usually smaller in the model, the velocities tend to be higher.

EXAMPLE 6-4

A 300-ft-long ship with a speed of 35 ft/s is to be modeled. Both viscous and gravity forces are considered important. Design a model capable of performing the necessary study.

SOLUTION:

At the present, the length scale is arbitrary. However, we must have both
$$\text{Fr}_m = \text{Fr}_p$$
and
$$\text{Re}_m = \text{Re}_p$$

if complete dynamic similitude is to be achieved. Eliminating velocity between the two expressions,

$$\left(\frac{V}{\sqrt{gL}}\right)_m = \left(\frac{V}{\sqrt{gL}}\right)_p$$

and

$$\left(\frac{VL}{\nu}\right)_m = \left(\frac{VL}{\nu}\right)_p$$

gives

$$\left(\frac{L_m}{L_p}\right)^{1/2} = \frac{L_p}{L_m}\frac{\nu_m}{\nu_p}$$

or

$$\frac{\nu_m}{\nu_p} = \left(\frac{L_m}{L_p}\right)^{3/2}$$

It is most desirable for the model fluid to be water, but this requires a full-scale model. Hence, a different fluid is required for the model. If the biggest possible model is 10 ft long, the viscosity ratio becomes

$$\frac{\nu_m}{\nu_p} = \left(\frac{10}{300}\right)^{3/2}$$

Assuming

$$\nu_p \approx 10^{-5} \text{ ft}^2/\text{s}$$

as the viscosity of the prototype gives

$$\nu_m = (10^{-5})\left(\frac{10}{300}\right)^{3/2} = 6.09 \times 10^{-8} \text{ ft}^2/\text{s}$$

Referring to the kinematic viscosity curves of Fig. A-2, there are no fluids with such a low viscosity. Perhaps a larger model would bring us into the range of mercury, but its use is obviously not feasible. The practical resolution of the problem is illustrated in Example 9-4. Basically, the gravity forces are modeled according to the Froude relationship, while the friction forces are calculated directly through the techniques developed in Chapter 9.

The phenomenon of cavitation must also be kept in mind in model studies. If the pressure in either model or prototype approaches the vapor pressure p_v, then this variable must also be considered. This is usually introduced as the variable $p - p_v$, where p is the absolute ambient pressure. Combining with the repeating variables used to obtain Eq. 6-5 gives the cavitation number

$$C = \frac{p - p_v}{\rho V^2/2}$$

Correct modeling requires that the cavitation number of the model and prototype be equal.

PROBLEMS

Sec. 6-1

6-1. Derive an equation for the discharge Q through an orifice of diameter d at the end of a pipe of diameter D if the discharge is a function only of d, D, the fluid density ρ, and the difference between the pressure p_0 and the ambient atmospheric pressure.

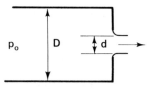

6-2. Repeat Prob. 6-1 for the case where a liquid of specific weight γ discharges into the atmosphere and the jet is therefore significantly affected by gravitational effects.

6-3. Repeat Prob. 6-1 when compressibility effects (E) must also be included.

6-4. Devise an expression for the drag force F on a sphere of diameter d exposed to a velocity V of a fluid of density ρ and viscosity μ.

6-5. If a square bar with length L and side dimensions a by a is placed in a high-speed air flow and its angular position indicated by θ, determine the drag force F on the bar as a function of a, L, θ, V, the density of air ρ, the viscosity of air μ, and the modulus of compressibility E.

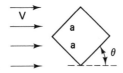

6-6. Repeat Prob. 6-5 if the velocity V is so high that viscous effects as represented by μ are unimportant.

6-7. Repeat Prob. 6-5 if the velocity V is sufficiently low that compressibility effects are unimportant.

6-8. Derive an equation for the discharge per unit length, q, over a weir of height P as a function of head H, weir height P and the fluid properties γ and ρ.

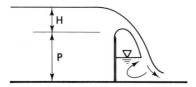

6-9. Repeat Prob. 6-8 if viscosity μ is also important.

6-10. Repeat Prob. 6-8 if both viscosity μ and surface tension σ are important.

6-11. Develop an expression for the power requirement for a ship. Assume that the power depends upon the following parameters: the length of the ship L, its velocity V, the viscosity of the water μ, the density of water ρ, and wave forces as indicated by the specific weight of water γ.

6-12. Use dimensional analysis to determine an expression for the height of capillary rise of a liquid in a circular glass tube.

6-13. Develop expressions for the lift and drag on an airplane flying at supersonic speed.

Sec. 6-2

6-14. Apply the Froude law to a model study of an overflow spillway for a dam. If the scale is $\frac{1}{48}$, what model velocity will correspond to a prototype spillway velocity of 80 ft/s?

6-15. If a model scale of $\frac{1}{100}$ is chosen for the spillway of Prob. 6-14, what would be the model velocity corresponding to a maximum prototype spillway velocity of 25 m/s?

6-16. A $\frac{1}{100}$ scale model of a tidal basin has been constructed. Assuming the Froude law applies, what time period in the model will correspond to a tidal cycle of 24 hr?

6-17. What velocity of air at 80°F in a 2-in.-diameter pipe would be dynamically similar to the flow of 80°F carbon tetrachloride at 10 gpm through a 1-in.-diameter pipe? Use the Reynolds number for modeling.

6-18. A model study is to be made of a flood flow through a residential area such as would occur if a levee failed. The model scale is $\frac{1}{100}$.
  (a) If the model flood velocity has an average value of 1 ft/s, what is the corresponding prototype velocity?
  (b) If the discharge past a section of 1 ft in width in the model is 0.1 cfs, what is the discharge per foot of width (q_p) in the prototype?
  (c) If the drag force on a typical model house is 0.05 lb what is the corresponding drag on a real house?

6-19. A $\frac{1}{100}$ scale model of a 10-mile length of river is to be operated according to the Froude law. What is the model flow corresponding to a prototype discharge of 150,000 cfs? If it requires 12 min for a flood peak to pass through the length of the model, what would be the estimated travel time for the corresponding flood peak to pass through the actual river section?

6-20. What velocity of water at 20°C in a 10-cm-diameter pipe would be dynamically similar to air at 80°C passing through a 0.5-m circular duct at 15 m/s? Use the Reynolds criteria.

6-21. A $\frac{1}{100}$ scale model of a 300-ft tanker is to be used in fresh water to study wave forces on the prototype. If the prototype ship has an operating speed of 20 ft/s, at what velocity must the model ship be towed? If it is found that the model requires a force of 0.3 lb to overcome wave forces, what is the corresponding force on the prototype? What power will be required by the tanker? Use density of salt water as 1.99 slugs/ft³.

6-22. A new valve design for use in a gasoline-handling system is to be modeled with water. The model is to be one-half the size of the prototype. The gasoline will be at 60°F and the water at 70°F. What discharge through the water system will be dynamically similar to a gasoline flow of 0.9 cfs? If the pressure drop through the model valve is measured as 2.5 psi, what will be the corresponding pressure drop in the prototype?

6-23. A $\frac{1}{10}$ scale model of a missile is to be tested in a high-pressure wind tunnel to study a prototype missile flying at 3500 fps in air at 0°F and 5 psia. The wind tunnel will be operated at 80°F and at a pressure of 6 atm. What is the required wind tunnel velocity? Assume that $E = kp$ from Eq. 1-14.

6-24. If the same fluid is used in both model and prototype, determine the force ratio (i.e., (F_m/F_p) as a function of the length ratio, if the similarity criterion is (a) Reynolds number, (b) Froude number, (c) Weber number, (d) Mach number.

6-25. If the same fluid is used in both model and prototype, determine the power ratio (i.e., power$_m$/power$_p$) as a function of the length ratio, if the similarity criterion is (a) Reynolds number, (b) Froude number, (c) Weber number, (d) Mach number.

6-26. Very small ripples 0.01 ft high on a tank of turpentine are interfering with an industrial process. It is desired to study these ripples. Both gravity and surface tension effects are involved, but viscous effects can be ignored. Water is chosen for the model fluid and the following information is known:

Turpentine

Height of turpentine ripples	0.01 ft
Surface tension	1.8×10^{-3} lb/ft
Specific gravity	0.87

Water

Surface tension	5×10^{-3} lb/ft
Density	1.94 slugs/ft^3

Waves of what height are required in the water for dynamic similitude?

6-27. If the overflow spillway of a large dam must pass a peak flood flow of 300 m^3/s, what is the maximum length ratio, L_m/L_p, which may be used in a model study if the available laboratory flow rate is 0.3 m^3/s? If the design gate-opening time on the prototype is 15 min, what is the corresponding time on the model?

6-28. Cavitation at a pipe valve is to be studied at reduced pressure in a water tunnel in which the overall pressure level can be controlled. The model has a scale ratio of 1/40. The water tunnel is operated at an ambient pressure which is one-fourth that of ambient conditions surrounding the prototype valve. If the water temperature is 20°C in the model and 15°C in the prototype, what model velocity would correspond to a prototype velocity of 10 m/s?

REFERENCES

BRIDGEMAN, P. W., *Dimensional Analysis*. New Haven, Conn.: Yale University Press, 1931.

HICKOX, G. H., "Hydraulic Models," in *Handbook of Applied Hydraulics*, C. V. Davis (ed.). New York: McGraw-Hill, 1952.

HOLT, M., "Dimensional Analysis," Chapter 15 in *Handbook of Fluid Dynamics*, V. L. Streeter (ed.). New York: McGraw-Hill, 1961.

Hydraulic Models, ASCE Manual in Engineering Practice No. 25. New York: ASCE, 1942.

LANGHAAR, H. L., *Dimensional Analysis and Theory of Models*. New York: Wiley, 1951.

ROUSE, H., *Advanced Mechanics of Fluids*. New York: Wiley, 1959.

WARNOCK, J. E., "Hydraulic Similitude," Chapter 2 in *Engineering Hydraulics*, H. Rouse (ed.). New York: Wiley, 1950.

7

Laminar Flow and Turbulence

This chapter will first examine, as exactly as possible, different types of laminar flows. This portion will be built on the information of Section 1-3, involving viscosity. Only Newtonian fluids will be considered, compressibility will be ignored, and most of the applications will be restricted to steady, uniform flows. Although most flows that the engineer has to deal with are turbulent, there are many important types of laminar flows. The broad subject areas of groundwater flow, lubrication theory, and the handling of viscous fluids all involve primarily laminar flows. Laminar flow also has the advantage, from the education point of view, of being more susceptible to mathematical analysis, as this chapter will demonstrate. Section 7-2 discusses and subsequently applies the general equations of motion, known as the Navier–Stokes equations.

Finally, the chapter will develop further insight into the subject of turbulence. The theory will be developed only insofar as is needed for the particular applications of the succeeding chapters. After the physical characteristics of turbulence are presented, its effect on the Navier–Stokes equations will be mentioned. Finally, an empirical approach will be considered based on phenomenological observations.

7–1 BASIC RELATIONSHIPS: CONDUIT FLOW

Shear Stress/Pressure Gradient Relationships

Previously, we have studied two results associated with a pressure gradient. One was the resulting acceleration imparted by a pressure difference; the relationship explained by Newton's second law. The other was the more simple exchange that takes place between elevation and pressure heads in the nonhorizontal conduit flow of liquids. This latter effect can be written using Eq. 5-5a for uniform flow in the arbitrary s directions as

$$\frac{\partial p}{\partial s} = -\gamma \frac{\partial y}{\partial s} \tag{7-1}$$

Here y is the vertical direction and there is no acceleration. If the flow is nonuniform, the effect of elevation on the pressure is given by Eq. 7-1, and this may be algebraically added to the change in pressure gradient due to the acceleration $(-\rho a_s)$ to give the combined effect of elevation change and acceleration on the pressure gradient.

In this chapter we will find that a pressure gradient will also be required to overcome viscous effects. The accelerational, gravitational, and the yet-to-be-determined viscous effects may all be added algebraically to determine the pressure gradient. However, this becomes quite difficult and we will generally consider only steady, uniform[1] flows, where at most only Eq. 7-1 need be considered along with the viscous effects.

In Section 1-3 a Newtonian fluid was defined by Eq. 1-5, where μ, the viscosity, was constant for a given temperature. In more complicated flow situations it is sometime necessary to use a shearing stress based on a more general equation. Those occasions will not arise here, however. Consider in rectangular Cartesian coordinates a two-dimensional steady, uniform flow to the right with a velocity distribution, as shown in Fig. 7-1. Initially, the flow will be assumed to occur in an horizontal direction so that the relationship can be developed without the inclusion of gravitational effects. Forces on the differential element shown will be summed in the x direction. Only the forces acting in the x direction are shown in this figure, and the length of the element in the z direction is taken as unity. The usual convention of taking a clockwise shear couple as positive is followed, and so shown in Fig. 7-1. Thus, after canceling terms, the net forces in the positive x direction due to pressure and shear stress are

$$-\frac{\partial p}{\partial x} dx\, dy + \frac{\partial \tau}{\partial y} dy\, dx = 0$$

---

[1]The use of the term *uniform* is consistent with the definition given in Section 3-3. Thus the streamlines are straight and parallel and although there is a velocity variation in the plane perpendicular to the flow, this velocity distribution remains unchanged from section to section.

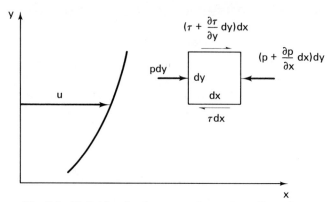

Fig. 7-1. Definition for shear stress in steady, uniform flow.

or

$$\frac{\partial \tau}{\partial y} = \frac{\partial p}{\partial x} \tag{7-2}$$

We see at once that a pressure gradient must exist in the direction of the flow if there is a shear-stress variation in the direction perpendicular to the flow. This pressure gradient is required to overcome frictional effects. Note that this equation applies equally to laminar or turbulent flow, since the shear stress has not yet been specified. Equally important, the velocity distribution must be the same across every section (i.e., for each value of x), since the flow has been assumed to be uniform. Consequently, the frictional effects must be the same at every cross section, and therefore the pressure gradient must be a constant along each streamline. Since the pressure distribution must be hydrostatic normal to the flow direction at every section, the pressure must drop by the same amount along each streamline over a given length. Therefore, the pressure gradient must be a constant along all streamlines. On this basis, recognizing also that the shear stress can vary with y only, we can also write

$$\frac{d\tau}{dy} = \frac{dp}{dx} = \text{constant} \tag{7-3}$$

in steady uniform flow.

The counterpart to Eq. 7-2 or Eq. 7-3 for axisymmetric flow through a pipe is more conveniently obtained if we start with the cylindrical element of Fig. 7-2. A velocity distribution is assumed; the steady, uniform flow is to the right, in the plus x direction; and $r = 0$ is taken as the centerline. The cylindrical element has radius r and length dx. The forces due to the pressure on each end are shown, as is the shear stress, which is now constant over the surface of the element due to symmetry. As in the past, the pressure acts over the area of the end of the element, whereas the shear stress acts over the area of the cylindrical surface. Summing forces in the direction of flow,

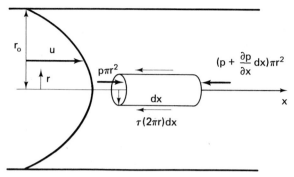

Fig. 7-2. Shear stress in axisymmetric flow.

$$-\frac{\partial p}{\partial x}\pi r^2\,dx - \tau(2\pi r)\,dx = 0$$

or

$$\tau = -\frac{r}{2}\frac{\partial p}{\partial x}$$

By the same reasoning as used before, the pressure gradient must have the same constant value along all streamlines; hence,

$$\tau = -\frac{r}{2}\frac{dp}{dx} \qquad (7\text{-}4)$$

Again, this relationship applies to both laminar and turbulent flows. At the boundary of a circular conduit of radius r_0, we have the wall shear stress given by

$$\tau_0 = -\frac{r_0}{2}\frac{dp}{dx} \qquad (7\text{-}5)$$

The shear stress decreases linearly from a maximum value at the wall given by Eq. 7-5, to zero at the pipe centerline. The relationships developed up to this point in the chapter are valid for both laminar and turbulent flows. They will now be applied to conditions of laminar flow. The assumption that a given flow is laminar will be taken without proof in this chapter. The criteria necessary to distinguish between laminar and turbulent flows will be mentioned in Section 7-3 and developed in Section 8-1.

Two-Dimensional Laminar Flow
Between Parallel Boundaries

The laminar flow between parallel boundaries will be considered first. End effects will be ignored and the flow assumed to be two-dimensional, as in Fig. 7-3. Starting with Eq. 7-3 and integrating with respect to y,

$$\tau = \left(\frac{dp}{dx}\right)y + C_1 \qquad (7\text{-}6)$$

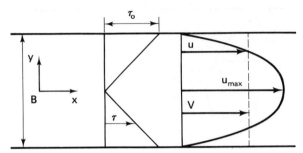

Fig. 7-3. Laminar flow between parallel boundaries.

Since the velocity must vary symmetrically about its maximum value along the centerline, decreasing to zero at the two boundaries, the velocity gradient du/dy must equal zero at the center. Consequently, from Eq. 1-5,

$$\tau = \mu \frac{du}{dy} = 0$$

at the centerline. The constant of integration in Eq. 7-6 can now be evaluated since at $y = 0$. Eq. 7-6 becomes

$$\tau = 0 = \left(\frac{dp}{dx}\right)(0) + C_1$$

or $C_1 = 0$. Thus, in general,

$$\tau = \left(\frac{dp}{dx}\right)y \tag{7-7}$$

It was not necessary to impose the symmetry condition at this point as the zero velocity at the upper and lower boundaries would provide sufficient boundary conditions to evaluate the two constants that would be present after a second integration. The preceding procedure is more direct, however. Substituting for τ using Eq. 1-5 and integrating again,

$$u = \frac{1}{\mu}\left[\left(\frac{dp}{dx}\right)\frac{y^2}{2} + C_2\right]$$

As $u = 0$ when $y = \pm B/2$, the equation above becomes

$$u = -\frac{1}{\mu}\left(\frac{dp}{dx}\right)\left(\frac{B^2}{8} - \frac{y^2}{2}\right) \tag{7-8}$$

The parabolic velocity distribution is shown in Fig. 7-3 along with the shear stress from Eq. 7-7. The maximum velocity is given by

$$u_{\text{max}} = -\frac{1}{\mu}\left(\frac{dp}{dx}\right)\frac{B^2}{8} \tag{7-9}$$

and since the average value of a parabolic curve is two-thirds of its peak value, the average velocity is immediately

$$V = -\frac{1}{\mu}\left(\frac{dp}{dx}\right)\frac{B^2}{12} \tag{7-10}$$

Further, the discharge per unit width (in the z direction) becomes

$$q = -\frac{1}{\mu}\left(\frac{dp}{dx}\right)\frac{B^3}{12} \tag{7-11}$$

Note that the velocity varies inversely with the viscosity and that the pressure gradient required to maintain the flow is directly proportional to the velocity. The minus sign in the foregoing equations is appropriate and consistent with the decreasing pressure in the direction of flow. Integration of Eq. 7-10 over a length L in the x direction gives the pressure drop in that length L,

$$p_1 - p_2 = \frac{12\mu VL}{B^2} \tag{7-12}$$

If the flow is inclined as in Fig. 7-4, the pressure gradient required to maintain the flow is, from Eq. 7-10,

$$\left(\frac{dp}{ds}\right)_{\text{friction}} = -\frac{12\mu V}{B^2}$$

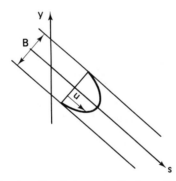

Fig. 7-4. Laminar flow between inclined parallel boundaries.

while the pressure gradient related to gravitation effects is, by Eq. 7-1 (refer also to Figs. 5-2 and 5-3),

$$\left(\frac{dp}{ds}\right)_{\text{gravity}} = -\gamma\frac{\partial y}{\partial s}$$

The actual pressure gradient is the sum of the above:

$$\frac{dp}{ds} = -\gamma\frac{\partial y}{\partial s} - \frac{12\mu V}{B^2}$$

Rewriting,

$$\frac{d}{ds}\left(\frac{p}{\gamma} + y\right) = \frac{dh}{ds} = -\frac{12\mu V}{\gamma B^2} = -\frac{12\nu V}{gB^2} \tag{7-13}$$

Thus, Eq. 7-13 relates the change in piezometric head to the characteristics of laminar flow between parallel boundaries. This equation now applies whether the flow is inclined or horizontal. In turn, if this equation is integrated in the s direction over a length L, we get the companion equation to Eq. 7-12,

$$h_1 - h_2 = \frac{12\mu VL}{\gamma B^2} = \frac{12\nu VL}{gB^2} \qquad (7\text{-}14)$$

In the case of a circular conduit which follows, a complete derivation is included for an inclined conduit.

If a steady, uniform laminar flow with a free surface occurs, as in Fig. 7-5, it may be treated as the lower half of the flow between sloping parallel

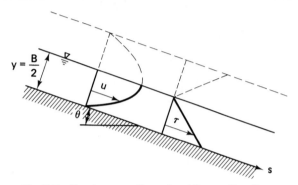

Fig. 7-5.   Laminar two-dimensional free surface flow.

boundaries, since the zero shear on the free surface of the former is similar to the centerline condition of the latter. Taking the slope S^2 as

$$S = \sin \theta = -\frac{\partial h}{\partial s}$$

and replacing B with $2y$ in Eq. 7-12 gives

$$S = \frac{3\mu V}{\gamma y^2} \qquad (7\text{-}15)$$

This expression would apply to situations where either very shallow or very viscous liquids flow over an inclined plane surface. We will see that generally, free surface flows are turbulent. This expression may also be derived directly following the procedures used earlier in the section.

EXAMPLE 7-1

Oil with a kinematic viscosity of 4×10^{-3} ft²/s and a specific gravity of 0.9 flows between two parallel, horizontal plates spaced 1 in. apart. If the flow rate is 0.1 cfs/ft, what is the pressure drop in 10 ft of length? Also determine the centerline velocity and the shear stress at the boundaries.

---

[2]Later the slope will be defined more conventionally as $S = \tan \theta$. Most open-channel flows have such a small slope that $\tan \theta \approx \sin \theta$. For large slopes the $\sin \theta$ must be used.

SOLUTION:

Assuming that the flow is laminar, the centerline velocity must be $\frac{3}{2}$ of the average velocity; hence,

$$u_{max} = \frac{3}{2}V = \left(\frac{3}{2}\right)\left(\frac{q}{B}\right) = \left(\frac{3}{2}\right)\left(\frac{0.1}{1/12}\right) = 1.80 \text{ ft/s}$$

Substituting now into Eq. 7-12 with

$$\mu = \rho v = (0.9)(1.94)(4 \times 10^{-3}) = 6.98 \times 10^{-3} \text{ lb-s/ft}^2$$

and $V = 1.2$ ft/s gives

$$p_1 - p_2 = \frac{(12)(6.98 \times 10^{-3})(1.2)(10)}{(\frac{1}{12})^2} = 144.7 \text{ lb/ft}^2$$

Noting that the pressure gradient must decrease at the rate

$$\frac{dp}{dx} = \frac{144.7}{10} = 14.47 \text{ lb/ft}^2/\text{ft}$$

the shear stress at the boundary, by Eq. 7-7, becomes

$$\tau = (14.47)(\tfrac{1}{24}) = 0.603 \text{ lb/ft}^2$$

EXAMPLE 7-2

The oil of Example 7-1 flows down a 40° slope which has a width of 10 m. If the depth is 1 cm, determine the flow rate.

SOLUTION:

In SI units the oil has a specific weight

$$\gamma = (9800)(0.9) = 8820 \text{ N/m}^3$$

and viscosity

$$\mu = (6.98 \times 10^{-3})(47.88) = 0.334 \text{ N·s/m}^2$$

the conversion factor for viscosity being given on the bottom of Fig. A-1. From Eq. 7-15,

$$V = \frac{\gamma y^2 S}{3\mu}$$

$$= \frac{(8820 \text{ N/m}^3)(0.01 \text{ m})^2(\sin 40°)}{(3)(0.334 \text{ N·s/m}^2)} = 0.565 \text{ m/s}$$

Therefore, the discharge of oil is

$$Q = AV = (0.01 \text{ m})(10 \text{ m})(0.565 \text{ m/s}) = 0.057 \text{ m}^3/\text{s}$$

Laminar Flow in a Circular Conduit

Laminar flow through a circular conduit or pipe is generally referred to as *Poiseuille flow*, after one of the experimenters responsible for much of the early work in this area. Although the initial formulation again assumes a horizontal flow, this is immediately followed by a more general derivation in Example 7-3. Referring to Fig. 7-6, note that Eq. 1-5 may be rewritten to reflect the change in direction from radially inward ($+y$ on Fig. 7-6) to radial-

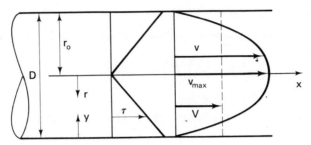

Fig. 7-6. Laminar flow in a circular tube.

ly outward $(+r)$. That is,

$$\tau = \mu \frac{\partial v}{\partial y} = -\mu \frac{\partial v}{\partial r} = -\mu \frac{dv}{dr} \tag{7-16}$$

The total derivative dv/dr is appropriate, since in a steady, uniform flow $v = f(r)$ only. Substituting Eq. 7-16 into Eq. 7-4 now gives

$$\frac{dv}{dr} = \frac{r}{2\mu}\left(\frac{dp}{dx}\right)$$

Integrating with respect to r,

$$v = \frac{r^2}{4\mu}\left(\frac{dp}{dx}\right) + C_3$$

and, since $v = 0$ at $r = r_0$,

$$C_3 = -\frac{r_0^2}{4\mu}\left(\frac{dp}{dx}\right)$$

Therefore, the velocity distribution for laminar flow through a pipe is the parabolic expression given by

$$v = -\frac{1}{4\mu}\left(\frac{dp}{dx}\right)(r_0^2 - r^2) \tag{7-17}$$

The maximum velocity again occurs at the center and is equal to

$$v_{\max} = -\frac{r_0^2}{4\mu}\left(\frac{dp}{dx}\right) \tag{7-18}$$

This time, since the distribution is a paraboloid of revolution, the average velocity must equal one-half of the maximum value, or

$$V = -\frac{r_0^2}{8\mu}\left(\frac{dp}{dx}\right) \tag{7-19}$$

whereas the discharge itself becomes

$$Q = -\frac{\pi r_0^4}{8\mu}\left(\frac{dp}{dx}\right) \tag{7-20}$$

As with flow between parallel plates, Eq. 7-19 when rearranged and integrated over a length L, from a section 1 to a section 2 gives the corresponding pressure drop in a horizontal pipe,

$$p_1 - p_2 = \frac{8\mu VL}{r_0^2} = \frac{32\mu VL}{D^2} \tag{7-21}$$

As before, the effect of elevation change can be incorporated directly to give the decrease in piezometric head in the direction of flow:

$$h_1 - h_2 = \frac{32\mu VL}{\gamma D^2} = \frac{32\nu VL}{gD^2} \tag{7-22}$$

The power required to maintain flow of velocity V equals the force required to overcome friction (i.e., the frictional force itself) times the velocity. Since the frictional force is the product of the pressure drop due to viscous effects and the conduit area, the power becomes

$$P = (\Delta pA)V = Q \,\Delta p = Q(p_1 - p_2) \tag{7-23}$$

The reader should verify that this force (ΔpA) is identical to the product of the wall shear stress τ_0 and the surface area over which it acts.

EXAMPLE 7-3

Commencing with the element shown in the inclined circular tube of Fig. 7-7, derive equations similar to the foregoing appropriate to the inclined case.

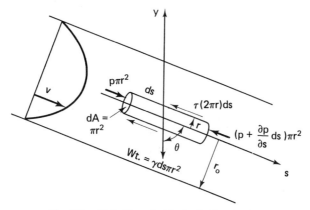

Fig. 7-7. Definition sketch for inclined tube.

SOLUTION:

The pressure, shear stress, and weight are shown on the axisymmetric element of radius r. Summing forces in the s direction gives

$$-\frac{\partial p}{\partial s} \, ds \, \pi r^2 - \tau(2\pi r) \, ds + \gamma \, ds \, \pi r^2 \cos\theta = 0$$

Noting, as before, that $\cos\theta = -\partial y/\partial s$ and rearranging,

$$\tau = -\frac{r}{2} \frac{\partial}{\partial s}(p + \gamma y)$$

The quantity $(p + \gamma y)$ does not vary in the r direction and, as before, its derivative with s must be constant in order to maintain a constant value of h normal to the flow direction. Substituting Eq. 1-5 with the velocity gradient expressed in terms of r gives

$$- \mu \frac{dv}{dr} = - \frac{r}{2} \frac{d}{ds}(p + \gamma y)$$

Upon integrating and setting $v = 0$ at $r = r_0$,

$$v = - \frac{1}{4\mu} \left[\frac{d}{ds}(p + \gamma y) \right](r_0^2 - r^2)$$

$$= - \frac{\gamma}{4\mu} \frac{dh}{ds}(r_0^2 - r^2)$$

The average velocity is therefore

$$V = - \frac{\gamma r_0^2}{8\mu} \frac{dh}{ds}$$

and when integrated over a length L this becomes

$$h_1 - h_2 = \frac{8\mu VL}{\gamma r_0^2} = \frac{32\mu VL}{\gamma D^2}$$

or, once again, Eq. 7-22.

EXAMPLE 7-4

Oil with a kinematic viscosity of 4×10^{-3} ft²/s and a specific gravity of 0.9 is pumped through a horizontal 4-in. pipe at a rate causing a pressure drop of 24,000 psf/mile. Determine the average velocity in the pipe, the power required to maintain the flow, and the velocity and shearing stress $\frac{1}{2}$ in. from the pipe wall.

SOLUTION:

The absolute viscosity is

$$\mu = (4 \times 10^{-3})(0.9)(1.94) = 6.98 \times 10^{-3} \text{ lb-s/ft}^2$$

Substituting into Eq. 7-21, the average velocity is found as

$$V = \frac{\Delta p D^2}{32\mu L} = \frac{(24,000)(\frac{4}{12})^2}{(32)(6.98 \times 10^{-3})(5280)} = 2.26 \text{ ft/s}$$

The power consumed, using Eq. 7-23, is

$$P = \frac{V \pi r_0^2 (p_1 - p_2)}{550} = \frac{(2.26)(\pi)(\frac{2}{12})^2(24,000)}{550} = 8.61 \text{ hp/mile}$$

At a distance of $\frac{1}{2}$ in. from the pipe wall,

$$r = \tfrac{3}{2} \text{ in.}$$

and the pressure gradient is

$$\frac{dp}{dx} = - \frac{24,000}{5280} = -4.55 \text{ psf/ft}$$

Thus, from Eq. 7-4 the shearing stress is

$$\tau = \frac{\frac{3}{2}}{(12)(2)}(4.55) = 0.284 \text{ psf}$$

and from Eq. 7-17 the velocity is

$$v = \frac{4.55}{(4)(6.98 \times 10^{-3})}\left[\left(\frac{2}{12}\right)^2 - \left(\frac{1.5}{12}\right)^2\right] = 1.98 \text{ ft/s}$$

EXAMPLE 7-5

Determine the flow rate through the 2-cm pipe shown in Fig. 7-8. Oil with a specific weight of 8800 N/m³ and dynamic viscosity of 0.20 N·s/m² flows from left to right, and pressures of 150 kN/m² and 100 kN/m² are recorded at sections 1 and 2, respectively.

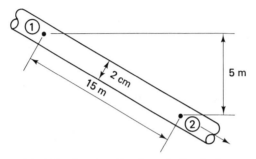

Fig. 7-8. Laminar flow in an inclined tube.

SOLUTION:

From Eq. 7-22, with the piezometric head separated into pressure and elevation heads, we have

$$\left(\frac{p_1}{\gamma} + y_1\right) - \left(\frac{p_2}{\gamma} + y_2\right) = \frac{32\mu VL}{\gamma D^2}$$

or

$$\left(\frac{150{,}000 \text{ N/m}^2}{8800 \text{ N/m}^3} + 5 \text{ m}\right) - \left(\frac{100{,}000 \text{ N/m}^2}{8800 \text{ N/m}^3} + 0\right) = \frac{(32)(0.20 \text{ N·s/m}^2)(V \text{ m/s})(15 \text{ m})}{(8800 \text{ N/m}^3)(0.02 \text{ m})^2}$$

Solving, $V = 0.39$ m/s for a flow rate of

$$Q = (0.39 \text{ m/s})\left(\frac{\pi}{4}\right)(0.02 \text{ m})^2 = 1.23 \times 10^{-4} \text{ m}^3/\text{s}$$

or 0.123 ℓ/s.

7–2 NAVIER–STOKES EQUATIONS

A set of differential equations, known as the Navier–Stokes equations, has been derived to describe the motion of Newtonian fluids.[3] A variety of exact solutions for specific flows have been found; however, the equations have not been solved in general. Their derivation is lengthy, and beyond the level and scope of this book. A brief outline of their derivation is appropriate, however.

[3]Refer to the references at the end of the chapter.

By equating pressure and gravitational forces to the product of the mass and the acceleration, we previously derived the Euler equations. Aligning the y axis of rectangular Cartesian coordinates with the vertical direction gave Eqs. 5-1, while more general rectangular Cartesian coordinates resulted in Eqs. 5-7. Repeating this procedure, but this time including the shear stresses on the different faces of the rectangular element (note that each face is subjected to shear stress in two directions) gives rise to similar equations, differing only by the inclusion of the derivatives of the shear stresses. The various shear stresses may be related to the different velocity gradients (rates of strain) through a generalization of Eq. 1-5. By a series of manipulations, many of which involve the symmetry of the various terms, the Navier–Stokes equations for an incompressible flow are obtained. In rectangular Cartesian coordinates they are as follows. In these equations and those that follow the vertical direction is again (see Fig. 5-4) taken as η.

$$\frac{\partial u}{\partial t} + u\frac{\partial u}{\partial x} + v\frac{\partial u}{\partial y} + w\frac{\partial u}{\partial z} = -\frac{1}{\rho}\frac{\partial p}{\partial x} - g\frac{\partial \eta}{\partial x}$$
$$+ v\left(\frac{\partial^2 u}{\partial x^2} + \frac{\partial^2 u}{\partial y^2} + \frac{\partial^2 u}{\partial z^2}\right) \tag{7-24a}$$

$$\frac{\partial v}{\partial t} + u\frac{\partial v}{\partial x} + v\frac{\partial v}{\partial y} + w\frac{\partial v}{\partial z} = -\frac{1}{\rho}\frac{\partial p}{\partial y} - g\frac{\partial \eta}{\partial y}$$
$$+ v\left(\frac{\partial^2 v}{\partial x^2} + \frac{\partial^2 v}{\partial y^2} + \frac{\partial^2 v}{\partial z^2}\right) \tag{7-24b}$$

and

$$\frac{\partial w}{\partial t} + u\frac{\partial w}{\partial x} + v\frac{\partial w}{\partial y} + w\frac{\partial w}{\partial z} = -\frac{1}{\rho}\frac{\partial p}{\partial z} - g\frac{\partial \eta}{\partial z}$$
$$+ v\left(\frac{\partial^2 w}{\partial x^2} + \frac{\partial^2 w}{\partial y^2} + \frac{\partial^2 w}{\partial z^2}\right) \tag{7-24c}$$

The Navier–Stokes equations in polar-cylindrical coordinates are written below. The notation used here is consistant with the polar coordinate system introduced in Section 3-3 and defined by Fig. 3-15.

$$\frac{\partial v_r}{\partial t} + v_r\frac{\partial v_r}{\partial r} + \frac{v_\theta}{r}\frac{\partial v_r}{\partial \theta} + v_z\frac{\partial v_r}{\partial z} - \frac{v_\theta^2}{r}$$
$$= -\frac{1}{\rho}\frac{\partial p}{\partial r} - g\frac{\partial \eta}{\partial r} + v\left(\nabla^2 v_r - \frac{v_r}{r} - \frac{2}{r^2}\frac{\partial v_\theta}{\partial \theta}\right) \tag{7-25a}$$

$$\frac{\partial v_\theta}{\partial t} + v_r\frac{\partial v_\theta}{\partial r} + \frac{v_\theta}{r}\frac{\partial v_\theta}{\partial \theta} + v_z\frac{\partial v_\theta}{\partial z} + \frac{v_r v_\theta}{r}$$
$$= -\frac{1}{\rho r}\frac{\partial p}{\partial \theta} - \frac{g}{r}\frac{\partial \eta}{\partial \theta} + v\left(\nabla^2 v_\theta + \frac{2}{r^2}\frac{\partial v_r}{\partial \theta} - \frac{v_\theta}{r^2}\right) \tag{7-25b}$$

and

$$\frac{\partial v_z}{\partial t} + v_r \frac{\partial v_z}{\partial r} + \frac{v_\theta}{r} \frac{\partial v_z}{\partial \theta} + v_z \frac{\partial v_z}{\partial z}$$

$$= -\frac{1}{\rho} \frac{\partial p}{\partial z} - g \frac{\partial \eta}{\partial z} + v(\nabla^2 v_z) \tag{7-25c}$$

Here the velocity components in the r, θ, and z directions are v_r, v_θ, and v_z, respectively, and

$$\nabla^2(\ ) = \frac{\partial^2(\ )}{\partial r^2} + \frac{1}{r} \frac{\partial(\ )}{\partial r} + \frac{1}{r^2} \frac{\partial^2(\ )}{\partial \theta^2} + \frac{\partial^2(\ )}{\partial z^2}$$

In vector notation the equations resolve to

$$\mathbf{a} = \frac{\partial \mathbf{V}}{\partial t} + (\mathbf{V} \cdot \nabla)\mathbf{V} = -\frac{\nabla p}{\rho} - g \nabla \eta + v \nabla^2 \mathbf{V} \tag{7-26}$$

From these equations the basic relationships of Section 7-1 can be obtained rather easily. Consider a two-dimensional flow in the x direction where $u = f(y)$ only, $v = w = 0$, and the y axis is vertical. Equations 7-24 simplify to

$$0 = -\frac{1}{\rho} \frac{\partial p}{\partial x} + v \frac{d^2 u}{dy^2} \tag{7-27a}$$

$$0 = -\frac{1}{\rho} \frac{\partial p}{\partial y} - g \tag{7-27b}$$

$$0 = -\frac{\partial p}{\partial z} \tag{7-27c}$$

The third equations merely says that the pressure is not a function of z. Integration of the second gives

$$p = -\gamma y + f(x, z)$$

but reduces to

$$p = -\gamma y + f(x)$$

in the light of the third equation. Taking the derivative of the above with respect to x gives

$$\frac{\partial p}{\partial x} = 0 + f'(x)$$

where $f'(x)$ denotes differentiation of $f(x)$ with respect to x. By this equation $\partial p/\partial x$ can be a function of x only. When this is compared to Eq. 7-27a, which says that the pressure gradient is given by

$$\frac{\partial p}{\partial x} = \mu \frac{d^2 u}{dy^2} \tag{7-28}$$

or a function of y only, it can be concluded immediately that the pressure gradient

$$\frac{\partial p}{\partial x} = \frac{dp}{dx} = \text{constant}$$

This is, of course, the result previously rationalized in the argument leading up to Eq. 7-3. In fact, if you substitute Eq. 1-5 into Eq. 7-27a, you now get Eq. 7-3. Note also that Eq. 7-27b shows that the pressure varies hydrostatically in the y direction.

Applications of the Navier–Stokes Equations to Laminar Flow

The two-dimensional flow between parallel plates shown in Fig. 7-3 will be briefly considered first. For this type of flow the Navier–Stokes equations have been reduced to Eq. 7-28, which for the constant pressure gradient becomes

$$\frac{d^2u}{dy^2} = \frac{1}{\mu}\frac{dp}{dx}$$

Integrating twice, we get

$$u = \frac{1}{\mu}\left(\frac{dp}{dx}\right)\frac{y^2}{2} + C_1 y + C_2$$

Substituting the boundary conditions

$$U = 0 \quad \text{at} \quad y = \pm B/2$$

gives

$$0 = \frac{1}{\mu}\left(\frac{dp}{dx}\right)\frac{B^2}{8} + \frac{C_1 B}{2} + C_2$$

and

$$0 = \frac{1}{\mu}\left(\frac{dp}{dx}\right)\frac{B^2}{8} - \frac{C_1 B}{2} + C_2$$

Thus

$$C_1 = 0 \quad \text{and} \quad C_2 = -\frac{1}{\mu}\left(\frac{dp}{dx}\right)\frac{B^2}{8}$$

and finally,

$$u = -\frac{1}{\mu}\left(\frac{dp}{dx}\right)\left(\frac{B^2}{8} - \frac{y^2}{2}\right)$$

which is Eq. 7-8 derived previously.

The solution of the circular pipe flow problem of Fig. 7-6 is somewhat more difficult. We will assume the pipe to be inclined and use notation consistent with Eqs. 7-25. Thus, for steady uniform flow in the z direction,

$$v_r = v_\theta = 0$$

and

$$v_z = f(r) \quad \text{only}$$

With these constraints, Eqs. 7-25 reduce to the following:

$$0 = -\frac{1}{\rho}\frac{\partial p}{\partial r} - g\frac{\partial \eta}{\partial r} \tag{7-29a}$$

$$0 = -\frac{1}{\rho r}\frac{\partial p}{\partial \theta} - \frac{g}{r}\frac{\partial \eta}{\partial \theta} \tag{7-29b}$$

$$0 = -\frac{1}{\rho}\frac{\partial p}{\partial z} - g\frac{\partial \eta}{\partial z} + \nu\frac{d^2v_z}{dr^2} + \frac{\nu}{r}\frac{dv_z}{dr} \tag{7-29c}$$

These may be rewritten as

$$0 = -\frac{\partial}{\partial r}\left(\frac{p}{\rho} + g\eta\right) \tag{7-30a}$$

$$0 = -\frac{1}{r}\frac{\partial}{\partial \theta}\left(\frac{p}{\rho} + g\eta\right) \tag{7-30b}$$

$$0 = -\frac{\partial}{\partial z}\left(\frac{p}{\rho} + g\eta\right) + \nu\frac{d^2v_z}{dr^2} + \frac{\nu}{r}\frac{dv_z}{dr} \tag{7-30c}$$

The first two equations now show that the quantity $p/\rho + g\eta$ cannot vary with either r or θ. But differentiation of this same quantity with respect to z shows, when compared to the third equation, that

$$\frac{\partial}{\partial z}\left(\frac{p}{\rho} + g\eta\right)$$

must be a constant. Since η is the vertical direction, just as y was in Fig. 5-2, the quantity $(p/\gamma + \eta)$ is the piezometric head (compare with Eq. 5-6). Therefore, across the flow section the pressure varies hydrostatically, while in the flow direction

$$\nu\left(\frac{d^2v_z}{dr^2} + \frac{1}{r}\frac{dv_z}{dr}\right) = \frac{d}{dz}\left(\frac{p}{\rho} + g\eta\right)$$

Rewriting and combining the first two terms gives the more easily integrated expression

$$\frac{1}{r}\frac{d}{dr}\left(r\frac{dv_z}{dr}\right) = -\frac{1}{\nu}\frac{d}{dz}\left(\frac{p}{\rho} + g\eta\right)$$

Integrating twice with respect to r,

$$r\frac{dv_z}{dr} = -\frac{r^2}{2\nu}\frac{d}{dz}\left(\frac{p}{\rho} + g\eta\right) + C_1$$

and

$$v_z = \frac{r^2}{4\nu}\frac{d}{dz}\left(\frac{p}{\rho} + g\eta\right) + C_1\ln r + C_2$$

Since the velocity must remain finite at $r = 0$, we have $C_1 = 0$, and since the velocity must go to zero at the pipe wall ($r = r_0$),

$$C_2 = -\frac{r_0^2}{4\nu}\frac{d}{dz}\left(\frac{p}{\rho} + g\eta\right)$$

Therefore, the velocity distribution becomes

$$v_z = -\frac{1}{4\nu}\left[\frac{d}{dz}\left(\frac{p}{\rho} + g\eta\right)\right](r_0^2 - r^2) \qquad (7\text{-}31)$$

Although a slightly different notation has been used (for convenience in Section 7-1, v_z was replaced by v), this reduces immediately to Eq. 7-17 for the case when the pipe is horizontal. The average velocity and the other quantities previously derived for pipe flow can, of course, be obtained from Eq. 7-31 as well.

A variety of other laminar flow problems can be solved using the Navier–Stokes equations. As a rather extreme example, the laminar flow through the rectangular conduit of Fig. 7-9, where $u = f(y, z)$, is described by the Navier–Stokes equation in the reduced from

$$\frac{\partial^2 u}{\partial y^2} + \frac{\partial^2 u}{\partial z^2} = \frac{1}{\mu}\frac{dp}{dx}$$

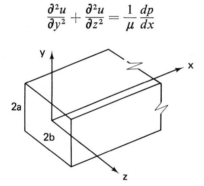

Fig. 7-9. Definition sketch for laminar flow in a rectangular conduit.

Solution of this equation gives rise to the velocity distribution

$$u = -\frac{1}{\mu}\frac{dp}{dx}\left\{\frac{b^2}{2} - \frac{y^2}{2} - \sum_{n=0}^{\infty}\frac{(-1)^n(2b^2)}{(2n+1)^3}\left(\frac{2}{\pi}\right)^3\right.$$
$$\left.\times\frac{\cosh\left[(2n+1)(\pi z/2b)\right]}{\cosh\left[(2n+1)(\pi a/2b)\right]}\cos\left[\frac{(2n+1)\pi y}{2b}\right]\right\} \qquad (7\text{-}32)$$

By integration over the area, the discharge is given by

$$Q = -\frac{1}{\mu}\frac{dp}{dx}\left\{\frac{4}{3}ab^3 - 8b^4\left(\frac{2}{\pi}\right)^5\sum_{n=0}^{\infty}\frac{1}{(2n+1)^5}\tanh\left[\frac{(2n+1)\pi a}{2b}\right]\right\} \qquad (7\text{-}33)$$

In addition to the exact solutions to the Navier–Stokes equations, a few of which we have examined, there are also a multitude of approximate solutions as well. We will have cause to return to the Navier–Stokes equations from time to time in the future.

7–3 INTRODUCTION TO TURBULENCE

After develping in considerable detail the mechanics of steady, uniform laminar flow it would seem desirable to follow this with the corresponding development for turbulent flow. However, the complexities involved make it necessary to consider first a relatively brief introduction to fluid turbulence, followed by a more extensive study of surface resistance and the effect of the surface itself on the turbulent velocity distribution.

The onset of turbulence and the changing of a laminar flow to a turbulent one is a very complicated phenomenon and accordingly will receive very little attention here. Let it suffice to state that as long as viscous forces predominate over inertial forces, a flow will remain laminar since any instabilities that tend to form in the flow will be suppressed by the viscous effects. Thus, as will be discussed further in Section 8-1, both the flow regime and the change from the laminar to turbulent regime must depend on a Reynolds number. For any laminar flow the changing of conditions so that the Reynolds number increases must eventually result in a turbulent flow.

Turbulence

The subject of turbulence was introduced in Section 3-4. At that time the apparent randomness of the flow was indicated, and the technique of resolving the instantaneous velocity into time-averaged mean and fluctuating components was mentioned (Eq. 3-22). The mathematical procedure for obtaining the time-averaged velocity was also given (Eq. 3-23).

Let us now compare and contrast what we know about laminar flow with the more obvious characteristics of turbulent flow. Figure 7-10a shows the steady, uniform velocity distribution for a two-dimensional laminar flow between parallel boundaries. A turbulent flow with equal discharge is given in Fig. 7-10b. This is indicated by the same average velocity V for each case. For the laminar flow we know that the average velocity is two-thirds of the maximum velocity, or in terms of the flow rate, it is the discharge divided by the area, which may also be determined by integration. Thus,

$$V_{\text{lam}} = \frac{2}{3}u_{\text{max}} = \frac{Q}{A} = \frac{1}{A}\int_A u\, dA$$

The turbulent flow gives a fluctuating distribution such as Fig. 7-10b that varies with both position and time. The distribution shown represents the velocity distribution at any instant. At the next instant this distribution will change. If, however, we examine the velocity at some point, say y_1, we would get a trace as in Fig. 3-18. Repeating the procedure at some point y_2 further into the flow would give a similar graph except that the time-averaged velocity at y_2 would be greater in magnitude than that at y_1. Repeating this process

219

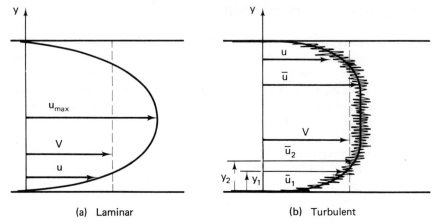

(a) Laminar   (b) Turbulent

Fig. 7-10.   Sketch of laminar and instantaneous turbulent profiles between parallel boundaries.

for every point across the flow would give the distribution of the time-averaged velocity, $\bar{u}$. This curve is also shown on Fig. 7-10b. The average velocity here, as with the laminar flow, can be related to the velocity distribution by integration of the time-averaged velocity over the area:

$$V_{\text{turb}} = \frac{Q}{A} = \frac{1}{A} \int_A \bar{u}\, dA$$

We are not able at this point to relate the centerline velocity to the average velocity; however, we can predict that they will be much closer to each other in value, since the mixing of the turbulent flow tends to even out the distribution.

We will now restrict our thinking to a steady, uniform flow such as that shown in Fig. 7-10b. Note that when we refer to a turbulent flow as steady, it is in terms of the time-averaged velocity, as of course the instantaneous velocity is changing continuously with time. The instantaneous velocity components in the x, y, and z directions of Cartesian coordinates will be u, v, and w, respectively. Resolving each into its time-averaged and fluctuating components, we have

$$u = \bar{u} + u' \tag{7-34a}$$

$$v = \bar{v} + v' = v' \tag{7-34b}$$

$$w = \bar{w} + w' = w' \tag{7-34c}$$

Since there is no net flow in the y or z directions, $\bar{v}$ and $\bar{w}$ are zero. The fluctuations represent the instantaneous velocity relative to the mean (in the latter two equations the mean happened to be zero), and consequently the average of the fluctuations must equal zero. This can be shown mathematically. Letting the bar represent the process of time averaging, Eq. 7-34a can be averaged as follows:

$$u = \bar{u} + u'$$

Taking the average of each side of the equation,

$$\bar{u} = \overline{\bar{u} + u'}$$

But the average of the sum equals the sum of the averages; hence,

$$\bar{u} = \bar{u} + \overline{u'}$$

and

$$\overline{u'} = 0$$

Since the mean of the fluctuations vanishes, we must define another term to describe the fluctuations in any direction. This is the intensity of the turbulence, obtained by first squaring the individual values of u' (to make them all positive), then taking the time average, and finally the square root of the result. That is, the intensity of the turbulence is the root mean square (or rms) of the fluctuations $\overline{(u'^2)}^{1/2}$.

Although the mean of the fluctuations is zero, this does not imply that the average of such products as $u'v'$ vanishes. In fact, not only does the mean of $u'v'$ (i.e., $\overline{u'v'}$) not vanish, but we can show that, in general,

$$\overline{u'v'} < 0 \tag{7-35}$$

To do this consider the velocity profile for $\bar{u}$ shown in Fig. 7-11. Consider

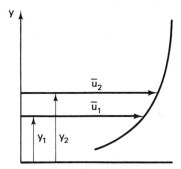

Fig. 7-11. Definition sketch for explanation of turbulent shear stress.

the velocities at points y_1 and y_2 to be as shown, where y_2 is only slightly greater than y_1. At instances when there is a positive vertical fluctuation $(+v')$ at point y_1, fluid with an average velocity of $\bar{u}_1$ will be carried up toward point y_2, thus temporarily lowering the velocity at the upper point. This reduction represents a negative fluctuation in the x direction $(-u')$. Conversely, a negative vertical fluctuation $(-v')$ at point y_2 carries down a velocity which on the average equals $\bar{u}_2$. This temporarily increases the velocity at point y_1 above the average value of $\bar{u}_1$, which corresponds to a positive fluctuation $(+u')$. Consequently, positive vertical fluctuations are usually accompanied by negative horizontal fluctuations, and vice versa.

It is now necessary to show that the quantity $\overline{u'v'}$ when multiplied by the mass density gives the turbulent shear stress,

$$\tau = -\rho \overline{u'v'} \tag{7-36}$$

Consider the positive vertical velocity fluctuation through the horizontal unit area given in Fig. 7-12. This carries a mass discharge of magnitude $\rho v' A$

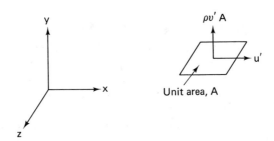

Fig. 7-12. Turbulent velocity components as momentum flux.

vertically across the horizontal surface. If the corresponding velocity change in the x direction is u', the change in momentum flux in the x direction is the product $\rho v' A u'$. By the momentum principle this equals the force in the x direction acting on the area A. Thus, the average force per unit area or shear stress is given by Eq. 7-36. The negative sign is required as a result of the previous inequality (Eq. 7-35).

Reynolds Equations

In a different vein, the Navier–Stokes equations (Eqs. 7-24) can be subjected to the same averaging process as was Eq. 7-34a previously. The velocities and pressure in the Navier–Stokes equations can be treated as the instantaneous values for turbulent flows, whereupon Eqs. 7-34 and a similar equation for pressure may be substituted. If each of the terms is now averaged, then, after a considerable amount of manipulation beyond the level of this book, the results are a set of equations usually referred to as the Reynolds equations. They take the following form in rectangular Cartesian coordinates for steady, incompressible, turbulent flow:

$$\bar{u}\frac{\partial \bar{u}}{\partial x} + \bar{v}\frac{\partial \bar{u}}{\partial y} + \bar{w}\frac{\partial \bar{u}}{\partial z} = -\frac{1}{\rho}\frac{\partial \bar{p}}{\partial x} - g\frac{\partial \eta}{\partial x}$$

$$+ \nu\left(\frac{\partial^2 \bar{u}}{\partial x^2} + \frac{\partial^2 \bar{u}}{\partial y^2} + \frac{\partial^2 \bar{u}}{\partial z^2}\right) - \frac{\partial(\overline{u'u'})}{\partial x} - \frac{\partial(\overline{v'u'})}{\partial y} - \frac{\partial(\overline{w'u'})}{\partial z} \tag{7-37a}$$

$$\bar{u}\frac{\partial\bar{v}}{\partial x} + \bar{v}\frac{\partial\bar{v}}{\partial y} + \bar{w}\frac{\partial\bar{v}}{\partial z} = -\frac{1}{\rho}\frac{\partial\bar{p}}{\partial y} - g\frac{\partial\eta}{\partial y}$$
$$+ \nu\left(\frac{\partial^2\bar{v}}{\partial x^2} + \frac{\partial^2\bar{v}}{\partial y^2} + \frac{\partial^2\bar{v}}{\partial z^2}\right) - \frac{\partial(\overline{u'v'})}{\partial x} - \frac{\partial(\overline{v'v'})}{\partial y} - \frac{\partial(\overline{w'v'})}{\partial z}$$

(7-37b)

$$\bar{u}\frac{\partial\bar{w}}{\partial x} + \bar{v}\frac{\partial\bar{w}}{\partial y} + \bar{w}\frac{\partial\bar{w}}{\partial z} = -\frac{1}{\rho}\frac{\partial\bar{p}}{\partial z} - g\frac{\partial\eta}{\partial z}$$
$$+ \nu\left(\frac{\partial^2\bar{w}}{\partial x^2} + \frac{\partial^2\bar{w}}{\partial y^2} + \frac{\partial^2\bar{w}}{\partial z^2}\right) - \frac{\partial(\overline{u'w'})}{\partial x} - \frac{\partial(\overline{v'w'})}{\partial y} - \frac{\partial(\overline{w'w'})}{\partial z}$$

(7-37c)

They differ from the Navier–Stokes equation only in the addition of a series of derivatives of quantities like $\overline{u'v'}$, which represent the turbulent stresses. Because of their complexity we will make little use of Eqs. 7-37, their introduction at this point being justified primarily as a backup to the physical arguments used previously in this section.

It is of interest to briefly note that for the steady, uniform, two-dimensional turbulent flow similar to that of Fig. 7-3, Eq. 7-37a reduces to

$$0 = -\frac{1}{\rho}\frac{\partial\bar{p}}{\partial x} + \nu\frac{\partial^2\bar{u}}{\partial y^2} - \frac{\partial(\overline{u'v'})}{\partial y}$$

Rewriting,

$$0 = -\frac{\partial\bar{p}}{\partial x} + \frac{\partial}{\partial y}\left(\mu\frac{\partial\bar{u}}{\partial y} - \rho\overline{u'v'}\right)$$

(7-38)

Comparing this latter equation with the equilibrium analysis of Section 7-1 and the resulting Eq. 7-3, valid for either laminar or turbulent flow, indicates that for turbulent flow the total shear stress may be written as

$$\tau = \mu\frac{\partial\bar{u}}{\partial y} - \rho\overline{u'v'}$$

(7-39)

The shear stress is apparently due to two components—one the result of viscous effects and the other due to the turbulent fluctuations.

Empirical Approach

After the basically theoretical, but difficult to apply arguments of the preceding pages, we will now consider an empirical and very approximate approach. This will be based on an eddy viscosity and the concept of a mixing length associated with the eddy size. No attempt will be made to completely develop this theory; rather, only those portions necessary for the subsequent development of an equation describing the velocity distribution that prevails in some turbulent flows will be pursued.

The first assumption that needs to be made is that credited to J. Boussinesq.[4] We have seen that the turbulent shear $-\rho\overline{u'v'}$ can be combined with

---

[4]See the reference at the end of the chapter.

the viscous contribution to shear $\mu \partial \bar{u}/\partial y$ to give the total shear as per Eq. 7-39. Boussinesq assumed that an analogy could be made between the molecular action responsible for viscous shear and the much larger eddies causing the turbulent stress. He consequently defined an eddy viscosity η such that the turbulent stress would be equal to $\eta \partial \bar{u}/\partial y$. Thus,

$$-\rho \overline{u'v'} = \eta \frac{\partial \bar{u}}{\partial y}$$

and from Eq. 7-39 the total shear stress becomes

$$\tau = \mu \frac{\partial \bar{u}}{\partial y} + \eta \frac{\partial \bar{u}}{\partial y} = (\mu + \eta) \frac{\partial \bar{u}}{\partial y} \qquad (7\text{-}40)$$

Upon dividing η by the density, the kinematic eddy viscosity ϵ is obtained and hence an alternative form of Eq. (7-40) is

$$\tau = \rho(v + \epsilon) \frac{\partial \bar{u}}{\partial y} \qquad (7\text{-}41)$$

Whereas the absolute and kinematic viscosities are properties of the fluid and can be obtained from graphs or tables with relative ease, the two eddy viscosities defined here are properties of the flow itself. They often vary from point to point throughout a fluid and vanish altogether when flow ceases or becomes laminar. Nevertheless, the form of Eqs. 7-40 and 7-41 will serve its purpose.

It is reasonable to assume that sufficiently near a boundary, at least if it is smooth, the turbulence will be suppressed by the presence of the boundary itself and Eqs. 7-40 and 7-41 will revert back to the viscous flow equations. On the other hand, since mixing is so much more intense in a turbulent flow than in a laminar flow, the eddy viscosities will generally have much larger magnitudes than their laminar counterparts throughout most of the flow region. Consequently we can generally express the shear stress by simply

$$\tau = \eta \frac{\partial \bar{u}}{\partial y} = \rho \epsilon \frac{\partial \bar{u}}{\partial y} \qquad (7\text{-}42)$$

The second empirical relationship, which will now be formulated, is due to L. Prandtl.[5] This is referred to as the *mixing-length hypothesis* and Fig. 7-13, similar to Fig. 7-11, will be helpful. The points y_1 and y_2 measured from the boundary are chosen so that they are separated by a distance l equal to the average eddy size; that is,

$$y_2 - y_1 = l$$

The corresponding time-averaged velocities are indicated as $\bar{u}_1$ and $\bar{u}_2$. Thus, as discussed previously, a positive vertical fluctuation $(+v')$ at y_1 causes a reduction in the x component of the instantaneous velocity at y_2 which is

[5]See the reference at the end of the chapter.

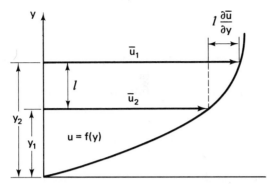

Fig. 7-13. Definition sketch for mixing-length hypothesis.

approximately proportional to the difference in mean velocities. Roughly, then, at y_2:

$$u' \approx -(\bar{u}_2 - \bar{u}_1) \approx -l\frac{\partial \bar{u}}{\partial y} \qquad (7\text{-}43)$$

where the last relationship assumes a linear velocity variation over the distance l. Ignoring viscous contributions we have, at least approximately,

$$\tau = -\rho\overline{u'v'} \approx \rho v'l\frac{\partial \bar{u}}{\partial y} \qquad (7\text{-}44)$$

whence, by comparison with Eq. 7-42,

$$\epsilon \approx v'l \qquad (7\text{-}45)$$

Thus, the kinematic eddy viscosity, which can be thought of as a mixing coefficient, is seen to depend on both the magnitude of the turbulent fluctuations and the size of the eddies.

If v' is assumed to be more-or-less equal in magnitude to u', Eq. 7-44 can be further written as

$$\tau = \rho l^2 \frac{\partial \bar{u}}{\partial y}\left|\frac{\partial \bar{u}}{\partial y}\right| \qquad (7\text{-}46)$$

The absolute value signs are placed around the one velocity gradient so that the shear stress will algebraically reflect the sign of the gradient. For a positive velocity gradient, the absolute value signs can be ignored and the equation rearranged to

$$\sqrt{\frac{\tau}{\rho}} = l\frac{\partial \bar{u}}{\partial y} \qquad (7\text{-}47)$$

In order to obtain a velocity distribution from this expression, the variation with y of both τ and l must be known or at least estimated. Since the eddy size must be depressed near a boundary, Prandtl made the simplest assumption that the eddy size, or mixing length, was directly proportional to the distance from the boundary y, or

$$l = \kappa y \qquad (7\text{-}48)$$

where κ (Greek lowercase kappa) is the constant of proportionality. He further assumed that if y is kept sufficiently small, the shear stress τ can be replaced by the wall shear stress τ_0. Introducing these assumptions, Eq. 7-47 becomes

$$\sqrt{\frac{\tau_0}{\rho}} = \kappa y \frac{\partial \bar{u}}{\partial y} \qquad (7\text{-}49)$$

Conventionally, the wall shear stress term is replaced by u_*, the shear velocity (so called because it has dimensions of LT^{-1}), defined by

$$u_* = \sqrt{\frac{\tau_0}{\rho}} \qquad (7\text{-}50)$$

and Eq. 7-49 takes the final form

$$u_* = \kappa y \frac{\partial \bar{u}}{\partial y} \qquad (7\text{-}51)$$

Because of the similarity between Eq. 7-42 and Eq. 1-3, it is reasonable to expect that the turbulent velocity profile can be obtained by integration as was the laminar case previously. Equation 7-51 now permits this. Upon separating variables and integrating,

$$\frac{\bar{u}}{u_*} = \frac{1}{\kappa} \ln y + C \qquad (7\text{-}52)$$

The constant of integration, which depends upon conditions at the boundary, will be evaluated later. For the present, consider the significant relationship between $\bar{u}$ and $\ln y$. The restrictive assumptions that have been made should limit the range of validity of Eq. 7-52 to a region near the wall (but outside any laminar portion in the immediate vicinity of the wall). Yet, it has been found that the logarithmic relationship holds reasonably well throughout the turbulent boundary layer, which will be considered in Chapter 9. Even more surprising, the logarithmic velocity distribution applies across almost the entire pipe cross section when turbulent flow occurs in a pipe. This is in spite of the assumed constant shear stress $\tau = \tau_0$. In fact, we have found that the shear must actually vary linearly from the boundary to zero at the centerline. Further, it is more logical that the eddy size in a pipe should depend to some extent on the pipe diameter rather than just on the distance from the boundary itself. Rouse[6] has offered one technique for resolving these inconsistencies. He suggests that the linear shear stress

$$\tau = \tau_0 \left(1 - \frac{y}{r_0}\right) \qquad (7\text{-}53)$$

[6]See the reference at the end of the chapter.

can be substituted into Eq. 7-47 if Eq. 7-48 is replaced by the equally reasonable hypothesis that

$$l = \kappa y \left(1 - \frac{y}{r_0}\right)^{1/2} \tag{7-54}$$

so that Eq. 7-48 when integrated still produces Eq. 7-52 for a pipe. Whatever the rationale for its evaluation, we will make considerable use of the logarithmic velocity distribution that has been obtained here.

PROBLEMS

Sec. 7-1

7-1. Determine the flow of glycerin at 60°F in gallons per minute (gpm) per foot of width for the two-dimensional flow between flat plates separated by a gap of 1 in. if the pressure drop is 0.10 psi per foot of length. What is the maximum shear stress?

7-2. What is the pressure gradient in a fluid with a dynamic viscosity of 3×10^{-2} lb-s/ft² flowing between parallel plates spaced 0.05 ft apart if the velocity at the centerline is 4.17 ft/s? What is the velocity at points midway between the centerline and the plates?

7-3. If a laminar flow occurs between parallel flat plates separated a distance B, at what distance from the boundaries is the velocity just equal to the average velocity?

7-4. Prove that the centerline velocity in a flow between parallel boundaries is three-halves the average velocity if the flow is laminar.

7-5. Determine the total rate of flow of water over a parking lot that is 800 ft wide and slopes downward at the rate of $\frac{1}{2}$ in./10 ft in the direction of flow. Its average depth is 0.01 ft and the temperature of the water is 60°F.

7-6. Glycerin at 20°C flows down a 10-m-wide flat surface that has a 45° slope. What is the discharge if the thickness of the sheet of glycerin is 1 cm? 2 cm?

7-7. Glycerin flows down a 10-m-wide plane surface that has a slope of 45°. What is the discharge if the thickness of the glycerin is 2 cm and the temperature is 15°C? 30°C?

7-8. For a laminar velocity distribution as given by Eq. 7-17, show by integration that the average velocity is indeed given by Eq. 7-19.

7-9. What is the pressure drop in a length of 1000 ft of horizontal 1-in.-diameter pipe if fuel oil at 100°F is pumped at a rate of 20 gpm? What is the power consumption?

7-10. If fuel oil at 110°F is pumped at the rate of 20 gpm through a 4-in.-diameter horizontal pipe, what will be the pressure drop in a length of 1000 ft? What horsepower would be required to move the fluid through this length? What is the shear stress at the boundary?

7-11. If SAE 30 oil at 25°C flows through a 5-cm-diameter pipe at the rate of 10^{-3} m³/s, what is the pressure drop in a length of 100 m if the pipe is horizontal? What is the shear stress at the boundary?

7-12. If the pipe of Prob. 7-11 slopes upward at 20°, what is the pressure drop in a length of 100 m?

7-13. What is the difference in pressure between points A and B if 0.2 cfs of SAE 10 oil at 65°F flows upward as shown through a 2-in.-diameter pipe?

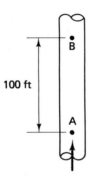

7-14. What is the difference in pressure between points A and B if the oil of Prob. 7-13 flows downward at the rate specified?

7-15. At what flow rate and direction would the oil given in Prob. 7-13 have to flow if the pressure at A equaled the pressure at B?

7-16. If laminar flow occurs in a circular tube, at what radial distance is the velocity just equal to the average velocity?

7-17. Forty feet of $\frac{1}{4}$-in. tubing is connected to the bottom of a tank of fuel oil. If the outlet of the tubing is 4 ft below the free surface in the tank, what will be the discharge of oil? The oil temperature is 80°F.

Sec. 7-2

7-18. Derive the hydrostatic relationships from the Navier–Stokes equations.

7-19. Using Eqs. 7-24 determine the vertical pressure distribution in a tank of water that is falling freely.

7-20. Show that the velocity profile for steady, uniform flow in a circular pipe, as given by Eq. 7-31, satisfies both the continuity equation and the Navier–Stokes equations.

7-21. through 7-23. Determine for the following three problems the velocity profile and the shear stress at both boundaries if two horizontal parallel plates are separated a distance B by a fluid with viscosity μ.

7-21. The upper plate is moved to the right with velocity V_1 and the pressure gradient is $dp/dx = 0$.

7-22. The upper plate is moved to the right with velocity V_1 and the pressure gradient is $dp/dx < 0$.

7-23. The upper plate is moved to the right with velocity V_1, the lower plate is moved to the left with velocity V_2, and the pressure gradient is $dp/dx < 0$.

7-24. If a rectangular duct has dimensions of 1 in. by 2 in., what is the flow rate of SAE 30 oil at 80°F if the pressure drop is 0.05 psf/ft?

7-25. If a rectangular duct has dimensions of 2 cm by 6 cm, what is the pressure drop in 20 m if SAE 30 oil at 30°C flows at the rate of 4×10^{-4} m^3/s?

7-26. What is the ratio of maximum to average velocity if laminar flow occurs in a square duct?

7-27. Develop an equation for the laminar flow in the annular region between the inner core $r = r_1$ and the outer cylinder at $r = r_2$.

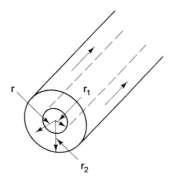

7-28. Compare the solution to Prob. 7-27 with the simpler solution (valid when $r_2 - r_1$ is small) obtained by treating the annular cross section as a rectangle of thickness $r_2 - r_1$ and width equal to the circumference.

7-29. If the inner cylindrical surface of Prob. 7-27 is eccentric (i.e., not centered as shown), would a greater or lesser discharge result, everything else being unchanged? Why?

Sec. 7-3

7-30. Demonstrate that substitution of Eqs. 7-53 and 7-54 into Eqs. 7-47 leads to Eq. 7-52.

7-31. Assuming that $\kappa = 0.4$, plot the magnitude of the mixing length versus radial distance in a 1-ft-diameter conduit according to Eq. 7-54.

7-32. Repeat Prob. 7-31 if κ is reduced in magnitude to 0.3.

REFERENCES

BATCHELOR, G. K., *The Theory of Homogenous Turbulence*. Cambridge: Cambridge University Press, 1960.

BOUSSINESQ, J., "Théorie de l'écoulement tourbillant," *Mem. Pres. Acad. Sci.*, Vol. XXIII (1877), 46.

HENNEKES, H., and J. L. LUMLEY, *A First Course in Turbulence*. Cambridge, Mass.: MIT Press, 1972.

HINZE, J. O., *Turbulence*. New York: McGraw-Hill, 1959.

LIN, C. C., *Statistical Theories of Turbulence*. Princeton, N.J.: Princeton University Press, 1961.

MONIN, A. S., and A. M. YAGLOM, *Statistical Fluid Mechanics: Mechanics of Turbulence*, J. L. Lumley (ed.). Cambridge, Mass.: MIT Press, 1971.

PAI, S. I., "Laminar Flow," Chapter 5 in *Handbook of Fluid Dynamics*, V. L. Streeter (ed.). New York: McGraw-Hill, 1961.

PRANDTL, L., *Essentials of Fluid Dynamics*. New York: Hafner, 1952.

ROSENHEAD, L. (ed.), *Laminar Boundary Layers*. Oxford: Oxford University Press, 1963.

ROUSE, H., *Advanced Mechanics of Fluids*. New York: Wiley, 1959.

TOWNSEND, A. A., *The Structure of Turbulent Shear Flow*. Cambridge: Cambridge University Press, 1953.

TOWNSEND, A. A., "Turbulence," Chapter 10 in *Handbook of Fluid Dynamics*, V. L. Streeter (ed.). New York: McGraw-Hill, 1961.

Steady, Uniform Turbulent Flow

Now that the subject of turbulence has been introduced and selected characteristics examined, we can return to steady, primarily uniform flows. It is initially necessary to consider the criteria that determine whether a given flow is laminar or turbulent. Subsequently, we can apply our knowledge of turbulence, in particular the logarithmic velocity distribution, to develop solutions for steady, uniform turbulent flows. As the solutions depend on the boundary characteristics, hydrodynamically smooth and hydrodynamically rough boundaries will be considered separately.

In addition, a general resistance equation will be formulated applicable to laminar as well as turbulent flows. This will be applied to noncircular as well as circular conduits. This equation will also be compared with the more empirical resistance equations; and resistance in open channels as well as conduits examined. Finally, the resistance will be included in the energy equation, along with the "minor losses" of pipe fittings, and other appurtenances.

8–1 THE REYNOLDS NUMBER

The significance of the Reynolds number for the modeling of flows in which viscous effects are important was emphasized in Chapter 6. It should thus be evident that once the Reynolds number has been defined for a given type of flow, the magnitude of the Reynolds number will characterize or uniquely define the flow. One aspect of this can be demonstrated at this point by the following arguments, part of which corresponds to the classic experiments of Osborne Reynolds.[1] In the nineteenth century Reynolds set up the apparatus shown schematically in Fig. 8-1. A reservoir of water was

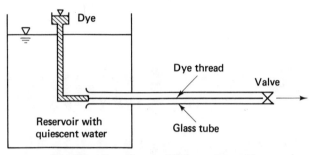

Fig. 8-1. Experiment of Osborne Reynolds.

allowed to sit for a sufficient time such that all initial disturbances were dissipated. Then the downstream valve was slightly opened and a small thread of dye subsequently introduced along the centerline of the glass tube. At small flow rates it was found that the dye traveled the length of the tube with very little wavering or dispersion. Since the flow was laminar, any mixing that occurred had to depend on molecular activity alone. This condition prevailed for ever-increasing flow rates until finally the thread of dye began to waver and ultimately, with still higher velocity, to break up and disperse rapidly across the tube. Reynolds, by considering tube diameter as well, identified a critical value for this onset of turbulence in terms of the dimensionless parameter VD/ν. As a result of his pioneering effort, this parameter now bears his name.

We will return to his results shortly. First, let us consider some variations on his experiment and the significance of their outcome. The experiment could be run repeatedly, each time increasing the pipe diameter, and correspondingly setting the valve so that the same average velocity prevailed. Just as with a constant diameter where it was found that above a certain "critical" velocity the flow became turbulent, it would now be found that above a "critical" diameter the flow would be turbulent.

Finally, a given pipe could be chosen and the valve operated so that a constant average velocity was again maintained. The variable in this set of experiments would be the fluid, in particular the kinematic viscosity. If the experiments were repeated such that each succeeding fluid had a lower vis-

[1]O. Reynolds, "An Experimental Investigation of the Circumstances Which Determine Whether the Motion of Water Shall Be Direct or Sinuous and of the Law of Resistance in Parallel Channels," *Phil. Trans. Roy. Soc.*, Vol. 174 (1883), 935.

cosity, a "critical" viscosity would this time be identified. In this case, opposite to the previous results, when the viscosity became sufficiently low, the onset of turbulence would occur. Thus, it is not a single variable alone that is important but rather the combination of increasing velocity or diameter and decreasing viscosity. In particular, it is their combination that is most significant: the dimensionless parameter that we have previously defined as the Reynolds number,

$$\text{Re} = \frac{VD}{\nu} \tag{8-1}$$

The physical significance of each of the variables as it affects the transition from laminar to turbulent flow is also important. The arguments will be seen to be somewhat similar to those of Section 6-2 leading to Eq. 6-9c. The magnitude of the viscosity is proportional to the viscous forces, tending to dampen out any instability of the flow. Consequently, the lower the viscosity, the less likely it is that the viscous forces will be able to suppress the tendency for eddies to form. Increasing the velocity, on the other hand, increases the inertia of the flow and also the inertia of any instabilities that tend to form in the flow. Hence, it becomes increasingly difficult for the viscous forces to maintain the laminar flow. The clearest effect of tube diameter is the constraint it places on eddy size. Obviously, the greater the diameter, the greater is the size of the largest eddies. Conversely and more to the point, the smaller the tube diameter, the better is its ability to suppress any eddies that materialize in the flow. Summing up, it is to be expected that the value of the Reynolds number would indicate whether flow is laminar or turbulent, since (from Section 6-2) it represents the ratio of inertial to viscous forces. In this role it indicates the relative importance of each of the two types of forces.

Reynolds found that the flow became unstable when VD/ν exceeded 12,000. We now know that that particular value is not significant but is dependent on the equipment used and the care taken. Repeating the experiments with the same equipment but with a few refinements in both procedure and setup, turbulence was observed to occur only when the Reynolds number exceeded 50,000. Similarly, flow in commercial pipes generally becomes turbulent by the time a value of 4000 is reached. However, it is found in all cases that as the Reynolds number decreases, turbulent flows revert to laminar flow at roughly a value of 2000. Thus, in a pipe a lower critical Reynolds number of 2000 is well defined and we can say with reasonable certainty that if the Reynolds number of the flow is below this value, the flow will be laminar. Furthermore, an upper critical value cannot be identified other than in particular instances. From a practical point of view we will usually assume that pipe flow is turbulent if the Reynolds number exceeds 4000.

For conduits or channels with noncircular cross sections the critical Reynolds number will depend upon the shape of the cross section and on the length chosen to define the Reynolds number. For example, a wide rectangular open channel with a width b and depth y will have a critical Reynolds number of 500 if the Reynolds number is defined by

$$\text{Re} = \frac{Vy}{\nu} \tag{8-2}$$

The lack of consistency regarding the upper critical limit can be explained by consideration of the behavior of a flow in the vicinity of a specific disturbance. The pipe flow shown on Fig. 8-2 has an average velocity V and is exposed to a significant disturbance at point A.

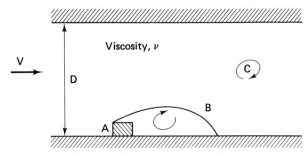

Fig. 8-2. Sketch of flow instability.

At very low values of V, such that $VD/\nu \ll 2000$,[2] the flow will deflect past the obstacle quickly returning to follow the original boundary and at all times remaining laminar. As V increases, a zone of separation will form (line B) as shown. Since an eddy persists in this region, this could be considered a type of turbulence. If VD/ν is still less than 2000, the remainder of the flow will still be laminar. Eventually, a point will be reached where the disturbance will not only create a zone of separation but will also shed eddies into the flow (C). If the Reynolds number is still below 2000, these eddies will damp out rapidly as they flow downstream and the flow will return to its laminar state. As the flow rate further increases and the Reynolds number rises above 2000, the eddies (C) will no longer be dissipated but will instead disturb the surrounding flow, creating more eddies, which will soon spread across the tube. Thus, at this value of V, the flow upstream of the disturbance will remain laminar, whereas downstream of the disturbance, turbulent flow will prevail. As the Reynolds number increases still more, the flow itself will become unstable and will become everywhere turbulent.

It is the disturbance itself, therefore, that gives rise to the upper critical number. If the disturbance were more pronounced, it would more readily trigger eddies that would break up the laminar flow. As we attempt to remove

[2]The symbol $\ll$ may be read "very much smaller than."

the possible disturbances, the likelihood of maintaining a laminar flow is thus increased.

This chapter will deal almost exclusively with uniform flows. This condition does not occur immediately at the start of a pipe but must develop in essentially the same way as the boundary layer development to be considered in Chapter 9. For example, in a pipe leading from a reservoir, a distance x must be traversed by the flow before the flow pattern becomes completely uniform and the flow is said to be fully developed. In laminar flow x is approximated by

$$\frac{x}{D} = 0.07\frac{VD}{\nu} \tag{8-3}$$

If the flow is turbulent, roughly 50 diameters,

$$\frac{x}{D} = 50 \tag{8-4}$$

are required to ensure completely uniform[3] conditions. In the pipe problems to be considered throughout this chapter, these initial length conditions will usually be ignored.

EXAMPLE 8-1

What is the greatest discharge of (a) water (70°F) and (b) glycerin (70°F) that we can pump through a 1-in.-diameter pipe if we want to be sure that the flow remains laminar? (c) Why is it sufficient to specify the critical Reynolds number in terms of the average velocity when, in fact, the velocity must vary from a value of zero at the walls to a maximum value at the centerline which exceeds the average velocity?

SOLUTION:

(a) The maximum allowable velocity must correspond to a Reynolds number equal to 2000.

Since $\nu_{water} = 1.05 \times 10^{-5}$ ft²/s at 70°F, we have

$$\frac{VD}{\nu} = \frac{V(1/12)}{1.05 \times 10^{-5}} = 2000$$

Solving, we obtain

$$V = 0.252 \text{ ft/s}$$

and hence for water

$$Q_{max} = VA = (0.252 \text{ ft/s})(0.00545 \text{ ft}^2) = 0.00137 \text{ cfs}$$

(b) Repeating for glycerin with $\nu_{gly} = 6 \times 10^{-3}$ ft²/s,

$$\frac{V(1/12)}{6 \times 10^{-3}} = 2000$$

and

$$V = 144.0 \text{ ft/s}$$

---

[3] For most purposes, turbulent flow can be treated as uniform after 15 diameters.

corresponding to a discharge of

$$Q_{max} = (144.0)(0.00545) = 0.785 \text{ cfs}$$

This is, of course, an exceedingly high, nonrealistic flow rate for a 1-in. pipe.

(c) The average velocity is sufficient, since it always bears a prescribed relationship to the velocity distribution. We have already seen this for laminar pipe flow, where the average velocity equals exactly one-half of the centerline or maximum velocity. We will find in turbulent flow (see Eq. 8-30) that the ratio between centerline velocity and average velocity is no longer constant but depends only on the Reynolds number for flow in a smooth tube.

EXAMPLE 8-2

How far downstream from the start of a 2-cm pipe should a pressure tap be placed if it is always to be in the region of completely uniform flow? The fluid is SAE 30 oil and the flow rate must always be 1.09 ℓ/s, although the temperature may fluctuate between 30°C and 60°C.

SOLUTION:

The minimum viscosity and therefore maximum Reynolds number will occur at the highest temperature. This will require the greatest length of pipe for uniform flow development provided that the Reynolds number does not exceed 2000. Checking,

$$V = \frac{(1.09 \ \ell/\text{s})(0.001 \ \text{m}^3/\ell)}{(\pi/4)(0.02 \ \text{m})^2} = 3.47 \ \text{m/s}$$

while at 60°C = 140°F,

$$v = (5 \times 10^{-4} \ \text{ft}^2/\text{s})(0.0929 \ \text{m}^2/\text{ft}^2) = 4.65 \times 10^{-5} \ \text{m}^2/\text{s}$$

giving a Reynolds number

$$\text{Re} = \frac{VD}{v} = \frac{(3.47 \ \text{m/s})(0.02 \ \text{m})}{4.65 \times 10^{-5} \ \text{m}^2/\text{s}} = 1490$$

Since this value is less than 2000, the flow is laminar throughout the temperature range and the maximum length x is

$$x = (0.07D)\left(\frac{VD}{v}\right) = (0.07D) \ \text{Re}$$

$$= (0.07)(0.02 \ \text{m})(1490) = 2.09 \ \text{m}$$

8-2 TURBULENT VELOCITY DISTRIBUTION

The criteria for predicting whether a flow will be laminar or turbulent have now been considered. We will for the present assume a turbulent flow and develop the appropriate velocity profile, particularly with regard to steady, uniform flow in a circular conduit. Recalling the equation, for a logarithmic velocity distribution (Eq. 7-52) from Chapter 7, we have

$$\frac{u}{u_*} = \frac{1}{\kappa} \ln y + C$$

Since the fluctuating components of the turbulence will not be considered further, the overbars used in Chapter 7 will be dropped. It will be assumed when dealing with turbulent flows that the velocities and pressures are the time-averaged values. As y is measured from the boundary inward, it has the opposite sense to the radial direction, r. Repeated plotting of u versus $\ln y$ from various sets of data permits experimental determination of the value of κ, which can be readily evaluated from the slope of the semilogarithmic graphs. It has been found, within a small variation, that κ is very nearly a constant value. This constant, $\kappa = 0.40$, is generally referred to as the *von Kármán universal constant*. In certain cases it can vary considerably, as for example in sediment-laden flows, where κ may drop as low as 0.20. Here, we will take the 0.40 value and consequently Eq. 7-52 becomes

$$\frac{u}{u_*} = 2.5 \ln y + C \qquad (8\text{-}5)$$

Attempting to apply Eq. 8-5 at the boundary where $y = 0$ leads to a negatively infinite velocity, as shown in Fig. 8-3. The first step toward

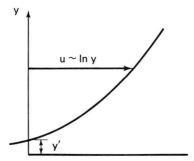

Fig. 8-3. Sketch for evaluation of constant of integration for logarithmic velocity profiles.

circumventing the difficulty is to locate the point of zero velocity shown as y'. Upon substituting this point into Eq. 8-5,

$$0 = 2.5 \ln y' + C$$

and therefore

$$\frac{u}{u_*} = 2.5 \ln \left(\frac{y}{y'} \right) \qquad (8\text{-}6)$$

Converting to logarithms to the base 10 gives the equivalent equation,

$$\frac{u}{u_*} = 5.75 \log_{10} \left(\frac{y}{y'} \right) \qquad (8\text{-}7)$$

To proceed further in the evaluation of y', it is necessary to consider the nature of the surface itself.

Velocity Profile over a Smooth Boundary

The velocity profile for a turbulent flow over a smooth boundary will be obtained by a combination of theoretical and physical reasoning, coupled with the results of a series of classic experiments. We will leave the practical definition of "smooth" and "rough" boundaries until later and assume that the boundary is smooth. In Fig. 8-4 the profile of Eq. 8-7 (shown dashed) has been superimposed over the actual velocity profile (curve I). The deviation

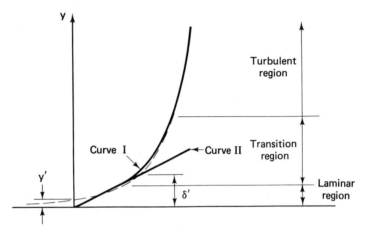

Fig. 8-4.   Laminar and turbulent regions near a smooth boundary.

is due in part to the no-slip condition, imposing in reality that the velocity must equal zero at the boundary. More important to our present thinking, there must be a region very near a smooth boundary where because of the low velocity, the flow will be laminar. This region, known as the *laminar sublayer* and designated as δ', must persist no matter how intensely turbulent (as reflected by a high Reynolds number) the main region of the flow actually is. It should be expected, however, that the higher the Reynolds number, the thinner this layer will be.

The thinness of the laminar sublayer permits the substitution of a linear relation $u \sim y$ for the more correct but less convenient parabolic form. This (curve II) must now be matched to the logarithmic curve. Note first that the flow transition from laminar to turbulent as y exceeds δ' should depend on an appropriate Reynolds number. A Reynolds number may be defined based on distance from the wall, $U_0 y \rho / \mu$, where U_0 is taken as the velocity at the edge of the laminar sublayer. The critical value will occur at the point $y = \delta'$, and setting this value equal to a constant C^2 gives

$$\frac{U_0 \delta' \rho}{\mu} = C^2 \tag{8-8}$$

Further, the shear stress at the wall (from Eq. 1-5) as modified by the assumed linear profile (curve II of Fig. 8-4) may be written as

$$\tau_0 = \mu \frac{du}{dy} = \mu \frac{u}{y} = \frac{\mu U_0}{\delta'} \tag{8-9}$$

Eliminating the velocity between the Eqs. 8-8 and 8-9 gives

$$C = \frac{\sqrt{\tau_0/\rho}\ \delta'}{\nu} = \frac{u_* \delta'}{\nu} \tag{8-10}$$

Here the critical conditions have been expressed in terms of what may descriptively be called a shear-velocity Reynolds number. Solving for δ' and assuming from dimensional considerations that δ' and y' will both vary in the same manner,

$$\delta' = \frac{C\nu}{u_*} = C'y' \tag{8-11}$$

Upon substituting Eq. 8-11 into Eq. 8-7, we get

$$\frac{u}{u_*} = 5.75 \log_{10}\left(\frac{yu_*}{\nu}\frac{C'}{C}\right)$$

or

$$\frac{u}{u_*} = 5.75 \log_{10}\left(\frac{u_* y}{\nu}\right) + 5.75 \log_{10}\left(\frac{C'}{C}\right)$$

Experiments by J. Nikuradse[4] have shown that the last term equals 5.5, whereupon

$$\frac{u}{u_*} = 5.75 \log_{10}\left(\frac{u_* y}{\nu}\right) + 5.5 \tag{8-12}$$

Thus we have a dimensionless, universal profile for turbulent flow over a smooth boundary. The equation is known as the *von Kármán–Prandtl equation* for a smooth boundary.

Returning to the velocity profile in the laminar sublayer, we have from Eq. 8-9,

$$u = \frac{\tau_0}{\mu} y$$

which by rearrangement yields

$$\frac{u}{u_*} = \frac{u_* y}{\nu} \tag{8-13}$$

Taking δ' as the intersection of Eqs. 8-12 and 8-13 (see Fig. 8-4), and combining the equations at the point $y = \delta'$ gives

$$\frac{u_* \delta'}{\nu} = 5.75 \log_{10}\left(\frac{u_* \delta'}{\nu}\right) + 5.5$$

[4] Described in all three references listed at the end of the chapter.

Upon solving for δ', we get

$$\delta' = \frac{11.6\nu}{u_*} \qquad (8\text{-}14)$$

Thus, it has been determined that $C = 11.6$. With only a little more effort, we can also obtain $C' = 107$.

In summary, the velocity distribution for flow over a smooth boundary is given in the laminar sublayer by Eq. 8-13 and in the remaining turbulent region by Eq. 8-12:

$$\frac{u}{u_*} = \frac{u_* y}{\nu} \qquad \text{(laminar sublayer)} \qquad (8\text{-}13)$$

$$\frac{u}{u_*} = 5.75 \log_{10}\left(\frac{u_* y}{\nu}\right) + 5.5 \qquad \text{(turbulent region)} \qquad (8\text{-}12)$$

For purposes of applying these equations, the thickness of the laminar sublayer is given by Eq. 8-14. Of little physical significance but nevertheless of some mathematical interest, the point of zero velocity as given by the logarithmic profile is

$$y' = \frac{\delta'}{107} \qquad (8\text{-}15)$$

Before proceeding further, refer to the experimental verification of these equations shown in Fig. 8-5. The semilogarithmic plot distorts the linear

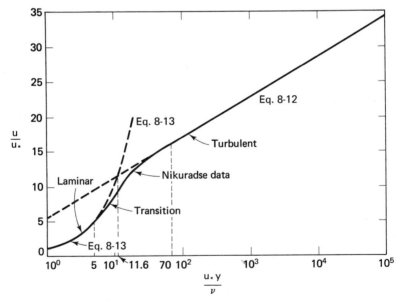

Fig. 8-5. Velocity distribution for laminar and turbulent flow over a smooth boundary.

portion, but nevertheless note that the experimental observations (indicated by the curve labeled Nikuradse data) follow the mathematical curves except in the vicinity of the intersection where they deviate slightly. In fact, a true laminar sublayer has less thickness that the δ' given by Eq. 8-14 and a transition or buffer zone exists between the two types of flows. The actual limits as taken from Fig. 8-5 are as follows:

$$0 < \frac{u_* y}{\nu} < 5 \qquad \text{laminar flow} \qquad\qquad (8\text{-}16a)$$

$$5 < \frac{u_* y}{\nu} < 70 \qquad \text{transition zone} \qquad\qquad (8\text{-}16b)$$

$$70 < \frac{u_* y}{\nu} \qquad \text{turbulent flow} \qquad\qquad (8\text{-}16c)$$

These regions are also shown qualitatively on Fig. 8-4.

Velocity Profile over a Rough Boundary

If the boundary is rough (and we still have not addressed the question of what is a rough boundary), it is very unlikely that a laminar sublayer could exist except possibly in small, disconnected areas. Instead, a roughness height k is defined as shown in Fig. 8-6. It will be assumed that this roughness

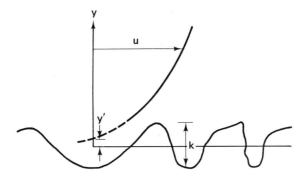

Fig. 8-6.   Sketch of flow over a rough boundary.

measure accounts for the effects of both the form of the roughness and its distribution as well as its magnitude. Thus, the cases of isolated roughness elements, specific patterns of roughness elements, or distinct geometric shapes are not systematically identified.

It is reasonable that y' should now depend on the roughness height, and expressing this relationship by introducing a constant of proportionality B gives

$$k = By' \qquad\qquad (8\text{-}17)$$

Substituting into the logarithmic profile, Eq. 8-7 becomes

$$\frac{u}{u_*} = 5.75 \log_{10}\left(\frac{y}{k}\right) + 5.75 \log_{10} B \tag{8-18}$$

By experiment with uniform size sand of diameter k cemented to the inside of pipes, Nikuradse found that the last term equaled 8.5, and hence $B = 30$. This gives rise to the von Kármán–Prandtl equation for flow over a rough boundary,

$$\frac{u}{u_*} = 5.75 \log_{10}\left(\frac{y}{k}\right) + 8.5 \tag{8-19}$$

which is a universal velocity distribution for rough pipes.

The question of whether a boundary is smooth or rough is going to depend on the relative magnitudes of the calculated values of δ' and k in each case. If k is sufficiently large, it will break up the laminar sublayer as previously described. If, on the other hand, δ' is relatively large, it will "submerge" the roughness elements and the boundary is then known as *hydraulically smooth*. Since k is fixed, a boundary may be hydraulically smooth to one flow rate and hydraulically rough to another. Recalling from Eq. 8-14 that $\delta' \sim v/u_*$, we have

$$\frac{k}{\delta'} \sim \frac{u_* k}{v} \tag{8-20}$$

This ratio of k/δ', which is a roughness factor, is seen to depend on a shear velocity/roughness Reynolds number. Nikuradse, using the aforementioned sand-roughened pipes, found that the pipe is smooth if

$$0 < \frac{u_* k}{v} < 5 \tag{8-21a}$$

in transition if

$$5 < \frac{u_* k}{v} < 70 \tag{8-21b}$$

and rough if

$$70 < \frac{u_* k}{v} \tag{8-21c}$$

In the first and third cases, Eqs. 8-12 and 8-19 apply, respectively. In the transition region, enough of the roughness elements penetrate the laminar layer to effect the resistance and hence the velocity distribution as well.

These ranges can be seen on Fig. 8-7, which also gives the velocity profile for all ranges. The Nikuradse data had modest scatter in the transition range. This complete universality is achieved by choosing an ordinate which in the smooth range reverts back to Eq. 8-12 and in the rough range is the constant 8.5 of Eq. 8-19. Note that the rough/transition/smooth criteria of Eqs. 8-21 can also be expressed directly in terms of δ'/k through the use of Eq. 8-14.

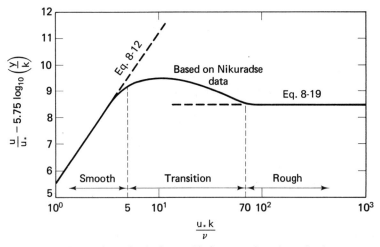

Fig. 8-7. Universal velocity profile for smooth and rough pipes.

EXAMPLE 8-3

The velocity distribution in a 1-ft-diameter pipe with absolute roughness $k = 0.001$ ft is plotted on Fig. 8-8. Assume water with $\nu = 10^{-5}$ ft²/s. Determine:
(a) The wall shear stress τ_0 if the boundary is rough.
(b) That the boundary is indeed rough.

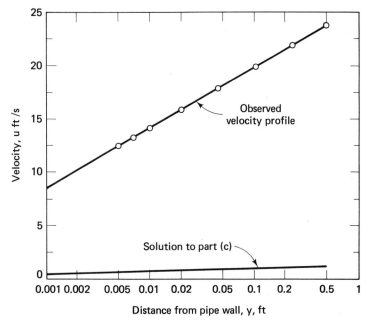

Fig. 8-8. Turbulent velocity profiles.

(c) The velocity distribution corresponding to the maximum flow rate for which this same pipe would be considered smooth.
(d) The velocity at the centerline and at $y = 0.1$ ft for both profiles.

SOLUTION:

(a) The equation for the measured velocity distribution Fig. 8-8 is found to be

$$u = 5.71 \log_{10} y + 25.53$$

Assuming that this represents flow over a rough boundary, for which Eq. 8-19 is appropriate, we may write

$$\frac{u}{u_*} = 5.75 \log_{10} \left(\frac{y}{0.001}\right) + 8.5$$

By comparison with the equation determined from the data of Fig. 8-8, we get

$$u_* = 0.992 \text{ ft/s}$$

Then from $\tau_0/\rho = u_*^2$,

$$\tau_0 = (0.992 \text{ ft/s})^2(1.94 \text{ slugs/ft}^3) = 1.91 \text{ lb/ft}^2$$

(b) Evaluating the shear velocity/roughness Reynolds number,

$$\frac{u_* k}{\nu} = \frac{(0.992)(10^{-3})}{10^{-5}} = 99.2 > 70$$

Thus, for this flow the boundary is hydraulically rough and the use of Eq. 8-19 was justified.
(c) The condition for which the boundary just becomes hydraulically smooth occurs when

$$\frac{u_* k}{\nu} = 5$$

Hence

$$u_* = \frac{(5)(10^{-5})}{10^{-3}} = 5 \times 10^{-2} \text{ ft/s}$$

Equation 8-12 now applies and

$$\frac{u}{5 \times 10^{-2}} = 5.75 \log_{10} \frac{(5 \times 10^{-2})y}{10^{-5}} + 5.5$$

or

$$u = 0.288 \log_{10} y + 1.338$$

This curve is plotted on Fig. 8-8 for comparison.
(d) To get the point velocities, the appropriate y values must be substituted into the velocity equations of parts (a) and (d). For the centerline $y = 0.5$ ft and hence

$$u_{\text{rough}} = 23.8 \text{ ft/s} \qquad u_{\text{smooth}} = 1.25 \text{ ft/s}$$

At $y = 0.1$ ft (at 0.4 ft from the centerline),

$$u_{\text{rough}} = 19.8 \text{ ft/s} \qquad u_{\text{smooth}} = 1.05 \text{ ft/s}$$

Compare with the graphed values.

8–3 RESISTANCE TO FLOW

The preceding section dealt basically with velocity profiles, with little mention of resistance or friction. However, the form of the equations and the experimental coefficients are due to the resistance that the flow must overcome. This section will first develop a resistance equation for steady, uniform pipe flow. (The equation will ultimately be applied more generally to other types of steady, uniform flows.) Through use of this equation the velocity equations of Section 8-2 will be converted to resistance equations.

Dimensional Analysis of the Resistance Problem

It is instructive to approach the resistance to flow from dimensional considerations, even though alternative derivations are available. The concept of resistance (in either laminar or turbulent flow) was responsible for the equilibrium equation (Eq. 7-5) developed previously, and we could use this equation as a starting point. We will return to Eq. 7-5 presently, but we will now proceed with a dimensional analysis of the resistance problem. For the present the flow may again be either laminar or turbulent. Taking the pressure gradient required to overcome viscous effects as the dependent variable, it may be expressed as a function of the independent parameters as follows:

$$\frac{dp}{dx} = \phi(D, k, V, \rho, \mu) \tag{8-22}$$

Here V is the average velocity, D the pipe diameter, and k the roughness.

The best choice of repeating variables is D, V, and ρ, and three pi terms may be expected. Evaluating the first,

$$\pi_1 = \left(\frac{dp}{dx}\right)^1 D^x V^y \rho^z$$

$$F^\circ L^\circ T^\circ = (FL^{-3})^1 (L)^x (LT^{-1})^y (FT^2 L^{-4})^z$$

from which

$$F: \quad 0 = 1 + z$$

$$T: \quad 0 = -y + 2z$$

$$L: \quad 0 = -3 + x + y - 4z$$

and immediately

$$z = -1, \qquad y = -2, \qquad \text{and} \qquad x = 1$$

or

$$\pi_1 = \frac{(dp/dx)D}{\rho V^2}$$

245

Repeating the process (or by inspection)

$$\pi_2 = \frac{k}{D} \quad \text{and} \quad \pi_3 = \frac{VD\rho}{\mu} = \text{Re}$$

Thus,

$$\frac{dp}{dx} = \frac{1}{D}\frac{\rho V^2}{2}f\left(\frac{k}{D}, \text{Re}\right)$$

where a 2 has been arbitrarily inserted on the right-hand side to create the more conventional term $\rho V^2/2$, which is also the dynamic pressure of the flow. Realizing that the pressure drop must vary linearly with pipe length and considering the functional relation indicated by f to be a resistance coefficient, this may be rewritten

$$\Delta p = f\frac{L}{D}\frac{\rho V^2}{2} \tag{8-23a}$$

where

$$f = f\left(\frac{k}{D}, \text{Re}\right) \tag{8-23b}$$

More frequently, it will be a loss in head rather than pressure drop which is of interest. Dividing through by γ will give the head loss due to friction,

$$h_\ell = f\frac{L}{D}\frac{V^2}{2g} \tag{8-24}$$

This equation, known as the *Darcy–Weisbach equation*, will be applied to the solution of engineering problems in the following section. It provides a means of evaluating the head loss due to frictional effects, but there still remains the necessary task of relating the resistance coefficient f to the Reynolds number and the relative roughness k/D. This will be done at the end of the section. The results are given on Fig. 8-12.

If the foregoing relationship involving the pressure gradient is substituted into Eq. 7-5, we get

$$\tau_0 = -\frac{r_0}{2}\left(\frac{1}{D}\frac{\rho V^2}{2}f\right)$$

which simplifies to

$$\frac{\tau_0}{\rho} = \frac{f}{8}V^2 \tag{8-25}$$

or

$$u_* = V\sqrt{\frac{f}{8}} \tag{8-26}$$

This equation will eventually provide a means of evaluating the shear stress.

Resistance Equations

The velocity profiles can be integrated over the pipe cross-sectional area to get the flow rate and average velocity. This perforce must introduce a small error, since the logarithmic equations break down at the wall and further do

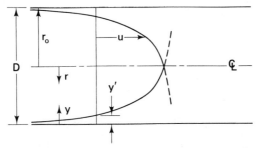

Fig. 8-9. Sketch for development of resistance equations.

not give a zero slope at the centerline, as can be seen in Fig. 8-9. Continuing, for a smooth pipe with the velocity v given by Eq. 8-12 (v has been substituted for u to be more consistent with the polar cylindrical coordinate system of Fig. 8-9),

$$Q = \int_0^{r_0} v(2\pi r)\, dr$$

$$= \int_0^{r_0} u_* 2\pi r \left[5.75 \log_{10}\left(\frac{u_*(r_0 - r)}{v}\right) + 5.5 \right] dr$$

$$= \pi r_0^2 u_* \left[5.75 \log_{10}\left(\frac{u_* r_0}{v}\right) + 1.75 \right]$$

Dividing through by the area πr_0^2 gives the average velocity,

$$V = u_* \left[5.75 \log_{10}\left(\frac{u_* r_0}{v}\right) + 1.75 \right] \tag{8-27}$$

Repeating with the rough boundary equation (Eq. 8-19) gives

$$V = u_* \left[5.75 \log_{10}\left(\frac{r_0}{k}\right) + 4.75 \right] \tag{8-28}$$

If the average velocity equations are now subtracted from the respective velocity profiles (i.e., Eq. 8-27 from Eq. 8-12 and Eq. 8-28 from Eq. 8-19), we get in either case the identical equation,

$$\frac{v - V}{u_*} = 5.75 \log_{10}\left(\frac{y}{r_0}\right) + 3.75$$

which upon introduction of Eq. 8-26 becomes

$$\frac{v - V}{V\sqrt{f}} = 2 \log_{10}\left(\frac{y}{r_0}\right) + 1.32$$

This gives the velocity distribution, as referenced to the average velocity, as a function of the resistance coefficient only. Because of the approximations that have been made, the equation deviates slightly from experimental data.

Correcting the equation so as to better agree with measurements, it becomes

$$\frac{v - V}{V\sqrt{f}} = 2.15 \log_{10}\left(\frac{y}{r_0}\right) + 1.43 \tag{8-29}$$

Upon setting $y = r_0$, the centerline or maximum velocity is given as

$$\frac{v_{max}}{V} = 1.43\sqrt{f} + 1 \tag{8-30}$$

The foregoing equations all relate the resistance coefficient to characteristics of the velocity distribution. It now remains to go one step further and derive equations that more directly yield the resistance coefficient. For smooth boundaries, this can be attained by substitution of Eq. 8-26 into Eq. 8-27. This gives

$$V = V\sqrt{\frac{f}{8}}\left[5.75 \log_{10}\left(\frac{V\sqrt{f/8}\,r_0}{\nu}\right) + 1.75\right]$$

Upon replacing r_0 by $D/2$ and combining the numerical values, there results

$$\frac{1}{\sqrt{f}} = 2.03 \log_{10}\left(\frac{VD}{\nu}\sqrt{f}\right) - 0.91$$

Again the numerical values require some correction, whereupon

$$\frac{1}{\sqrt{f}} = 2 \log_{10}(\text{Re}\sqrt{f}) - 0.8 \tag{8-31}$$

This equation is known as the *von Kármán–Prandtl resistance equation* for pipe flow over a hydraulically smooth boundary. Although hard to apply because of the inconvenient placing of f, we will see that it plays an important role in the general resistance scheme. If Eq. 8-26 is now substituted into Eq. 8-28, rearranged, and numerical values slightly altered to better fit measurements, there results the corresponding von Kármán–Prandtl resistance equation for turbulent pipe flow over rough boundaries,

$$\frac{1}{\sqrt{f}} = 2 \log_{10}\left(\frac{r_0}{k}\right) + 1.74 \tag{8-32}$$

It is apparent that for smooth boundaries the resistance coefficient is dependent only on the Reynolds number, and for rough boundaries it is solely dependent on the relative roughness. For the transition region it clearly must be dependent upon both parameters. This is completely consistent with the results of the dimensional considerations given in Eq. 8-23b.

If we again make use of Eq. 8-26, this time by substituting into the ratio of δ'/r_0 as given by Eq. 8-14, we get

$$\frac{\delta'}{r_0} = \frac{11.6\nu}{u_* r_0} = \frac{65.6}{\text{Re}\sqrt{f}}$$

Thus, the ratio k/δ', which earlier was found proportional to u_*k/v, subsequently used as the abscissa of Fig. 8-7, is also proportional to $\mathrm{Re}\sqrt{f}/(r_0/k)$. Since the ordinate of Fig. 8-7 [from the von Kármán–Prandtl equation (Eq. 8-19) for flow over a rough boundary] is directly related to the corresponding von Kármán–Prandtl resistance equation (Eq. 8-32), the curve may also be considered an universal resistance equation. Figure 8-7 is redrawn as Fig. 8-10 with both sets of axes included.

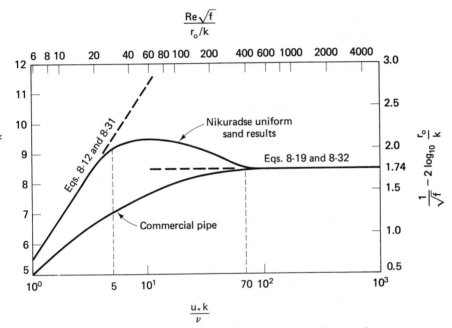

Fig. 8-10. Universal velocity profile and resistance diagram for smooth and rough pipes.

The experimental curve shown in Figs. 8-7 and 8-10 was due to the artificial, uniform sand roughness used by Nikuradse. Commercial pipes have been found not to follow the universal curve in the transition, but rather to scatter about the lower curve shown. This is due to the tendency for the commercial roughness to be somewhat nonuniform and the few larger roughness elements to trigger roughness characteristics in the transition range which are out of proportion to the "average" roughness of the pipe. Colebrook[5]

[5]C. F. Colebrook, "Turbulent Flow in Pipes, with Particular Reference to the Transition Region Between the Smooth and Rough Pipe Laws," *J. Inst. Civil Engrs., London*, February 1939.

has found that the equation

$$\frac{1}{\sqrt{f}} - 2 \log_{10}\left(\frac{r_0}{k}\right) = 1.74 - 2 \log_{10}\left(1 + \frac{18.7 r_0/k}{\text{Re}\sqrt{f}}\right) \qquad (8\text{-}33)$$

does a generally adequate job of representing the commercial pipe data. The values of k, incidentally, are obtained for commercial pipes by experimentally determining the head loss and then through the Darcy–Weisbach equation calculating the resistance coefficient. For those values corresponding to a rough boundary, a value of k can then be obtained from Eq. 8-32. These k values, a measure of the absolute roughness of commercial pipes, indicate fully rough characteristics identical to uniform sand of diameter k. Hence, the values of k for commercial pipes are known as the *equivalent sand grain roughness*. Values for different types of pipe material are given in Table 8-1.

Table 8-1   Absolute Boundary Roughness, k

Material	k (ft)
Corrugated metal pipe	0.1–0.2
Riveted steel	0.003–0.03
Concrete	0.001–0.01
Wood stave	0.0006–0.003
Cast iron	0.00085
Galvanized iron	0.0005
Asphalted cast iron	0.0004
Commercial steel, wrought iron	0.00015
Drawn tubing	0.000005

Although the curves of Fig. 8-10 represent universal functions, an additional representation on the basis of Eq. 8-23b, using the relative roughness and Reynolds number as parameters, makes for more convenient application. Figure 8-11, again based on the original Nikuradse uniform sand data, expresses this functional form over a wide range of parameters. Note that the previous resistance equations are manifest when displayed in this form. Below a Reynolds number of 2000, the combining of the Poiseuille flow equation (Eq. 7-22) with the Darcy–Weisbach equation (Eq. 8-24) gives

$$\frac{32\nu VL}{gD^2} = f\frac{L}{D}\frac{V^2}{2g}$$

or

$$f = \frac{64}{\text{Re}} \qquad (8\text{-}34)$$

This is indicated on the laminar range of Fig. 8-11. The smooth boundary turbulent flow follows Eq. 8-31. However, in the moderate Reynolds range from 4000 to 100,000, the flow has been found to fit slightly better a simpler

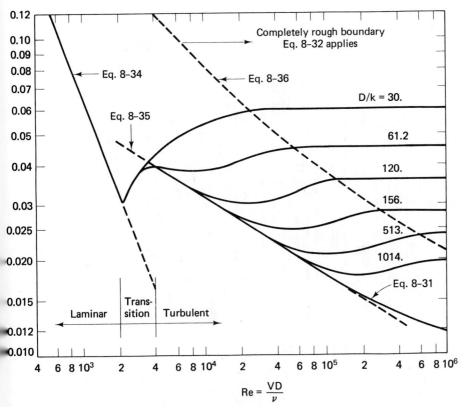

Fig. 8-11.   Resistance coefficient for smooth and uniformly roughened pipes.

empirical relation developed by Blasius,

$$f = \frac{0.316}{Re^{1/4}} \tag{8-35}$$

To the right of the slashed line indicating the lower limit of hydraulically rough boundaries and given by the approximately equivalent expressions

$$\frac{u_* k}{\nu} = 70 \tag{8-36a}$$

or

$$\frac{Re \sqrt{f}}{D/k} = 200 \tag{8-36b}$$

from Fig. 8-10, the flow passes over a fully rough boundary, which may be expressed by Eq. 8-32.

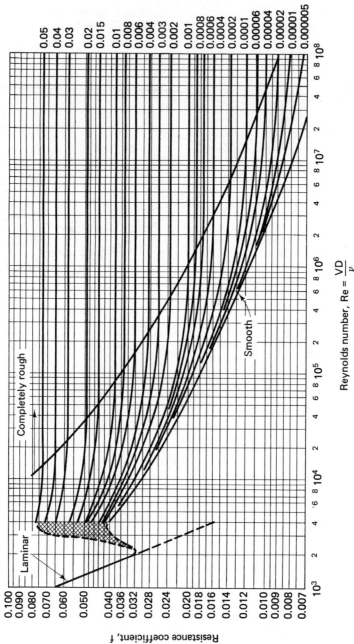

Relative roughness, k/D

Reynolds number, $Re = \dfrac{VD}{\nu}$

Resistance coefficient, f

Completely rough

Laminar

Smooth

Fig. 8-12. Moody resistance diagram for Darcy–Weisbach equation.

A similar approach by Moody,[6] involving commercial pipes and the appropriate curve in the transition region of Fig. 8-10, leads to Fig. 8-12, known as the *Moody resistance diagram*. The next section will be devoted to the solution of engineering problems involving the Moody diagram and pipe friction.

EXAMPLE 8-4

A discharge of 11 ℓ/s is passed through a set of 6-cm-diameter pipes of different roughnesses. As the equivalent sand grain roughness k varies from smooth to 0.01 ft in the 6-cm-diameter pipes, what is the corresponding range of the centerline or maximum velocity? The fluid has kinematic viscosity of 10^{-5} m²/s.

SOLUTION:

The velocity is

$$V = \frac{Q}{A} = \frac{(11 \ \ell/\text{s})(0.001 \ \text{m}^3/\ell)}{(\pi/4)(0.06 \ \text{m})^2} = 3.89 \ \text{m/s}$$

and the Reynolds number accordingly is

$$\text{Re} = \frac{VD}{\nu} = \frac{(3.89 \ \text{m/s})(0.06 \ \text{m})}{10^{-5} \ \text{m}^2/\text{s}} = 2.33 \times 10^4$$

Using Fig. 8-12, the resistance coefficient for a smooth pipe is $f = 0.024$.
    The roughest pipe, with $k = 0.01$ ft $= 0.00305$ m, and relative roughness

$$\frac{k}{D} = \frac{0.00305}{0.06} = 5.08 \times 10^{-2}$$

has a resistance coefficient $f = 0.072$ (by Fig. 8-12 or Eq. 8-32). The centerline velocity is given by Eq. 8-30. For the smooth pipe

$$\begin{aligned}
v_{\text{max}} &= V(1.43\sqrt{f} + 1) \\
&= (3.89 \ \text{m/s})[(1.43)(0.024)^{1/2} + 1] \\
&= 4.75 \ \text{m/s}
\end{aligned}$$

and for the roughest pipe

$$\begin{aligned}
v_{\text{max}} &= (3.89)[(1.43)(0.072)^{1/2} + 1] \\
&= 5.38 \ \text{m/s}
\end{aligned}$$

8–4 APPLICATIONS OF THE DARCY– WEISBACH EQUATION

As we have seen in the development in the preceding section, the head loss over a length of pipe is given by the Darcy–Weisbach equation. The resistance coefficient f contained therein is, in general, a function of the Reynolds number and relative roughness. Although a number of equations are available, this function is best summarized in the Moody diagram (Fig. 8-12). The absolute roughness, in turn, is obtained from Table 8-1.

[6]L. F. Moody, "Friction Factors for Pipe Flow," *Trans. ASME*, Vol. 66 (1944).

Pipe Problems

In engineering problems involving pipe friction, the variables of concern to the engineer will generally be those included in Eqs. 8-22 through 8-24. Although pressure drops (or sometimes pressure gradients) are of equal interest, particularly in connection with air flows, we will presently set up problems in terms of the head loss and use the Darcy–Weisbach equation, as given by Eq. 8-24. The conversion from head to pressure is easily accomplished when desired, since the product of friction head loss times specific weight gives the pressure drop due to fluid resistance. Other quantities, such as power requirements, can be calculated from these variables as needed. In any given problem it is possible that any of the variables $h_\ell, f, L, D, k, V, Q, \rho$, or ν might be requested. However, most problems can be classified into one of three types.

The first and simplest is the determination of head loss when the type of fluid, the discharge, and the pipe material, diameter, and length are given. For the pipe material specified, Table 8-1 gives the absolute roughness k, and the relative roughness k/D is easily determined. Although Q is usually specified rather than V, the average velocity and then the Reynolds number may also be calculated. The resistance coefficient f can next be read directly from Fig. 8-12, based on the relative roughness and Reynolds number, and finally the head loss calculated.

A second common type of problem arises when the head loss is specified along with the fluid and the pipe material, length, and diameter; and the discharge is required. Hence, the average velocity is unknown and neither the resistance coefficient nor the Reynolds number can be directly calculated. A trial-and-error solution is necessary, but note that the relative roughness curves of Fig. 8-12 are generally quite flat. Therefore, Fig. 8-12 may be entered with the known k/D value and the range of possible f values will be greatly restricted. For water flows or large diameters, read straight across horizontally (i.e., assume that the pipe is completely rough) to get a trial f value. This permits the calculation of trial values of V and Re so that a new f value can be obtained from Fig. 8-12. If significantly different from the first f, a second iteration involving the new f is required, but the convergence is usually very rapid. For more viscous fluids or small diameters, following the k/D curve back to the lower Reynolds number range will give a slightly higher and hopefully closer starting f value.

The third type to be discussed is the design problem of determining the correct pipe size, when the flow rate and head loss are both given. It is assumed also that the length, pipe material, and the fluid are known. In this case, none of the three parameters of Fig. 8-12 can be calculated and the starting point for a trial-and-error solution is not apparent. Consider the relationship, however, between D and f in the Darcy–Weisbach equation after the discharge has been introduced in place of the velocity.

$$h_\ell = f \frac{L}{D} \frac{V^2}{2g} = f \frac{L}{D} \frac{Q^2}{2g(\pi D^2/4)^2}$$

Rearranging,

$$D = f^{1/5} \left[\frac{8LQ^2}{\pi^2 g h_\ell} \right]^{1/5} \tag{8-37}$$

In the type of problem under examination, the bracketed variables are all given, and D therefore varies as $f^{1/5}$. The advantage of this formulation lies in the realization that the fifth root is not a very sensitive function (i.e., for given changes in f the value of D will change far more slowly). This suggests that the best starting point is to estimate f (usually somewhere in the middle range) and calculate a trial D. Trial values of Re and k/D may be calculated and a new f obtained from Fig. 8-12. This must be repeated to convergence; however, it is again a rapid process.

In all cases the temperature may have to be estimated. Further, the absolute roughness is never known exactly. An average value of k for the particular pipe material will usually suffice. In cases where a maximum or minimum flow is of concern, the appropriate limiting value of roughness should be chosen.

Frequently, the friction loss will be required in a problem involving Eq. 5-41 or other forms of the energy equation. The head loss is due to the dissipation of flow energy, ultimately as heat. It may be included in the energy equation, as was previously done in the development of Eq. 5-40. For values of α equal to unity, Eq. 5-40 becomes

$$\frac{p_1}{\gamma} + y_1 + \frac{V_1^2}{2g} = \frac{p_2}{\gamma} + y_2 + \frac{V_2^2}{2g} + h_\ell \tag{8-38}$$

where h_ℓ represents the head loss due to friction between sections 1 and 2. The pipe system of Fig. 5-19 would be modified as shown in Fig. 8-13 to

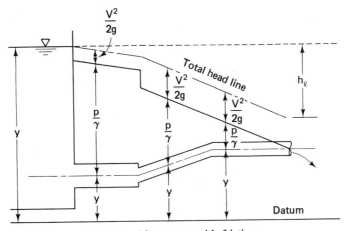

Fig. 8-13. Pipe system with friction.

reflect the friction loss. Note the pressure gradient now required to overcome frictional effects and the greater total head line slope in the smaller pipe, which has the greater rate of friction loss.

EXAMPLE 8-5

Determine the head loss in 5 miles of 12-in. (diameter) commercial steel pipe if 2.5 cfs of gasoline (sp. gr. $= 0.68$) are to be pumped. Consider the answer with respect to a temperature range 32 to 80°F.

SOLUTION:

Take $k = 0.0002$ ft, $v_{32°} = 6.1 \times 10^{-6}$ ft²/s and $v_{80°} = 4.5 \times 10^{-6}$ ft²/s. Then the relative roughness is

$$\frac{k}{D} = \frac{0.0002}{1} = 0.0002$$

and for an average velocity

$$V = \frac{Q}{A} = \frac{2.5}{0.785} = 3.18 \text{ ft/s}$$

the Reynolds numbers are

$$\text{Re}_{32°} = \frac{(3.18)(1)}{6.1 \times 10^{-6}} = 5.21 \times 10^5$$

and

$$\text{Re}_{80°} = \frac{(3.18)(1)}{4.5 \times 10^{-6}} = 7.07 \times 10^5$$

From Fig. 8-12 the corresponding resistance coefficients are

$$f_{32°} = 0.0154 \quad \text{and} \quad f_{80°} = 0.0150$$

(In general, accuracy of neither the Moody diagram nor the known variables warrants expressing f to three significant figures. They are kept here only to demonstrate the minor effect of temperature on head loss.) The desired head loss at the two temperatures is given by Eq. 8-24.

$$h_\ell = \frac{(0.0154)(5280)(5)(3.18)^2}{(1)(64.4)} = 63.8 \text{ ft at } 32°F$$

and

$$h_\ell = \frac{(0.0150)(5280)(5)(3.18)^2}{(1)(64.4)} = 62.2 \text{ ft at } 80°F$$

EXAMPLE 8-6

What diameter of concrete pipe is required to carry 15 cfs of water at 70°F if the head loss must not exceed 4.8 ft/1000 ft of length?

SOLUTION:

To guarantee that flow will not exceed the allowable head loss, take the maximum absolute roughness for concrete, $k = 0.01$ ft. Then, in terms of the discharge, we may write the following equations:

$$\text{Re} = \frac{VD}{v} = \frac{4Q}{\pi Dv} = \frac{(4)(15)}{\pi(1.05 \times 10^{-5})D} = \frac{1.82 \times 10^6}{D}$$

$$D = f^{1/5}\left[\frac{8LQ^2}{\pi^2 gh_\ell}\right]^{1/5} = f^{1/5}\left[\frac{(8)(1000)(15)^2}{\pi^2(32.2)(4.8)}\right]^{1/5} = 4.12\,f^{1/5}$$

(The latter is from Eq. 8-37). Assume $f = 0.025$ as a trial value. Then $D = (4.12)(0.025)^{1/5} = 1.97$ ft. For this value of D,

$$\frac{k}{D} = \frac{0.01}{1.97} = 0.0051$$

and

$$\text{Re} = \frac{1.82 \times 10^6}{1.97} = 9.24 \times 10^5$$

From Fig. 8-12, the corresponding value of f is

$$f = 0.030$$

Since this value is in the fully rough range, it will undoubtedly be correct. Continuing, so as to verify this f value, new values are

$$D = (4.12)(0.030)^{1/5} = 2.04 \text{ ft}$$

$$\frac{k}{D} = \frac{0.01}{2.04} = 0.0049$$

and

$$\text{Re} = \frac{1.82 \times 10^6}{2.04} = 8.91 \times 10^5$$

Comparing with Fig. 8-12 this verifies the f value of 0.030. Thus, the necessary size is 2.04 ft. Since this is just over the standard 2-ft pipe size, it would be better to ensure that some care is taken to control the roughness rather than going to the more expensive, larger size.

EXAMPLE 8-7

A 6-cm pipe carries 20°C water at the rate of 12 ℓ/s. If the pressure drop over a 50-m length is 142 kN/m², what is the absolute roughness of the pipe?

SOLUTION:

The average velocity and Reynolds number are

$$V = \frac{Q}{A} = \frac{(12 \,\ell/\text{s})(0.001 \text{ m}^3/\ell)}{(\pi/4)(0.06)^2} = 4.24 \text{ m/s}$$

and

$$\text{Re} = \frac{VD}{v} = \frac{(4.24 \text{ m/s})(0.06 \text{ m})}{1.007 \times 10^{-6} \text{ m}^2/\text{s}} = 2.53 \times 10^5$$

Since a pressure drop is specified, Eq. 8-23a may be applied to solve for f:

$$\Delta p = f\frac{L}{D}\frac{\rho V^2}{2}$$

$$1.42 \times 10^5 \text{ N/m}^2 = \frac{(f)(50 \text{ m})(998.2 \text{ kg/m}^3)(4.24 \text{ m/s})^2}{(0.06 \text{ m})(2)}$$

or

$$f = 0.019$$

Figure 8-12 may now be used to obtain the relative roughness. For Re $= 2.53 \times 10^5$ and $f = 0.019$, the chart gives $k/D = 0.0006$, or

$$k = (0.0006)(0.06) = 3.6 \times 10^{-5} \text{ m} = 1.2 \times 10^{-4} \text{ ft}$$

Pipe Systems

Pipes arranged in series (i.e., sequentially) were briefly considered in conjunction with Fig. 8-13. With reference to that figure, Eq. 8-38 may be applied directly, bearing in mind that the head loss due to friction will require a separate formulation for each size or type of pipe. Thus, the Darcy–Weisbach equation can be used for each section, with the overall head loss being given by the sum of the head losses in each section.

It is sometimes convenient for calculation purposes to replace a number of pipes which are in series by a single pipe of some constant diameter and roughness. This requires that values of diameter, length, and resistance coefficient be chosen for the equivalent pipe so that it will have the same head loss as does the original system for a given discharge. The resulting equivalent pipe will be valid over a range of discharges provided that the resistance coefficient does not change significantly.

EXAMPLE 8-8

Determine what diameter pipe with $f = 0.20$, and length equal to that of the overall system, would be equivalent to the following series of pipe:

$$\text{Pipe (a):} \quad D = 6 \text{ cm} \quad L = 500 \text{ m} \quad k = 1.5 \times 10^{-4} \text{ m}$$
$$\text{Pipe (b):} \quad D = 8 \text{ cm} \quad L = 700 \text{ m} \quad k = 1.5 \times 10^{-4} \text{ m}$$
$$\text{Pipe (c):} \quad D = 10 \text{ cm} \quad L = 600 \text{ m} \quad k = 1.5 \times 10^{-4} \text{ m}$$

if the discharge of water (at 20°C) is 700 ℓ/min.

SOLUTION:

$$Q = (700 \ \ell/\text{min})(0.001 \text{ m}^3/\ell)(\tfrac{1}{60} \text{ min/s}) = 0.0117 \text{ m}^3/\text{s}$$

Therefore, the following are calculated:

$$\nu = 1.007 \times 10^{-6} \text{ m}^2/\text{s}, \quad \text{Re} = \frac{VD}{\nu}, \quad V = \frac{Q}{A}, \quad \text{and} \quad h_\ell = f\frac{L}{D}\frac{V^2}{2g}$$

Thus,

Pipe	V (m/s)	Re	k/D	f (from Fig. 8-12)	h_ℓ (m)
(a)	4.13	2.45×10^5	2.5×10^{-3}	0.025	181
(b)	2.32	1.84×10^5	1.9×10^{-3}	0.024	57.6
(c)	1.49	1.48×10^5	1.5×10^{-3}	0.023	15.6
					$\Sigma = 254$

Also, $\Sigma L = 1800$ m.

The equivalent pipe may be found from

$$h_\ell = f \frac{L}{D} \frac{V^2}{2g} = f \frac{L}{D^5} \frac{Q^2}{2g(\pi/4)^2}$$

or

$$254 = \frac{(0.020)(1800)(0.0117)^2}{D^5(2)(9.81)(\pi/4)^2}$$

Solving yields

$$D = 0.069 \text{ m}$$

Thus, a pipe with $D = 6.9$ cm and length of 1800 m will be equivalent to the three original pipes.

Two or more pipes may be connected in parallel as shown in Fig. 8.14. The regions upstream of A and downstream of B are connected in series with

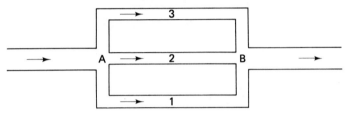

Fig. 8-14. Parallel pipe system.

the parallel pipe system. Ignoring those portions for the present, note first that the discharge arriving at point A, say Q, must be distributed among the various branches. Thus, continuity requires that

$$Q = Q_1 + Q_2 + Q_3 \tag{8-39}$$

The second important point is that all branches leading from A have the same piezometric head, namely h_A, and when they rejoin at B they must again have a common piezometric head, h_B. Consequently, the head loss must be the same in each branch,

$$h_{\ell_1} = h_{\ell_2} = h_{\ell_3} \tag{8-40}$$

If the piezometric head at points A and B is known, the discharge in each branch may be calculated as if the branch were a single line, and the total discharge obtained by summing. Trial and error will be required only to the extent that the resistance coefficient is unknown and trial values have to be assumed.

If, instead, the discharge Q is given, both head loss and flow distribution are unknown and the problem is more difficult. In the case of three parallel pipes,[7] we may write

$$f_1 \frac{L_1}{D_1^5} \frac{Q_1^2}{2g} \left(\frac{4}{\pi}\right)^2 = f_2 \frac{L_2}{D_2^5} \frac{Q_2^2}{2g} \left(\frac{4}{\pi}\right)^2 = f_3 \frac{L_3}{D_3^5} \frac{Q_3^2}{2g} \left(\frac{4}{\pi}\right)^2$$

[7] Although only three branches are chosen here, the equations may be generalized for any number.

and assuming that lengths and diameters are known, this may be rewritten as

$$C_1 f_1 Q_1^2 = C_2 f_2 Q_2^2 = C_3 f_3 Q_3^2 \qquad (8\text{-}41)$$

where $C_i = L_i / D_i^5$. The discharge through each branch may now be determined by simultaneously solving Eqs. 8-39 and 8-41. Since the values of f are unknown, highest accuracy requires that f values are first assumed and then the solution repeated until the discharge in each pipe verifies the correctness of the f values. Usually, however, the uncertainties surrounding an engineering problem of this type do not justify this accuracy and a more rapid solution using nonchanging f values is often preferred.

Again, for computational purposes an equivalent pipe may be substituted for a number of pipes in parallel. The Darcy–Weisbach equation,

$$h_l = f \frac{L}{D} \frac{V^2}{2g} = \frac{fL}{D^5} \frac{Q^2}{2g} \left(\frac{4}{\pi} \right)^2$$

arranges to

$$Q = \left(\frac{h_l 2 g \pi^2}{16} \right)^{1/2} \left(\frac{D^5}{fL} \right)^{1/2}$$

Therefore, for three parallel pipes, Eq. 8-39 yields

$$Q = Q_1 + Q_2 + Q_3$$
$$= \left(\frac{h_l 2 g \pi^2}{16} \right)^{1/2} \left[\left(\frac{D_1^5}{f_1 L_1} \right)^{1/2} + \left(\frac{D_2^5}{f_2 L_2} \right)^{1/2} + \left(\frac{D_3^5}{f_3 L_3} \right)^{1/2} \right]$$
$$= \left(\frac{h_l 2 g \pi^2}{16} \right)^{1/2} \left(\frac{D_e^5}{f_e L_e} \right)^{1/2}$$

where the subscript e indicates equivalent pipe components. Thus, the equivalent pipe may be chosen to satisfy

$$\left(\frac{D_e^5}{f_e L_e} \right)^{1/2} = \left(\frac{D_1^5}{f_1 L_1} \right)^{1/2} + \left(\frac{D_2^5}{f_2 L_2} \right)^{1/2} + \left(\frac{D_3^5}{f_3 L_3} \right)^{1/2} \qquad (8\text{-}42)$$

EXAMPLE 8-9

If the discharge of water through the system of Fig. 8-15 is 2 cfs, what portion of the flow goes through each of the parallel pipes? Assume that the flow is over a fully rough boundary with $k = 0.0008$ ft in each case.

(2) L = 200 ft , D = 1 ft

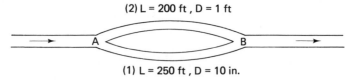

(1) L = 250 ft , D = 10 in.

Fig. 8-15. Parallel pipe system.

SOLUTION:

Since f will not be permitted to vary with Re and the pipe flows are specified as fully rough, we may immediately write

$$\frac{k}{D_1} = \frac{0.0008}{\frac{10}{12}} = 0.00096, \qquad f_1 = 0.020$$

$$\frac{k}{D_2} = \frac{0.0008}{1} = 0.0008, \qquad f_2 = 0.019$$

Also,

$$C_1 = \frac{250}{(\frac{10}{12})^5} = 622$$

$$C_2 = \frac{200}{(1)^5} = 200$$

and therefore

$$(622)(0.020)Q_1^2 = (200)(0.019)Q_2^2$$

From Eq. 8-39,

$$Q = 2 = Q_1 + Q_2$$

Upon solving simultaneously, $Q_1 = 0.71$ cfs, or 36% of the total flow, while $Q_2 = 1.29$ cfs, or 64% of the flow.

Typical of another type of pipe problem is the branching pipe system shown in Fig. 8-16. Whereas there can be no question of the flow direction in

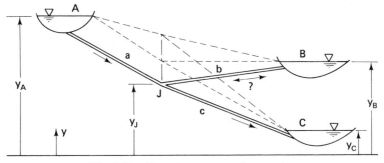

Fig. 8-16.   Three interconnected reservoirs.

lines a and c, the flow may be either into or out of reservoir B. If the piezometric head at the junction J (as indicated by the long dashed lines) lies above the level of reservoir B, flow will be into B. Conversely, flow must be out of reservoir B if the piezometric head at the junction is lower than the free surface at B.

Since the head loss varies as the velocity squared in the Darcy–Weisbach equation, the magnitude of the head loss is not affected by the sign (and therefore direction) of the velocity when calculated by the Darcy–Weisbach equation. Thus, one cannot write an equation in which the sign on the velocity in pipe b will take care of itself. We can approach the problem in the following manner, first noting that the respective f values will usually be held constant, and that the velocity heads will be ignored in the formulation. (What would you use for the velocity head at the junction anyway?) Assume that the piezometric head at the junction equals that at B—an unlikely possibility, but nevertheless a good starting point. (See Fig. 8-16, short dashed lines.) Then there is no flow in line b and $Q_a = Q_c$. Thus,

$$h_J = \frac{p_J}{\gamma} + y_J = y_B$$

Further

$$h_{\ell_a} = y_A - h_J = f_a \frac{L_a}{D_a} \frac{V_a^2}{2g} = f_a \frac{L_a}{D_a^5} \left(\frac{4}{\pi}\right)^2 \frac{Q_a^2}{2g} \qquad (8\text{-}43\text{a})$$

and

$$h_{\ell_c} = h_J - y_C = f_c \frac{L_c}{D_c^5} \left(\frac{4}{\pi}\right)^2 \frac{Q_c^2}{2g} \qquad (8\text{-}43\text{b})$$

Since the elevations of the reservoirs are known, the foregoing equations may be solved for Q_a and Q_c. In the event that $Q_a = Q_c$, the assumption was correct. Otherwise, if $Q_a > Q_c$, the flow must be into B and h_J must lie above Y_B, while $Q_a < Q_c$ indicates that the reverse is true.

At this point a trial-and-error procedure is necessary. If it has been determined that flow is into B, then a new value of h_J is assumed, somewhat higher than Y_B. The headloss equations (Eqs. 8-43a and b), along with

$$h_{\ell_b} = h_J - y_B = f_b \frac{L_b}{D_b^5} \left(\frac{4}{\pi}\right)^2 \frac{Q_b^2}{2g} \qquad (8\text{-}43\text{c})$$

may be solved for their respective discharges. The discharges may then be checked against continuity at the junction:

$$Q_a = Q_b + Q_c \qquad (8\text{-}43\text{d})$$

and new values of h_J assumed until continuity is achieved. Conversely, if flow is out of reservoir B, the head loss equations are Eqs. 8-43a and b, along with

$$h_{\ell_b} = y_B - h_J = f_b \frac{L_b}{D_b^5} \left(\frac{4}{\pi}\right)^2 \frac{Q_b^2}{2g} \qquad (8\text{-}43\text{e})$$

The calculated discharge must now be compared with continuity requirements at the junction in the form of

$$Q_a + Q_b = Q_c \qquad (8\text{-}43\text{f})$$

Many other types of pipe systems can be considered, up to complicated pipe networks such as a city water distribution system. This last type of problem requires an iterative procedure which can best be solved using electronic computers. For moderate-size networks the technique developed by

Hardy Cross[8] minimizes hand calculations. This procedure is fully developed in references listed at the end of the chapter.

Noncircular Cross Sections

Conduits, or even channels of noncircular cross section can be handled by the Darcy–Weisbach equation. However, for shapes differing markedly from circular there is an increasing loss of accuracy. To develop a means of applying Eq. 8-24 it is necessary to repeat the equilibrium analysis that led to Eq. 7-5. Assuming steady uniform flow through the noncircular but constant cross-sectional conduit of Fig. 8-17, the resisting shear stress τ_0 now represents the average shear around the perimeter. The cross-sectional area is A

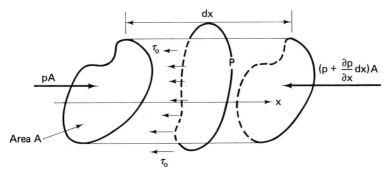

Fig. 8-17.   Definition sketch for shear stress in noncircular cross sections.

and the perimeter or distance around the cross section is P. For equilibrium between pressure and resistance forces,

$$-\frac{dp}{dx} A = \tau_0 P$$

Integrating over a length L, dividing by γ to convert to dimensions of head, and rearranging,

$$\tau_0 = \gamma \frac{h_\ell}{L} \frac{A}{P} = \gamma \frac{h_\ell}{L} R \qquad (8\text{-}44)$$

The ratio of cross-sectional area to perimeter is defined as the hydraulic radius R:

$$R = \frac{A}{P} \qquad (8\text{-}45)$$

For flow with a free surface, Eq. 8-44 will give the average shear stress along that portion of the boundary which is resisting the flow (air drag ignored) if

---

[8] Hardy Cross, "Analysis of Flow in Networks of Conduits and Conductors," *Univ. Illinois Eng. Exp. Sta. Bull. 286*, 1936.

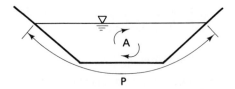

Fig. 8-18. Wetted perimeter and area of trapezoidal open channel.

the appropriate perimeter P (See Fig. 8-18) is chosen, for use in Eqs. 8-44 and 8-45. This length is significantly called the "wetted" perimeter. Further, the channel bottom, water surface, and total head line must all have the same slope in order for an open-channel flow to be uniform. Whereupon, the ratio of headloss to length h_ℓ/L can be replaced by the slope S. If the hydraulic radius for a circular pipe flowing full,

$$R = \frac{A}{P} = \frac{\pi D^2/4}{\pi D} = \frac{D}{4} \tag{8-46}$$

is substituted into Eq. 7-33, we obtain the pipe resistance equation,

$$\tau_0 = \gamma \frac{h_\ell}{L} \frac{D}{4}$$

Note in this equation that the product of head loss and specific weight is equal to the pressure drop, and therefore this equation is identical to the the earlier equation for pipe resistance (Eq. 7-5).

This equivalency obtained by relating pipe diameter to hydraulic radius may be applied to all the parameters associated with Fig. 8-12. Thus, the Darcy–Weisbach equation becomes

$$h_\ell = f \frac{L}{4R} \frac{V^2}{2g} \tag{8-47a}$$

where f is given by Fig. 8-12 as a function of

$$\frac{k}{D} = \frac{k}{4R} \tag{8-47b}$$

and

$$\text{Re} = \frac{4VR}{\nu} \tag{8-47c}$$

This procedure is also applicable in the laminar range, but its accuracy decreases rapidly as the shape becomes less circular. This is not too surprising when you compare this simple procedure with the complex solutions of Chapter 7, such as Eqs. 7-32 and 7-33. In fact, for either turbulent or laminar flow, the use of the hydraulic radius to represent the entire cross section geometry becomes less and less satisfactory as the cross section becomes more angular.

EXAMPLE 8-10

What head loss will occur over a 100-m length as water at 15°C flows through a 1-m-square wooden ($k = 3 \times 10^{-4}$ m) conduit at a discharge of 3.8 m³/s?

SOLUTION:

At 15°C,

$$\nu = 1.141 \times 10^{-6} \text{ m}^2/\text{s}$$

$$V = \frac{Q}{A} = \frac{3.80 \text{ m}^3/\text{s}}{(1 \text{ m})(1 \text{ m})} = 3.8 \text{ m/s}$$

and

$$R = \frac{A}{P} = \frac{1 \text{ m}^2}{4 \text{ m}} = 0.25 \text{ m}$$

Using the relations of Eqs. 8-47,

$$\frac{k}{4R} = \frac{3 \times 10^{-4} \text{ m}}{(4)(0.25 \text{ m})} = 3 \times 10^{-4}$$

$$\text{Re} = \frac{4VR}{\nu} = \frac{(4)(3.8 \text{ m/s})(0.25 \text{ m})}{1.141 \times 10^{-6} \text{ m}^2/\text{s}} = 3.33 \times 10^6$$

From Fig. 8-12, $f = 0.015$, so

$$h_\ell = f \frac{L}{4R} \frac{V^2}{2g}$$

$$= \frac{(0.015)(100 \text{ m})(3.8 \text{ m/s})^2}{(4)(0.25 \text{ m})(2)(9.81 \text{ m/s}^2)} = 1.10 \text{ m}$$

EXAMPLE 8-11

A trapezoidal channel, Fig. 8-19, is to have a depth $y = 1$ m, a bottom width $b = 3$ m, and side slopes of 2 on 1. The water discharge is 10 m³/s and $\nu = 10^{-6}$ m²/s.

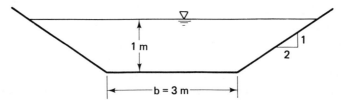

Fig. 8-19. Trapezoidal channel for Example 8-11.

What is the minimum roughness height k for which the flow will be fully rough? What are the corresponding channel slope and average boundary shear stress?

SOLUTION:

For the given discharge,

$$V = \frac{Q}{A} = \frac{10 \text{ m}^3/\text{s}}{(3 \text{ m})(1 \text{ m}) + (1 \text{ m})(2 \text{ m})} = 2 \text{ m/s}$$

$$R = \frac{A}{P} = \frac{(3 \text{ m})(1 \text{ m}) + (1 \text{ m})(2 \text{ m})}{(3 \text{ m}) + 2\sqrt{(1 \text{ m})^2 + (2 \text{ m})^2}} = 0.669 \text{ m}$$

and

$$\text{Re} = \frac{4VR}{\nu} = \frac{(4)(2 \text{ m/s})(0.669 \text{ m})}{10^{-6} \text{ m}^2/\text{s}} = 5.36 \times 10^6$$

Entering Fig. 8-12 with the value of Re given above and reading vertically up to the first k/D curve, which is "completely rough," the relative roughness is found to be 0.00025 and the minimum absolute roughness is therefore obtained from

$$\frac{k}{4R} = \frac{k}{(4)(0.669)} = 0.00025$$

Solving for the absolute roughness,

$$k = 6.69 \times 10^{-4} \text{ m} = 0.67 \text{ mm}$$

Corresponding to the foregoing relative roughness, $f = 0.014$ in Fig. 8-12, whereby Eq. 8-47a gives

$$\frac{h_\ell}{L} = S = \frac{f}{4R}\frac{V^2}{2g} = \frac{(0.014)(2)^2}{(4)(0.669)(2)(9.81)} = 1.07 \times 10^{-3}$$

Thus, for an absolute roughness of 0.67 mm, the channel must have a slope $S = 1.07 \times 10^{-3}$. From Eq. 8-44 the average shear stress is

$$\tau_0 = \gamma RS = (9800 \text{ N/m}^3)(0.669 \text{ m})(1.07 \times 10^{-3}) = 7.02 \text{ N/m}^2$$

8–5 EMPIRICAL RESISTANCE EQUATIONS

The most purely empirical equation in common use for pipe flow is that of Hazen and Williams, which in simplest form becomes

$$V = 1.32C_H R^{0.63} S^{0.54} \tag{8-48}$$

Here C_H is a discharge coefficient (the reciprocal of a resistance coefficient) for which a few values are given in Table 8-2, R is the hydraulic radius, and S is the slope of the total head line (or h_ℓ/L). Although only applicable to water flows, it has been well verified over a wide range of pipe sizes. Hazen and Williams have presented extensive tables permitting rapid, direct solutions, and this has led to wide use of this equation in the fields of water supply and sewage disposal. The Hazen–Williams equation ignores viscous effects (which corresponds to the assumption of fully rough flow), which is an advantage in terms of ease of application, but it may under certain conditions cause significant errors.

Table 8-2 Hazen–Williams Coefficient for Pipes, C_H

Pipe Description	C_H
Extremely smooth and straight	140
Very smooth	130
Smooth wood or masonry	120
Vitrified clay or new riveted steel	110
Ordinary brick or old cast iron	100
Old riveted steel	95
Old pipes in bad condition	60–80

The next relationship is not entirely empirical, since it comes rather logically from the Darcy–Weisbach equation. Substituting S for the head loss per unit length and solving for V, Eq. 8-47a becomes

$$V = \sqrt{\frac{8g}{f}}\sqrt{RS}$$

Replacing the first radical by a coefficient C, we get the *Chezy equation*,

$$V = C\sqrt{RS} \tag{8-49}$$

This equation is more often applied to open-channel flow than conduit flow. The value of the Chezy C can be obtained directly from the two foregoing equations which give C as a function of f, namely,

$$C = \sqrt{\frac{8g}{f}} \tag{8-50}$$

The value of C can also be obtained from Eq. 8-53, to be introduced shortly. Noting that the Chezy C has dimensions of $g^{1/2}$, a dimensionless constant $C' = C/\sqrt{g}$ is sometimes introduced such that

$$V = C'\sqrt{gRS} \tag{8-51}$$

A final empirical equation known as the *Manning equation* is currently the most common resistance equation used in the analysis of open-channel flows. It also finds some use in conduit problems. It essentially assumes that the Chezy C is proportional to $R^{1/6}$ rather than a pure constant, and introduces a resistance coefficient rather than a discharge coefficient. The Manning equation originally presented in the metric system was as follows:

$$V = \frac{1}{n}R^{2/3}S^{1/2} \tag{8-52a}$$

When the equation was converted to English units it was felt desirable to keep the magnitude of the roughness coefficient n values unchanged. Thus, it now appears as

$$V = \frac{1.49}{n}R^{2/3}S^{1/2} \tag{8-52b}$$

Here V, R, and S are again the average velocity, hydraulic radius, and slope and the additional variable known as the Manning n is given in Table 8-3. The Manning n has dimensions of length to the one-sixth power and the constant 1.49 consequently has dimensions of $g^{1/2}$. Being dimensional in form, it is applicable only to water flows. By comparison with the Chezy equation,

$$C = \frac{1.49}{n}R^{1/6} \tag{8-53}$$

and when further compared with Eq. 8-50,

$$\frac{1}{\sqrt{f}} = \frac{1.49}{\sqrt{8g}}\frac{R^{1/6}}{n} \tag{8-54}$$

Table 8-3   Manning *n*

Boundary Surface	Manning n
Very smooth surface (glass, plastic, machined metal)	0.010
Planed timber	0.011
Unplaned wood	0.012–0.015
Smooth concrete	0.012–0.013
Unfinished concrete	0.013–0.016
Brickwork	0.014
Vitrified clay	0.015
Rubble masonry	0.017
Earth channels smooth, no weeds	0.020
Firm gravel	0.020
Earth channels with some stones and weeds	0.025
Earth channels in bad condition, winding natural streams	0.035
Mountain streams	0.040–0.050
Sand channels (with flat bed) (d = mean grain diameter, ft)	$0.034d^{1/6}$

All of the foregoing resistance equations involve either slope S or the head loss per unit length h_ℓ/L. For conduits flowing full, this refers to the slope of the total head line. For open channels or conduits flowing partly full, so that there is a free surface, the slope will be the channel or conduit slope if the flow is uniform. Under the conditions of uniform flow this will also equal the water surface slope. If, on the other hand, the flow is nonuniform the slope must be interpreted as the gradient of the total head line.

In an open channel the depth is usually defined as the vertical distance from the water surface to the lowest point of the channel cross section. If the flow is uniform, the corresponding depth is known as the normal depth. The Manning equation is usually used to calculate this depth. The trial-and-error procedure is illustrated in the following example.

EXAMPLE 8-12

A trapezoidal channel that was cut through bare earth has side slopes of 2 on 1 and a bottom width of 8 ft (see Fig. 8-20). If the channel slope is 0.001 and the flow rate is 340 cfs, determine the normal depth, y_n.

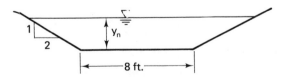

Fig. 8-20.   Trapezoidal channel.

SOLUTION:

Assuming that $n = 0.025$, the Manning equation (Eq. 8-52b) may be written in terms of the discharge as

$$Q = AV = \frac{1.49}{n} AR^{2/3} S^{1/2} = \frac{1.49}{n} \frac{A^{5/3}}{P^{2/3}} S^{1/2}$$

where for the trapezoid

$$A = 8y_n + 2y_n^2$$

and

$$P = 8 + 2\sqrt{y_n^2 + 2^2 y_n^2}$$
$$= 8 + 2y_n\sqrt{5}$$

Separating the known from the unknown quantities and substituting,

$$\frac{Qn}{1.49 S^{1/2}} = \frac{(340)(0.025)}{(1.49)(0.001)^{1/2}} = \frac{(8y_n + 2y_n^2)^{5/3}}{(8 + 2y_n\sqrt{5})^{2/3}}$$

Solving by trial and error, the normal depth is

$$y_n = 4.93 \text{ ft}$$

For comparison, the hydraulic radius is 2.93 ft.

EXAMPLE 8-13

Plot values of Chezy C versus depth for Example 8-12.

SOLUTION:

The Chezy C is related to the Manning n by Eq. 8-53. Assuming that the Manning n value is a constant $n = 0.025$ (from Example 8-12), typical values may be determined thus:

$$C = \frac{1.49}{n} R^{1/6} = \frac{1.49 R^{1/6}}{0.025} = 59.6 R^{1/6}$$

R	1	2	3	4	5	6	7
C	59.6	66.9	71.6	75.1	77.9	80.3	82.4

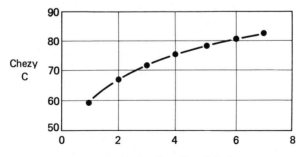

Fig. 8-21. Chezy C versus R for Example 8-13.

8–6 MINOR LOSSES

In addition to the pipe wall friction which we have considered in some detail, changes in direction, valves, transitions in pipe size—in fact, all fittings—cause additional losses of head or energy. These losses are actually due to local nonuniformity of the flow, but because of their importance in practical pipe problems, they are nevertheless introduced in this chapter, which is concerned primarily with uniform flow. These losses are generally expressed as a loss coefficient times a velocity head:

$$H_L = C_L \frac{V^2}{2g} \tag{8-55}$$

and for the most part are applicable only to turbulent flow. They are included in the energy equation by the simple addition of all the individual energy losses. Thus, Eq. 8-38 may be modified to read

$$\frac{p_1}{\gamma} + y_1 + \frac{V_1^2}{2g} = \frac{p_2}{\gamma} + y_2 + \frac{V_2^2}{2g} + h_\ell + \sum H_L \tag{8-56}$$

The various loss coefficients are in some cases determined theoretically, but the majority are entirely empirical, being based on actual tests. These losses are treated as if they were point losses and the length over which the loss actually occurs is ignored. This shows up on diagrams such as Fig. 8-26, where the losses are shown as abrupt decreases in head. The use of the term "minor" in reference to these losses is largely by convention, since there are many circumstances (e.g., a very short pipe or a nearly closed valve) in which they become more significant than friction loss. The following minor losses are by no means all inclusive but merely a representative selection.

Pipe Entrances and Outlets

Typical pipe entrances and associated average loss coefficients are shown in Fig. 8-22. Because the flow must turn a corner when entering a pipe, separation at the entrance can be reduced only by increasing the radius of curvature r. By proper rounding (Fig. 8-22a), the loss coefficient can be reduced nearly to zero. The value of 0.05 that is given is only a typical value. At the other extreme, the reentrant tube of Fig. 8-22c, the coefficient will be nearly unity if the pipe walls are very thin. As the pipe wall increases in thickness, the coefficient decreases in magnitude, with its lower limit being similar to the square-edged entrance of Fig. 8-22b.

Submerged pipe outlets always give rise to energy loss, since all the kinetic energy of the exiting flow must be dissipated as eddies in the surrounding fluid. Thus, the loss coefficient must equal unity (see Fig. 8-23, where V_o is the pipe velocity and V_E is the exit velocity). By use of a gradual expansion, the exit velocity (and hence the head loss) can be reduced, however.

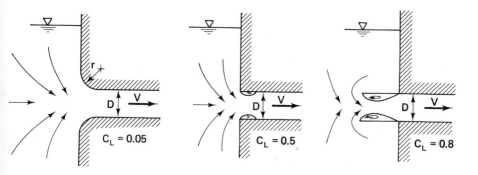

(a) Rounded entrance   (b) Square entrance   (c) Re-entrant entrance

Fig. 8-22.   Pipe entrances.

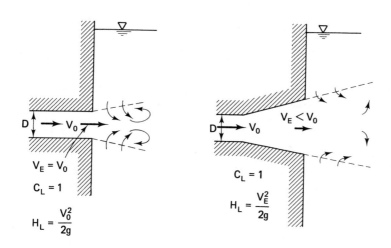

(a) Standard exit.   (b) Expanded exit section.

Fig. 8-23.   Pipe exit sections.

Abrupt Expansion and Contraction

The abrupt expansion (Fig. 8-24) was considered previously in Example 5-15 for a specific numerical problem. If repeated with the notation of Fig. 8-24a, the combining of the continuity, momentum, and energy equations (see Prob. 8-79 at the end of the section) yields

$$H_L = \left(1 - \frac{D_1^2}{D_2^2}\right)^2 \frac{V_1^2}{2g} \tag{8-57a}$$

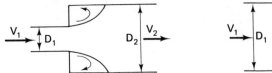 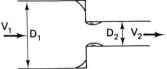

(a) Abrupt expansion   (b) Abrupt contraction

Fig. 8-24. Abrupt transitions.

and hence the loss coefficient for an abrupt expansion is

$$C_L = \left(1 - \frac{D_1^2}{D_2^2}\right)^2 \tag{8-57b}$$

Note that the pipe outlet considered previously (Fig. 8-23a) is a special case of the abrupt expansion where $D_2 \rightarrow \infty$.

The abrupt contraction shown in Fig. 8-24b may also be expressed relative to the diameter ratio. For

$$H_L = C_L \frac{V_2^2}{2g} \tag{8-58}$$

C_L is given experimentally in Fig. 8-25. The limiting case where D_2/D_1 goes to zero gives the loss coefficient for the square-edged pipe entrance of Fig. 8-22b.

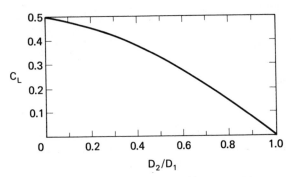

Fig. 8-25. Loss coefficient for sudden contraction.

Pipe Fittings and Bends

Loss coefficients for additional fittings and pipe bends are given in Table 8-4. All losses can be expressed by

$$H_L = C_L \frac{V^2}{2g} \tag{8-59}$$

where V is the pipe velocity. Most losses are primarily due to separation in the vicinity of the fitting. The bends and elbows have additional loss due to

Table 8-4 Loss Coefficients for Pipe Fittings and Appurtenances

90° Bend of Radius r		Elbows	
r/D	C_L	Short radius 90° elbow	$C_L = 0.9$
1.0	0.40	Medium radius 90° elbow	0.8
1.5	0.32	Long radius 90° elbow	0.6
2.0	0.27	45° elbow	0.4
3.0	0.22		
4.0	0.20		
Gate Valves		*Other Valves (Open)*	
Fully open	$C_L = 0.2$	Globe valve	$C_L = 10$
3/4 open	1	Angle valve	5
1/2 open	5.6	Swing check valve	2.5
1/4 open	24		

secondary currents set up by the centrifugal forces. These secondary currents persist for a considerable distance downstream, where they are eventually damped.

Figure 5-19, modified in Fig. 8-13 for wall friction, can now be further modified to include minor losses, as shown in Fig. 8-26. In any of these prob-

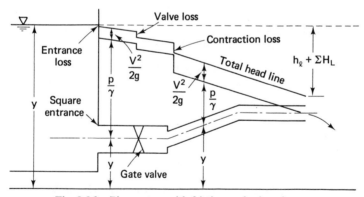

Fig. 8-26. Pipe system with friction and minor losses.

lems a pump or turbine can be accommodated as per Fig. 5-21, and of course the head change can be included in the energy equation.

EXAMPLE 8-14

Consider the pipe system of Fig. 8-26 to consist of 1000 ft of 1-ft-diameter commerical steel pipe followed by 2000 ft of 8-in. pipe of the same material. The reservoir elevation is 200 ft and the pipe outlet is at 100 ft. The entrance is square-edged and the gate valve is fully open. Determine the flow rate (a) ignoring all losses; (b) including only the wall friction; (c) by including all losses. Use $k = 0.0002$ ft for the absolute roughness.

SOLUTION:

(a) Writing the energy equation (Eq. 5-41) between the water surface in the reservoir and the outlet and ignoring all losses,

$$200 = 100 + \frac{V_8^2}{2g}$$

Thus,

$$V = 80.2 \text{ ft/s} \quad \text{and} \quad Q = (80.2)(0.349) = 28.0 \text{ cfs}$$

(b) To include the friction loss,

$$k = 0.0002 \text{ ft}$$

and therefore

$$\left(\frac{k}{D}\right)_{12} = \frac{0.0002}{1} = 0.0002$$

$$\left(\frac{k}{D}\right)_8 = \frac{0.0002}{\frac{8}{12}} = 0.0003$$

Assume f values of

$$f_{12} = 0.014$$

and

$$f_8 = 0.015$$

on the basis of the relative roughnesses only as recommended in Section 8-4 when discharge is unknown. Substituting into Eq. 8-38,

$$200 = 100 + \frac{V_8^2}{2g} + (0.014)\frac{1000}{1}\frac{V_{12}^2}{2g} + (0.015)\frac{2000}{\frac{8}{12}}\frac{V_8^2}{2g}$$

and combining with continuity in the form of

$$V_8(8)^2 = V_{12}(12)^2$$

gives upon solving, a velocity

$$V_8 = 11.49 \text{ ft/s}$$

Assuming that the viscosity $v = 10^{-5}$ ft²/s, we can calculate trial Reynolds numbers

$$Re_{12} = \frac{(11.49)(\frac{2}{3})^2(1)}{10^{-5}} = 5.11 \times 10^5$$

$$Re_8 = \frac{(11.49)(\frac{2}{3})}{10^{-5}} = 7.66 \times 10^5$$

This gives improved resistance coefficients of

$$f_{12} = 0.016$$

and

$$f_8 = 0.016$$

accordingly. Repeating,

$$200 = 100 + \frac{V_8^2}{2g} + (0.016)\frac{1000}{1}\frac{V_{12}^2}{2g} + (0.016)\frac{2000}{\frac{8}{12}}\frac{V_8^2}{2g}$$

and

$$V_8 = 11.11 \text{ ft/s}$$

This velocity substantiates the above f values; thus,

$$Q = (11.11)(0.349) = 3.88 \text{ cfs}$$

(c) The following minor losses need to be included:
Entrance (square-edged):

$$C_L = 0.5$$

Gate valve (open):

$$C_L = 0.2$$

Contraction:

$$\frac{D_2}{D_1} = \frac{8}{12}, \qquad C_L = 0.23$$

Using the f values from part (b) to get started, the energy equation in the form of Eq. 8-56 becomes

$$200 = 100 + \frac{V_8^2}{2g} + (0.016)\frac{1000}{1}\frac{V_{12}^2}{2g} + (0.016)\frac{2000}{\frac{8}{12}}\frac{V_8^2}{2g}$$

$$+ (0.5)\frac{V_{12}^2}{2g} + (0.2)\frac{V_{12}^2}{2g} + (0.23)\frac{V_8^2}{2g}$$

Again eliminating V_{12} using continuity, the velocity in the smaller pipe is

$$V_8 = 11.07 \text{ ft/s}$$

and therefore

$$Q = (11.07)(0.349) = 3.86 \text{ cfs}$$

In this case the minor losses were insignificant; therefore, the f values are satisfactory. If the gate valve had been only $\frac{1}{4}$ open, a $C_L = 24$ for the valve would reduce the flow to 3.70 cfs.

PROBLEMS

Sec. 8-1

8-1. Air at a temperature of 25°C blows through a 0.5-m circular duct at the rate of 120 m³/min. What is the Reynolds number of the flow?

8-2. Air with a temperature of 80°F and pressure of 50 psia is blown through a 1-ft-diameter circular tube at 2 lb/min. What is the Reynolds number?

8-3. Water is pumped at 10 ft/s through a 2-in. pipe. What is the Reynolds number if the temperature is 40°F? 150°F?

8-4. Water is pumped at 0.005 m³/s through a 2.5-cm pipe. Determine the Reynolds number if the temperature is 10°C.

8-5. Determine the kinematic viscosity of a fluid if $Re = 10^6$ when it flows at the rate of 0.19 m³/s through a 0.3-m-diameter circular tube.

8-6. Glycerin at 60°F flows through a 2-in.-diameter pipe. What is the maximum flow rate for which you can be sure the flow is laminar? What is the corresponding centerline velocity?

8-7. Glycerin at 25°C flows through a 10-cm-diameter pipe. What is the maximum centerline velocity for which you can be sure the flow will be laminar?

8-8. If laminar flow occurs in a pipe of diameter D, what length must be traversed before the flow is fully developed if $Re = 2000$? Why is this greater than the length required for turbulent flow?

8-9. What initial length of pipe is required for uniform flow to be established if fuel oil at 25°C is pumped through a 20-cm pipe at the rate of 3×10^{-2} m³/s?

8-10. If water at 60°F flows along a 1% slope, what is the depth y and average velocity V corresponding to $Re = 500$? (*Hint:* Refer back to Section 7-1 for a second relationship.)

8-11. If water at 70°F flows in a wide, open channel with an average velocity of 1 ft/s, what is the maximum depth if the flow is to remain laminar?

8-12. Water at 20°C flows in a wide, open channel. If the depth is 1 cm, what is the maximum average velocity if the flow is laminar? What is the corresponding free surface velocity?

8-13. Fuel oil at 90°F flows over a flat surface with an average velocity of 2 ft/s. What is the maximum depth for which the flow will remain laminar?

Sec. 8-2

8-14. Wind-velocity measurements are made at elevations of 10 and 20 ft above the ground. The respective velocities are 21 and 22 ft/s. What is the magnitude of y'? What is the velocity at a height of 2 ft? 100 ft?

8-15. Assume that the ground surface of Prob. 8-14 is smooth. What is the boundary shear stress? What is the viscosity of the air? What is the thickness of the laminar sublayer? Determine the actual limits of the laminar and turbulent zones.

8-16. Assume that the boundary of Prob. 8-14 is rough. What is the boundary shear stress? What is the roughness height?

8-17. Assume that the velocity profile of Example 8-3 occurred as an unknown fluid flowed through a 1-ft-diameter smooth pipe. What is the magnitude of the shear stress at the pipe wall? What would be the thickness of the laminar sublayer? What is the velocity at the edge of the laminar sublayer?

8-18. Determine the magnitude of y' if wind velocities of 10 and 11 m/s are recorded at heights of 1 m and 4 m, respectively. What is the velocity at a height of 20 m?

8-19. Water at 20°C flows over a flat surface with a velocity such that the shear stress is 10 N/m². Determine the maximum roughness height that will still result in a smooth boundary and the minimum roughness height for which the boundary will still be rough.

8-20. Verify that the curve labeled Eq. 8-12 in Fig. 8-7 does indeed represent that equation.

Sec. 8-3

8-21. Show that a value of the parameter $u_* k / v = 70$ corresponds to

$$\frac{\text{Re}\sqrt{f}}{D/k} = 200$$

8-22. If the head loss in 100 ft of 6-in.-diameter pipe carrying water at 70°F is 6 ft when $Q = 2$ cfs, what is the value of roughness k? What is the centerline velocity?

8-23. If the head loss in 100 m of 15-cm-diameter pipe is 6 m when the water discharge is 0.05 m³/s, what is the value of the roughness k? What is the centerline velocity?

8-24. Sand with a diameter of 1 mm is cemented to the inside of a 100-ft-long 2-in.-diameter pipe. What is the head loss if the water discharge is 0.2 cfs? The temperature is 70°F.

8-25. If SAE 30 oil at 65°F is used rather than water in Prob. 8-24, what is the head loss in feet of water?

8-26. What is the minimum flow rate of water (70°F) in a 4-in. pipe with relative roughness $D/k = 120$, for which the flow is fully rough? What is the corresponding pressure drop in 100 ft?

8-27. Show that it is impossible for the centerline velocity in turbulent pipe flow to equal twice the average velocity, as it does for the laminar counterpart.

Sec. 8-4

8-28. What is the head loss in 100 ft of 2-in. galvanized iron pipe if the flow rate is 0.27 cfs and the fluid is water at 50°F? What is the pressure drop over that length?

8-29. What is the head loss (in feet of water) if SAE 10 oil at 170°F is pumped through a 500-ft-long, 4-in.-diameter commercial steel pipe at 500 gpm?

8-30. Determine the head loss (in meters of water) when gasoline at 20°C is pumped at 50 ℓ/min through 4-cm-diameter, 30-m-long drawn tubing.

8-31. What is the pressure drop if water at 5°C is pumped through a 2-cm-diameter, 15-m-long smooth pipe at the rate of 2 ℓ/s?

8-32. Determine the pressure drop in a length of 100 m, if benzene at 30°C is pumped at the rate of 0.032 m³/s through a 10-cm-diameter horizontal cast iron pipe.

8-33. What flow rate may be expected through 1000 ft of horizontal, smooth, 3-in.-diameter pipe, if the fluid is gasoline at 60°F, and pressure gages at either end of the 1000-ft section indicate a pressure difference of 11.6 psi?

8-34. What discharge of water at 20°C may be expected through 300 m of horizontal, smooth, 8-cm-diameter tubing, if a pressure drop of 80 kN/m² occurs over the length?

8-35. What discharge of turpentine at 120°F would occur through a 1-in.-diameter galvanized iron pipe if a head loss of 20 ft of water occurs in a length of 200 ft?

8-36. Water at 40°F flows in a new 12-in.-diameter riveted steel pipe ($k = 0.005$ ft). If the pressure drop in the 400-ft horizontal pipe is 15 psi, what is the discharge rate?

8-37. Estimate the discharge range that can be expected if a 2-ft-diameter corrugated metal pipe has a head loss of 0.5 ft/100 ft of length when flowing full of water at 50°F.

8-38. What diameter of concrete pipe ($k = 0.003$) is required to carry 15 cfs of water at 70°F if the head loss must not exceed 0.25 ft/1000 ft of length?

8-39. What diameter of galvanized iron pipe is required to carry 0.02 m³/s of gasoline at 15°C if the head loss must be less than 1 m/100 m of length?

8-40. Determine the diameter of smooth pipe required to carry 15 ℓ/s of 20°C gasoline if the head loss is to be 2 m/100 m.

8-41. What diameter of corrugated metal pipe ($k = 0.15$ ft) must be used if a flow rate of 5 cfs (water at 40°F) and head loss of 1 ft/100 ft are required?

8-42. Calculate the flow rate in cfs for the system shown. The fluid is water at 55°F. The pipe is cast iron with a diameter of 6 in. What is the pressure at point A?

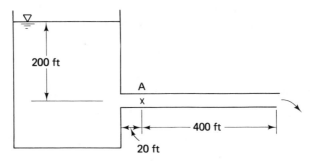

8-43. What pipe diameter (riveted steel, $k = 0.01$ ft) is required for the system of Prob. 8-42 if a flow rate of 10 cfs is required? The fluid is water at 60°F.

8-44. What diameter of cast iron pipe is required by the system of Prob. 8-42 if the flow rate is to be 0.1 m³/s of water (20°C)? The head in the reservoir is 60 m and the pipe length is 100 m.

8-45. A siphon is used to transport water from the upper reservoir to the lower reservoir as shown. The line is 15 cm in diameter and 600 m long, with a resistance coefficient $f = 0.015$. The pipe must pass over an obstruction one-third of the way from the upper reservoir. What is the maximum height Δz if the pressure in the line cannot drop below 6000 N/m²(abs)? The difference in reservoir elevation is 15 m.

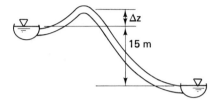

8-46. A 0.6-m-diameter pipe has a discharge of 2.8 m³/s. If one point on the line has an elevation of 300 m and a pressure of 100 kN/m² and a second point 200 m away has an elevation of 290 m and a pressure of 440 kN/m², what is the magnitude of the resistance coefficient f? What is the absolute roughness of the pipe, in meters? (Assume water with $v = 10^{-6}$ m²/s.)

8-47. If the discharge through the three series pipes of Example 8-8 is doubled, what diameter pipe will be equivalent to the given system?

8-48. Refer to the system specified in Example 8-8. What length of smooth pipe of 0.1-m diameter would be equivalent to the given system?

8-49. What length of 18-in. pipe with $k = 0.0008$ ft would be equivalent to the parallel pipes of Example 8-9?

8-50. A 20-cm-diameter, 200-m-long pipe with absolute roughness $k = 0.001$ ft carries water (20°C) at the rate of 0.30 m³/s. Determine what diameter would be required if the given pipe is replaced by a pair of identical diameter pipes equivalent to the original pipe. Each is to have $k = 0.001$ ft and a length of 200 m.

8-51. Determine the discharge of water through each pipe in the system of Example 8-9 if pipe 1 has a diameter of 10 cm, pipe 2 has a diameter of 15 cm, and each has a length of 100 m. The total discharge is 0.25 m³/s. Assume a temperature of 20°C and $k = 0.0008$ ft for each pipe.

8-52. Repeat Prob. 8-51 if both the pipes are smooth.

8-53. The three reservoirs of Fig. 8-16 have water surface elevations of 150 ft, 120 ft, and 60 ft, respectively. Pipes a and b each have a diameter of 8 in. and pipe c has a diameter of 12 in. All three pipes have lengths of 500 ft and resistance coefficient $f = 0.020$. Determine the discharge in each pipe.

8-54. The three reservoirs of Fig. 8-16 have water surface elevations of 200 m, 140 m, and 120 m, respectively. All three pipes have diameters of 20 cm, lengths of 300 m, and resistance coefficients $f = 0.025$. Determine the discharge in each pipe.

8-55. What is the pressure drop in 100 ft of air duct if the cross section is 3 in. by 14 in. and the average velocity is 20 ft/s? The air temperature is 100°F and $k = 0.0001$ ft.

8-56. What is the pressure drop in the air duct of Prob. 8-55 if the duct is smooth and the air temperature is 140°F?

8-57. What is the discharge of water (80°F) through a smooth, 420-ft triangular duct, 6 in. on a side, if it is used to replace the 420-ft-long pipe in Prob. 8-42?

8-58. Determine the discharge through the channel of Fig. 8-19 if the slope is 0.005 and the absolute roughness is 0.002 ft. The depth is 1 m.

Sec. 8-5

8-59. What is the flow rate is a 10-ft-wide rectangular brick channel laid on a slope of 1 ft/1000 ft if the depth of water in the channel is 4 ft?

8-60. What is the flow rate if the channel of Prob. 8-59 is trapezoidal with a bottom width of 10 ft, depth of 4 ft, and side slopes of 3 on 1?

8-61. If the flow rate in Prob. 8-59 is 50 cfs, what would be the corresponding normal depth?

8-62. A trapezoidal channel with a slope of 0.5 ft/1000 ft has side slopes of 4 on 1 and a bottom width of 15 ft. If the flow rate is 300 cfs and the channel is cut through sand with a diameter of 0.5 mm, what is the normal depth?

8-63. What is the discharge in a rectangular flume of unplaned wood if the width is 10 ft, the depth is 3 ft, and the slope is 4 ft/1000 ft?

8-64. What is the normal depth in Prob. 8-63 if the flow rate is 100 cfs?

8-65. What flow rate may be expected in a trapezoidal smooth earth channel if the bottom width is 4 m, the side slopes 2 on 1, the depth is 2 m, and the channel slope is 0.0005?

8-66. What is the normal depth in the channel of Prob. 8-65 if the discharge is 60 m³/s?

8-67. A brick trapezoidal channel is to be constructed on a slope of 0.0004 to carry a maximum flow of 3.4 m³/s. If the side slopes are 2.5 on 1, and the depth must not exceed 0.7 m, what bottom width is required?

8-68. A circular pipe flowing partly full has the following relationships:

$$A = r^2(\theta - \tfrac{1}{2}\sin 2\theta)$$
$$P = 2r\theta$$

where θ is measured in radians. Assuming a constant value of Manning n, calculate and plot V/V_{full} as a function of y_n/d.

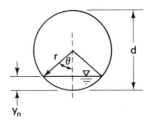

8-69. With reference to Prob. 8-68, calculate and plot the ratio Q/Q_{full} as a function of y_n/d.

8-70. Assuming a fully rough boundary, determine the general relationship between Manning n and the absolute roughness k. What is the specific relationship for a pipe with a diameter of 1 ft? What is the effect on n of doubling the value of k?

8-71. By comparison of Manning n and the Darcy–Weisbach resistance coefficient f through Eq. 8-54, and assuming the Blasius relationship for a smooth pipe (Eq. 8-35), determine the relationship between n and the Reynolds number for a smooth pipe. From this, estimate a practical minimum for values of n.

Sec. 8-6

8-72. What is the flow rate for the system shown if the gate valve is open?

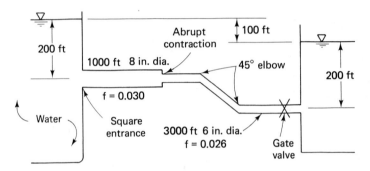

8-73. Repeat Prob. 8-72 if the gate valve is only one-fourth open.

8-74. How much horsepower is required to pump 5 cfs of water (temperature 60°F) into the upper reservoir? The pipe is commercial steel with a diameter of 10 in. The pipe length is 700 ft, it has a square entrance, two fully open gate valves, a check valve, four medium-radius 90° elbows, and four 90° bends, each with a 2-ft radius.

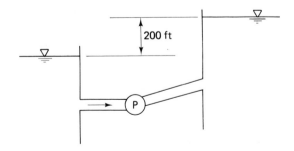

8-75. Water discharges into the atmosphere through a short (ignore friction) 6-in.-diameter tube located 50 ft below the free surface of a reservoir. Compare flow rates for the three entrance conditions of Fig. 8-22.

8-76. Repeat Prob. 8-75 if the tube diameter is 25 cm and the reservoir lies 30 m above the outlet.

8-77. Calculate the flow rate for the system shown.

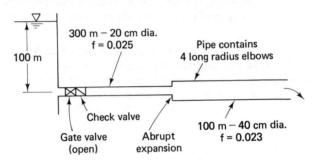

8-78. Repeat Prob. 8-77 if the gate valve is only one-fourth open and the second pipe is connected directly to a reservoir with a water surface level 90 m above the pipe outlet.

8-79. Using Fig. 8-24a, develop the equation for head loss at an abrupt expansion using the continuity, energy, and momentum equations.

REFERENCES

PRANDTL, L., *Essentials of Fluid Dynamics*. New York: Hafner, 1952.

ROUSE, H., *Elementary Mechanics of Fluids*. New York: Wiley, 1946.

SCHLICHTING, H., *Boundary Layer Theory*, 6th ed. New York: McGraw-Hill, 1968.

9

Flow Past Immersed Bodies: Lift and Drag

Drag, or resistance to flow, has already been applied in several instances in preceding sections. The first type of drag to be considered at this time is *surface drag*. Although it will now be considered in reference to a flat (or nearly flat) surface, it is the same type of resisting force which was introduced in Chapter 8 and which gave rise to conduit and even open-channel friction. In fact, some of the relationships previously introduced were originally applied to pipe flow on the basis of similarity between the velocity distributions over a flat plate and in a pipe.

If a flow fails to follow the boundary, separation will occur. This gives rise to what is known as *form drag* (or sometimes *separation drag*). The minor losses that resulted from those pipe fittings which created zones of separation were of this type. The final type of drag is known as *deformation drag*. This occurs only at exceedingly low flow rates, sometimes called *creeping flows*. In addition to the various drag forces, lift force will be considered at the end of the chapter.

9–1 SURFACE DRAG: BOUNDARY LAYER THEORY

If a thin flat plate is pulled through a fluid which is at rest, shear stress will be exerted along the boundary. The presence of the plate will affect the fluid only in a region very near the plate. This region of retarded fluid, known as a *boundary layer*, will have increasing thickness at points farther and farther away from the leading edge. Thus, flow conditions will be nonuniform. We will develop the theory of flow in a boundary layer from the steady-state counterpart of the preceding example, that is, from the steady, initially uniform approach flow past a stationary thin, flat plate.

The development of a boundary layer over a thin, flat plate exposed to a uniform approach velocity V_0 is shown in Fig. 9-1. For very small values

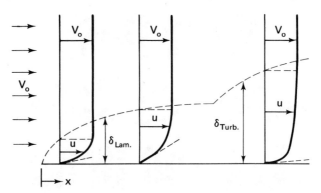

Fig. 9-1.   Boundary layer development along a flat plate.

of x (i.e., near the leading edge) the velocity gradient at the boundary will be very high, corresponding to the thin boundary layer. Thus, the shear stress will also be large. Moving downstream, the slow velocity near the boundary will retard additional fluid farther from the plate, and the velocity distribution will smooth out, the gradient decrease, and the shear stress drop.

The low velocity in the boundary layer plus the presence of the plate will tend to suppress the formation of eddies and initially the boundary layer flow will be laminar. Moving downstream to regions of ever-thickening boundary layer, the flow will eventually become turbulent. However, as with the smooth pipe, it may be expected that if the plate is smooth, a laminar sublayer will still exist immediately above the boundary itself. Further, this transition from laminar to turbulent boundary layer will depend on some kind of a Reynolds number.

The thickness of the boundary layer δ is the distance measured out from the boundary to the point where the velocity u just equals the free stream velocity V_0. Since this is approached asymptotically, δ will be defined more practically as the distance out to the point where the velocity reaches 99 % of V_0. This limit is shown in Fig. 9-1 for both the laminar and turbulent regions.

Laminar Boundary Layer

An approximate analysis of the boundary layer using previously developed concepts will be followed. Certain numerical constants will subsequently be adjusted in the light of more precise analysis and experimental results. In

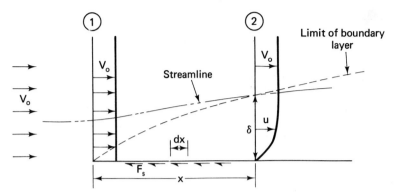

Fig. 9-2. Definition sketch for the analysis of boundary layers.

Fig. 9-2, for purposes of momentum analysis, a control volume can be identified of length x. This volume is bounded below by the plate and above by the streamline passing through the outer limit of the boundary layer at the downstream end of the region. The expansion of the streamline in the downstream direction is due to the ever-increasing amount of retarded fluid between it and the plate. Because of the thinness of the boundary layer, it is assumed that there is no pressure gradient across it, and the constant free stream velocity precludes a pressure gradient in the flow direction. Therefore, there is no pressure variation in any direction, and the only force is the resisting surface drag F_s of the plate on the fluid. Applying the momentum principle with β values included (Eq. 5-55), on a per unit width basis between the sections identified as 1 and 2, gives

$$-F_s = \rho q(V_2\beta_2 - V_1\beta_1)$$

Here q is the discharge per unit width and F_s is the drag force exerted by the plate on an area x units long by a unit width. At section 1 the average velocity V_1 equals V_0 and $\beta_1 = 1$. At the downstream section the velocity profile can be assumed parabolic and hence the average velocity $V_2 = 2V_0/3$ (see Prob. 3-12), $\beta_2 = \frac{6}{5}$ (as per Prob. 5-71), and $q = V_2\delta = \frac{2}{3}V_0\delta$. Thus, the momentum equation becomes

$$-F_s = \rho\left(\frac{2V_0\delta}{3}\right)\left[\left(\frac{2V_0}{3}\right)\left(\frac{6}{5}\right) - V_0\right]$$

or

$$F_s = 0.133\rho V_0^2\delta \tag{9-1}$$

That portion of F_s acting on a differential length dx (shown in Fig. 9-2) may be written

$$dF_s = \tau_0\, dx$$

where τ_0 is the shear stress at the plate and therefore is a function of x.

The shear stress at the plate is given by[1]

$$\tau_0 = \mu \left(\frac{du}{dy}\right)_{y=0}$$

and the parabolic velocity distribution can be expressed as

$$u = V_0 - \frac{V_0}{\delta^2}(\delta - y)^2$$

Thus, upon differentiating, the shear stress is given by

$$\tau = \mu \frac{2V_0}{\delta^2}(\delta - y)$$

and therefore at the plate

$$\tau_0 = \frac{2\mu V_0}{\delta} \tag{9-2}$$

Continuing by differentiating Eq. 9-1,

$$\tau_0 = \frac{dF_s}{dx} = 0.133\rho V_0 \frac{d\delta}{dx}$$

which when combined with Eq. 9-2 yields

$$\delta \, d\delta = \frac{15\mu}{\rho V_0} \, dx$$

Integrating over the length x, during which the boundary layer thickness will range from zero at the leading edge to δ at the other limit, gives

$$\frac{\delta^2}{2} = \frac{15\mu x}{\rho V_0}$$

Solving for the ratio of δ to x,

$$\frac{\delta}{x} = \frac{5.48}{\sqrt{V_0 x \rho / \mu}}$$

This introduces a significant Reynolds number defined in terms of the distance from the leading edge,

$$\mathrm{Re}_x = \frac{V_0 x \rho}{\mu} \tag{9-3}$$

whereupon

$$\frac{\delta}{x} = \frac{5.48}{\mathrm{Re}_x^{1/2}} \tag{9-4}$$

This equation, which gives the growth of the boundary layer, may now be substituted into Eq. 9-1 to give, after some rearrangement,

$$F_s = \frac{1.463}{\mathrm{Re}_x^{1/2}} \frac{x \rho V_0^2}{2} \tag{9-5a}$$

[1] The notation used here indicates that the derivative must be evaluated at $y = 0$.

where a drag coefficient

$$C_f = \frac{1.463}{\text{Re}_x^{1/2}} \tag{9-5b}$$

may conveniently be introduced. Substituting Eq. 9-4 into Eq. 9-2 for δ gives another useful equation,

$$\tau_0 = \frac{0.732}{\text{Re}_x^{1/2}} \frac{\rho V_0^2}{2} \tag{9-6a}$$

and a local drag coefficient

$$c_f = \frac{0.732}{\text{Re}_x^{1/2}} \tag{9-6b}$$

may be defined.

On the basis of more rigorous analysis, coupled with experimental verification, the constants in Eqs. 9-4, 9-5, and 9-6 should be changed from 5.48 to 5.2, 1.463 to 1.328, and 0.732 to 0.664, respectively. With the inclusion of the improved values for the numerical constants, the laminar boundary layer thickness is given by

$$\frac{\delta}{x} = \frac{5.2}{\text{Re}_x^{1/2}} \tag{9-7}$$

Further, the drag force on a flat plate of breadth B and length L is

$$F_s = C_f BL \frac{\rho V_0^2}{2} \tag{9-8a}$$

where the mean drag coefficient is

$$C_f = \frac{1.328}{\text{Re}_L^{1/2}} \tag{9-8b}$$

The drag force on the first x ft may be obtained by substituting x for L. The average shear, over the length L, is simply the force per unit area, or

$$\tau_{0_{av}} = C_f \frac{\rho V_0^2}{2} \tag{9-9}$$

Finally, the shear stress, as a function of x, is given by

$$\tau_0 = c_f \frac{\rho V_0^2}{2} \tag{9-10a}$$

where the local drag coefficient is

$$c_f = \frac{0.664}{\text{Re}_x^{1/2}} \tag{9-10b}$$

Note that the mean coefficient (Eq. 9-8b) is used to give the shear force or the average stress over a length of surface and the local coefficient (Eq. 9-10b) is used to give the shear stress at a specific point.

EXAMPLE 9-1

Plot the boundary layer thickness and shear stress along a thin plate pulled through glycerin at 25°C. The velocity is 1.5 m/s and the plate is 1 m long.

SOLUTION:

For $T = 25°C = 77°F$,

$$\nu = (4.4 \times 10^{-3} \text{ ft}^2/\text{s})(0.0929 \text{ m}^2/\text{ft}^2) = 4.09 \times 10^{-4} \text{ m}^2/\text{s}$$

The boundary layer thickness is given by

$$\delta = \frac{5.2x}{\text{Re}_x^{1/2}}$$

and the shear stress by

$$\tau_0 = c_f \frac{\rho V_0^2}{2} = \frac{(c_f)(1258 \text{ kg/m}^3)(1.5 \text{ m/s})^2}{2} = 1415 c_f$$

where

$$c_f = \frac{0.664}{\text{Re}_x^{1/2}}$$

and

$$\text{Re}_x = \frac{Vx}{\nu} = \frac{(1.5)x}{4.09 \times 10^{-4}} = 3667x$$

Typical values are calculated in the following table, and the results are plotted on Fig. 9-3.

x (m)	Re	δ (m)	τ_0 (N/m²)
0.02	73.3	0.012	109.7
0.05	183	0.019	69.5
0.1	367	0.027	49.0
0.2	733	0.038	34.7
0.4	1467	0.054	24.5
1.0	3667	0.086	15.5

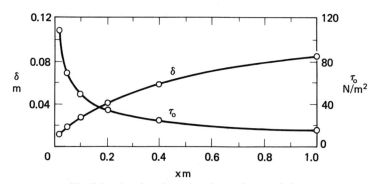

Fig. 9-3. Laminar boundary layer characteristics.

Turbulent Boundary Layer

As the Reynolds number Re_x increases, the boundary layer will eventually become unstable. This condition will occur in the vicinity of the section where the Reynolds number exceeds 400,000. Downstream of this point the flow in the boundary layer will be turbulent. As the flow instability is dependent on both the nature of the free stream flow and the conditions at the boundary, the foregoing value is very approximate. Once the boundary layer becomes turbulent (see Fig. 9-1), the increased mixing causes both an accelerated growth of the boundary layer thickness and an increased velocity gradient at the boundary. This latter aspect means that the shear stress will become larger as the transition from the laminar zone to the turbulent zone is passed. Proceeding downstream the shear stress will again decrease with distance, however.

An analysis similar to the laminar boundary layer can be used to develop relations similar to Eqs. 9-7 through 9-10. The analysis assumes that a turbulent boundary layer exists over the entire surface and that the velocity in the boundary layer varies as the seventh root of the distance from the boundary:

$$\frac{u}{V_0} = \left(\frac{y}{\delta}\right)^{1/7} \tag{9-11}$$

Repeating the momentum analysis (using the control volume specified in Fig. 9-2 and the velocity at section 2 as specified by Eq. 9-11) gives the results which follow. The numerical constants have again been altered slightly to better fit actual data.

$$\frac{\delta}{x} = \frac{0.38}{\text{Re}_x^{1/5}} \tag{9-12}$$

$$C_f = \frac{0.074}{\text{Re}_L^{1/5}} \tag{9-13}$$

$$c_f = \frac{0.059}{\text{Re}_x^{1/5}} \tag{9-14}$$

The mean and local drag coefficients given above apply in the general drag force and shear stress equations given previously as Eqs. 9-8a and 9-10a, respectively. These three turbulent boundary layer equations (Eqs. 9-12, 9-13, 9-14) are valid only as long as the one-seventh power law of Eq. 9-11 gives a good representation of the actual velocity profile. This occurs up to a Reynolds number of 2×10^7. Above this number the deviation of the velocity profile results in an underestimation of the actual drag. The velocity distribution at Reynolds numbers greater than 2×10^7 is better described by a logarithmic relation. A more exact analysis using this relationship yields the *von Kármán–Schoenherr equation*,

$$\frac{1}{\sqrt{C_f}} = 4.13 \log_{10} (\text{Re}_L C_f) \tag{9-15}$$

The similarity between boundary layer and pipe flows can be seen by comparison of Eq. 9-15 with the von Kármán–Prandtl equation (Eq. 8-31). A more convenient and only slightly less accurate expression in the range of

Reynolds numbers from 10^6 to 10^9 has been developed by Schlichting. This equation is

$$C_f = \frac{0.455}{(\log_{10} \text{Re}_L)^{2.58}}$$

(9-16)

The equations for the mean drag coefficient C_f (Eqs. 9-8b, 9-13, and 9-15) are graphed in Fig. 9-4. The usual ranges of validity are shown as continuous

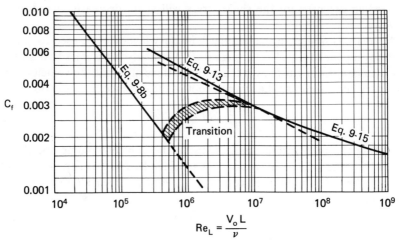

Fig. 9-4.   Mean drag coefficient.

lines and possible extensions as dashed lines. The curves have been well substantiated by experimental data. Recall that the turbulent relations were developed on the basis of a turbulent boundary layer starting at the leading edge. This is a good approximation if the plate is very long, if the free stream flow is highly turbulent, or if the front portion of the plate is roughened. More generally, however, the initial portion is laminar up to $\text{Re}_L = 400,000$, beyond which the boundary layer is turbulent. Above about $\text{Re}_L = 10^7$, the laminar portion represents an insignificant area of the plate, and the theoretical curves become quite accurate. In the intermediate range between 4×10^5 and 10^7, the combined drag due to the two regions can best be evaluated from the empirical transition shown as the shaded curve.

Although the preceding discussion has assumed a flow over a flat surface, the equations that have been developed give reasonably good solutions to flow over curved surfaces, provided that the flow does not separate from the boundary. The subject of separation provides the introduction to the next section on form drag. Finally, conditions in the boundary layer become important in many engineering problems. In fact, a boundary layer type of adjustment generally occurs during the transition from one boundary geometry to another. Of particular importance to modern transportation, the control of the boundary layer is a major factor in the design of aircraft wings.

EXAMPLE 9-2

A flat surface 40 ft wide by 200 ft long is exposed to a 80-ft/s wind (80°F) blowing in the direction of the 200-ft length. Assuming an initial laminar boundary layer followed by a turbulent boundary layer, determine:
(a) The length of the laminar boundary layer.
(b) The shear stress and boundary layer thickness at the end of the laminar region.
(c) The shear stress at the end of the 200 ft.
(d) The total force on the first 100 ft.
(e) The total force on the final 100 ft.

SOLUTION:

At 80°F, $\rho = 0.00228$ slug/ft^3 and $\nu = 1.69 \times 10^{-4}$ ft^2/s.
(a) Assuming that the laminar portion ends at $\text{Re}_x = 400,000$,

$$\text{Re}_x = \frac{(80)x}{1.69 \times 10^{-4}} = 400,000$$

and $x = 0.845$ ft. Thus, less than 1 ft of the total length will be laminar.
(b) At the point $x = 0.845$ ft, $\text{Re}_x = 400,000$, and from Eqs. 9-10,

$$\tau_0 = \frac{0.664}{(400,000)^{1/2}} \frac{(0.00228)(80)^2}{2} = 0.00766 \text{ lb/ft}^2$$

while from Eq. 9-7,

$$\delta = \frac{(0.845)(5.2)}{(400,000)^{1/2}} = 0.00695 \text{ ft}$$

(c) At the end of the surface, $x = 200$ ft and

$$\text{Re}_{200} = \frac{(80)(200)}{1.69 \times 10^{-4}} = 9.47 \times 10^7$$

Although this is beyond the range of validity of Eq. 9-14, using it, for lack of a better relationship, as a first approximation in conjunction with Eq. 9-10a gives

$$\tau_0 = \frac{0.059}{(9.47 \times 10^7)^{1/5}} \frac{(0.00228)(80)^2}{2} = 0.01093 \text{ lb/ft}^2$$

(d) For the first 100 ft,

$$\text{Re}_{100} = \frac{(80)(100)}{1.69 \times 10^{-4}} = 4.73 \times 10^7$$

and from Fig. 9-4 (or Eq. 9-15),

$$C_f = 0.0023$$

Thus, from Eq. 9-8a,

$$F_{100} = (0.0023)(40)(100)\frac{(0.00228)(80)^2}{2} = 67.1 \text{ lb}$$

(e) Repeating part (d) for the entire length where $\text{Re}_{200} = 9.47 \times 10^7$ and $C_f = 0.0021$ gives

$$F_{200} = (0.0021)(40)(200)\frac{(0.00228)(80)^2}{2} = 122.7 \text{ lb}$$

The force on the total length is a little less than twice the force on the first 100 ft. Finally, the force on the last 100 ft is the difference

$$F_{200} - F_{100} = 122.7 - 67.1 = 55.6 \text{ lb}$$

EXAMPLE 9-3

Evaluate the surface drag force on a 1-m by 1-m plate as water ($\nu = 10^{-6}$ m²/s) flows over it with a velocity of 1 m/s. Assume that:
(a) The boundary layer remains laminar.
(b) The boundary layer is entirely turbulent.
(c) The boundary layer is laminar up to $Re_x = 400,000$.

SOLUTION:

The Reynolds number Re_L is given by

$$Re_L = \frac{V_0 L}{\nu} = \frac{(1 \text{ m/s})(1 \text{ m})}{10^{-6} \text{ m}^2/\text{s}} = 10^6$$

From Fig. 9-4 the mean drag coefficient in each of the specified cases is given as follows:
(a) Laminar curve: $C_f = 0.00137$
(b) Turbulent curve: $C_f = 0.0047$
(c) Transition curve: $C_f = 0.0028$ (approximate)
Since the force is given by

$$F_s = C_f BL \frac{\rho V_0^2}{2} = \frac{(C_f)(1 \text{ m})(1 \text{ m})(998 \text{ kg/m}^3)(1 \text{ m/s})^2}{2}$$

$$= 499 C_f$$

the force in each case is as follows:
(a) Laminar boundary layer: $F_s = (499)(0.00137) = 0.68$ N
(b) Turbulent boundary layer: $F_s = (499)(0.0047) = 2.35$ N
(c) Transition: $F_s = (499)(0.0028) = 1.40$ N

EXAMPLE 9-4

Consider the 300-ft-long ship of Example 6-4 and assume that it has a surface area of 20,000 ft² below the water line. Example 6-4 previously demonstrated the diffi-culty of achieving equality of both the Reynolds and Froude numbers as required for complete modeling of friction and gravity forces. Consequently, a 10-ft model will be used and gravity forces will be scaled using the Froude law, while the fric-tion forces will be evaluated according to the relationships of this section. Assume that the prototype will operate in salt water ($\rho = 1.99$ slug/ft³ and $\nu = 1.2 \times 10^{-5}$ ft²/s) and that the model will be towed in fresh water at 70°F ($\rho = 1.94$ slug/ft³ and $\nu = 1.05 \times 10^{-5}$ ft²/s). From Example 6-4 the prototype maximum velocity is 35 ft/s. When the model is towed at the corresponding scale velocity, the total drag is measured as 4.03 lb. What is the total drag on the full-size ship?

SOLUTION:

Using the Froude law,

$$V_m = V_p \left(\frac{L_m}{L_p}\right)^{1/2} = (35)(\tfrac{1}{30})^{1/2} = 6.39 \text{ ft/s}$$

This must be the velocity at which the model was towed when the drag force of

4.03 lb was measured. In order to calculate friction drag forces,

$$Re_m = \frac{(6.39)(10)}{1.2 \times 10^{-5}} = 5.33 \times 10^6$$

and

$$Re_p = \frac{(35)(300)}{1.05 \times 10^{-5}} = 10^9$$

whereupon from Fig. 9-4, $C_{f_m} = 0.0031$ and $C_{f_p} = 0.0016$. The friction drag is given by Eq. 9-8a for both model and prototype:

$$F_f = \frac{C_f A \rho V^2}{2}$$

The area A for the model is

$$A_m = \frac{A_p}{(L_p/L_m)^2} = \frac{20,000}{(30)^2} = 22.2 \text{ ft}^2$$

Thus,

$$F_{f_m} = \frac{(0.0031)(22.2)(1.94)(6.39)^2}{2} = 2.73 \text{ lb}$$

$$F_{f_p} = \frac{(0.0016)(20,000)(1.99)(35)^2}{2} = 39,000 \text{ lb}$$

The wave forces on the model are

$$F_{w_m} = F_m - F_{f_m} = 4.03 - 2.73 = 1.30 \text{ lb}$$

Since this force is properly scaled by the Froude relationship, the wave force on the prototype is

$$F_{w_p} = F_{w_m} \frac{\rho_p}{\rho_m}\left(\frac{L_p}{L_m}\right)^3 \qquad \text{(refer to Example 6-2)}$$

or

$$F_{w_p} = (1.30)\frac{1.99}{1.94}(30)^3 = 36,000 \text{ lb}$$

The total force on the prototype is the sum of wave and friction forces; hence,

$$F_p = F_{w_p} + F_{f_p}$$
$$= 36,000 + 39,000 = 75,000 \text{ lb}$$

9–2 SEPARATION, FORM DRAG, AND DEFORMATION DRAG

Separation

Up to this point in the chapter we have considered drag only over flat plates. Curved surfaces alter the relationships; however, for moderate curvature the equations of the preceding section may be used as a first approximation. If the boundary is curved so as to accelerate the flow, the pressure will decrease in the flow direction. This condition, known as a *favorable pressure gradient*, tends to keep the boundary layer thinner and to prolong both the tendency for the laminar boundary layer to become turbulent and the flow to separate from the boundary. If, on the other hand, the boundary curvature causes deceleration of the flow, the pressure will increase in the flow direction, creating an adverse pressure gradient, increasing the onset of turbulence as well as the likelihood of separation.

The subject of *separation*, which gives rise to additional resistance beyond that of surface drag, will be considered first as the logical extension of a boundary layer flow subjected to an adverse pressure gradient. The situation is shown in Fig. 9-5, where the flow over an expanding boundary is shown.

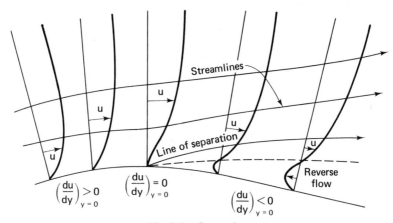

Fig. 9-5. Separation.

The flow is decelerating and the velocity near the boundary decreases. The velocity at the boundary is already zero, however, and as the surrounding fluid is retarded, the velocity gradient du/dy necessarily goes to zero at some point along the boundary. Farther downstream the continued expansion results in a negative velocity gradient and a reversal of the flow. The line of zero velocity is shown in Fig. 9-5, as is the line demarking the zone of separation. The latter is located so as to satisfy the demands of continuity. On any cross section below the line of separation, the forward flow rate exactly equals that of the return flow, and above the zone of separation, continuity of the main flow prevails. Note that this region of separation, unlike the foregoing boundary layer, is usually quite thick.

The point of separation is determined by the zero velocity gradient at the boundary. It is generally very difficult to predict this point of separation in advance, as it depends on too many variables. It can be noted, however, that since the point of separation requires that $du/dy = 0$, a turbulent flow with its considerably steeper velocity gradient is more resistant to separation than is a laminar flow. Hence, we will see shortly that the separation associated with flow past a sphere or other rounded body will occur farther forward if the boundary layer is laminar and jump farther downstream toward the rear when the boundary layer becomes turbulent.

In addition to the separation associated with a boundary layer and the attempt to decelerate an already zero velocity, separation will also occur if the radius of curvature is too short. In the situation depicted in Fig. 9-6, the fluid, unable to flow smoothly around the short radius with its resulting high convective acceleration V^2/R, separates as shown. If the corner were

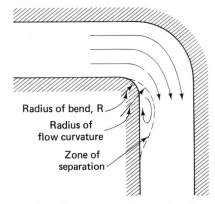

Radius of bend, R

Radius of flow curvature

Zone of separation

Fig. 9-6. Separation due to a short radius of curvature.

square or mitered so that the inside radius goes to zero, this would require an infinite acceleration, which is clearly impossible. In either case the eddy losses in the zone of separation give rise to the minor losses considered previously in Section 8-7. More to the specific point of this chapter is the separation accompanying flow around a shape such as the disk of Fig. 9-7. Again, the flow cannot turn the sharp corner at the edge and instead adjusts to a configuration that provides compatible accelerations and pressure distribution. Flow of this type will be considered in more detail presently. For now, note that unlike the boundary layer separation of Fig. 9-5, the point of separation here will be at a fixed location over a wide range of flow conditions.

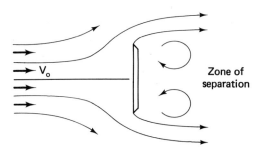

V_0

Zone of separation

Fig. 9-7. Separation behind a disk.

In conclusion, separation is most likely to occur when a boundary layer flow is exposed to an adverse pressure gradient or when the flow is directed around a short radius of curvature.

Flow Around a Sphere

The drag on many objects is a combination of both boundary layer and separation effects at moderate to high velocities and dependent on an altogether different mechanism in the lower range. Since a particular type of drag cannot usually be identified with a specific shape, it is desirable to examine how the flow pattern, and consequently the drag force, behaves under a range of conditions for a given shape. This will be illustrated for flow past a sphere. The various conditions are shown on Fig. 9-8. As should

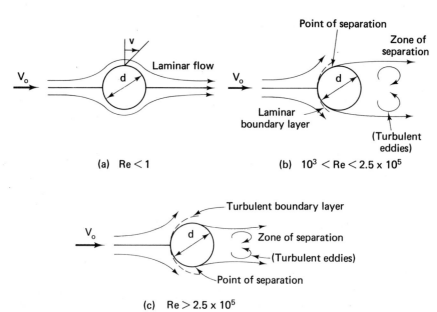

(a)   Re < 1

(b) $10^3 <$ Re $< 2.5 \times 10^5$

(c)   Re $> 2.5 \times 10^5$

Fig. 9-8.   Separation behind a sphere.

be anticipated, the flow will be best characterized by a Reynolds number. In this case the reference length will be the sphere diameter and therefore, in terms of the approach velocity and kinematic viscosity,

$$\text{Re} = \frac{V_0 d}{\nu} \tag{9-17}$$

The importance of this parameter will shortly be revealed further by dimensional considerations.

At very slow velocities the inertial effects become less important. Assuming that they may be ignored, Stokes simplified the Navier–Stokes equations (Eqs. 7-24) by setting the left-hand side of each equal to zero. On this basis he obtained an equation for the total drag force on a sphere. The derivation is quite lengthy and requires the integration of the components of the pressure and shear stress in the flow direction. The resulting expression for the drag force is known as the *equation of Stokes,*

$$F_D = 3\pi\mu V_0 d \qquad (9\text{-}18)$$

This equation has been found valid up to a Reynolds number close to unity, at which point the acceleration terms, ignored in the derivation, start to become significant.

The physical situation is perhaps easier to grasp if we consider the unsteady counterpart of a slowly moving sphere through fluid at rest. At higher velocities the sphere passes by before any of the fluid, except that in the immediate vicinity of the sphere, can be set in motion. At very low velocities, however, the sphere passes through very slowly, essentially pushing the fluid out of the way. Under these slow conditions the affected fluid pushes additional fluid and because of the lack of inertia, the effect is very widespread. In fact, fluid up to 100 diameters from the sphere may be affected. This type of drag is known as *deformation drag,* after the "deforming" of the fluid that takes place. Every shape will experience this type of drag at a sufficiently low Reynolds number; however, an analytic solution such as the Stokes equation is usually not available.

As the Reynolds number increases, which means an increasing velocity for a given fluid and sphere, the flow deviates more and more from the deformation drag assumptions. By the time $\text{Re} = 1000$, the flow slips by the sphere without widespread lateral effect, a laminar boundary layer has formed on the front portion, and a large zone of separation covers the remainder. This condition, which exists up to about $\text{Re} = 2.5 \times 10^5$, is shown in Fig. 9-8b. As discussed previously, the laminar boundary layer on the curved surfaces extends to the point where the adverse pressure gradient caused by the curvature results in separation. The shear stress due to the velocity gradient in the boundary layer contributes to the total drag. Of more importance, however, are the normal stresses or pressure. A relatively high positive pressure prevails over much of the front of the sphere, reaching a maximum at the stagnation point. As the point of separation occurs somewhat before the midpoint, this is a region of high velocity and therefore low pressure. As the pressure is nearly constant throughout the zone of separation, the rear portion is exposed to a low, in fact, negative (relative to ambient conditions), pressure throughout. The positive pressure over the front face and the negative pressure over the rear both contribute to a drag force in the direction of flow. This type of drag will be here designated as *form drag* (the terms *pressure* or *separation drag* are also frequently used).

At approximately $Re = 2.5 \times 10^5$, depending on the roughness of the sphere and the turbulence of the free stream flow, the boundary layer itself becomes turbulent. As this results in a much steeper velocity gradient at the boundary, the point of separation is postponed to some point behind the midsection, as shown in Fig. 9-8c. The point of separation is now in a region of lower velocity and therefore higher pressure (slightly above the ambient pressure). The positive pressure over the front still results in a drag force, but it is considerably less than the previous case with a laminar boundary layer at the same velocity.

Drag Force

Thus far in this section, the subjects of separation, pressure distribution around a body, deformation, and form drag have been discussed. It is now necessary to first tie these concepts together so as to have a complete picture of the drag force problem and second, to solve the corresponding engineering problems.

Backing up briefly, consider the total drag force on a body for which a length dimension L can be defined. Assuming that the approach velocity V_0 is not so high as to cause compressibility effects and that the surface is smooth, we may write

$$F_D = f(\text{geometry}, L, V_0, \rho, \mu)$$

The geometry term is included to avoid the number of length ratios required to define a complicated shape. It is sufficient since we are interested in a specific shape (which means the geometry variable is constant) in a given problem.

Selecting L, V_0, and ρ as repeating variables, dimensional analysis gives

$$\frac{F_D}{\rho L^2 V_0^2} = \phi\left(\text{geometry}, \frac{V_0 L \rho}{\mu}\right)$$

Since L^2 is proportional to an area A, the equation may be rewritten as

$$\frac{F_D}{\rho A V_0^2/2} = \phi_1(\text{geometry}, Re) \tag{9-19}$$

where the factor 2 has been once again added arbitrarily to the denominator.

For a specific shape, both the area A and the length dimension in the Reynolds number must be properly defined. Nevertheless, Eq. 9-19 is a general drag equation and for a specific shape, ϕ_1, can be replaced by a drag coefficient C_D so that

$$F_D = C_D A \frac{\rho V_0^2}{2} \tag{9-20}$$

where C_D is a function only of the Reynolds number.

Note first that if the problem in question involves a thin surface with flow over it (or an approximation thereof), then by taking A as the surface area and the length as the surface length in the direction of flow, the surface drag equations of Section 9-1 are obtained. Equation 9-20 becomes the equivalent of Eq. 9-8a, where the coefficient is given by Eqs. 9-8b, 9-13, 9-15, 9-16, or Fig. 9-4 as a function of Re_L.

For other shapes the drag will consist of form drag, form plus surface drag, or deformation drag. The coefficient of Eq. 9-20 is denoted as C_D to distinguish it from the surface drag coefficient C_f. Generally, C_D must be determined experimentally. Curves of C_D versus Re for selected shapes are given in Figs. 9-9 and 9-10 and typical values for other shapes are included in Table 9-1. The discussion of flow around a sphere has revealed that the drag on a sphere is due to pressure differences involving separation and shear stress along the surface. It is not practical to separate the various stresses. Therefore, the experimental drag coefficients in the curves and table include the effect of shear as part of the form drag. Since the shear stress is usually of less importance, the area A is chosen to correspond best with the normal stresses and the zone of separation. Therefore, in calculations involving form drag, the area is the projected area of the body perpendicular to the flow direction. The reference length must be defined for each shape. Whenever possible a diameter is used; otherwise, the length will be specified for the specific shape. The drag coefficient for the airship hull included in Fig. 9-9 is primarily due to surface drag, while at the other extreme, shear stress contributes virtually nothing to the drag on a circular disk perpendicular to the flow. A comparison of the two drag coefficients not only gives a measure of the magnitude of the two types of drag but also demonstrates the importance of streamlining toward reducing form drag.

The curve of drag coefficient for a sphere includes the range of deformation drag (Re < 1). By equating the equation of Stokes (Eq. 9-18) with the general drag equation (Eq. 9-20), we have

$$3\pi\mu V_0 d = C_D A \frac{\rho V_0^2}{2}$$

Since the projected area of a sphere is $\pi d^2/4$, this reduces to

$$C_D = \frac{24}{\mathrm{Re}} \tag{9-21}$$

This equation for C_D (labeled on Fig. 9-9) when used in conjunction with the drag equation (Eq. 9-20) is therefore an alternative form of the equation of Stokes. The point at which the boundary layer on a sphere becomes turbulent can also be detected in Fig. 9-9, as the Reynolds number at which the drag coefficient drops rather abruptly in value from 0.5 to 0.2.

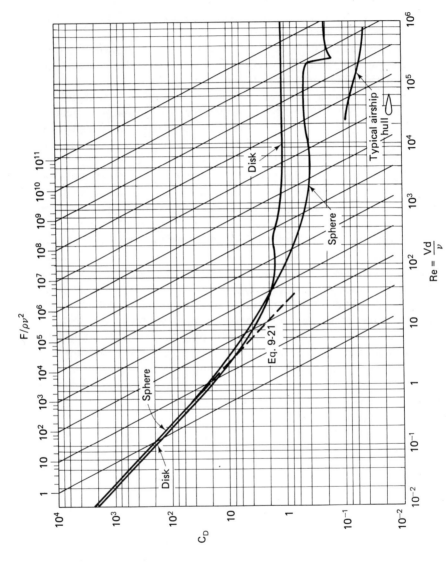

Fig. 9-9. Coefficients of drag for bodies of revolution.

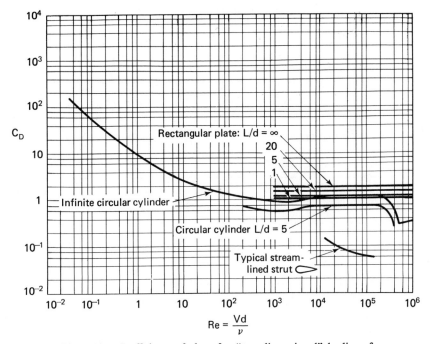

Fig. 9-10. Coefficients of drag for "two-dimensional" bodies of infinite and finite length.

For many engineering problems it is the drag force that must be evaluated. If the velocity is known, the drag coefficient may be determined and the force calculated directly. Another frequently encountered problem involves the terminal velocity at which a body rises or falls through a fluid. For example, the descent of a parachute, the removal of particles in a settling basin, and the rising of bubbles in an aeration tank all involve a velocity as an unknown variable. As Example 9-6 will demonstrate, the resisting force is known and it is the velocity that must be calculated. The C_D–Re curves require a trial-and-error solution, but this can be avoided by properly combining the parameters. Eliminating the velocity between

$$F_D = \frac{C_D A \rho V_0^2}{2} \quad \text{and} \quad \text{Re} = \frac{V_0 d}{\nu}$$

gives

$$\frac{F_D}{\rho \nu^2} = \frac{A}{2d^2} C_D \text{Re}^2 \tag{9-22}$$

For a sphere or other shape with a circle as projected area, this becomes

$$\frac{F_D}{\rho \nu^2} = \frac{\pi}{8} C_D \text{Re}^2 \tag{9-23}$$

Table 9-1 Typical Drag Coefficients for Various Body Forms

BODY (flow from left to right)	L/d	Re = Vd/ν	C_D
Bodies of revolution			
1) Sphere:		10^5 $> 3 \times 10^5$	0.50 0.20
2) Hemispherical Shell:		$> 10^3$	1.33 0.34
3) Ellipsoid:		$> 2 \times 10^5$	0.07
4) Circular cylinder axis ‖ to flow:	0 1 2 4 7	$> 10^3$	1.12 0.91 0.85 0.87 0.99
5) Circular disk ⊥ to flow:		$> 10^3$	1.12
6) Tandem disks ⊥ to flow (L = Spacing)	0 1 2 3	$> 10^3$	1.12 0.93 1.04 1.54
"Two-dimensional" flow (finite and infinite length)			
7) Circular cylinder axis ⊥ to flow:	1 5 20 ∞ 5 ∞	10^5 $> 5 \times 10^5$	0.63 0.74 0.90 1.20 0.35 0.33
8) Elliptical cylinder: 2:1 4:1 8:1		4×10^4 10^5 $2.5 \times 10^4 - 10^5$ 2.5×10^4 2×10^5	0.6 0.46 0.32 0.29 0.20
9) Rectangular Plate: L = length d = width	1 5 20 ∞	$> 10^3$	1.16 1.20 1.50 1.90
10) Square cylinder:		3.5×10^4 $10^4 - 10^5$	2.0 1.6

It is now possible to construct lines of constant $F_D/\rho v^2$ as has been done in Fig. 9-9. The value of $F_D/\rho v^2$ for a specific problem can then be entered and the intersection of the $F_D/\rho v^2$ line with the appropriate C_D–Re curve permits calculation of the desired velocity.

EXAMPLE 9-5

Determine the drag force on a cylindrical chimney that is 80 m high by 10 m in diameter when the wind ($T = 15°C$) velocity is 120 km/hr.

SOLUTION:

Assuming standard atmospheric pressure, $\rho = 1.226$ kg/m³, and for $T = 15°C = 59°F$,

$$\nu = (1.57 \times 10^{-4} \text{ ft}^2/\text{s})(0.0929 \text{ m}^2/\text{ft}^2) = 1.46 \times 10^{-5} \text{ m}^2/\text{s}$$

Therefore, the Reynolds number is

$$\text{Re} = \frac{V_0 d}{\nu}$$

$$= \frac{(120 \text{ km/hr})(1000 \text{ m/km})(10 \text{ m})}{(3600 \text{ s/hr})(1.46 \times 10^{-5} \text{ m}^2/\text{s})} = 2.28 \times 10^7$$

From Table 9-1, section 7, for

$$\frac{L}{d} = \frac{80}{10} = 8$$

$$C_D = 0.34 \quad \text{(approximately)}$$

Hence, the drag force is

$$F_D = \frac{C_D A \rho V_0^2}{2}$$

$$= \frac{(0.34)(80 \text{ m})(10 \text{ m})(1.226 \text{ kg/m}^3)(33.3 \text{ m/s})^2}{2}$$

$$= 1.85 \times 10^5 \text{ N}$$

EXAMPLE 9-6

Two tandem disks, each with a diameter of 0.7 m spaced 1.6 m apart, are towed behind a ship through 18°C fresh water at 6 m/s. What power is consumed in pulling the disks?

SOLUTION:

At $T = 18°C$,

$$\nu = 1.061 \times 10^{-6} \text{ m}^2/\text{s}$$

and

$$\text{Re} = \frac{(6 \text{ m/s})(0.7 \text{ m})}{1.061 \times 10^{-6} \text{ m}^2/\text{s}} = 3.96 \times 10^6$$

Since this is well in excess of $Re = 10^3$, Table 9-1, section 6, may be used. For $L/d = 1.6/0.7 = 2.29$, $C_D = 1.19$ and

$$F_D = \frac{C_D A \rho V_0^2}{2}$$

$$= \frac{(1.19)(\pi/4)(0.7 \text{ m})^2(998 \text{ kg/m}^3)(6 \text{ m/s})^2}{2}$$

$$= 8230 \text{ N}$$

Thus, the power required becomes

$$P = F_D V = (8230)(6) = 49,400 \text{ N·m/s}$$

EXAMPLE 9-7

Determine the velocity at which a wooden (sp. gr. $= 0.65$) sphere 2 in. in diameter would rise through water at 60°F.

SOLUTION:

At 60°F,

$$\rho = 1.94 \text{ slugs/ft}^3 \quad \text{and} \quad \nu = 1.21 \times 10^{-5} \text{ ft}^2/\text{s}$$

If the sphere is traveling at a uniform (terminal) velocity, the net lifting force of buoyancy minus weight must equal the drag force on the sphere. Thus,

$$F_D = \frac{\pi}{6} d^3 \gamma_{\text{water}} - \frac{\pi}{6} d^3 \gamma_{\text{wood}}$$

$$= \frac{\pi}{6}\left(\frac{2}{12}\right)^3 (62.4)(1 - 0.65)$$

$$= 0.0529 \text{ lb}$$

Then

$$\frac{F_D}{\rho \nu^2} = \frac{0.0529}{(1.94)(1.21 \times 10^{-5})^2} = 1.86 \times 10^8$$

From Fig. 9-9, $C_D = 0.5$. Finally, from Eq. 9-20,

$$V_0 = \sqrt{\frac{2F_D}{C_D A \rho}} = \sqrt{\frac{(2)(0.0529)}{(0.5)(\pi/4)(\frac{2}{12})^2(1.94)}} = 2.236 \text{ ft/s}$$

9–3 LIFT AND DRAG

The objects considered thus far have all been symmetrically shaped and have been aligned symmetrically with respect to the flow. Consequently, the drag force has always been in the flow direction. If the body itself is not symmetrical or if a symmetrical body is not aligned with the flow, the resultant total drag force may still be determined. Of course, it now acts at some angle relative to the flow. It is customary, however, to resolve this force into two components—a *drag force* in the flow direction and a *lift force* perpendicular to the flow. This leads immediately to the subject of lift on wings and aerodynamics. Because of its obvious importance, this is an area that has been widely studied and highly developed. The subject will only be introduced at this point, however.

As with the drag force before, both the lift and drag will be related to the flow by lift and drag coefficients, respectively. Thus, with reference to Fig. 9-11, we will write

$$F_L = C_L Bc \frac{\rho V_0^2}{2} \tag{9-24}$$

$$F_D = C_D Bc \frac{\rho V_0^2}{2} \tag{9-25}$$

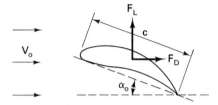

Fig. 9-11. Definition sketch for lift, drag, and angle of attack of an air foil.

The subscript L is introduced to indicate lift and the most representative area is the product of chord length c and wing span (or length) B (in the direction perpendicular to the cross section shown on Fig. 9-11). For accuracy the coefficients C_L and C_D must be determined experimentally. Approximate solutions for lift can be obtained analytically; these will be considered in Chapter 12, which deals with ideal flows.

Note before continuing, however, that the actual forces are, as always, directly related to the pressure distributions. The curvature of the wing surface results in increased velocity over the wing and reduced velocity below. Accordingly, the pressure is reduced above and increased below, giving rise to the net upward force of lift.

Typical curves of C_L and C_D for a wing of infinite length are given in Fig. 9-12. As Fig. 9-11 indicates, they are primarily a function of the angle of attack α_0. In general, the coefficients should depend on both the Reynolds number and the Mach number. Restricting our consideration to incompressible flow, only viscous effects have to be considered. Since the Reynolds numbers are usually very high, the viscous effects are insignificant and can be ignored, leaving the angle of attack as the most significant parameter. The infinite wing corresponds to two-dimentional flow and end effects can be ignored. This is achieved in the laboratory by placing flat plates over the ends of the wing section.

Refer now to Fig. 9-12. The lift coefficient is considerably greater than

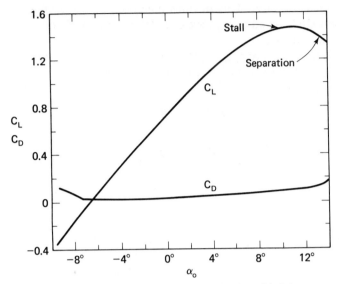

Fig. 9-12. Coefficients of lift and drag for a wing of infinite span.

the drag coefficient, the ratio indicating a measure of the efficiency of the wing. Of interest also is the positive lift that occurs even for a negative angle of attack and the nearly linear relationship for lift coefficient as α_0 increases over a wide range of angles. Eventually, the C_L curve turns downward as the point of maximum lift is passed. This dropoff, known as *stall*, occurs as the flow over the wing suddenly separates. Note that this also causes an increase in drag.

EXAMPLE 9-8

Assume that the curves of Fig. 9-12 are valid for a plane weighing 9000 lb and flying at a velocity of 180 ft/s. The wing span is 60 ft and the average chord length is 7 ft. Assume that $p_{\text{atmos}} = 11$ psia and $T = 25°F$. Determine the corresponding drag force and the horsepower required to overcome this drag.

SOLUTION:

In level flight the lift force must equal the weight of the plane. The density is given by

$$\rho = \frac{p}{gRT} = \frac{(11)(144)}{(32.2)(53.3)(485)} = 0.001903 \text{ slug/ft}^3$$

From Eq. 9-24,

$$C_L = \frac{F_L}{Bc\rho V_0^2/2} = \frac{(2)(9000)}{(60)(7)(0.001903)(180)^2} = 0.695$$

From Fig. 9-12 the corresponding drag coefficient is $C_D = 0.04$; and the drag, by

Eq. 9-25, is

$$F_D = (0.04)(60)(7)(0.001903)\frac{(180)^2}{2} = 517.9 \text{ lb}$$

Thus, the horsepower required to overcome the drag is

$$P = \frac{(517.9)(180)}{550} = 169.5 \text{ hp}$$

EXAMPLE 9-9

Determine the stall speed for the plane of Example 9-8.

SOLUTION:

In Example 9-8 the coefficient of lift was $C_L = 0.695$. At stall, Fig. 9-12 indicates that the lift coefficient will have just reached $C_L = 1.48$. Hence, Eq. 9-24 becomes

$$9000 \text{ lb} = \frac{(1.48)(60 \text{ ft})(7 \text{ ft})(0.001903 \text{ slug/ft}^3)(V_0 \text{ ft/s})^2}{2}$$

Solving, the stall velocity is $V_0 = 123.4$ ft/s.

Induced Drag

Thus far an infinite span length has been assumed, thereby avoiding end (or wingtip) effects. The modifications that result for wings of finite length are shown in Fig. 9-13. As with the two-dimensional case, the flow passes

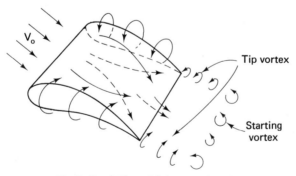

Fig. 9-13. Effect of finite span length.

over the wing with a higher velocity than that passing below except at the trailing edge, where, because of the shape of the air foil, the velocity below is greater than that above. This leads to a velocity discontinuity and a transverse vortex formation known as the *starting vortex*. This occurs on both the infinite and finite length spans. Although this starting vortex is important in the mathematical explanations of lift, it is not of immediate concern here.

The pressure difference between the lower and upper surfaces cannot remain two-dimensional over the entire span, as this would create a pressure discontinuity at the end of the wing. Rather, a smooth pressure gradient is established over the ends. This is accompanied, however, by the setting up of a secondary flow over the end from the high-pressure side to the low-pressure side, known as a *tip vortex*. The secondary flow pattern over and under the wing, as well as the tip vortices, are shown on Fig. 9-13. These tip vortices, with their accompanying reduction in pressure and temperature, sometimes cause condensation patterns in high-level flight similar to the *vapor trails* from the engine blast.

The tip vortices induce a downward component of velocity V_i known as *downwash*, which can be treated as shown in Fig. 9-14. Thus, the finite length

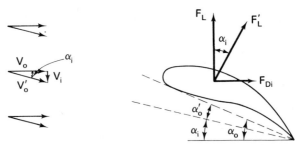

Fig. 9-14. Definition sketch for consideration of induced drag.

can be treated as an infinite length span with approach velocity V_0' and reduced angle of attack α_0'. This effective angle of attack is given by

$$\alpha_0' = \alpha_0 - \alpha_i \qquad (9\text{-}26)$$

where

$$\alpha_i = \tan^{-1}\left(\frac{V_i}{V_0}\right) \qquad (9\text{-}27)$$

Since lift is defined as the force perpendicular to the approach velocity, this reduced angle of attack results in a slightly reduced lift. Further, Fig. 9-14 shows that the lift F_L' based on V_0' can be resolved into two components, the actual lift F_L and an induced drag F_{D_i}, which must be added to the normal drag, now written F_{D_0}. Therefore,

$$F_D = F_{D_0} + F_{D_i} \qquad (9\text{-}28)$$

The induced drag may also be written

$$F_{D_i} = C_{D_i} B c \frac{\rho V_0^2}{2} \qquad (9\text{-}29)$$

thereby defining an induced drag coefficient C_{D_i}. For small induced angle of attack α_i, we may write

$$\tan \alpha_i \approx \sin \alpha_i \approx \alpha_i \quad \text{(radians)} \tag{9-30a}$$

and

$$\cos \alpha_i \approx 1 \tag{9-30b}$$

Thus, the following approximate relationships will hold:

$$F_L = F'_L, \quad V_0 = V'_0, \quad \text{and} \quad F_{D_i} = F_L \alpha_i \tag{9-31}$$

On the basis of an assumed elliptical distribution of lift along a wing, the induced drag coefficient has been determined as

$$C_{D_i} = \frac{C_L^2}{\pi B/c} \tag{9-32}$$

whence from Eq. 9-31, along with Eqs. 9-24 and 9-29,

$$\alpha_i = \frac{C_L}{\pi B/c} \quad \text{(radians)} \tag{9-33}$$

EXAMPLE 9-10

Reinvestigate Example 9-8 in light of its finite wing length.

SOLUTION:

The lift force remains the same and by Eq. 9-31 the coefficient of lift also is unchanged. Assuming an elliptic distribution of lift force, the induced angle of attack may be calculated:

$$\alpha_i = \frac{C_L}{\pi B/c} = \frac{0.695}{\pi(\frac{60}{7})} = 0.0258 \text{ rad}$$

Therefore, the induced drag is

$$F_{D_i} = F_L \alpha_i = (9000)(0.0258) = 232.3 \text{ lb}$$

and the total drag is now

$$F_D = 517.9 + 232.3 = 750.2 \text{ lb}$$

The increase power required is

$$\Delta P = \frac{(232.3)(180)}{550} = 76.0 \text{ additional horsepower}$$

PROBLEMS

Sec. 9-1

9-1. Air at 70°F blows at 82 ft/s along a 2-ft-long flat surface in a wind tunnel. On the same graph, plot the variation of shear stress along the length assuming that (a) the boundary layer is laminar for the entire length; (b) the entire boundary layer is turbulent. What is the average shear stress in each case?

9-2. Water at 20°C flows at the rate of 40 m/s over a 1-m-long flat surface. Plot the the boundary layer thickness along the length of the plate, assuming that (a) the boundary layer is laminar over the entire length; (b) the entire boundary layer is turbulent. (c) Over what length is the boundary layer most likely to be laminar?

9-3. At what maximum velocity may a very thin, flat plate 4-ft by 4-ft be pulled through water at 60°F if the drag force is not to exceed 10 lb?

9-4. At what maximum velocity may a very thin, 2-m by 2-m flat plate be pulled through fuel oil at 50°C if the drag force is not to exceed 80 N?

9-5. At what maximum velocity may the plate of Prob. 9-4 be pulled if the entire boundary layer is to remain laminar and the fluid is water at 50°C?

9-6. What is the surface drag on a ship if its length is 300 ft and the submerged area is 25,000 ft²? Its speed is 20 ft/s through 50°F water. What power is required to overcome the surface drag?

9-7. What is the thickness of the boundary layer at the stern of the ship of Prob. 9-6? What portion of the length has a laminar boundary layer?

9-8. Determine the surface drag on a 100-m ship with a surface area below the Plimsoll mark (waterline) of 3000 m² if its speed is 7 m/s through water at 15°C.

9-9. Repeat Prob. 9-7 for the ship of Prob. 9-8.

9-10. What is the surface drag on a blimp 60-m long with a surface area of 1400 m² if it cruises at 20 m/s through air at 17°C? What power is required?

9-11. A streamlined train with a length of 300 m and a perimeter of 8m has a speed of 145 km/hr. What is the surface drag on the train if the air temperature is 20°C?

9-12. Determine the boundary layer thickness at the end of the train of Prob. 9-11. What portion of the length will have a laminar boundary layer?

Sec. 9-2

9-13. What is the drag on a sphere of 10-ft diameter exposed to an air flow of 60 ft/s at 70°F?

9-14. What is the drag on a 1-ft-diameter sphere pulled through 60°F water at (a) 1 ft/s; (b) 10 ft/s?

9-15. What is the drag on a 10-m-diameter spherical balloon when held in a wind of 8 m/s? The air temperature is 25°C.

9-16. Plot a graph of the force on a 1-ft-diameter sphere exposed to air flows ranging from 0.1 ft/s to 100 ft/s. Assume that the air temperature is 60°F.

9-17. A 1-ft-diameter circular disk is pulled at the rate of 1 ft/s through a tank of fuel oil at 110°F. What force is required?

9-18. Compare the force required to pull a 6-ft by 6-ft thin plate at a velocity of 20 ft/s through 70°F water when the plate is perpendicular to the flow and when it is parallel to the flow. What power is required in each case?

9-19. At what terminal velocity will a sand grain (sp. gr. = 2.65) with diameter of 0.5 mm fall through water (temperature 60°F) at rest?

9-20. At what terminal velocity will a 1-mm-diameter sand grain (sp. gr. = 2.65) fall through water at 5°C?

9-21. At what terminal velocity will a 10-ft-diameter hydrogen balloon rise through air at 70°F? Assume the hydrogen to be at atmospheric pressure.

9-22. At what terminal velocity will a 1-cm-diameter air bubble rise through water that is at 30°C?

9-23. Assuming a parachute to be a hemispherical shell, at what terminal velocity will a man (weight 200 lb) fall if the chute has a diameter of 20 ft? Assume an air temperature of 50°F.

9-24. What diameter parachute (see Prob. 9-23) would be necessary for a man weighing 800 N if he is to land with a velocity less than 5.5 m/s?

9-25. What diameter of parachute (see Prob. 9-23) would be required for an object weighing 3000 lb with a landing velocity of 22 ft/s?

9-26. A pair of hemispherical shells is oriented toward the flow as shown. Each has a diameter of 4 cm and an arm of 10 cm connecting it to a hinge support. What is the net thrust and moment on the hinge? Assume air at 20°C and atmospheric pressure.

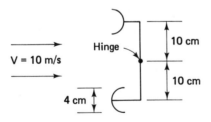

9-27. Determine the drag on an electrical cable that has a diameter of 1 cm and a length of 70 m between supports when the wind velocity is 20 m/s. Assume air at 15°C and atmospheric pressure.

Sec. 9-3

9-28. For the plane of Examples 9-8 and 9-9, determine the drag force at the point of stall.

9-29. For the wing of Fig. 9-12, plot the ratio of lift to drag coefficient versus the angle of attack. Determine the angle α of greatest efficiency and the maximum lift/drag ratio.

9-30. Keeping the wing area unchanged, but increasing the ratio of wing span to chord length up to 12 for the wing of Example 9-10, what would be the percent reduction in (a) induced drag; (b) total drag?

9-31. Develop Eq. 9-33 according to the procedure indicated.

9-32. Use the curves of Fig. 9-12 for a plane that weighs 40 kN and flies at a velocity of 60 m/s with a wing span of 20 m and an average chord length of 2 m. Assume standard atmospheric pressure and a temperature of 25°C. Calculate the drag force on the plane and the power required to overcome this drag.

9-33. Determine the stall velocity and corresponding drag force for the plane of Prob. 9-32.

9-34. Calculate the induced drag on the plane of Fig. 9-32 and resulting increase in power required to offset the induced drag.

REFERENCES

DEAN, R. C., "Separation and Stall," Section 11 in *Handbook of Fluid Dynamics*, V. L. Streeter (ed.). New York: McGraw-Hill, 1961.

LANDWEBER, L., "Motion of Immersed and Floating Bodies," Section 13 in *Handbook of Fluid Dynamics*, V. L. Streeter (ed.). New York: McGraw-Hill, 1961.

MILNE-THOMSON, L. M., *Theoretical Hydrodynamics*, 5th ed. New York: Macmillan, 1968.

ROSENHEAD, L. (ed.), *Laminar Boundary Layers*. Oxford: Oxford University Press, 1963.

ROUSE, H., *Elementary Mechanics of Fluids*. New York: Wiley, 1946.

SCHLICHTING, H., *Boundary Layer Theory*, 6th ed., New York: McGraw-Hill, 1968.

10

Open-Channel Flow

Each of the next three chapters examines an area of fluid mechanics that is frequently expanded into a complete course or set of courses. Consequently, it may be expected that these chapters will serve only as introductions to the specific subject matter. In the present chapter, for example, dealing with flow in open channels, much of the material is very applied in nature and of interest primarily to the civil engineering profession.

In the following sections, the characteristics of open channel (or free surface) flows will be discussed. Resistance to flow, already considered in Chapter 8, will be expanded somewhat. The nonuniform flow associated with the short transition section from one channel cross section to another will be analyzed in one section, while the nonuniform flow involving friction and long transitions will be treated in another. The importance of the Froude number will be emphasized, and flow problems involving waves and surges will be examined.

10–1 CHARACTERISTICS OF OPEN-CHANNEL FLOW: RESISTANCE

Open-channel flow encompasses any flow situation involving a free surface. It is thereby restricted to the flow of liquids, and the liquid in most applications is water. Because of the free surface, gravity usually plays an important role and we can expect that the Froude number will be an important parameter. The terms "steady" and "unsteady" bear their usual significance. Examples that can be made steady by the concept of relative motion will be considered later. "Uniformity" also carries its usual meaning; however, an additional distinction must be made. A completely confined flow will be uniform if and only if the conduit is straight and its cross section has a constant size and shape. An open-channel flow, to be uniform, must also have a straight, constant-shape channel. However, it must also be in equilibrium; that is, the component of the liquid weight in the direction of flow must equal the resistance of the channel boundary. If this condition is satisfied, the surface of the liquid in the direction of flow will be parallel to the channel bottom and the flow uniform. It should be clear from the preceding discussion that uniform flow is not possible in a horizontal channel since equilibrium can never exist.

This equilibrium analysis for uniform flow may be applied to an irregular but uniform, cross section A, as indicated in Fig. 10-1, with the following results:

$$\gamma LA \sin \theta = \tau_0 PL$$

or

$$\tau_0 = \gamma \frac{A}{P} \sin \theta = \gamma R \sin \theta$$

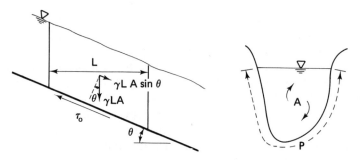

Fig. 10-1.   Open-channel resistance.

As in Section 8-4, R is the hydraulic radius and τ_0 represents the average shear stress around the wetted perimeter, that portion of the boundary which is resisting the flow. For open-channel flows θ is generally small, so the slope S is

$$S = \tan \theta \approx \sin \theta$$

and

$$\tau_0 = \gamma RS \qquad (10\text{-}1)$$

This is essentially the resistance equation derived earlier (Eq. 8-44), since the slope may be considered as the slope of the total head line as well as the channel slope for uniform flow.

If the constant-cross-section channel has a nonuniform flow, which may be the case in the vicinity of a change in grade or upstream or downstream of a control structure, such as a weir or sluice gate, then the analysis is further complicated. It is usually assumed, to good effect, that the empirical resistance equations, such as the Manning equation, still apply, the only difference being that the slope involved must be the slope of the total head line rather than the channel slope. Under these circumstances, Eqs. 8-52 become

$$V = \frac{1}{n} R^{2/3} S_f^{1/2} \tag{10-2a}$$

in SI units and

$$V = \frac{1.49}{n} R^{2/3} S_f^{1/2} \tag{10-2b}$$

in English units, where S_f is the slope of the total head line, usually called the *friction slope*. To avoid confusion, the channel slope will now be denoted as S_0.

Pressure Distribution

Generally, the relatively flat slope associated with uniform free surface flow permits the usual assumption of hydrostatic pressure distribution in the vertical direction. As the slope increases, as in the case of flow over a spillway, down a steep chute, or flow down an incline during an industrial process, the effect of the slope itself on the pressure distribution cannot be neglected. The situation will be developed with respect to Fig. 10-2.

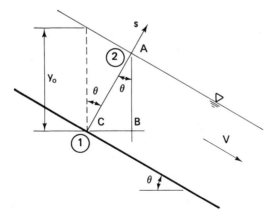

Fig. 10-2.   Pressure distribution on very steep slopes.

Start with Eq. 5-2, which may readily be written for an open-channel flow as

$$\frac{\partial}{\partial s}\left(\frac{p}{\gamma} + y\right) = -\frac{a_s}{g} \tag{10-3}$$

Recalling that a_s, from Eq. 5-2, was the acceleration in an arbitrary (not necessarily streamline) direction, the equation may be applied in the s direction of Fig. 10-2, for which the acceleration is zero. Immediately,

$$\frac{p}{\gamma} + y = \text{constant}$$

or

$$\frac{p_1}{\gamma} + y_1 = \frac{p_2}{\gamma} + y_2$$

where points 1 and 2 are at the bottom of the channel and at the surface of the liquid, respectively, but do not lie on a vertical line. The pressure $p_2 = 0$, and in the notation of Fig. 10-2, $y_2 - y_1$ equals the vertical distance AB. Thus, the pressure at point 1 is

$$p_1 = \gamma(AB)$$

In terms of the length AC, which is the liquid thickness,

$$AB = AC \cos \theta$$

so that

$$p_1 = \gamma(AC) \cos \theta \tag{10-4}$$

Finally, if the pressure is calculated from the vertical thickness (or depth y_0),

$$AC = y_0 \cos \theta$$

and

$$p_1 = \gamma y_0 \cos^2 \theta \tag{10-5}$$

The pressure distribution is still linear; however, some care must be used in its calculation. As the slope becomes small, $\cos^2 \theta$ approaches unity, and the usual equation for pressure distribution results.

Resistance Problems

One problem associated with open-channel flow occurs when channel shape gets too extreme. The most graphic example of this is the very typical river channel in which the normal water surface elevation, or stage, is confined to a main channel, but flood stage spreads out over a wide floodplain (Fig. 10-3).

This may be handled by the following technique. The channel is divided into two regions, as shown. The discharge in each portion is then related to the same channel slope and to the geometry of the specific portion. Then, for

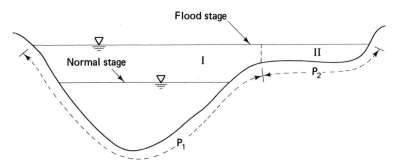

Fig. 10-3. Overbank problem.

either uniform or nonuniform flow,

$$Q = Q_I + Q_{II}$$
$$= \frac{1.49}{n_1} A_1 \left(\frac{A_1}{P_1}\right)^{2/3} S_f^{1/2} + \frac{1.49}{n_2} A_2 \left(\frac{A_2}{P_2}\right)^{2/3} S_f^{1/2}$$

or

$$Q = 1.49 S_f^{1/2} \left(\frac{A_1^{5/3}}{n_1 P_1^{2/3}} + \frac{A_2^{5/3}}{n_2 P_2^{2/3}}\right) \tag{10-6}$$

If the flow is uniform, $S_f = S_0$. Further, P_1 and P_2 (as shown in Fig. 10-3) will generally be chosen so as to ignore the common fluid boundary between the two regions.[1] This is tantamount to saying that no shear stress exists between the two sections, which is not exactly true if V_1 is considerably greater than V_2. The foregoing procedure may be easily generalized to cover any number of regions into which it may be desirable to subdivide the cross section for reasons of varying cross-sectional shape or even varying Manning n.

Another, perhaps even more difficult problem associated with open-channel flow is the estimation of boundary roughness or, more specifically, the Manning n value. Table 8-3 gives typical values of n; however, considerable judgment and experience are required, particularly when dealing with natural channels. The problem is even more complicated in sand bed channels, where a variety of bed forms (ripples, dunes, and bars, among others) each give rise to a different magnitude of roughness. Without going into further detail, the final expression of Table 8-3 may be used to give an estimate of Manning n for flat-bed sand channels.

EXAMPLE 10-1

Estimate the flow rate for the river cross section approximated in Fig. 10-4. The main channel (I) has a sand bed with a mean grain size of 0.5 mm, and the overbank portion (II) is largely grass and small shrubs. The slope is approximately 1 ft/mi.

---

[1]Shown as a dashed line separating regions I and II on Fig. 10-3.

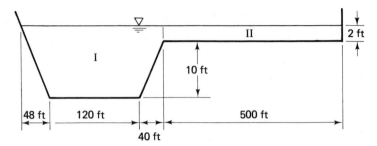

Fig. 10-4. Example of overbank problem.

SOLUTION:

For the main channel (assuming a flat bed),

$$n_1 = 0.034d^{1/6}$$

$$= (0.034)\left(\frac{0.5}{304.8}\right)^{1/6} = 0.012$$

Assume for the overbank portion that

$$n_2 = 0.050$$

From the channel geometry,

$$A_1 = (120)(10) + (40)(10)(\tfrac{1}{2}) + (48)(12)(\tfrac{1}{2}) + (2)(160)$$

$$= 2008 \text{ ft}^2$$

$$A_2 = (2)(500) = 1000 \text{ ft}^2$$

Also,

$$P_1 = 120 + \sqrt{(48)^2 + (12)^2} + \sqrt{(40)^2 + (10)^2} = 210.7 \text{ ft}$$

and

$$P_2 = 500 + 2 = 502 \text{ ft}$$

Therefore, from Eq. 10-6,

$$Q = \frac{(1.49)(2008)^{5/3}}{(0.012)(210.7)^{2/3}}\left(\frac{1}{5280}\right)^{1/2} + \frac{(1.49)(1000)^{5/3}}{(0.050)(502)^{2/3}}\left(\frac{1}{5280}\right)^{1/2}$$

$$= 16,000 \text{ cfs}$$

10–2 SPECIFIC ENERGY: FROUDE NUMBER

This section will concentrate on steady open-channel flow through channel transitions which are sufficiently short that energy loss and friction can be ignored. As with the analysis of flows through other types of transitions, it is to be expected that the energy equation will be a major tool. We will, in fact, see repeated use of the energy concept throughout the remainder of the chapter. However, for some purposes it is advantageous to adopt it in a modified form, referred to as the *specific energy*. To illustrate the need, first consider flow at depth y in a rectangular channel of constant width b. It is desired to determine what will happen to the depth or water surface elevation if it encounters a change in bottom elevation Δz as shown on Fig. 10-5.

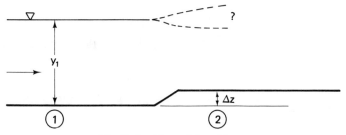

Fig. 10-5.   Channel transition.

Flow is from left to right, and assuming that section 2 is reasonably close to section 1, channel friction may be ignored in this type of analysis. Note that if flow at sections 1 and 2 is uniform (or nearly uniform) the pressure distribution vertically will be hydrostatic and the pressure and elevation heads may be replaced by the water surface elevation relative to a horizontal datum. Immediately,

$$y_1 + \frac{V_1^2}{2g} = (y_2 + \Delta z) + \frac{V_2^2}{2g} \tag{10-7}$$

Assuming that the flow rate is known, this expression can be put in terms of only one unknown, y_2, through use of continuity in its two-dimensional form,

$$q = y_1 V_1 = y_2 V_2 \tag{10-8}$$

The result is

$$y_1 + \frac{q^2}{2gy_1^2} = \Delta z + y_2 + \frac{q^2}{2gy_2^2} \tag{10-9}$$

Although this equation can be solved by trial and error, it is a cubic equation and we cannot even say which is the correct root, as there will usually be two positive roots. To circumvent this impasse, we define a quality known as the specific energy, H_0. By definition the specific energy is the total head relative to the channel bottom. Thus, in general,

$$H_0 = y + \frac{V^2}{2g} \tag{10-10}$$

and in a rectangular channel,

$$H_0 = y + \frac{q^2}{2gy^2} \tag{10-11}$$

Note at this point that the values of specific energy at the two sections of Fig. 10-5 are

$$H_{0_1} = y_1 + \frac{q^2}{2gy_1^2}$$

and

$$H_{0_2} = y_2 + \frac{q^2}{2gy_2^2}$$

and that they are related, in this case, through the conventional energy equation as follows:

$$H_{0_1} = H_{0_2} + \Delta z$$

To apply the specific energy concept, it is appropriate at this point to consider Eq. 10-11 in some detail.

Specific Energy Diagram

If Eq. 10-11 for specific energy in a rectangular channel is plotted with H_0 as the abscissa and depth y as the ordinate, we will get a curve as shown in Fig. 10-6 for constant q, the discharge per unit width. (For a rectangular channel of constant width, q will of course remain constant if the flow is

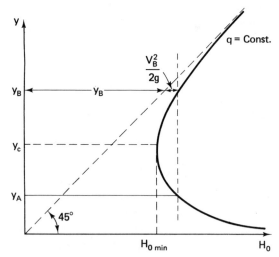

Fig. 10-6. Specific energy diagram.

steady, since the actual discharge Q is constant.) As the depth goes to zero, H_0 tends to infinity, giving the lower limb of the curve. As the depth gets larger and larger, y approaches H_0 in value, and the upper limb asymptotically approaches the 45° line as shown. Thus, for any value of H_0 above some $H_{0_{\min}}$, there are two possible flow depths. They are indicated in Fig. 10-6 as y_A and y_B. Since at depth y_B the horizontal distance over to the 45°

line is also y_B, the remaining distance, by Eq. 10-10, must be equal to the velocity head $V_B^2/2g$.

This geometric relationship is applicable to any depth. Therefore, the two possible flow states for a given value of H_0 consist of a relatively deep flow (y_B) and low velocity (as indicated by $V_B^2/2g$) and a relatively shallow flow (y_A) and high velocity (V_A). The former is called *subcritical flow* and the latter *supercritical flow*.

Below a certain minimum value of specific energy, the flow is not possible. It is this minimum that will be considered next. If Eq. 10-11 is differentiated with respect to y and the result set equal to zero, the minimum point of the curve can be located. Namely,

$$\frac{dH_0}{dy} = 1 - \frac{q^2}{gy^3} = 0$$

We will refer to this depth as the critical depth y_c. Hence, upon solving,

$$y_c = \sqrt[3]{\frac{q^2}{g}} \qquad (10\text{-}12)$$

With critical depth defined in this manner it will be noted that for

$$\text{Subcritical flow:} \quad y > y_c$$
$$\text{Supercritical flow:} \quad y < y_c$$

In terms of velocities,

$$\text{Subcritical flow:} \quad V < V_c$$
$$\text{Supercritical flow:} \quad V > V_c$$

The critical velocity (V_c) associated with critical depth is obtained from

$$V_c = \frac{q}{y_c}$$

We may also write

$$H_{0min} = y_c + \frac{V_c^2}{2g}$$

and, combining this with Eq. 10-12 in the form

$$y_c^3 = \frac{V_c^2 y_c^2}{g}$$

or

$$y_c = 2\left(\frac{V_c^2}{2g}\right)$$

gives

$$H_{0min} = \tfrac{3}{2} y_c \qquad (10\text{-}13)$$

This equation gives the relationship between H_{0min} and y_c, but as a word of caution, the minimum value of specific energy cannot be found from a given value of depth by using this equation. Neither can be critical depth be found from Eq. 10-13 by taking two-thirds of a given value of H_0.

Return now to the problem associated with Fig. 10-5. Since q, y_1, and Δz were given, we can calculate H_{0_1}, y_c, and H_{0_2}, the latter from

$$H_{0_1} = H_{0_2} + \Delta z$$

If $y_1 > y_c$, the problem can be analyzed per Fig. 10-7 as follows. Passing

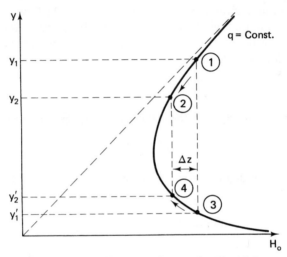

Fig. 10-7. Specific energy diagram for Fig. 10-5.

from section 1 to section 2, H_0 must decrease by the amount Δz, but since q is constant, the flow must follow the solution line of Fig. 10-7. Thus, moving to the left from point 1 (so as to lower H_0), you drop down to some point 2. The associated depth, y_2, is the required solution. Not only is the depth less, but since the vertical distance from the water surface to the total head line ($V^2/2g$) increases, the water surface elevation must drop as well. If the flow at section 1 were supercritical, the depth $y_2'^2$ is less than y_c. This solution starts on the lower limb at point 3 with energy H_{0_1} and moving to the left as H_0 decreases, the depth increases to some value y_2' at point 4, which is the required solution for the supercritical flow. Both solutions are shown in Fig. 10-8.

Further increases of Δz would lower y_2 or increase y_2' until Δz just equals $H_{0_1} - H_{\min}$. This condition would make either y_2 or y_2' just equal to y_c. Additional increase of Δz would drop H_{0_2} below $H_{0_{\min}}$, an impossible state.[3]

[2]The prime is added here only to permit showing both solutions on the same diagram without confusion.

[3]At this point the transition becomes a "choke." We will see a similar situation arise for compressible flows in Chapter 11.

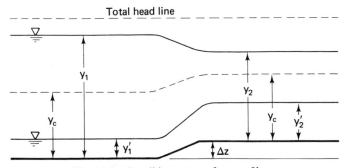

Fig. 10-8. Possible water surface profiles.

Rather, the flow would adjust to this larger increase in Δz by adjusting upstream so as to increase the value of H_{0_1} to the extent that the flow would pass over the hump with H_{0_2} just equal to $H_{0_{\min}}$. If the flow were subcritical, this adjustment would take the form of a gentle swell that would move upstream, altering the flow condition. The result would be a greater depth, lower velocity, but greater specific energy. If, on the other hand, the flow were supercritical, the adjustment would require that a surge (see the next section) move upstream, and the new conditions would be the same subcritical flow as in the previous case of initially subcritical flow.

A drop in channel bottom would be analyzed in the same fashion, with H_{0_2} being greater than H_{0_1}. As the amount of drop increases, there is no limit such as was considered in the preceding discussion with increasing channel bottom.

Another type of rectangular channel transition consists of a constant bottom elevation and a change in channel width. In this case H_0 must remain constant through the transition, but the discharge per unit width will change even though the flow is steady. If the channel varies in width as shown in Fig. 10-9, the narrower width at section 2 will result in $q_1 < q_2$. In this case a specific energy diagram similar to that of Fig. 9-5 can be constructed for each value of q, as shown in Fig. 10-10. It can easily be shown that the curve for q_2 will be to the right of that for q_1 and y_{c_2} will be greater than y_{c_1}. The

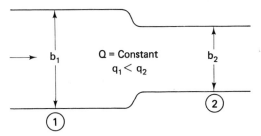

Fig. 10-9. Channel width constriction.

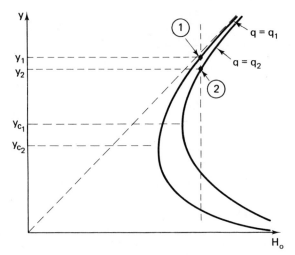

Fig. 10-10.   Specific energy diagram for transition of Fig. 10-9.

solution to the change in width problem must lie on a line of constant H_0, such as the vertical dashed line in Fig. 10-10. Consider the case when the flow at section 1 is subcritical (point 1 on Fig. 10-10). As the flow passes from section 1 to 2 at constant specific energy, the depth must change from y_1 on the q_1 curve of Fig. 10-10 to point 2 on the q_2 curve. Consequently, the depth must decrease in the constricted section. Other channel contractions and expansions would be handled identically. A transition that involves both a change in bottom elevation and a change in width can be treated by combining the two individual methods. As the examples will illustrate, the actual solution to a given problem may still require solving a cubic equation. But the specific energy diagram will tell us in advance which root we are interested in, and will set specific limits within which the solutions must fall.

Froude Number

If the depth and average velocity at a section are taken as the defining quantities for the Froude number, the Froude number for that section becomes

$$Fr = \frac{V}{\sqrt{gy}} \tag{10-14}$$

If the depth changes from section to section, as in the preceding examples, then, of course, the Froude number must change as well. Consider the value of the Froude number at critical conditions,

$$Fr_c = \frac{V_c}{\sqrt{gy_c}}$$

but as before,

$$y_c = \frac{V_c^2}{g}$$

Hence,

$$\text{Fr}_c = 1$$

Referring now to Eq. 10-14, as y becomes greater than y_c, and correspondingly V becomes less than V_c, the value of the Froude number decreases and hence must be less than unity. Conversely, if $y < y_c$, the Froude number will exceed unity. In summary, we have:

Subcritical flow:	$y > y_c$	$\text{Fr} < 1$
Critical flow:	$y = y_c$	$\text{Fr} = 1$
Supercritical flow:	$y < y_c$	$\text{Fr} > 1$

and the significance of the Froude number for the characterizing of open-channel flows is established. The following section will make more use of this important parameter.

If the differentiation of specific head with y is again considered, we note that

$$\frac{dH_0}{dy} = 1 - \frac{q^2}{gy^3} = 1 - \frac{V^2}{gy} = 1 - \text{Fr}^2 \qquad (10\text{-}15)$$

which immediately shows that at critical conditions for which $dH_0/dy = 0$, the Froude number must equal unity.

EXAMPLE 10-2

Determine the downstream depth in a 3-m-wide rectangular channel in which the channel bottom or invert drops 0.1 m. The flow rate is 5.5 m³/s and the upstream depth 0.4 m.

SOLUTION:

The channel and specific energy diagram (not to same scale) are shown in Fig. 10-11. The discharge per unit width is

$$q = \frac{Q}{b} = \frac{5.5 \text{ m}^3/\text{s}}{3 \text{ m}} = 1.83 \text{ (m}^3/\text{s)/m}$$

and the critical depth is

$$y_c = \sqrt[3]{\frac{q^2}{g}}$$

$$= \sqrt[3]{\frac{(1.83 \text{ m}^2/\text{s})^2}{9.81 \text{ m/s}^2}} = 0.70 \text{ m}$$

Since $y = 0.40 \text{ m} < 0.70 \text{ m}$, the flow is supercritical and y_1 is on the lower limb, as shown on the specific energy diagram. In passing from section 1 to section 2 the

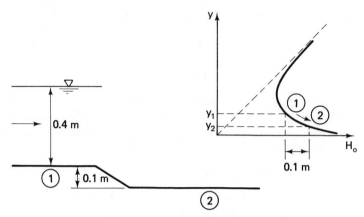

Fig. 10-11.   Rectangular channel with drop in invert (or bottom elevation).

specific energy must increase by 0.1 m and hence y_2 must be less than y_1. Solving,

$$H_{0_1} = y_1 + \frac{q^2}{2gy_1^2} = (0.4) + \frac{(1.83)^2}{(2)(9.81)(0.4)^2} = 1.467 \text{ m}$$

$$H_{0_2} = H_{0_1} + 0.1 \text{ m} = 1.567 \text{ m}$$

and finally

$$H_{0_2} = y_2 + \frac{q^2}{2gy_2^2}$$

or

$$1.567 = y_2 + \frac{(1.83)^2}{(2)(9.81)y_2^2} = y_2 + \frac{0.171}{y_2^2}$$

The downstream depth must lie in the range $0 < y_2 < y_1$. Upon solving by trial and error, the solution is found to be $y_2 = 0.38$ m.

EXAMPLE 10-3

Determine the maximum possible infringement due to bridge approaches in the rectangular channel shown in Fig. 10-12 that will not create upstream changes. The flow rate is 3200 cfs, the original width is $b_1 = 100$ ft, and the original depth is 8 ft.

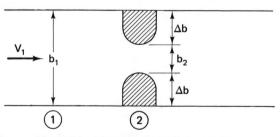

Fig. 10-12.   Example of width constriction.

SOLUTION:

For the approach conditions the average velocity is

$$V_1 = \frac{3200}{(100)(8)} = 4 \text{ ft/s}$$

and the Froude number is

$$Fr_1 = \frac{4}{\sqrt{(8)(32.2)}} = 0.249$$

Hence, the flow is subcritical. The initial discharge per unit width is

$$q_1 = V_1 y_1 = (4)(8) = 32 \text{ cfs/ft}$$

The specific energy diagram appropriate to q_1 is shown in Fig. 10-13 with conditions at section 1 identified. Since we desire the maximum possible constriction, we must

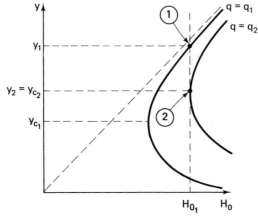

Fig. 10-13. Specific energy diagram for maximum constricted section.

find the value of the maximum possible discharge per unit width. This will be q_2, the curve that just intersects the line of constant specific energy $H_0 = H_{0_1}$. This value of H_0 is

$$H_{0_1} = y_1 + \frac{V_1^2}{2g}$$

$$= 8 + \frac{(4)^2}{64.4} = 8.248 \text{ ft}$$

Since conditions at the constricted section will be critical,

$$y_{c_2} = \tfrac{2}{3} H_{0_1} = 5.50 \text{ ft}$$

Then, from Eq. 10-12,

$$q_2 = \sqrt{gy_c^3}$$
$$= \sqrt{(32.2)(5.50)^3} = 73.5 \text{ cfs/ft}$$

Therefore, the required channel width is

$$b_2 = \frac{3200 \text{ cfs}}{73.5 \text{ cfs/ft}} = 43.5 \text{ ft}$$

The maximum intrusion on both sides, Δb, is

$$\Delta b = \frac{b_1 - b_2}{2} = \frac{100 - 43.5}{2} = 23.2 \text{ ft}$$

Bridge piers with an infringement less than 23.2 ft per side will have no effect on upstream flow conditions. At $\Delta b = 23.2$ ft, the constricted section becomes a choke. Further infringement out into the flow would result in alteration to the upstream depth.

EXAMPLE 10-4

If a 2.5-m-wide rectangular channel with a flow of 5.0 m³/s at a depth of 1.0 m must pass through a transition in which the channel bottom rises 0.2 m, what new width is required if the water surface is to remain unchanged?

SOLUTION:

Although this type of problem can generally be worked through use of appropriate specific energy diagrams, the fact that in this case the water surface must remain horizontal leads to a direct solution. Friction being ignored in the transition, the total head line is parallel to the water surface, and the velocity head must therefore be constant. From continuity, the cross-sectional areas must also remain unchanged and

$$y_1 b_1 = y_2 b_2$$

from which

$$b_2 = \frac{y_1 b_1}{y_2} = \frac{(1 \text{ m})(2.5 \text{ m})}{1.0 - 0.2 \text{ m}} = 3.13 \text{ m}$$

Nonrectangular Cross Sections

Although the emphasis in this chapter is on rectangular cross sections, it is instructive to briefly consider nonrectangular channels and to generalize the basic relationships. As we have already seen, the Manning equation can be used to determine normal depth whether the section is rectangular or not. If we have a nonrectangular cross section as shown in Fig. 10-14, the total head is

$$H = z + y + \frac{V^2}{2g}$$

where V is the average velocity over the section ($V = Q/A$). Similarly, the

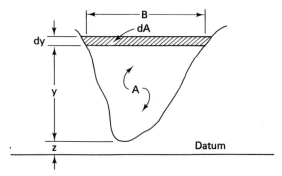

Fig. 10-14. Nonrectangular cross section.

specific energy, defined relative to the channel bottom as before, is

$$H_0 = y + \frac{V^2}{2g} = y + \frac{Q^2}{2gA^2}$$

Differentiating with respect to y and setting the derivative equal to zero,

$$\frac{dH_0}{dy} = 1 - \frac{Q^2}{gA^3}\frac{dA}{dy} = 0$$

If an incremental increase in depth occurs then, as can be seen from the shaded area of Fig. 10-14, $dA = B\,dy$, where B is the top width. Hence, the preceding equation becomes

$$1 - \frac{Q^2 B}{gA^3} = 0$$

or

$$\frac{A^3}{B} = \frac{Q^2}{g} \qquad\qquad (10\text{-}16)$$

Since both A and B are functions of the depth, this equation can now be solved to obtain the critical depth. When the section is rectangular, the equation reduces to Eq. 10-12.

If for nonrectangular cross sections the length variable in the Froude number is chosen as the ratio A/B, then a generalized Froude number becomes

$$\mathrm{Fr} = \frac{V}{\sqrt{g(A/B)}} \qquad\qquad (10\text{-}17)$$

Upon rearrangement of Eq. 10-16, we get at critical conditions

$$\frac{Q^2/A^2}{g(A/B)} = \frac{V^2}{g(A/B)} = \mathrm{Fr}^2 = 1$$

which is consistent with the value of the critical Froude number in a rectangular channel. Further, Eq. 10-17 reverts to Eq. 10-14 when a channel is rectangular.

10–3 WAVES AND SURGES:
HYDRAULIC JUMP

This section will examine the behavior of various types of waves and surges. In so doing, the significance of the Froude number as the parameter of primary importance will be emphasized. That the Froude number is of paramount importance should be expected after our previous considerations of dimensional analysis. Similarly, in Chapter 11 the Mach number will overshadow all other parameters. As moving waves and surges are unsteady, it will once again be necessary to apply the concept of relative motion in order that a steady flow may be analyzed.

Waves

Because of the near absence of viscous effects in the motion of waves, the describing equations have been subjected to considerable mathematical analysis. Therefore, it is possible to find complete mathematical solutions to many wave problems. The interested reader will find reference to these at the end of the chapter. The subject will receive only introductory treatment here.

We will start with a small wave and examine its progress as it spreads outward from the point of disturbance or generation. Such a wave traveling through a fluid at rest is shown in Fig. 10-15a. The wave with height Δy moves with velocity c to the left as shown. We will define the rate of wave advance relative to the fluid as its celerity, c. In order to apply previously derived relationships, the unsteady wave has been brought to rest in Fig. 10-15b by the principle of relative motion. The Bernoulli and continuity

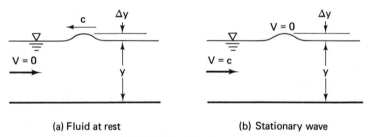

(a) Fluid at rest   (b) Stationary wave

Fig. 10-15.   Small wave.

equations are now to be applied between the approach section with velocity equal to the celerity c, and the section at the stationary wave where the depth is $y + \Delta y$. This leads directly to

$$y + \frac{V^2}{2g} = (y + \Delta y) + \frac{V^2}{2g}\left(\frac{y}{y + \Delta y}\right)^2$$

Solving for the celerity,

$$c = \sqrt{g}\left[\frac{2\Delta y}{1 - \left(\dfrac{y}{y + \Delta y}\right)^2}\right]^{1/2}$$

and after some rearrangement

$$c = \sqrt{g}\left[\frac{2(y + \Delta y)}{1 + \left(\dfrac{y}{y + \Delta y}\right)}\right]^{1/2} \tag{10-18}$$

This may be reduced in two stages for moderately small and very small waves. First, if Δy is small relative to the depth Eq. 10-18 becomes

$$c = \sqrt{g}\,(y + \Delta y)^{1/2}$$

or

$$c = \sqrt{gy}\left(1 + \frac{\Delta y}{y}\right)^{1/2} \tag{10-19}$$

Second, if $\Delta y \ll y$, then we get simply

$$c = \sqrt{gy} \tag{10-20}$$

the equation for the celerity of a very small wave. Since the depth played a major role in the derivation and resulting equations, these waves are known as *shallow water waves*. In other words, the wave is affected by the underlying bed.

For comparison, a theoretical solution based on the wave length λ (Greek lowercase lambda) as well as the depth gives

$$c = \sqrt{\frac{g\lambda}{2\pi}}\left[\tanh\left(\frac{2\pi y}{\lambda}\right)\right]^{1/2} \tag{10-21}$$

If the depth y is large relative to the wave length, this equation becomes

$$c = \sqrt{\frac{g\lambda}{2\pi}} \tag{10-22}$$

the *deep water wave equation*. On the other hand, when the depth is small relative to the wave length,

$$\tanh\left(\frac{2\pi y}{\lambda}\right) \approx \frac{2\pi y}{\lambda}$$

and Eq. 10-21 becomes

$$c = \sqrt{\frac{g\lambda}{2\pi}}\sqrt{\frac{2\pi y}{\lambda}}$$

or

$$c = \sqrt{gy}$$

which is again the shallow water wave equation. Thus, it is the ratio of wave length to depth that distinguishes shallow water waves from deep water waves.

The tidal waves or tsunami, which travel across the Pacific Ocean, move because of their extreme length as shallow water waves.

In all of the preceding equations the velocity c is the velocity of the wave relative to the water (i.e., the celerity). In problems involving waves as they move through flowing water, the celerity must be added algebraically to the water velocity to get the absolute velocity of the wave.

Consideration of the Froude number as applied to a flow of velocity V and depth y such that

$$\text{Fr} = \frac{V}{\sqrt{gy}} \qquad (10\text{-}23)$$

shows that the Froude number can be considered as the ratio of the flow velocity to the celerity of a small wave. Therefore, a Froude number of unity when compared with Eq. 10-20 takes on the added significance that at critical depth (Fr = 1) the flow velocity just equals the celerity of a small wave. Hence, a small wave can move upstream against a subcritical flow but cannot travel upstream when the flow is supercritical. The spreading of a small wave under different flow conditions is summarized in Fig. 10-16.

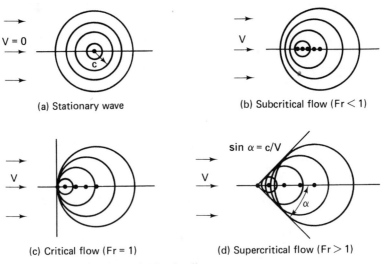

(a) Stationary wave

(b) Subcritical flow (Fr < 1)

(c) Critical flow (Fr = 1)

(d) Supercritical flow (Fr > 1)

Fig. 10-16. Small wave patterns.

In part (a) the water is stationary and small waves spread radially from the point of generation. A series of outward-moving concentric circles results, similar to the ripple pattern that forms when a pebble is tossed into a pond. In part (b) of Fig. 10-16, the spreading waves still assume a circular form. However, as they spread they are also affected by the stream velocity V. Since V is less than c, the waves move upstream more slowly than downstream, hence the nonsymmetric pattern shown. Part (c) is the limiting case where V just equals c, so there can be no propagation upstream and a wave front forms. In the final portion V exceeds c and the wave front itself is swept downstream, with the angle α indicating the relative velocities as shown. Note in conclusion that larger waves can, according to Eqs. 10-18 and 10-19, move upstream against a supercritical flow.

Hydraulic Jump and Surges

The stationary surge or hydraulic jump was considered previously in Example 5-16. The sketch of the two-dimensional hydraulic jump is redrawn as Fig. 10-17. The ratio of downstream to upstream depth was found in

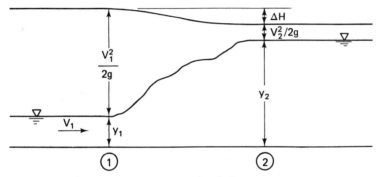

Fig. 10-17.   Hydraulic jump.

Example 5-16 to be

$$\frac{y_2}{y_1} = \frac{1}{2}\left(\sqrt{1 + \frac{8V_1^2}{gy_1}} - 1\right) \tag{10-24}$$

Noting that the Froude number at section 1 is

$$\mathrm{Fr}_1 = \frac{V_1}{\sqrt{gy_1}}$$

Eq. 10-24 becomes

$$\frac{y_2}{y_1} = \tfrac{1}{2}(\sqrt{1 + 8\mathrm{Fr}_1^2} - 1) \tag{10-25}$$

As a matter of convenience it is sometimes desirable to express the depth ratio in terms of downstream conditions. A similar derivation leads to

$$\frac{y_1}{y_2} = \tfrac{1}{2}(\sqrt{1 + 8\mathrm{Fr}_2^2} - 1) \tag{10-26}$$

In the same way the equation for energy loss from Example 5-16,

$$\frac{\Delta H}{y_1} = 1 + \frac{V_1^2}{2gy_1} - \frac{y_2}{y_1} - \left(\frac{y_1}{y_2}\right)^2 \frac{V_1^2}{2gy_1} \tag{10-27}$$

becomes

$$\frac{\Delta H}{y_1} = 1 + \tfrac{1}{2}Fr_1^2 - \tfrac{1}{2}(\sqrt{1 + 8Fr_1^2} - 1) - \frac{2Fr_1^2}{(\sqrt{1 + 8Fr_1^2} - 1)^2} \tag{10-28}$$

Hence, the hydraulic jump is characterized by the Froude number, as might be expected for a free surface phenomenon. These curves are shown graphically in Fig. 10-18, along with an experimental curve for jump length, L_j. By combining the energy, momentum, and continuity equations (see Example 5-16) so as to eliminate both velocities V_1 and V_2 and solving for the head

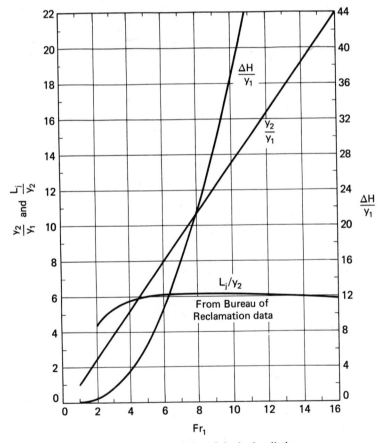

Fig. 10-18. Characteristics of the hydraulic jump.

loss gives an alternative equation,

$$\Delta H = \frac{(y_2 - y_1)^3}{4y_1 y_2} \tag{10-29}$$

This is simpler to use than Eq. 10-28, but it requires knowledge of both upstream and downstream depths.

The stationary hydraulic jump occurs frequently in nature when a high-speed flow encounters a slower deeper flow. Its most important application is at the foot of spillways, where it effectively dissipates a large part of the energy of the very high velocity flow over a dam. By proper design the jump will occur in a concrete stilling basin and the water will be less likely to erode the natural river channel below the dam.

By the principle of relative motion, a moving surge may be brought to rest so that the procedures for the stationary jump can be applied to moving surges. This will be illustrated by Example 10-6, which follows. If the surge moves with a velocity V_s,[4] addition of a velocity $-V_s$ to all points in the flow field will bring the surge to rest and analysis can proceed based on the foregoing relationships. This is true regardless of whether the surge moves with or contrary to the flow direction. Generally, the solution will require that the continuity equation as it applies to the steady-state flow must be included. A rapidly opened gate or the failure of a dam can cause a surge to move downstream. Rapid closure of a gate may cause a surge to move upstream. Rivers in areas exposed to very large tidal fluctuations may have a surge form and move upstream. This type of surge is known as a *bore*.

It is also possible for an oblique surge to form in a supercritical flow. The oblique surge may assume an angle to the flow similar to that shown on Fig. 10-16 for small waves. As these surges tend to occur at changes in the boundary alignment, they are an important aspect in the design of channels that are to carry supercritical flow. However, like the oblique shock wave to be mentioned in Chapter 11, the oblique surge will not be considered further in this book.

EXAMPLE 10-5

Determine the head loss and power dissipation that occur in a hydraulic jump below a spillway. The upstream depth is 0.85 m and the downstream depth is 7.0 m. The cross section is rectangular, with a width of 25 m.

SOLUTION:

For a ratio $y_2/y_1 = 7.0/0.85 = 8.24$, Fig. 10-18 gives

$$\mathrm{Fr}_1 = \frac{V_1}{\sqrt{gy_1}} = 6.2$$

---

[4]Here V_s is the absolute wave velocity, not the relative velocity or celerity.

Thus,

$$V_1 = (6.2)\sqrt{(9.81 \text{ m/s}^2)(0.85 \text{ m})} = 17.90 \text{ m/s}$$

and

$$Q = V_1 A = (17.90 \text{ m/s})(0.85 \text{ m})(25 \text{ m}) = 380 \text{ m}^3/\text{s}$$

Also, from Fig. 10-18, $\Delta H/y_1 = 11.5$, so the head loss in the jump is

$$\Delta H = (11.5)(0.85 \text{ m}) = 9.78 \text{ m}$$

and the power dissipated becomes

$$P = Q\gamma \, \Delta H$$
$$= (380 \text{ m}^3/\text{s})(9800 \text{ N/m}^3)(9.78 \text{ m})$$
$$= 3.64 \times 10^7 \text{ m} \cdot \text{N/s} = 36.4 \text{ MW}$$

EXAMPLE 10-6

A 9-ft-wide rectangular channel carries 180 cfs at a depth of 2 ft. If a downstream gate is abruptly closed, at what velocity will the resulting surge move upstream and what will be the consequent depth?

SOLUTION:

The physical problem is shown in Fig. 10-19a, and the steady state that results upon adding the surge velocity V_s in the opposite direction is given in Fig. 10-19b. The

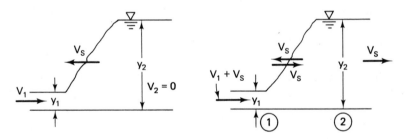

(a) Physical problem.   (b) Steady state conditions.

Fig. 10-19.   Surge due to gate closure.

hydraulic jump equations may now be applied to Fig. 10-19b. From Eq. 10-24,

$$\frac{y_2}{y_1} = \frac{1}{2}\left(\sqrt{1 + \frac{8(V_1 + V_s)^2}{gy_1}} - 1\right)$$

or

$$\frac{y_2}{2} = \frac{1}{2}\left(\sqrt{1 + \frac{(8)(10 + V_s)^2}{(32.2)(2)}} - 1\right)$$

and from continuity

$$(V_1 + V_s)y_1 = V_s y_2$$

or

$$(10 + V_s)(2) = V_s y_2$$

Thus, we have two equations which must be solved simultaneously for the two unknowns. Upon solving, we obtain

$$y_2 = 4.98 \text{ ft}$$

and

$$V_s = 6.72 \text{ ft/s}$$

Upon abruptly closing the gate, a surge will form and move upstream at 6.72 ft/s, leaving stationary water with a depth of 4.98 ft.

10–4 GRADUALLY VARIED FLOW

For purposes of analysis, nonuniform open-channel flows may be divided into two categories. The first type, of which Sections 10-2 and 10-3 form a part, are those flows in which the nonuniformity occurs over a relatively short length. Although the approach was different in each of those sections, they did share the common feature that the channel friction could be ignored because of the localized nonuniformity. The second type, as the title of this section implies, are those open-channel flows in which nonuniform regions extend over relatively long lengths. Consequently, frictional effects must be included in the formulation. As has been the case throughout most of this chapter, only constant-width rectangular cross sections will be considered. The more general solutions to both nonrectangular cross sections and non-constant cross sections are presented in the references found at the end of the chapter.

In general, the flow in a long, constant-slope channel will tend to be uniform. In fact, we have used an equilibrium analysis, balancing the component of the weight along the slope to the resistance around the (wetted) perimeter to calculate the average shear stress. Further, we have calculated the corresponding uniform depth, or normal depth, using the Manning equation. Many conditions can cause the flow to deviate from this normal depth, however. These include a change in channel slope (where, in fact, the water surface is adjusting from one normal depth to another), a dropoff at the end of a channel, and the termination of a channel into a reservoir.

The differential equation governing gradually varied flow may be obtained from the Bernoulli equation. With reference to Fig. 10-20, the total head at any section is

$$H = z + y + \frac{V^2}{2g} \tag{10-30}$$

Note that the elevation of the channel bed is measured relative to a horizontal datum, while y is the depth and is consequently relative to the channel bottom rather than a horizontal reference. The velocity V is the average velocity across the section and thereby is a function of x only. Further, the channel

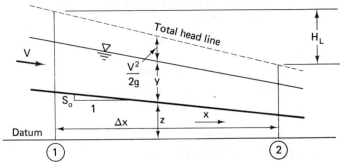

Fig. 10-20. Definite sketch for gradually varied flow.

slope is S_0 and the slope of the total head line, or friction slope, is S_f. The latter may be evaluated from the Manning relationship as given by Eq. 10-2 (or by the Chezy equation). By convention (and because the usual channel runs downhill), a downward slope is taken as positive. Consequently,

$$S_0 = -\frac{dz}{dx} \tag{10-31}$$

and

$$S_f = -\frac{dH}{dx} \tag{10-32}$$

One final point: in writing the total head as is done in Eq. 10-30, a hydrostatic pressure distribution is assumed. This implies that the streamlines are nearly parallel, an assumption that is usually, but not always met in a gradually varied flow.

Differentiating the total head with respect to x now leads to the governing equation:

$$\frac{dH}{dx} = \frac{d}{dx}\left(z + y + \frac{V^2}{2g}\right) = -S_f$$

or

$$\frac{d}{dx}\left(y + \frac{V^2}{2g}\right) = S_0 - S_f$$

which in terms of the specific head H_0 from Eq. 10-10 becomes

$$\frac{dH_0}{dx} = \frac{dH_0}{dy}\frac{dy}{dx} = S_0 - S_f$$

Finally, with the addition of Eq. 10-15,

$$\frac{dy}{dx}(1 - \text{Fr}^2) = S_0 - S_f \tag{10-33}$$

This equation now permits the qualitative analysis of all possible gradually varied flow profiles. Once the profiles have been systematically considered and classified, we will return to the details of their solution and subsequent application. In addition to the distinction (see Section 10-2) between subcritical and supercritical flow (and the limiting case of critical flow), we will now make an additional distinction based on the relative magnitudes of the normal depth and the critical depth. If for a given discharge $y_n > y_c$, the channel will be classified as having a mild slope. Conversely, if $y_n < y_c$, the channel will be called steep. The slope at which $y_n = y_c$ will be the critical slope. To facilitate the graphic display of the various conditions and profiles, the critical depth will be indicated by a series of short dashes and the normal depth by long dashes in Figs. 10-21 through 10-31. In addition, the slope will be exaggerated. An examination of the equations for critical depth and normal depth will show that under certain conditions (see Probs. 10-45 and 10-46) a channel will be mild for one range of discharges and steep for another. However, this will generally be of no concern to us. The calculation of normal and critical depth will usually be required when working gradually varied flow problems, even though the actual flow is not at either depth. Likewise, a mild slope does not mean that the flow is subcritical (i.e., $y_n > y_c$ does not imply that $y > y_c$). It does indicate that if the flow is at normal depth, it is in fact subcritical. However, there are a number of circumstances (e.g., flow discharging under a sluice gate) where the flow is supercritical even though the channel has a mild slope.

Let us first consider a mild slope (see Fig. 10-21). The possible profile in

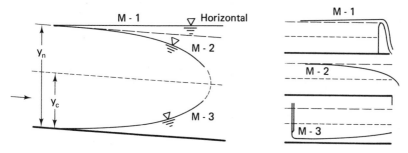

Fig. 10-21. Gradually varied flow on a mild slope.

each range is labeled as an M-1, M-2, or M-3 curve, and a typical situation that would create each type of curve is shown to the right. In the region $y > y_n$ the flow is subcritical; hence, Fr < 1. Also, from the Manning equation for constant width and discharge, if $y > y_n$, then $S_f < S_0$ at all points. Thus, from Eq. 10-33, since $S_0 > S_f$ and Fr < 1, dy/dx must be positive. Recall that y is measured from the channel bottom, not a horizontal datum. Therefore, $dy/dx > 0$ implies that the depth must increase in the x direction. Further, as $y \rightarrow y_n$, $S_f \rightarrow S_0$ also, but Fr does not approach unity. If Eq. 10-33 is to apply as the right-hand side goes to zero, then $dy/dx \rightarrow 0$, or in other words, the depth curve must approach the normal depth line asymptotically. Finally, as the depth increases (i.e., as $y \to \infty$), both Fr and $S_f \to 0$ and therefore $dy/dx \to S_0$. Since y is measured from the bottom, which has a slope of S_0, the quality $dy/dx = S_0$ defines a horizontal line, and the limit $dy/dx \to S_0$ means that the depth is asymptotically approaching a horizontal plane. The sum of these conditions is the M-1 curve shown.

With abbreviated comments, the remaining two curves are obtained as follows: In the range $y_c < y < y_n$, $S_f > S_0$, Fr < 1, and therefore dy/dx is negative and the depth decreases with x. As $y \to y_n$, $S_f \to S_0$, and as with the M-1 curve, $dy/dx \to 0$, so the M-2 profile must also approach normal depth asymptotically. As $y \to y_c$, $dy/dx \to \infty$, which implies that the water surface becomes vertical. This does not occur since the rapid curvature in the region violates the initial assumptions of nearly parallel streamlines and a hydrostatic pressure distribution. Nevertheless, this is sufficiently accurate to complete the M-2 curve as shown and, in fact, the slope of the surface does become quite large. For $0 < y < y_c$, $S_f > S_0$, Fr > 1, so dy/dx is again positive. As $y \to y_c$, again $dy/dx \to \infty$, with comments as above. As $y \to 0$, both Fr and S_f tend to infinity. Upon rearranging Eq. 10-33 to

$$\frac{dy}{dx} = S_0 + \frac{dy}{dx}\text{Fr}^2 - S_f$$

we see that dy/dx must approach some positive value so that the last two terms will remain in balance. The depth can never equal zero, but this provides sufficient guide so that the M-3 curve can be sketched.

The corresponding curves for steep channels are included in Fig. 10-22 with typical applications shown to the right. The reasoning that leads to these curves is similar to the foregoing and is left as an exercise (Prob. 10-47).

If the slope is critical, region 2 between normal and critical depths does

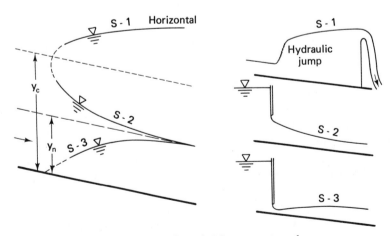

Fig. 10-22. Gradually varied flow on a steep slope.

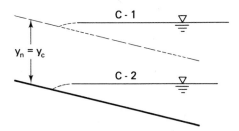

Fig. 10-23.   Gradually varied flow on a critical slope.

not exist (see Fig. 10-23). Analyzing Eq. 10-33 as before, in the region $y > y_n$ and y_c, $S_0 > S_f$, Fr < 1 and $dy/dx > 0$. As $y \to \infty$, $S_f \to 0$, Fr $\to 0$, and $dy/dx \to S_0$. As $y \to y_n$ and y_c, Fr $\to 1$ and $S_f \to S_0$; hence, dy/dx is indeterminate but apparently must possess a positive angle.

It is possible to better justify the forms of the C-1 curve shown by assuming a wide channel and modifying Eq. 10-33 as follows:

$$\frac{dy}{dx} = S_0 \frac{1 - S_f/S_0}{1 - \mathrm{Fr}^2}$$

But from the Manning equation,

$$q = \frac{1.49}{n} y^{5/3} S_f^{1/2} = \frac{1.49}{n} y_n^{5/3} S_0^{1/2}$$

or

$$\frac{S_f}{S_0} = \left(\frac{y_n}{y}\right)^{10/3}$$

and the Froude number yields

$$\mathrm{Fr}_c^2 = 1 = \frac{q^2}{g y_c^3}$$

$$\mathrm{Fr}^2 = \frac{V^2}{gy} = \frac{q^2}{g y^3} = \frac{y_c^3}{y^3}$$

Combining the equations above will give the following equation, where y_n and y_c will be equal at the critical slope:

$$\frac{dy}{dx} = S_0 \frac{1 - (y_n/y)^{10/3}}{1 - (y_c/y)^3} \tag{10-34}$$

Here S_0 is now the critical slope. This relationship shows that the quantity dy/dx will be a little greater than S_0 as $y \to y_c$, and will decrease to S_0 as y gets larger. The C-3 curve may be explained in a similar fashion. It is worth noting in passing that if the channel is assumed wide and the Chezy equation with constant coefficient C is used rather than the Manning equation, Eq. 10-33 will reduce to $dy/dx = S_0$ for all values of both the C-1 and C-3 curves. Both curves would then be straight horizontal lines.

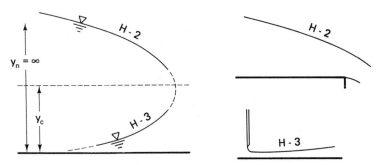

Fig. 10-24. Gradually varied flow in a horizontal channel.

A far more important case than the critical slope is the horizontal channel, for which $y_n \rightarrow \infty$ and we have only H-2 and H-3 curves as shown in Fig. 10-24. Except that $S_0 = 0$, the analysis is essentially similar to that of the M-2 and M-3 curves. The final set of curves results from a negative or adverse slope as shown in Fig. 10-25. The analysis of the two curves is again straightforward; note only that the right-hand side of Eq. 10-33 will always be negative.

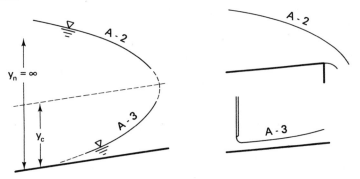

Fig. 10-25. Gradually varied flow on an adverse slope.

A little thought will show that whenever the flow is subcritical (which includes the M-1, M-2, S-1, H-2, and A-2 curves), the location of the curve must be determined from the downstream end. This is equivalent to saying that a subcritical flow has a downstream control. In some cases this is obvious. For example, the M-2 curve, which occurs at the dropoff at the end of a mild slope, will pass through critical depth at (or more exactly, a short distance upstream of) the brink. This locates the curve, whereas it would be impossible to predict from the upstream end alone where the curve begins to deviate from normal depth. The actual calculation of these profiles will start from a known depth at the downstream end and proceed upstream.

The situation is identical, but perhaps a little less obvious, in the case of the S-1 curve. The S-1 curve will generally follow a hydraulic jump, there being no steep channel profiles which allow the depth to smoothly increase above normal depth. But a hydraulic jump cannot be located from upstream conditions alone. Hence, the S-1 curve must be located at its downstream end (e.g., just at or above the crest of a spillway) and then projected upstream. The remaining curves, which are all supercritical, behave in exactly the opposite fashion. Their control is upstream and they can only be calculated by proceeding downstream.

Over the years, a variety of methods have been developed to calculate the actual profiles. Many of these are integration procedures based on integration of Eq. 10-33, after making various, usually limiting assumptions concerning the cross-sectional shape and the friction (or total head) slope. The references listed at the end of this chapter thoroughly cover this subject. The only procedure developed in detail here is a step method based on a difference formulation of the Bernoulli equation as applied between sections 1 and 2 of Fig. 10-20. Specifically,

$$z_1 + y_1 + \frac{V_1^2}{2g} = z_2 + y_2 + \frac{V_2^2}{2g} + H_L$$

Since

$$\frac{z_1 - z_2}{\Delta x} = S_0 \quad \text{and} \quad \frac{H_L}{\Delta x} = S_f$$

this becomes

$$S_0 \, \Delta x - S_f \, \Delta x = \left(y_2 + \frac{V_2^2}{2g}\right) - \left(y_1 + \frac{V_1^2}{2g}\right)$$

or

$$\Delta x = \frac{(y_1 + V_1^2/2g) - (y_2 + V_2^2/2g)}{S_f - S_0} \tag{10-35}$$

Theoretically, we can either assume a small change or step in y and calculate the distance Δx required, as Eq. 10-35 is set up to do, or assume a step in x and calculate the resulting change in y. Since the velocity can be expressed more readily as a function of y, the former is usually preferred. Starting from the control where y is known, a second value of y is assumed. This permits calculation of V_1, V_2, R_1, and R_2. The friction slope S_f may be calculated from either Chezy or Manning equations. From the latter,

$$S_f = \frac{n^2 V^2}{2.21 R^{4/3}} \tag{10-36a}$$

in English (lb-ft-s) units, and

$$S_f = \frac{n^2 V^2}{R^{4/3}} \tag{10-36b}$$

in SI (N-m-s) units. In either case, average values of n, V, and R can be used to determine the value of S_f in Eq. 10-35. The value of Δx may now be determined, a new value of y picked and the process repeated. To select y values that are in the correct direction, it is important that the type of water surface profile be known at the outset. The smaller the size of the increments in y, the greater will be the accuracy of the resulting profile. Obviously, this type of computational procedure can be readily programmed for an electronic computer, even one of the pocket type.

EXAMPLE 10-7

A discharge of 8 m³/s occurs in a 3-m-wide rectangular channel built on a slope of 0.0007. Assume that $n = 0.015$. If the channel ends in an abrupt dropoff, determine and plot the water surface profile.

SOLUTION:

As it is necessary to know the type of curve that will occur, both y_n and y_c must be calculated. For y_n,

$$Q = 8 \text{ m}^3/\text{s} = \frac{AR^{2/3}S_o^{1/2}}{n} = \frac{(3y_n)^{5/3}}{(3 + 2y_n)^{2/3}} \frac{(0.0007)^{1/2}}{0.015}$$

which by trial and error yields $y_n = 1.75$ m. The critical depth is

$$y_c = \sqrt[3]{\frac{q^2}{g}} = \sqrt[3]{\frac{(\frac{8}{3})^2}{9.81}} = 0.90 \text{ m}$$

Therefore, the channel has a mild slope and the profile leading to the brink must be a M-2 curve as shown in Fig. 10-26. Theoretically, the M-2 curve would be

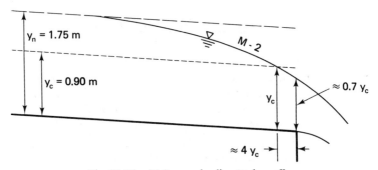

Fig. 10-26.   M-2 curve leading to dropoff.

expected to pass through the critical depth at the brink. However, this is a region of considerable curvature and definitely nonhydrostatic pressure distribution. In fact, the depth at the dropoff is more closely $0.7y_c$, and the actual critical depth occurs approximately $4y_c$ upstream. For the water surface profile computation we will start at $y_c = 0.90$ m, a distance $4y_c = 3.60$ m upstream of the brink. The computations required for Eq. 10-35 are given in tabular form in Table 10-1, and the subsequent profile is plotted in Fig. 10-27.

TABLE 10-1 Computation of M-2 curve (Example 10-7)

y	A	R	V	$\Delta\left(y + \dfrac{V^2}{2g}\right)$	V_{av}	R_{av}	S_f	Δx	$x = \sum \Delta x$
(m)	(m^2)	(m)	(m/s)	(m)	(m/s)	(m)		(m)	(m)
0.9	2.70	0.56	2.96	—	—	—	—	—	3.6
1.0	3.00	0.60	2.67	0.0168	2.81	0.58	3.67×10^{-3}	5.7	9.3
1.1	3.30	0.63	2.42	0.0352	2.55	0.62	2.79×10^{-3}	16.8	26.1
1.2	3.60	0.67	2.22	0.0527	2.32	0.65	2.15×10^{-3}	36.3	62.4
1.4	4.20	0.70	1.90	0.1367	2.06	0.68	1.59×10^{-3}	153.6	216.0
1.75	5.25	0.81	1.52	0.2799	1.71	0.75	9.59×10^{-4}	1080.7	1296.7

Most of Table 10-1 should be self-explanatory. The friction slope S_f is calculated from Eq. 10-36b and the final tabulation x includes the distance from the brink to the point of critical depth. In Fig. 10-27 the depths at calculated points are shown. The scale on the left-hand side gives the water surface elevation relative to the brink.

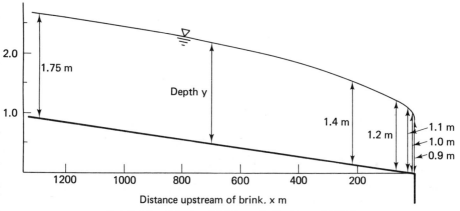

Fig. 10-27. Calculated M-2 profile for Example 10-7.

One must continually deal with the concept of control when attempting (preliminary to actual calculation) to sketch the gradually varied flow profile which results when there is a change in channel slope. Several of these are shown in Figs. 10-28 through 10-31. With a little study it becomes rela-

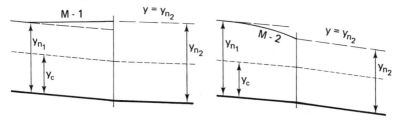

Fig. 10-28.   Transitions from mild slope to mild slope.

tively easy to determine the one or more possible profiles that exist in each case. To calculate the actual profiles or even to determine whether the slopes are steep or mild, it is necessary to first calculate the critical depth and the normal depths associated with each slope. With reference to the possible curves of Fig. 10-21, it will be seen that the transitions shown in Fig. 10-28 are the only ones possible. They also demonstrate the significance of the downstream control, since in both cases it is a downstream frictional control as related to the downstream normal depth which determines the location of the transition curve.

In the first transition of Fig. 10-29, note that there is no smooth curve by which the flow can deviate from normal depth. Hence, in this case, where no

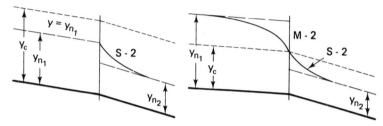

Fig. 10-29.   Transitions from steep to steep and mild to steep.

jump is possible, the water flows at normal depth until the break in grade. In the second case the break provides a downstream control for the subcritical section and and an upstream control for the supercritical section. Examination of the possible profiles should provide convincing evidence that no other transition is possible. It is assumed here that both sections are sufficiently long that at the upstream and downstream limits the flow will occur at the respective normal depths.

In certain cases there is no possible profile or profiles which the water surface can smoothly follow. The hydraulic jump is then the mechanism by which at least part of the transition is achieved. The water surface will "jump" from a depth y_1 to y_2 according to Eqs. 10-25 or 10-26. Figure 10-30 illustrates such a case. The flow can neither smoothly leave y_{n_1} on the steep slope nor can it

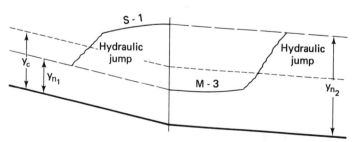

Fig. 10-30.   Transition with a hydraulic jump.

smoothly approach y_{n_2} on the subsequent mild slope. Two possibilities suggest themselves, although only one is possible for a given set of conditions. The flow might jump from y_{n_1} on the steep slope to a subcritical depth given by Eq. 10-25, which is then followed by an S-1 water surface profile. The second possibility is an M-3 curve commencing at the grade break, followed by the hydraulic jump. In this case y_{n_2} is known and Eq. 10-26 may be used to determine the depth from which the jump will occur.

It is possible at the outset to evaluate which situation will occur. Note that the ratio of depths y_2/y_1 in Eq. 10-25 gets larger as the Froude number increases, and vice versa. If, for the moment, the jump is assumed to occur at the grade break, then, based on the depth y_{n_1}, Eq. 10-25 can be used to calculate the corresponding downstream depth y_2. If $y_2 > y_{n_2}$, then the jump must actually be located downstream of the break and the M-3 curve will continue until the supercritical depth has increased sufficiently that the hydraulic jump will just reach y_{n_2}. Conversely, if $y_2 < y_{n_2}$ in the jump calculation, the M-3 curve would just make matters worse, as any jump from a greater depth on the M-3 curve would be even less able to reach y_{n_2}. Thus, the upstream jump shown on Fig. 10-30 must occur.

Finally, consider Fig. 10-31, which illustrates a few additional considerations. Here again the critical depth and the normal depths are assumed

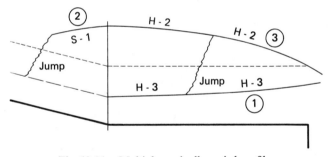

Fig. 10-31.   Multiple gradually varied profiles.

known. The downstream portion is horizontal and ends in an abrupt dropoff. There are three distinct profiles here, which depend to a large extent on the relative length of the horizontal section. If the horizontal section is relatively short, then the water will flow at normal depth to the break in grade and then follow an H-3 curve until it shoots off the brink (curve 1). Starting at the break in grade, the H-3 curve would be calculated (with $S_0 = 0$) according to Eq. 10-35. If the brink is reached without the water surface approaching critical depth, then this curve is correct. If the profile approaches y_c before reaching the dropoff, a hydraulic jump must occur which again can be either before or after the grade change (curves 2 and 3, respectively). Since there is no normal depth on the horizontal section, the analysis is more complicated. However, the curve may be computed and compared with Eq. 10-26 to locate the jump.

PROBLEMS

Sec. 10-1

10-1. The following data are collected at two gaging sections in a relatively straight portion of a river. Station 1 is 1000 ft upstream of Station 2, and the flow is 21,000 cfs. Estimate the Manning n value.

Station	Water Surface Elevation (ft)	Cross-sectional Area (ft²)	Wetted Perimeter (ft)
1	26.78	4150	730
2	26.21	4750	810

10-2. What is the average shear stress around the perimeter of the channel of Prob. 10-1?

10-3. What is the depth y_0 and thickness of a layer of water if the pressure at the bottom is 4 psi and the slope is 10%? Assume uniform flow.

10-4. Repeat Prob. 10-3 for a slope of 50%.

10-5. Repeat Prob. 10-3 for a slope of 100%.

10-6. What is the pressure at the bottom of a layer of water flowing uniformly down a 10% slope if the depth is 1.5 m?

10-7. Repeat Prob. 10-6 for a 100% slope.

10-8. What is the pressure at the bottom of a layer of water flowing uniformly if the depth is 1.7 m and the thickness of the water layer is 1.3 m?

10-9. Repeat Example 10-1 with the depth increased by an additional 10 ft. What percent of the flow is carried in the main channel?

10-10. What is the average shear stress around the perimeter of the channel in Prob. 10-9?

10-11. In the channel shown, the main channel has a Manning n of 0.020 and the overbank portions have an n value of 0.040. If the channel slope is 0.35 m/km, what is the flow rate?

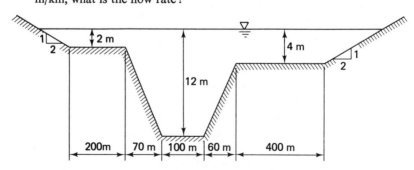

10-12. Estimate the average shear stress in each of the overbank portions and in the main channel of Prob. 10-11.

Sec. 10-2

10-13. A flow of 210 cfs in a 10-ft-wide rectangular channel occurs at a depth of 1.70 ft. What is the subsequent depth downstream of a transition at which the channel bottom drops 0.5 ft?

10-14. What is the subsequent depth in the channel of Prob. 10-13 if the initial depth is 1.0 ft?

10-15. What is the subsequent depth in the channel of Prob. 10-13 if the initial depth is 4.0 ft?

10-16. A flow of 8 m³/s occurs in a 3-m-wide rectangular channel. The depth is 0.5 m. What is the subsequent depth downstream of a transition at which the channel bottom drops 0.3 m?

10-17. What is the subsequent depth in the channel of Prob. 10-16 if the initial depth is 2.0 m?

10-18. A flow of 200 cfs occurs in a 10-ft-wide rectangular channel with a depth of 2.5 ft. How much of a channel drop is required for the water surface to rise 0.1 ft?

10-19. A flow of 10 m³/s occurs in a 3-m-wide rectangular channel. The initial depth is 1.5 m. Determine the subsequent depth if the channel bottom rises 0.15 m.

10-20. What is the maximum increase in channel bottom for which there will be no upstream effects for the flow of Prob. 10-19?

10-21. Analyze the consequences of raising the channel bottom of Prob. 10-19 by 1.0 m. What will be the subsequent upstream and downstream depths?

10-22. What is the maximum increase in the elevation of the channel bottom which can occur without upstream effect if the flow rate is 240 cfs and the initial depth is 5 ft in a 12-ft-wide rectangular channel?

10-23. Determine the subsequent depth in Prob. 10-13 if the bottom elevation remains constant but the width reduces to 9 ft.

10-24. Repeat Prob. 10-23 if the width is increased to 12 ft.

10-25. Determine the effect on the water surface elevation of a channel transition from a 12-ft-wide channel to 15 ft width if the bottom elevation also drops 1 ft. The flow rate is 300 cfs and the upstream depth is 5 ft.

10-26. Prove that if there is a reduction in width such as that shown in Fig. 10-9, the specific energy diagram for the constricted section will lie to the right of the diagram for the initial section. Prove further that the critical depth will be greater in the constricted section.

10-27. Show that Eqs. 10-16 and 10-17 revert to Eqs. 10-12 and 10-14 when the channel is rectangular.

Sec. 10-3

10-28. A small wave of height 0.1 ft moves through otherwise stationary water which has a depth of 1.0 ft. Calculate the wave celerity by Eqs. 10-18, 10-19, and 10-20.

10-29. Repeat Prob. 10-28 for a wave height of 1 cm in water with a depth of 10 cm.

10-30. What wave height Δy may be expected to cause a celerity of 6 m/s in water with a depth of 3 m?

10-31. Determine the percent error in wave celerity that is introduced by using Eqs. 10-19 and 10-20 rather than Eq. 10-18, if the depth is 10 ft and the wave height is 1 ft.

10-32. What will be the celerity of a wave with a wave length of 4 m in water with a depth of 10 m?

10-33. What is the celerity of a deep water wave with a wave length of 30 ft?

10-34. At what absolute velocity will a very small wave move upstream against a current of 1.1 m/s if the depth is 0.2 m?

10-35. Determine the velocity of a stream with a depth of 1 ft if a wave front forms with an angle α to the flow of 15°.

10-36. If a flow of 4000 cfs has a depth of 2 ft just upstream of a hydraulic jump in a 40-ft-wide rectangular channel, determine the downstream depth, length of jump, and power loss in horsepower.

10-37. Repeat Prob. 10-36 if the upstream depth is 1 ft.

10-38. An hydraulic jump occurs in a 30-ft-wide rectangular channel. If the two depths are 4 ft and 15 ft, what is the discharge? What is the head loss?

10-39. Determine the upstream and downstream Froude numbers in Prob. 10-38.

10-40. A channel with an upstream depth of 0.5 m and velocity of 15 m/s occurs in a wide rectangular channel. What are the downstream depth, the jump length, and the power loss?

10-41. An hydraulic jump occurs in a wide rectangular channel. The upstream and downstream depths are 1 m and 8 m, respectively. Determine the discharge per unit width and the upstream and downstream Froude numbers.

10-42. If the depth and velocity downstream of an hydraulic jump are 2 m and 0.6 m/s, respectively, what must be the upstream depth and the head loss in the jump?

10-43. A 5-m-wide rectangular channel carries water with a depth of 1.1 m and a velocity of 4 m/s. If a downstream gate is abruptly closed, at what velocity will a surge move upstream, and what will be the final depth?

10-44. A discharge of 450 cfs is flowing at a depth of 3 ft in a 15-ft-wide channel. What will be the subsequent conditions (depth, velocity, and surge velocity) if the upstream flow rate is abruptly doubled?

Sec. 10-4

10-45. Show that a wide rectangular channel (where $R \approx y$) is mild or steep depending on whether q is less than or greater than $(4.62n/S_0^{1/2})$ when English units are used.

10-46. Determine the criteria for Prob. 10-45 if SI units are used.

10-47. Determine from Eq. 10-33 the form of the three steep channel profiles S-1, S-2, and S-3.

10-48 through **10-53.** Sketch and label all possible profiles for each of the following. On mild or steep slopes, assume that the lengths are sufficiently long that transition curves may be completed in the length shown. Normal depth is indicated by the long dashes and critical depth by the short dashes. Flow is from left to right in each case.

10-48.

10-49.

10-50.

10-51.

10-52.

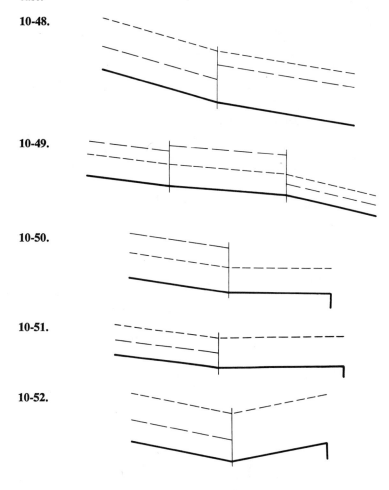

10-53.

10-54. An 8-ft-wide rectangular channel ($n = 0.014$) carries 130 cfs. Calculate and plot the transition if the channel slope changes abruptly from 1.3×10^{-3} to 6×10^{-4}.

10-55. Repeat Prob. 10-54 if the slope change is from 6×10^{-4} to 1.3×10^{-3}.

10-56. A discharge of 3.5 m³/s occurs in a 3-m-wide channel with $n = 0.012$. Calculate and plot the transition curve if the slope changes abruptly from 0.014 to 0.005.

10-57. Repeat Prob. 10-56 if the slope change is from 0.005 to 0.014.

10-58. Calculate and plot the water surface profile if a long, 10-ft-wide rectangular channel with a slope of 5×10^{-4} is followed by a 100-ft-long horizontal section that ends in an abrupt dropoff. The discharge is 220 cfs and $n = 0.014$.

10-59. Repeat Prob. 10-58 if the horizontal section is 2000 ft in length.

10-60. Water discharges under a sluice gate with an average velocity of 10 m/s and a depth of 0.5 m. The channel is 3 m wide with $n = 0.013$. Calculate and plot the water surface profile if the channel has a slope of 4×10^{-4}.

10-61. Repeat Prob. 10-60 if the channel is 300 m long, horizontal, and ends with an abrupt dropoff.

10-62. Repeat Prob. 10-60 if the channel has a slope of 1%.

REFERENCES

CHOW, VEN TE, "Open Channel Flow," Section 24 in *Handbook of Fluid Dynamics*, V. L. Streeter (ed.). New York: McGraw-Hill, 1961.

CHOW, VEN TE, *Open Channel Hydraulics*. New York: McGraw-Hill, 1959.

HENDERSON, F. M., *Open Channel Flow*. New York: Macmillan, 1966.

MAHMOOD, K., and V. YEVJEVICH (eds.), *Unsteady Flow in Open Channels* (3 vols.). Fort Collins, Colo.: Water Resources Publications, 1975.

POSEY, C. J., *Fundamentals of Open Channel Hydraulics*. Allenspark, Colo.: Rocky Mountain Hydraulic Laboratory, 1969.

11

Compressible Flow

The chapter is devoted to the consideration of the effects of fluid compressibility. Up to this point we have usually assumed that we have been dealing with an incompressible flow. Thus, we will be concerned with establishing when we may treat a flow as incompressible and when we must include compressibility effects. Many of the types of flows discussed in earlier chapters will be reexamined in the light of compressibility considerations. As in the treatment of open-channel flow in Chapter 10, this chapter will not attempt to be an in-depth study, but rather an introduction to the subject. However, the analogy between open-channel flow and compressible flow will be demonstrated, particularly as it concerns the similar roles of the Froude number and the Mach number in the respective flows.

11–1 ELASTIC WAVE: MACH NUMBER

Before proceeding with the analysis of compressible flows, it is desirable to discuss the spreading of an elastic wave and lead from this into a consideration of the Mach number, which was introduced in Chapter 6. An *elastic wave* is a pressure or density perturbation that spreads through a fluid in much the same way as did water waves in Chapter 10. Since the generation of sound is essentially the production of pressure variations, the celerity of elastic waves will be identically the speed of sound in the particular medium.

The analysis of the elastic wave which follows will be based on the Euler equations derived in Chapter 5. Figure 11-1, which is a relabeling of Fig. 10-15, shows a small pressure disturbance or elastic wave moving with celerity c through an otherwise stationary fluid. The pressure wave is shown as a

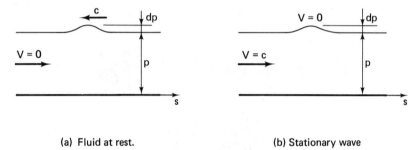

(a) Fluid at rest.   (b) Stationary wave

Fig. 11-1. Elastic wave.

small wave of amplitude dp in a fluid of otherwise constant pressure p. As with the water wave, analysis requires steady-state conditions. Through the use of the relative motion principle, this is given in Fig. 11-1b. The Bernoulli equation cannot be used, since it assumed an incompressible flow. The derivation of the Euler equations, which we will use, did not require this assumption, however. Starting with Eq. 5-2 and dropping the elevation term, we have

$$\frac{\partial p}{\partial s} = -\rho a_s = -\rho V \frac{\partial V}{\partial s} \tag{11-1}$$

where s is the coordinate direction so labeled in Fig. 11-1, and V is the velocity as shown in Fig. 11-1b.

Assuming that the cross-sectional area through which the wave passes does not change with s, the continuity equation (Eq. 4-15) becomes

$$\frac{\partial}{\partial s}(\rho V) = 0$$

This may be expanded to

$$V \frac{\partial \rho}{\partial s} + \rho \frac{\partial V}{\partial s} = 0 \tag{11-2}$$

By eliminating the velocity gradient $\partial V/\partial s$ between Eqs. 11-1 and 11-2, we get

$$\frac{dp}{ds} = V^2 \frac{dp}{ds} \tag{11-3}$$

where total derivations may be used, since p and ρ depend only on s. Upon solving for V,

$$V = \sqrt{\frac{dp/ds}{d\rho/ds}} = \sqrt{\frac{dp}{d\rho}} \tag{11-4}$$

Since the velocity V becomes the celerity in the unsteady situation (see Fig. 11-1), we may write

$$c = \sqrt{dp/d\rho} \tag{11-5}$$

This becomes the general equation for the speed of sound, or elastic wave. It may be interpreted as dependent on the ratio of pressure to density gradients, or simply as the ratio of pressure to density differentials.

Introducing the modulus of compressibility as defined by Eq. 1-10,

$$E = \rho \frac{dp}{d\rho}$$

the sonic velocity immediately becomes

$$c = \sqrt{\frac{E}{\rho}} \tag{11-6}$$

Assume first that the passing of the elastic wave is a constant-temperature or isothermal process. We would then have, from Eq. 1-12, that $E = p$. When introduced into Eq. 11-6, this gives

$$c = \sqrt{\frac{p}{\rho}} = \sqrt{gRT} \tag{11-7}$$

Similarly, if we assume that the wave passage is adiabatic (i.e., there is no heat transfer), then from Eq. 1-14, $E = kp$ and therefore

$$c = \sqrt{\frac{kp}{\rho}} = \sqrt{kgRT} \tag{11-8}$$

where k, as defined in Section 1-3, is the ratio of specific heats. Experiments bear out Eq. 11-8, implying that the process is, in fact, adiabatic. This is reasonable when you consider that the passage of the elastic wave is very rapid and there is therefore no time for the heat transfer necessary to maintain a constant temperature.

The preceding derivation is only appropriate for a small elastic wave, one in which the wave amplitude dp is small relative to the ambient pressure, p. For large pressure waves, the celerity will be increased over that indicated by Eq. 11-8, just as large water waves were found to move with a greater velocity than that predicted by Eq. 10-20.

EXAMPLE 11-1

Determine the speed of sound in water and in air at 70°F.

SOLUTION:

For water at 70°F, $E = 3.20 \times 10^5$ psi from Table A-V. Since E is known, Eq. 11-6 can be used to give

$$c = \sqrt{\frac{E}{\rho}}$$

$$= \sqrt{\frac{(3.20 \times 10^5)(144)}{1.94}} = 4870 \text{ ft/s}$$

For air at 70°F, we have $k = 1.4$, $R = 53.3$ ft/°R, and

$$T = 460 + 70 = 530°R$$

Thus, from Eq. 11-8,

$$c = \sqrt{kgRT} = \sqrt{(1.4)(32.2)(53.3)(530)} = 1130 \text{ ft/s}$$

Observe from these calculations that although air is thousands of times more compressible than water, the speed of sound in water is a little less than five times that of air.

Mach Number

The Mach number was previously introduced in Chapter 6, where it was defined in Eq. 6-6e as

$$\text{Ma} = \frac{V}{\sqrt{E/\rho}} \qquad (11\text{-}9)$$

For purposes of modeling it was shown in Eq. 6-9e to be the ratio of inertial force to elastic force. By comparison with Eq. 11-6, we see immediately that Eq. 11-9 may be written as

$$\text{Ma} = \frac{V}{c} \qquad (11\text{-}10)$$

Hence, the Mach number may also be considered as the ratio of the flow velocity to the celerity of an elastic wave. Once again, compare this result with the definition of the Froude number in Chapter 10. To further the analogy, note that the elastic wave may move upstream in a flow with a Mach number less than unity (subsonic flow), but the wave may only move downstream if the Mach number is greater than unity (supersonic flow). The situation may be summarized by Fig. 11-2, which is identical to Fig. 10-16. As the velocity increases relative to the celerity, we see that the concentric circles are increasingly swept downstream. When Ma > 1, a wave front forms and the angle α is known as the *Mach angle*. The tangent line, known as the *Mach line*, represents a reinforcement of the wave pattern. This gives rise to a shock wave. It is the passing of this Mach line or shock

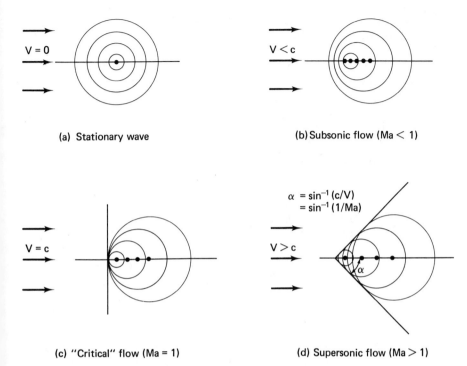

(a) Stationary wave   (b) Subsonic flow (Ma < 1)

(c) "Critical" flow (Ma = 1)   (d) Supersonic flow (Ma > 1)

Fig. 11-2.   Elastic wave pattern.

wave trailing behind an airplane in supersonic flight which we experience as a sonic boom.

EXAMPLE 11-2

A plane with a velocity of 500 m/s flies through air which has a temperature of 0°C and a pressure of 56 kN/m²(abs). What is the Mach number and associated Mach angle?

SOLUTION:

The speed of sound by Eq. 11-8 is

$$c = \sqrt{kgRT}$$
$$= \sqrt{(1.4)(9.81 \text{ m/s}^2)(29.2 \text{ m/}°\text{K})(273°\text{K})} = 331 \text{ m/s}$$

(Note that the air pressure does not enter the calculation.) The Mach number is

$$\text{Ma} = \frac{V}{c} = \frac{500 \text{ m/s}}{331 \text{ m/s}} = 1.51$$

and the Mach angle α is

$$\alpha = \sin^{-1}\left(\frac{1}{\text{Ma}}\right) = \sin^{-1}\left(\frac{1}{1.51}\right) = 41.5°$$

11–2 ENERGY EQUATION: FRICTIONLESS ADIABATIC FLOW

A general energy equation was developed in Chapter 5. We may take this equation (Eq. 5-29) as a starting point and note that for steady, compressible, frictionless flow with no shaft work it may be written as

$$\frac{dQ_H}{dt} = \int_{\substack{\text{control} \\ \text{surface}}} (p + e\rho)\mathbf{V} \cdot \mathbf{dA} \tag{11-11}$$

where e from Eq. 5-30 is

$$e = \frac{v^2}{2} + gy + gu \tag{11-12}$$

Here e is the energy per unit mass and the three right-hand terms of Eq. 11-12 are the kinetic energy, the potential energy, and the internal energy, respectively.

Further assuming adiabatic flow for which there is no heat transfer through the boundaries of the control volume, Eq. 11-11 may be written as

$$\int_{\substack{\text{control} \\ \text{surface}}} \left(\frac{p}{\rho} + e\right) \rho \mathbf{V} \cdot \mathbf{dA} \tag{11-13}$$

If the sections where the flow enters and leaves the control volume are essentially regions of uniform flow, the arguments of Section 5-5 again apply and the equation may be written between sections 1 and 2 of the control volume as follows:

$$\left(\frac{p_1}{\rho_1} + \frac{V_1^2}{2} + gy_1 + gu_1\right) \rho_1 V_1 A_1 = \left(\frac{p_2}{\rho_2} + \frac{V_2^2}{2} + gy_2 + gu_2\right) \rho_2 V_2 A_2 \tag{11-14}$$

The limitations discussed in Chapter 5 are again appropriate. An α value could have been introduced as in Section 5-5, but it has been deleted this time.[1] Since steady flow has been assumed, the mass rate of flow is constant and we get simply

$$\frac{p_1}{\rho_1} + \frac{V_1^2}{2} + gy_1 + gu_1 = \frac{p_2}{\rho_2} + \frac{V_2^2}{2} + gy_2 + gu_2 \tag{11-15}$$

In gas dynamics both the internal energy u and the pressure head p/γ are functions of temperature (the latter from $p/\gamma = RT$). The sum is frequently defined as a single quantity, the enthalpy h, such that

$$h = u + p/\gamma \tag{11-16}$$

---

[1]The correction factor α is generally deleted from compressible flows since they are nearly always turbulent leading to a value of α close to unity.

Here each term again represents energy per unit weight of fluid. The conventional use of h for the enthalpy should cause little confusion with the piezometric head, as the latter has little significance in compressible flow. Dividing through by the acceleration of gravity g, Eq. 11-15 may now be written either as

$$\frac{V_1^2}{2g} + y_1 + \frac{p_1}{\gamma_1} + u_1 = \frac{V_2^2}{2g} + y_2 + \frac{p_2}{\gamma_2} + u_2 \tag{11-17}$$

or, by inclusion of Eq. 11-16:

$$\frac{V_1^2}{2g} + y_1 + h_1 = \frac{V_2^2}{2g} + y_2 + h_2 \tag{11-18}$$

For purposes of application, certain thermodynamic relationships for perfect gases are required. Introducing c_p and c_v as the coefficients of specific heat at constant pressure and constant volume, respectively, we have, from thermodynamics,

$$k = c_p/c_v \tag{11-19}$$

and

$$c_p - c_v = R \qquad \left(\frac{\text{ft-lb}}{\text{lb-}^\circ\text{R}} \text{ or } \frac{\text{m}\cdot\text{N}}{\text{N}\cdot{}^\circ\text{K}}\right) \tag{11-20}$$

Combining, we obtain

$$c_p = \frac{Rk}{k-1} \tag{11-21}$$

Additionally, the thermodynamic relationship for internal energy,

$$u = c_v T \tag{11-22}$$

may be combined with the perfect gas law, Eq. 1-4, yielding for the enthalpy

$$h = u + p/\gamma$$
$$= c_v T + RT$$
$$= (c_v + R)T$$

and therefore from Eq. 11-20,

$$h = c_p T \tag{11-23a}$$

or, from Eq. 11-21,

$$h = \frac{RkT}{k-1} \tag{11-23b}$$

Thus, the energy equation becomes alternatively,

$$\frac{V_1^2}{2g} + y_1 + c_p T_1 = \frac{V_2^2}{2g} + y_2 + c_p T_2 \tag{11-24a}$$

or

$$\frac{V_1^2}{2g} + y_1 + \frac{RkT_1}{k-1} = \frac{V_2^2}{2g} + y_2 + \frac{RkT_2}{k-1} \tag{11-24b}$$

Although derived in this section for a control volume or streamtube, the equations will become increasingly more accurate as the streamtube is shrunk down to a single streamline.

Frictionless Adiabatic Flow Equations

With the exception of shock waves, the remainder of this section will be devoted to the application of Eqs. 11-24 to flows where both friction and heat transfer are negligible. The flow will therefore be frictionless and adiabatic, a condition referred to as *isentropic flow*.[2] We will also ignore the effects of elevation differences. The energy equation may immediately be expressed as either

$$\frac{V_1^2}{2g} + c_p T_1 = \frac{V_2^2}{2g} + c_p T_2 \qquad (11\text{-}25a)$$

or

$$\frac{V_1^2}{2g} + \frac{RkT_1}{k-1} = \frac{V_2^2}{2g} + \frac{RkT_2}{k-1} \qquad (11\text{-}25b)$$

The adiabatic constraint limits these equations either to insulated flows or to flow situations involving such rapid accelerations and correspondingly large pressure differences that there is insufficient time for significant heat exchange to occur. Ignoring friction further restricts most applications to the latter of the two cases.

For isentropic flow, Eq. 11-25b may be arranged to

$$\frac{V_2^2}{2g} - \frac{V_1^2}{2g} = \frac{Rk}{k-1}(T_1 - T_2) \qquad (11\text{-}26)$$

which in terms of pressures may be written,

$$\frac{V_2^2}{2g} - \frac{V_1^2}{2g} = \frac{k}{k-1}\left(\frac{p_1}{\gamma_1} - \frac{p_2}{\gamma_2}\right) \qquad (11\text{-}27)$$

Introducing the frictionless adiabatic relationship (Eq. 1-13),

$$\frac{p_1}{\gamma_1^k} = \frac{p_2}{\gamma_2^k} \qquad (11\text{-}28)$$

and combining the preceding two equations gives, after some rearranging,

$$\frac{V_2^2}{2g} - \frac{V_1^2}{2g} = \frac{k}{k-1}\left(\frac{p_1}{\gamma_1}\right)\left[1 - \left(\frac{p_2}{p_1}\right)^{(k-1)/k}\right] \qquad (11\text{-}29a)$$

or

$$\frac{V_2^2}{2g} - \frac{V_1^2}{2g} = \frac{k}{k-1}\left(\frac{p_2}{\gamma_2}\right)\left[\left(\frac{p_1}{p_2}\right)^{(k-1)/k} - 1\right] \qquad (11\text{-}29b)$$

---

[2] A thermodynamic property not heretofore mentioned is the entropy S. The entropy is defined through its differential dS which is the ratio of a differential influx of heat to the absolute temperature. Although the definition is specifically for a reversible process, our concern here is with conditions that lead to a state of constant entropy, i.e., an isentropic process. Since both friction in the system and heat transferred into the system increase the heat content of a system, the necessary condition for isentropic flow is that the flow be both frictionless and adiabatic.

These equations permit calculation of one or the other velocity when either p_1, γ_1, and p_2 or p_1, p_2, and γ_2 are known. It is more frequently necessary, however, to calculate pressures or pressure differences based on the velocities themselves. Solving Eq. 11-29a for p_2/p_1 yields

$$\frac{p_2}{p_1} = \left[1 + \frac{k-1}{2}\left(\frac{V_1^2 - V_2^2}{kp_1/\rho_1}\right)\right]^{k/(k-1)} \tag{11-30}$$

For the frictionless adiabatic conditions under consideration, Eq. 11-8 gives

$$c_1 = \sqrt{\frac{kp_1}{\rho_1}}$$

and with this addition Eq. 11-30 may also be written as

$$\frac{p_2}{p_1} = \left[1 + \frac{k-1}{2}\left(\frac{V_1^2 - V_2^2}{c_1^2}\right)\right]^{k/(k-1)} \tag{11-31}$$

Either of the equations above permits calculation of pressure changes resulting from prescribed changes in the velocity. The full significance of the equations may be more readily interpreted, however, if the right-hand side is expanded by the binominal theorem, which for reference is

$$(a + x)^n = a^n + na^{n-1}x + \frac{n(n-1)a^{n-2}x^2}{2!}$$
$$+ \frac{n(n-1)(n-2)a^{n-3}x^3}{3!} + \cdots$$

Thus, when Eq. 11-31 is expanded in powers of $k/(k-1)$, we get

$$\frac{p_2}{p_1} = 1 + \left(\frac{k}{k-1}\right)(1)\left(\frac{k-1}{2}\frac{V_1^2 - V_2^2}{c_1^2}\right)$$
$$+ \left(\frac{k}{k-1}\right)\left(\frac{k}{k-1} - 1\right)\left(\frac{1}{2!}\right)(1)\left(\frac{k-1}{2}\frac{V_1^2 - V_2^2}{c_1^2}\right)^2$$
$$+ \left(\frac{k}{k-1}\right)\left(\frac{k}{k-1} - 1\right)\left(\frac{k}{k-1} - 2\right)\left(\frac{1}{3!}\right)(1)\left(\frac{k-1}{2}\frac{V_1^2 - V_2^2}{c_1^2}\right)^3$$
$$+ \cdots$$

This relation readily simplifies to

$$\frac{p_2}{p_1} = 1 + \frac{k}{2}\left(\frac{V_1^2 - V_2^2}{c_1^2}\right) + \frac{k}{8}\left(\frac{V_1^2 - V_2^2}{c_1^2}\right)^2$$
$$+ \frac{k(2-k)}{48}\left(\frac{V_1^2 - V_2^2}{c_1^2}\right)^3 + \cdots \tag{11-32}$$

Rearranging so as to solve for the pressure difference and again utilizing Eq. 11-8, we obtain

$$p_2 - p_1 = \frac{\rho_1 c_1^2}{k}\left[\frac{k}{2}\left(\frac{V_1^2 - V_2^2}{c_1^2}\right)\right.$$
$$\left. + \frac{k}{8}\left(\frac{V_1^2 - V_2^2}{c_1^2}\right)^2 + \frac{k(2-k)}{48}\left(\frac{V_1^2 - V_2^2}{c_1^2}\right)^3 + \cdots\right]$$

or

$$p_2 - p_1 = \frac{\rho_1(V_1^2 - V_2^2)}{2}\left[1 + \frac{1}{4}\left(\frac{V_1^2 - V_2^2}{c_1^2}\right)\right. $$
$$\left. + \frac{2-k}{24}\left(\frac{V_1^2 - V_2^2}{c_1^2}\right)^2 + \cdots\right] \qquad (11\text{-}33)$$

If velocities or velocity differences are small relative to the sonic velocity, the equation reduces to

$$p_2 - p_1 = \frac{\rho_1(V_1^2 - V_2^2)}{2} \qquad (11\text{-}34)$$

which will be recognized as the Bernoulli equation previously developed for incompressible flow.

EXAMPLE 11-3

Air in a wind tunnel used to study flow past a body has a temperature of 25°C and a pressure of 100 kN/m²(abs). The tunnel velocity is 150 m/s and the air in the vicinity of the object reaches a maximum of 220 m/s. What is the temperature of the air at this point?

SOLUTION:

Because the velocity change is the product of an isentropic flow, Eq. 11-26 may be used to calculate the temperature change.

$$T_1 - T_2 = \frac{k-1}{Rk}\left(\frac{V_2^2}{2g} - \frac{V_1^2}{2g}\right)$$

or

$$25 - T_2 = \frac{1.4 - 1}{(29.2)(1.4)}\left[\frac{(220)^2}{(2)(9.81)} - \frac{(150)^2}{(2)(9.81)}\right]$$

Solving, we obtain $T_2 = 12.1°C$.

EXAMPLE 11-4

Determine the error in pressure difference that will result from the assumption of constant density in an airflow with a velocity change from 100 to 350 ft/s. The air temperature is 60°F and the pressure is 14.7 psia at section 1.

SOLUTION:

At 60°F, $\rho_1 = 0.00237$ slug/ft³. The required error can be evaluated with reasonable accuracy by considering only the second term in parentheses in Eq. 11-33:

$$\text{error} \approx \frac{1}{4}\frac{V_1^2 - V_2^2}{c_1^2}$$

where

$$c_1^2 = \frac{kp_1}{\rho_1} = \frac{(1.4)(14.7)(144)}{0.00237} = 1.252 \times 10^6 \text{ (ft/s)}^2$$

Therefore,

$$\text{error} \approx \frac{350^2 - 100^2}{(4)(1.252 \times 10^6)} = 2.25 \times 10^{-2}$$

or about $2\frac{1}{4}\%$.

The foregoing example gives some insight into the types of problems in which compressibility effects must be considered, and the minor influence compressibility has at low to moderate velocities. We will consider next a couple of situations leading first to relatively simple and then to more difficult solutions of various adiabatic flow problems.

Stagnation Point

Conditions at a stagnation point were considered in Section 5-3. The pressure rise that occurs when an incompressible flow is brought to rest at a stagnation point was given as

$$p_2 - p_1 = \frac{\rho V_1^2}{2}$$

If a compressible flow is similarly brought to rest at any point, we can anticipate that the process will be adiabatic because of the sudden accelerations and rapid pressure changes. With $V_2 = 0$, Eq. 11-33 becomes

$$p_2 - p_1 = \frac{\rho_1 V_1^2}{2}\left[1 + \frac{1}{4}\left(\frac{V_1}{c_1}\right)^2 + \frac{2-k}{24}\left(\frac{V_1}{c_1}\right)^4 + \ldots\right] \qquad (11\text{-}35a)$$

but from the definition of the Mach number,

$$\text{Ma} = \frac{V}{c}$$

we may also write

$$p_2 - p_1 = \frac{\rho_1 V_1^2}{2}\left(1 + \frac{1}{4}\text{Ma}_1^2 + \frac{2-k}{24}\text{Ma}_1^4 + \ldots\right) \qquad (11\text{-}35b)$$

Similar to the results of Example 11-4, Eq. 11-35b shows that at a Mach number of 0.3 the error in assuming the flow to be incompressible is about $2\frac{1}{4}\%$.

If the temperature change at a stagnation point is of interest, Eq. 11-26 gives

$$T_2 - T_1 = \frac{V_1^2}{2g}\frac{k-1}{Rk} \qquad (11\text{-}36)$$

Thus, the stagnation temperature (T_2) is

$$T_2 = T_1 + \frac{V_1^2}{2g}\frac{k-1}{Rk} \qquad (11\text{-}37)$$

and therefore

$$\frac{T_2}{T_1} = 1 + \frac{k-1}{2}\frac{V_1^2}{gkRT_1}$$

or

$$\frac{T_2}{T_1} = 1 + \frac{k-1}{2}\text{Ma}_1^2 \qquad (11\text{-}38)$$

which gives the temperature rise as a function of the Mach number. Note also that if Eq. 11-25a is written between an arbitrary point in the flow and the stagnation point, we get

$$\frac{V^2}{2g} + c_p T = c_p T_{\text{stagnation}} \qquad (11\text{-}39)$$

The stagnation temperature is thus a constant along the streamline. It may be expected to play much the same role in compressible flow as the total head does in incompressible flow.

EXAMPLE 11-5

What is the maximum air velocity that will not exceed a 2°F temperature rise at a stagnation point? Assume air at 70°F and 14.7 psia.

SOLUTION:

At 70°F, $\rho = 0.00233$ slug/ft³, so

$$c = \sqrt{\frac{kp}{\rho}} = \sqrt{\frac{(1.4)(14.7)(144)}{0.00233}} = 1128 \text{ ft/s}$$

Also,

$$T_1 = 70 + 460 = 530°\text{R}$$

and the stagnation temperature T_2 is

$$T_2 = 72 + 460 = 532°\text{R}$$

The maximum Mach number is given by Eq. 11-38:

$$\frac{532}{530} = 1 + \frac{1.4 - 1}{2}(\text{Ma}_1^2)$$

Solving, we obtain

$$\text{Ma}_1^2 = 0.0189$$

and

$$\text{Ma}_1 = 0.137$$

Finally,

$$\text{Ma}_1 = 0.137 = \frac{V_1}{1128}$$

and

$$V_1 = 153 \text{ ft/s}$$

EXAMPLE 11-6

Determine the error in the velocity measurement made by a Pitot tube if the flow is assumed incompressible and the equations of Section 5-3 applied. Assume that the air is at 20°C and the velocity is 120 m/s.

SOLUTION:

At 20°C the speed of sound is

$$c = \sqrt{kgRT}$$
$$= \sqrt{(1.4)(9.81 \text{ m/s}^2)(29.2 \text{ m/°K})(293°\text{K})} = 343 \text{ m/s}$$

and the Mach number

$$\text{Ma} = \frac{V}{c} = \frac{120 \text{ m/s}}{343 \text{ m/s}} = 0.350$$

From Eq. 11-36b, the pressure rise as sensed by the Pitot tube will be

$$p_2 - p_1 = \frac{\rho_1 V_1^2}{2}\left(1 + \frac{1}{4}\text{Ma}_1^2\right)$$

$$= \frac{\rho_1 V_1^2}{2}\left[1 + \frac{(0.350)^2}{4}\right] = \frac{\rho_1 V_1^2(1.0306)}{2}$$

If the incompressible flow equation is used to interprete the pressure rise,

$$V_{\text{inc}} = \sqrt{2(p_2 - p_1)/\rho}$$

$$= \sqrt{V_1^2(1.0306)}$$

Therefore,

$$V_{\text{inc}}/V_1 = \sqrt{1.0306} = 1.015$$

and the Pitot tube will overestimate the velocity by 1.5% if the flow is assumed to be incompressible.

One-Dimensional Compressible Flow

Within the constraints of isentropic (frictionless-adiabatic) flow, we are frequently concerned with flows exposed to relatively abrupt changes in cross-sectional geometry; that is, changes in cross section that cause pressure, velocity, and in the case of compressible flow, density and temperature changes, over a short length so that friction can be reasonably ignored. As with incompressible flow, the fundamental equations are continuity and energy. Between two sections they may be written as

$$\rho_1 V_1 A_1 = \rho_2 V_2 A_2 \tag{11-40}$$

which was derived previously as Eq. 4-15 and

$$\frac{V_1^2}{2} + \frac{k}{k-1}\frac{p_1}{\rho_1} = \frac{V_2^2}{2} + \frac{k}{k-1}\frac{p_2}{\rho_2} \tag{11-41}$$

which is a rearrangement of Eq. 11-27.

In a duct where V, p, and ρ are all subject to change with changing cross-sectional area A, we may best anticipate the results by differentiating the equations as follows. From continuity,

$$\rho V A = \text{constant}$$

Thus, changes in the flow direction s are related according to

$$\frac{\partial(\rho V A)}{\partial s} = V A \frac{\partial \rho}{\partial s} + \rho V \frac{\partial A}{\partial s} + \rho A \frac{\partial V}{\partial s} = 0 \tag{11-42}$$

Treating the energy equation (Eq. 11-41) in a similar manner,

$$\frac{\partial}{\partial s}\left(\frac{V^2}{2} + \frac{k}{k-1}\frac{p}{\rho}\right) = V\frac{\partial V}{\partial s} + \frac{k}{k-1}\left(\frac{1}{\rho}\frac{\partial p}{\partial s} - \frac{p}{\rho^2}\frac{\partial \rho}{\partial s}\right) \tag{11-43}$$

The former may be arranged to yield

$$\frac{1}{A}\frac{\partial A}{\partial s} = -\frac{1}{V}\frac{\partial V}{\partial s} - \frac{1}{p}\frac{\partial p}{\partial s} \tag{11-44}$$

If Eq. 11-43 is now solved for the pressure gradient $\partial p/\partial s$ and the result substituted into Eq. 11-44 along with

$$p = \rho g R T$$

and

$$c^2 = k g R T$$

we can obtain

$$\frac{1}{A}\frac{\partial A}{\partial s} = -\frac{1}{V}\frac{\partial V}{\partial s}\left(1 - \frac{V^2}{c^2}\right)$$

or

$$\frac{1}{V}\frac{\partial V}{\partial s} = \frac{(1/A)(\partial A/\partial s)}{\text{Ma}^2 - 1} \tag{11-45}$$

Equation 11-45 now permits the prediction of velocity changes due to area changes, the Mach number playing much the same role here as did the Froude number on the specific energy diagrams of Chapter 10. If a stream-tube expands in the flow direction ($\partial A/\partial s > 0$), and if $\text{Ma} > 1$ (supersonic), then from Eq. 11-45, $\partial V/\partial s > 0$ and the velocity will increase as it goes through the expansion. Conversely, if $\partial A/\partial s > 0$ while $\text{Ma} < 1$ (subsonic), then $\partial V/\partial s < 0$ and the velocity decreases as it passes through an expansion. Similarly, if $\partial A/\partial s < 0$ (a converging section), the velocity will increase with s if the flow is subsonic and decrease if supersonic. Finally, if $\text{Ma} = 1$, Eq. 11-45 requires that $\partial A/\partial s$ also equal zero. This may be satisfied only in a region of minimum cross section known as a *throat*, such as would occur between converging and diverging sections. This does not imply, however, that $\text{Ma} = 1$ in a throat. Rather, if $\text{Ma} \neq 1$ when $\partial A/\partial s = 0$ (the geometric condition at the throat), then $\partial V/\partial s = 0$ also. Thus, if the flow is subsonic ($\text{Ma} < 1$) in the throat, the velocity that has increased toward the throat will be a maximum in the throat, and if the throat velocity is supersonic ($\text{Ma} > 1$), the velocity in the throat will be a minimum.

Convergent Nozzle

The isentropic counterpart to incompressible ideal flow from a reservoir is the frictionless flow of gas from a large pressure tank. Consider the discharge from such a tank through a convergent nozzle with area A_2 as depicted in Fig. 11-3. At section 1 in the tank the fluid has pressure p_1, density ρ_1, and temperature T_1. As with a large reservoir, it will be assumed that $V_1 = 0$ and that the conditions remain constant. The mass rate of flow out G will depend on the existence of a pressure difference $p_1 - p_3$, where p_3 is the ambient (and usually atmospheric) pressure. We shall see that the pressure in the jet p_2 is not necessarily equal to the ambient pressure p_3.

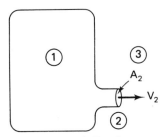

Fig. 11-3. Isentropic flow from a nozzle.

Starting with Eq. 11-29b and applying it between sections 1 and 2 of Fig. 11-3 gives

$$\frac{V_2^2}{2g} = \frac{k}{k-1}\frac{p_2}{\gamma_2}\left[\left(\frac{p_1}{p_2}\right)^{(k-1)/k} - 1\right] \tag{11-46}$$

The Mach number in the jet is

$$\text{Ma}_2 = \frac{V_2}{c_2} = \frac{V_2}{\sqrt{kgRT_2}} = \frac{V_2}{\sqrt{kgp_2/\gamma_2}}$$

Thus, by combining the two equations, we have

$$\text{Ma}_2^2 = \frac{2}{k-1}\left[\left(\frac{p_1}{p_2}\right)^{(k-1)/k} - 1\right] \tag{11-47}$$

which relates the nozzle and jet Mach number to the tank and jet pressure. The flow is initially at rest and there is no diverging section; hence, the velocity must increase in accordance with Eq. 11-45 but remain subsonic. If we consider the "critical" point when $\text{Ma}_2 = 1$ in the throat, the corresponding pressure ratio (p_2/p_1) is obtained from Eq. 11-47 as

$$\left(\frac{p_2}{p_1}\right)_c = \left(\frac{2}{k+1}\right)^{k/(k-1)} \tag{11-48}$$

The critical pressure ratio is dependent only on the fluid, and is independent of the tank and the ambient pressure p_3. Thus, when sonic velocity occurs in the throat, we will generally have $(p_1/p_3) > (p_1/p_2)_c$, and consequently p_2 will be greater than p_3.

The mass flow rate may be calculated from the general discharge equation,

$$G = \rho_2 V_2 A_2$$

with ρ_2 obtained from Eq. 11-28. If the velocity is subsonic, V_2 is given by Eq. 11-46, with $p_2 = p_3$, if the downstream (i.e., throat) density or specific weight is known. If the density or specific weight of the fluid in the tank is known, Eq. 11-29a is more appropriate. For $V_1 = 0$ this becomes

$$\frac{V_2^2}{2g} = \frac{k}{k-1}\frac{p_1}{\gamma_1}\left[1 - \left(\frac{p_2}{p_1}\right)^{(k-1)/k}\right] \tag{11-49}$$

If $Ma_2 = 1$, the velocity V_2 is most readily calculated by the equation for sonic velocity,

$$V_2 = \sqrt{kgRT_2} = \sqrt{\frac{kp_2}{\rho_2}}$$

along with Eqs. 11-48 and Eq. 11-28, the latter in the form

$$\frac{p_2}{p_1} = \left(\frac{\gamma_2}{\gamma_1}\right)^k = \left(\frac{\rho_2}{\rho_1}\right)^k$$

Thus, if $Ma_2 = 1$, the mass flow rate is

$$G = \rho_2 V_2 A_2 = \rho_2 A_2 \left(\frac{kp_2}{\rho_2}\right)^{1/2}$$

$$= A_2\left[k\rho_1 p_1 \left(\frac{p_2}{p_1}\right)^{1/k}\frac{p_2}{p_1}\right]^{1/2} = A_2\left[k\rho_1 p_1 \left(\frac{p_2}{p_1}\right)^{(k+1)/k}\right]^{1/2}$$

and finally, by Eq. 11-48,

$$G = A_2\left[k\rho_1 p_1 \left(\frac{2}{k+1}\right)^{(k+1)/(k-1)}\right]^{1/2} \qquad (11\text{-}50)$$

Once the flow reaches $Ma_2 = 1$, the mass discharge for a given nozzle is dependent only on the tank conditions. Reduction of the ambient pressure has no further effect on the flow. The throat has become a "choke," similar to the open-channel conditions described in Section 10-2.

EXAMPLE 11-7

Air discharges isentropically from a large tank through a 10-cm-diameter convergent nozzle. The temperature in the tank is 45°C and the ambient pressure is 100 kN/m²(abs). Calculate the flow rate, pressure, temperature, and velocity in the jet as it just leaves the nozzle if the tank pressure is (a) 800 kN/m²; (b) 50 kN/m².

SOLUTION:

For a gage pressure of 800 kN/m², the density of the air in the tank is

$$\rho_1 = \frac{p_1}{gRT_1} = \frac{800 \times 10^3 + 100 \times 10^3 \text{ N/m}^2}{(9.81 \text{ m/s}^2)(29.2 \text{ m/°K})(318°\text{K})} = 9.880 \text{ kg/m}^3$$

By Eq. 11-48, the critical pressure ratio is

$$\left(\frac{p_2}{p_1}\right)_c = \left(\frac{2}{1.4+1}\right)^{1.4/(1.4-1)} = 0.528$$

whereas the ambient pressure/tank pressure ratio is

$$\frac{p_3}{p_1} = \frac{100 \text{ kN/m}^2}{800 + 100 \text{ kN/m}^2} = 0.111$$

Thus, p_2 is greater than p_3, the throat velocity will be sonic, and

$$p_2 = (0.528)(900 \text{ kN/m}^2) = 475.2 \text{ kN/m}^2(\text{abs})$$

The discharge as obtained by Eq. 11-50 is

$$G = \left[\frac{\pi}{4}(0.1 \text{ m})^2\right]\left[(1.4)(9.88 \text{ kg/m}^3)(900 \times 10^3 \text{ N/m}^2)\left(\frac{2}{1.4+1}\right)^{(1.4+1)/(1.4-1)}\right]^{1/2}$$

$$= 16.04 \text{ kg/s}$$

The adiabatic relationship (Eq. 11-28) may be used to get the density in the jet,

$$\rho_2 = \rho_1\left(\frac{p_2}{p_1}\right)^{1/k} = (9.880 \text{ kg/m}^3)(0.528)^{1/1.4} = 6.261 \text{ kg/m}^3$$

The temperature of the jet may be obtained from the equation of state:

$$T_2 = \frac{p_2}{\rho_2 g R} = \frac{475.2 \times 10^3 \text{ N/m}^2}{(6.261 \text{ kg/m}^3)(9.81 \text{ m/s}^2)(29.2 \text{ m/}^\circ\text{K})}$$

$$= 265^\circ\text{K} = -8^\circ\text{C}$$

Finally, the sonic velocity of the jet is

$$V_2 = \sqrt{kgRT_2}$$

$$= \sqrt{(1.4)(9.81 \text{ m/s}^2)(29.2 \text{ m/}^\circ\text{K})(265^\circ\text{K})} = 326 \text{ m/s}$$

In part (b) the tank pressure is only 50 kN/m² or 150 kN/m²(abs); thus,

$$\rho_1 = \frac{p_1}{gRT_1} = \frac{150,000}{(9.81)(29.2)(318)} = 1.647 \text{ kg/m}^3$$

The critical pressure remains $(p_2/p_1)_c = 0.528$, while

$$\frac{p_3}{p_1} = \frac{100 \text{ kN/m}^2}{50 + 100 \text{ kN/m}^2} = 0.667$$

which indicates that the critical pressure ratio is not reached. Therefore, $p_2 = p_3 = 100 \text{ kN/m}^2(\text{abs})$, and the nozzle velocity will be something less than sonic. The density in the jet will be

$$\rho_2 = \rho_1\left(\frac{p_2}{p_1}\right)^{1/k}$$

$$= (1.647 \text{ kg/m}^3)\left(\frac{100 \times 10^3 \text{ N/m}^2}{150 \times 10^3 \text{ N/m}^2}\right)^{1/1.4} = 1.233 \text{ kg/m}^3$$

The jet velocity by Eq. 11-49 is

$$V_2 = \left\{\frac{2gk}{k-1}\frac{p_1}{\rho_1 g}\left[1 - \left(\frac{p_2}{p_1}\right)^{(k-1)/k}\right]\right\}^{1/2}$$

$$= \left\{\frac{(2)(1.4)(150 \times 10^3 \text{ N/m}^2)}{(1.4-1)(1.647 \text{ kg/m}^3)}\left[1 - \left(\frac{100 \times 10^3 \text{ N/m}^2}{150 \times 10^3 \text{ N/m}^2}\right)^{(1.4-1)/1.4}\right]\right\}^{1/2}$$

$$= 264.1 \text{ m/s}$$

The flow rate now is

$$G = \rho_2 V_2 A_2 = (1.233 \text{ kg/m}^3)(264.1 \text{ m/s})(\pi/4)(0.1 \text{ m})^2$$

$$= 2.558 \text{ kg/s}$$

and the temperature

$$T_2 = \frac{p_2}{p_2 g R} = \frac{100 \times 10^3 \text{ N/m}^2}{(1.233 \text{ kg/m}^3)(9.81 \text{ m/s}^2)(29.2 \text{ m/}^\circ\text{K})}$$
$$= 283^\circ\text{K} = 10^\circ\text{C}$$

It should be noted that although the velocity does not increase beyond the speed of sound, further increase in the tank pressure results in increased discharge because of the increase in density.

Convergent Conduit

If isentropic flow occurs through a section of reducing conduit, Eq. 11-45 is useful for predicting the directions in which changes will occur. The actual analysis is more difficult than that of the convergent nozzle, however, since the approach velocity V_1 cannot be ignored. Example 11-8 illustrates this type of problem.

EXAMPLE 11-8

Determine the pressure, density, temperature, and velocity in the reduced section of the circular duct of Fig. 11-4. The mass flow rate of air is 6.0 slugs/s. A pressure gage at section 1 reads 100 psi, and the temperature at that section is 80°F.

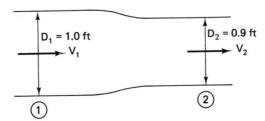

Fig. 11-4.   Frictionless adiabatic flow through a contraction.

SOLUTION:

Since $p_1 = 100 + 14.7 = 114.7$ psia and $T_1 = 80 + 460 = 540^\circ$R, the density is

$$\rho_1 = \frac{p_1}{g R T_1} = \frac{(114.7)(144)}{(32.2)(53.3)(540)} = 0.0178 \text{ slugs/ft}^3$$

and the velocity accordingly is

$$V_1 = \frac{6.0}{\rho_1 A_1} = \frac{6.0}{(0.0178)(0.785)} = 429 \text{ ft/s}$$

Since

$$c_1 = \sqrt{kg R T_1} = \sqrt{(1.4)(32.2)(53.3)(540)} = 1139 \text{ ft/s}$$

the Mach number becomes

$$\text{Ma}_1 = \frac{V_1}{c_1} = \frac{429}{1139} = 0.377$$

With reference to Eq. 11-45, the contracting section ($\partial A/\partial s < 0$) and the subsonic flow ($\text{Ma}_1 < 0$) require that the velocity must increase, and therefore V_2 will be greater than V_1. From Eq. 11-40,

$$6.0 = \rho_2 V_2 \left(\frac{\pi}{4}\right)(0.9)^2 = 0.636 \rho_2 V_2$$

while from Eq. 11-41,

$$\frac{(427)^2}{2} + \frac{1.4}{0.4}\frac{(114.7)(144)}{0.0178} = \frac{V_2^2}{2} + \frac{1.4}{0.4}\frac{p_2}{\rho_2}$$

and finally from Eq. 11-28 (originally Eq. 1-13),

$$\frac{(114.7)(144)}{[(0.0178)(32.2)]^{1.4}} = \frac{p_2}{[(32.2)\rho_2]^{1.4}}$$

Solving the three equations simultaneously,

$$V_2 = 554 \text{ ft/s}$$

Density and pressure may now be calculated from the preceding equations. They are

$$\rho_2 = \frac{6.0}{(0.636)(554)} = 0.0170 \text{ slugs/ft}^3$$

$$p_2 = \frac{(114.7)(0.0170)^{1.4}}{(0.0178)^{1.4}} = 107.5 \text{ psia} = 92.8 \text{ psi (gage)}$$

Using the equation of state, the final temperature may also be calculated as

$$T_2 = \frac{p_2}{\rho_2 g R} = \frac{(107.5)(144)}{(0.0170)(32.2)(53.3)} = 531°\text{R} = 71°\text{F}$$

It should be noted at this point that, as in Chapter 10, only an introduction to this specialized subject has been presented. The references at the end of the chapter cover isentropic flow in far more detail than is possible here. They include many graphic and tabular aids which make the actual problem solving considerably simpler. One additional type of nozzle will also be considered, the convergent–divergent nozzle. This will be treated as soon as the necessary material on the "shock wave" has been developed.

Normal Shock Wave

In the convergent nozzle we have examined an isentropic flow condition with an upper bound of $\text{Ma} = 1$. We will shortly consider a convergent–divergent nozzle, in which supersonic flows are possible as well. In the process, however, we will find that real upstream and downstream conditions may occur for which it is not possible to have a continuous isentropic process. This is analogous to the open-channel conditions of Chapter 10, in which a discontinuity in the form of a hydraulic jump occurred. As with the hydraulic jump, we will have a considerable energy loss, as well as an abrupt increase in pressure and, in this case, temperature and density. This phenomenon is known as a *shock* or *shock wave*. The text will only treat *normal shock*, that in which the shock wave is perpendicular to the flow, as the one-dimensional approach may then be used for the analysis. This is consistent with Chapter 10, where oblique hydraulic jump was only mentioned. In passing, oblique shock is of considerable importance in the aerospace industry, as shock waves forming in the vicinity of a high-speed body are generally oblique.

Like hydraulic jump, the analysis of normal shock waves follows from direct application of the momentum equation. The control volume is shown in Fig. 11-5. The shock may be treated as abrupt, since the shock takes place

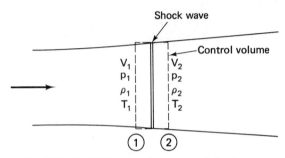

Fig. 11-5. Definition sketch for normal shock wave.

over a very short length which is on the order of a few times the mean free path of the molecules (approximately 10^{-3} mm). This means that the cross-sectional area will not change through the length of the shock and for sections 1 and 2 just upstream and downstream of the shock, respectively, $A_1 = A_2 = A$. Further, we will have $V_1, p_1, \rho_1,$ and T_1 as the average velocity, pressure, density, and temperature at section 1, with corresponding quantities $V_2, p_2, \rho_2,$ and T_2 at section 2. As in previous situations where a one-dimensional approach was applied, variation of each quantity across the section is ignored and the average value is taken to represent the section as a reasonable approximation. Applying the momentum equation to the control volume of Fig. 11-5 gives

$$(p_1 - p_2)A = G(V_2 - V_1) \tag{11-51}$$

where G, the mass rate of flow, is given by

$$G = \rho_1 V_1 A_1 = \rho_2 V_2 A_2 \tag{11-52}$$

Combining the two equations gives

$$p_2 - p_1 = \rho_1 V_1^2 - \rho_2 V_2^2 \tag{11-53}$$

which relates the pressure increase $p_2 - p_1$ to the upstream and downstream velocities. Making use of

$$\text{Ma}^2 = \left(\frac{V}{c}\right)^2 = \frac{V^2}{kp/\rho}$$

we may rewrite Eq. 11-53 as

$$p_2 - p_1 = kp_1\text{Ma}_1^2 - kp_2\text{Ma}_2^2$$

which, when rearranged, gives the pressure ratio p_2/p_1 in terms of the Mach number:

$$\frac{p_2}{p_1} = \frac{1 + k\text{Ma}_1^2}{1 + k\text{Ma}_2^2} \tag{11-54}$$

An additional relationship is needed at this point. We may note that although considerable internal friction occurs in the shock wave, no heat is added to or removed from the system. Hence, the adiabatic energy equation still applies. Choosing this equation in the form of Eq. 11-24b, it may be arranged as follows:

$$\frac{V_1^2}{kgRT_1} + \frac{2}{k-1} = \frac{V_2^2}{kgRT_1}\frac{T_2}{T_2} + \frac{2}{k-1}\frac{T_2}{T_1}$$

or

$$\text{Ma}_1^2 + \frac{2}{k-1} = \left(\text{Ma}_2^2 + \frac{2}{k-1}\right)\frac{T_2}{T_1}$$

When solved for T_2/T_1 we have an additional equation relating the temperature ratio to the upstream and downstream Mach numbers,

$$\frac{T_2}{T_1} = \frac{\text{Ma}_1^2 + \dfrac{2}{k-1}}{\text{Ma}_2^2 + \dfrac{2}{k-1}} \tag{11-55}$$

In a similar manner, the density ratio may be determined from the pressure and temperature ratios through the equation of state. Noting also that densities and velocities are related through Eq. 11-52, we have

$$\frac{\rho_2}{\rho_1} = \frac{V_1}{V_2} = \frac{p_2/gRT_2}{p_1/gRT_1} = \frac{p_2}{p_1}\frac{T_1}{T_2}$$

and hence

$$\frac{\rho_2}{\rho_1} = \frac{V_1}{V_2} = \frac{1 + k\text{Ma}_1^2}{1 + k\text{Ma}_2^2}\frac{\text{Ma}_2^2 + \dfrac{2}{k-1}}{\text{Ma}_1^2 + \dfrac{2}{k-1}} \tag{11-56}$$

In order to obtain a relationship between the Mach numbers, the equation of state and Eq. 11-52 may be combined as follows:

$$\frac{p_2}{p_1} = \frac{\rho_2}{\rho_1}\frac{T_2}{T_1} = \frac{V_1}{V_2}\frac{T_2}{T_1}$$

But

$$\frac{V_1}{V_2} = \frac{V_1}{\sqrt{kgRT_1}}\frac{\sqrt{kgRT_1}}{V_2}\frac{\sqrt{T_2}}{\sqrt{T_2}} = \frac{\text{Ma}_1}{\text{Ma}_2}\left(\frac{T_1}{T_2}\right)^{1/2}$$

Substituting this equation for V_1/V_2 into the previous equation for p_2/p_1 and solving for T_2/T_1 yields

$$\frac{T_2}{T_1} = \left(\frac{p_2}{p_1}\right)^2 \left(\frac{Ma_2}{Ma_1}\right)^2$$

Finally, if Eqs. 11-54 and 11-55 are substituted for T_2/T_1 and p_2/p_1, respectively, there results an equation in Ma_1 and Ma_2 only:

$$\frac{Ma_1^2 + \dfrac{2}{k-1}}{Ma_2^2 + \dfrac{2}{k-1}} = \left(\frac{1 + kMa_1^2}{1 + kMa_2^2}\right)^2 \frac{Ma_2^2}{Ma_1^2} \qquad (11\text{-}57)$$

After considerable algebraic manipulation, this equation may be solved to give

$$Ma_2^2 = \frac{Ma_1^2 + \dfrac{2}{k-1}}{\left(\dfrac{2k}{k-1}\right)Ma_1^2 - 1} \qquad (11\text{-}58)$$

This equation completes the set of equations necessary to determine conditions downstream of a shock wave given the upstream conditions. Based on Ma_1^2, Eq. 11-58 gives Ma_2^2, and Eqs. 11-54, 11-55, and 11-56 may then be used, as previously indicated, to obtain the downstream pressure, temperature and density, respectively. Alternatively, Eq. 11-58 may be directly substituted into the foregoing equations to give the pressure, temperature, density, and velocity ratios as functions of Ma_1 only. The resulting equations are

$$\frac{p_2}{p_1} = \frac{2kMa_1^2 - (k-1)}{k+1} \qquad (11\text{-}59)$$

$$\frac{T_2}{T_1} = \frac{2(k-1)}{(k+1)^2 Ma_1^2}\left(1 + \frac{k-1}{2}Ma_1^2\right)\left(\frac{2k}{k-1}Ma_1^2 - 1\right) \qquad (11\text{-}60)$$

and

$$\frac{\rho_2}{\rho_1} = \frac{V_1}{V_2} = \frac{Ma_1^2(k+1)}{2 + Ma_1^2(k-1)} \qquad (11\text{-}61)$$

These shock wave equations correspond to the hydraulic jump equation (Eq. 10-25), which related the depth ratio to the upstream Froude number. Also, similar to the hydraulic jump, which "abruptly" changes a supercritical flow to a subcritical flow, the shock wave can only occur when $Ma_1 > 1$. The downstream flow must therefore have $Ma_2 < 1$, according to Eq. 11-58. Any of the reference books at the end of the chapter will provide a complete proof that this is the only possible case.

By elimination of Ma_1 between Eqs. 11-59 and 11-61, the density ratio is given in terms of the pressure ratio as

$$\frac{p_2}{p_1} = \frac{1 + \dfrac{k+1}{k-1}\dfrac{p_2}{p_1}}{\dfrac{k+1}{k-1} + \dfrac{p_2}{p_1}} \tag{11-62}$$

This expression, known as the *Rankine–Hugoniot equation*, is compared with Eq. 11-28, the isentropic equation, in the form

$$\rho_2/\rho_1 = (p_2/p_1)^{1/k}$$

in Fig. 11-6 for a gas with $k = 1.4$. The figure shows that except for a weak shock, the process is not isentropic. In fact, the stronger the shock, the greater is the divergence between the two relationships.

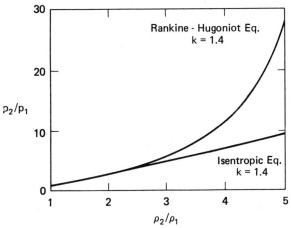

Fig. 11-6. Comparison of Rankine–Hugoniot and isentropic equations.

EXAMPLE 11-9

A normal shock occurs in an airflow with the following upstream conditions: $V_1 = 600$ m/s, $p_1 = 100$ kN/m²(abs), and $T_1 = 5°C$. Determine the downstream velocity, pressure, and temperature, and both the upstream and downstream densities and Mach numbers.

SOLUTION:

The equations that are available offer alternative computations for the various quantities requested. The procedure selected here is to first use Eq. 11-58 to obtain Ma_2 and then use Eqs. 11-54 through 11-56 for the other quantities. The reader would be advised to check that Eqs. 11-59 through 11-61 give the same results.

To use Eq. 11-58, we first need Ma_1, which is given by

$$Ma_1 = \frac{V_1}{\sqrt{kgRT_1}} = \frac{600 \text{ m/s}}{\sqrt{(1.4)(9.81 \text{ m/s})(29.2 \text{ m/}°K)(273 + 5°K)}} = 1.797$$

Then, from Eq. 11-58,

$$Ma_2^2 = \frac{(1.797)^2 + \dfrac{2}{1.4 - 1}}{\dfrac{(2)(1.4)}{1.4 - 1}(1.797)^2 - 1} = 0.3809$$

from which $Ma_2 = 0.6172$.

The pressure is obtained from Eq. 11-54:

$$\frac{p_2}{100 \times 10^3 \text{ N/m}^2} = \frac{1 + (1.4)(1.797)^2}{1 + (1.4)(0.6172)^2}$$

which gives

$$p_2 = 360 \times 10^3 \text{ N/m}^2(\text{abs}) = 360 \text{ kN/m}^2(\text{abs})$$

Next, using Eq. 11-55,

$$\frac{T_2}{273 + 5} = \frac{(1.797)^2 + \dfrac{2}{1.4 - 1}}{(0.6172)^2 + \dfrac{2}{1.4 - 1}}$$

and

$$T_2 = 425°K = 152°C$$

By Eq. 11-56,

$$\frac{600 \text{ m/s}}{V_2} = \frac{1 + (1.4)(1.797)^2}{1 + (1.4)(0.6172)^2} \frac{(0.6172)^2 + \dfrac{2}{1.4 - 1}}{(1.797)^2 + \dfrac{2}{1.4 - 1}}$$

and $V_2 = 254.8$ m/s. Finally, from the equation of state,

$$\rho_1 = \frac{p_1}{gRT_1} = \frac{100 \times 10^3}{(9.81)(29.2)(273 + 5)} = 1.256 \text{ kg/m}^3$$

and from

$$\frac{\rho_2}{\rho_1} = \frac{V_1}{V_2}$$

$$\rho_2 = \frac{(1.256 \text{ kg/m}^3)(600 \text{ m/s})}{254.8 \text{ m/s}} = 2.957 \text{ kg/m}^3$$

Convergent–Divergent Nozzle

This section will be concluded by a study of the convergent–divergent nozzle, such as that shown in Fig. 11-7. The analysis of this device ties together several aspects of compressible flow heretofore treated separately. Known as the *deLaval nozzle*,[3] it has important applications in the aerospace industry for both jet propulsion engines and rocket motors. Its primary function is the acceleration of the fluid to high velocity. Here, the behavior of the nozzle

---

[3]Developed by a Swedish engineer, Carl Gustaf Patrik deLaval (1845–1913).

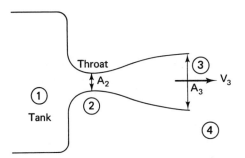

Fig. 11-7. Convergent–divergent nozzle.

under a range of flow conditions will be examined. The results of these different conditions are displayed in Fig. 11-8 as curves of pressure versus position along the nozzle.

The tank pressure is taken as a constant p_1 and the ambient pressure as p_4. If $p_1 = p_4$, then, of course, no flow occurs and the pressure distribution is a constant, as indicated by curve A on Fig. 11-8. As the ambient pressure is reduced, the flow accelerates in passing from the tank to the throat. Assuming that the sonic velocity is not reached at the throat, the flow will decelerate from that point to the exit according to Eq. 11-45. In the expanding section the pressure will increase as compression occurs (curve B). The pressure distribution can be determined from the isentropic equations, with the exit pressure p_3 equal to the ambient pressure p_4. Further reduction of the ambient pressure results in the sonic velocity being reached in the throat, at which

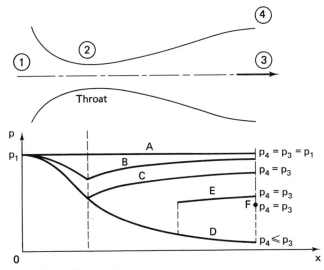

Fig. 11-8. Possible flows through the deLaval nozzle.

point the critical pressure ratio (Eq. 11-48) will occur. This requires that the ambient and hence exit pressure be exactly the correct value, however. The pressure distribution, shown as curve C, would again be found from the isentropic relations. At this condition, the throat has become a choke and any further reduction in the ambient pressure can have no effect either at the throat or upstream. The remaining cases to be considered all follow curve C up to the throat.

There is one remaining curve which results from purely isentropic flow. This case (curve D) occurs when the ambient pressure, and thereby the exit pressure, is reduced to the point shown. This also requires a specific pressure, but as it leads (isentropically) to supersonic flow, it is normally the design case. The fluid smoothly accelerates and expands as it passes through the divergent nozzle. As the discharge is fixed by the choke action of the throat, a further reduction in the ambient pressure will have no effect on the discharge or on the pressure distribution anywhere in the nozzle. It will result, however, in $p_3 > p_4$ and a further expansion of the fluid downstream of the exit of the nozzle. This expansion is accomplished through oblique shock waves not amenable to one-dimensional analysis.

If the ambient pressure falls anywhere between the end points of curves C and D, there is no completely isentropic solution. Rather, a normal shock must occur either at the exit or between segments of isentropic flow. (Curve E is typical, with curve D followed until the point of the shock.) The isentropic relationship will provide the upstream and downstream portions of the curve and Eq. 11-54 or 11-59 will apply to give the pressure increase at the shock wave. The shock wave will be located at the point where the pressure ratio for the shock is compatible with the isentropic flow curves downstream from the throat and upstream from the ambient (and exit) pressure. If the ambient pressure is just slightly below that for exit conditions leading to curve C, the shock will be relatively weak and located just shortly downstream of the throat. As the ambient pressure drops, the shock will intensify and move downstream. The limit occurs as the pressure drops to some value at point F where the ambient pressure is such that the shock wave will occur at the exit, following curve D to that point. If the ambient pressure drops to some point between point E and the terminus of curve D, then curve D will be followed to the exit, whereupon oblique shocks will occur beyond the exit to provide the necessary compression.

The two examples that follow will indicate the actual equations involved in the respective computations.

EXAMPLE 11-10

Air discharges from a pressure tank (with $p_1 = 100$ psia and $T_1 = 160°F$) through a convergent–divergent nozzle. The throat has a cross-sectional area of 0.00785 ft^2 and the exit area is 0.015 ft^2. Determine the ambient pressure required to isentropically produce a supersonic jet. Also calculate the mass flow rate and the exit temperature, velocity, and Mach number.

SOLUTION:

The required flow is similar to case D of Fig. 11-8. The throat must act as a choke and the flow rate is therefore given by Eq. 11-50. For an air density in the pressure tank which is found to be

$$\rho_1 = \frac{p_1}{gRT_1} = \frac{(100 \ \text{lb/in}^2)(144 \ \text{in}^2/\text{ft}^2)}{(32.2 \ \text{ft/s}^2)(53.3 \ \text{ft/°R})(160 + 460°R)}$$

$$= 0.01353 \ \text{slugs/ft}^3$$

the mass flow is

$$G = (0.00785 \ \text{ft}^2)\Big[(1.4)(0.01353 \ \text{slugs/ft}^3)(100 \times 144 \ \text{lb/ft}^2)$$

$$\times \left(\frac{2}{1.4 + 1}\right)^{(1.4+1)/(1.4-1)}\Big]^{1/2}$$

$$= 0.0751 \ \text{slugs/s}$$

In order to calculate the exit conditions, we may write the following three equations: First, the discharge equation is

$$G = \rho_3 V_3 A_3$$

or

$$0.0751 \ \text{slugs/s} = (\rho_3 \ \text{slugs/ft}^3)(V_3 \ \text{ft/s})(0.015 \ \text{ft}^2)$$

Second, the isentropic pressure–density relation (Eq. 11-28) gives

$$\frac{p_3 \ \text{lb/ft}^2}{(100 \ \text{lb/ft}^2)(144 \ \text{in.}^2/\text{ft}^2)} = \left(\frac{\rho_3 \ \text{slugs/ft}^3}{0.01353 \ \text{slugs/ft}^3}\right)^{1.4}$$

Finally, the isentropic energy equation in the form of Eq. 11-49 is

$$\frac{(V_3 \ \text{ft/s})^2}{2} = \frac{1.4}{1.4 - 1}\frac{100 \times 144 \ \text{lb/ft}^2}{0.01353 \ \text{slugs/ft}^3}\Big[1 - \left(\frac{p_3}{100 \times 144}\right)^{(1.4-1)/1.4}\Big]$$

Simultaneously solving these three equations for the exit velocity, we get $V_3 = 1889 \ \text{ft/s}$. The discharge equation then yields $\rho_3 = 2.650 \times 10^{-3} \ \text{slugs/ft}^3$, while the second equation gives $p_3 = 1470 \ \text{lb/ft}^2(\text{abs}) = 10.21 \ \text{psia}$. To meet the design conditions, this must be the ambient pressure outside the nozzle.

The exit temperature is

$$T_3 = \frac{p_3}{\rho_3 gR} = \frac{1470 \ \text{lb/ft}^2}{(2.650 \times 10^{-3} \ \text{slugs/ft}^3)(32.2 \ \text{ft/s}^2)(53.3 \ \text{ft/°R})}$$

$$= 323°R = -137°F$$

and the Mach number at the exit is

$$\text{Ma} = \frac{V}{\sqrt{kgRT}} = \frac{1889}{\sqrt{(1.4)(32.2)(53.3)(323)}} = 2.14$$

EXAMPLE 11-11

Determine the ambient pressure range that will cause a normal shock wave to form in the convergent–divergent nozzle of Example 11-10.

SOLUTION:

As a shock wave is to occur (or be on the verge of occurring), the velocity in the throat must again be sonic. Thus, the mass flow rate is 0.0751 slugs/s, as in Example 11-10. The upper pressure limit will be that ambient pressure which causes a shock to occur just downstream of the throat. This limit will correspond to curve C in Fig. 11-8, and the desired pressure at the exit will be that associated with this curve. This curve represents the second isentropic solution to the three equations solved simultaneously in Example 11-10. Solving the same three equations again, this time for a subsonic exit velocity, we get $V_3 = 389$ ft/s, $\rho_3 = 0.0129$ slugs/ft³, and hence $p_3 = 13{,}430$ lb/ft²(abs) $= 93.3$ psia.

The lower limit of ambient pressure that will cause a normal shock to occur in the divergent section will correspond to curve D of Fig. 11-8, with a pressure jump at the exit to point F. Hence, the results of Example 11-10 will apply up to the shock wave and the pressure just downstream of the shock is the required lower limit of ambient pressure. This pressure is given by Eq. 11-59,

$$\frac{p\ \text{lb/ft}^2}{1470\ \text{lb/ft}^2} = \frac{(2)(1.4)(2.14)^2 - (1.4 - 1)}{1.4 + 1}$$

Solving, we obtain

$$p = 7609\ \text{psf(abs)} = 52.8\ \text{psia}$$

In concluding this section it should be noted that the references listed at the end of the chapter, particularly the two volume set by Shapiro, contain extensive tables that simplify the analysis of both isentropic and shockwave problems.

11–3 ISOTHERMAL FLOW IN PIPES

As defined previously, isothermal flow is flow at constant temperature. In this section we will be concerned primarily with isothermal flow in pipes. The situation would occur most commonly in uninsulated pipes where heat flow through the pipe walls permits constant heat exchange and thereby maintenance of a constant temperature.

As in the pipe flows considered previously, wall friction is of major importance and cannot be ignored. In order to incorporate the resistance of the pipe walls, consider the element shown in Fig. 11-9. Applying Newton's second law in the flow direction from left to right gives

$$-\frac{dp}{dx}\,dx\frac{\pi D^2}{4} - \tau_0 \pi D\,dx = \rho V \frac{dV}{dx}\,dx\frac{\pi D^2}{4}$$

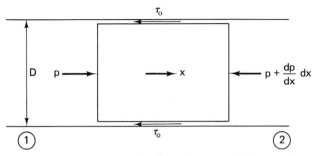

Fig. 11-9. Stresses on a fluid element in compressible pipe flow.

Even though the pipe is of uniform or constant cross section, the velocity changes that may now occur due to compressibility effects will result in fluid acceleration. Thus, the product of mass times acceleration is included on the right-hand side of the equation. Again the "one-dimensional" approach is employed and any variation of a quantity perpendicular to the flow direction is ignored. Replacing the wall shear stress by means of Eq. 8-25 and dividing through by the pipe area gives

$$-\frac{dp}{dx} - \frac{f}{D}\frac{\rho V^2}{2} = \rho V \frac{dV}{dx} \tag{11-63}$$

Note at this point that the Reynolds number,

$$\text{Re} = \frac{(V\rho)D}{\mu} \tag{11-64}$$

is dependent on the product $V\rho$ and, although both V and ρ may be varying, continuity requires that their product remain constant in a constant-area duct. Hence Re and therefore f will not vary with x. Additionally, because of the constant temperature (see Eq. 1-11),

$$\frac{p}{\rho} = \text{constant} \tag{11-65}$$

and from continuity as mentioned above,

$$\rho V = \text{constant} \tag{11-66}$$

Writing these two relationships between section 1 and an arbitrary downstream section, we have

$$\frac{p_1}{\rho_1} = \frac{p}{\rho}$$

or

$$\frac{p_1}{\rho} = \frac{p_1}{\rho}$$

and

$$\rho_1 V_1 = \rho V$$

or

$$\frac{p_1}{\rho} = \frac{V}{V_1}$$

By combining, this also implies that

$$\frac{p_1}{p} = \frac{V}{V_1}$$

Substituting these relationships into Eq. 11-63 and simplifying, we obtain

$$-\frac{dp}{dx} - \frac{f}{D}\frac{\rho_1 V_1^2}{2}\frac{p_1}{p} = -\frac{\rho_1 V_1^2 p_1}{p^2}\frac{dp}{dx}$$

Rearranging yields

$$\frac{dp}{dx}\left(\frac{\rho_1 V_1^2 p_1}{p} - p\right) = \frac{f}{D}\frac{\rho_1 V_1^2}{2}p_1 \qquad (11\text{-}67)$$

The only variable remaining is the pressure p and the equation can be easily integrated from section 1 to section 2, over the length L. Immediately,

$$\rho_1 V_1^2 \ln\left(\frac{p_2}{p_1}\right) - \frac{p_2^2 - p_1^2}{2} = f\frac{L}{D}p_1\frac{\rho_1 V_1^2}{2}$$

which rearranges to

$$\frac{p_1^2 - p_2^2}{2} = p_1\frac{\rho_1 V_1^2}{2}\left[f\frac{L}{D} + 2\ln\left(\frac{p_1}{p_2}\right)\right] \qquad (11\text{-}68)$$

Generally in long pipes, where isothermal flow is most likely anyway, the quantity

$$f\frac{L}{D} \gg 2\ln\left(\frac{p_1}{p_2}\right) \qquad (11\text{-}69)$$

and the equation further reduces to

$$\frac{p_1^2 - p_2^2}{2} = p_1 f\frac{L}{D}\frac{\rho_1 V_1^2}{2} \qquad (11\text{-}70)$$

By expanding the difference in the squares of the pressure terms according to

$$p_1^2 - p_2^2 = (p_1 - p_2)(p_1 + p_2)$$

the equation may be arranged to read

$$p_1 - p_2 = \frac{2}{1 + (p_2/p_1)}f\frac{L}{D}\frac{\rho_1 V_1^2}{2} \qquad (11\text{-}71)$$

Thus, the equation for pressure drop due to friction in isothermal pipe flow is identical to that for incompressible flow except for the initial multiplying factor

$$\frac{2}{1 + (p_2/p_1)}$$

This indicates that the greater the pressure change, as indicated by the deviation of p_2/p_1 from unity, the greater is the magnitude of the pressure difference, $p_1 - p_2$, from that of incompressible flow. For a given flow the ratio p_2/p_1 changes with the distance x between reference sections. Hence, the length of the conduit plays a far more important role in compressible flow than it does for incompressible flow. We will return to this matter shortly.

We may express the pressure drop as a function of a Mach number if Eq. 11-68 is first divided by p_1^2:

$$\frac{p_1^2 - p_2^2}{p_1^2} = \frac{\rho_1 V_1^2}{p_1}\left[f\frac{L}{D} + 2\ln\left(\frac{p_1}{p_2}\right)\right]$$

Then, since

$$c_1 = \sqrt{\frac{kp_1}{\rho_1}}$$

and

$$\mathrm{Ma}_1 = \frac{V_1}{c_1}$$

we get

$$\frac{p_1^2 - p_2^2}{p_1^2} = 1 - \frac{p_2^2}{p_1^2} = k\mathrm{Ma}_1^2\left[f\frac{L}{D} + 2\ln\left(\frac{p_1}{p_2}\right)\right] \tag{11-72}$$

Although Eqs. 11-71 and 11-72 reveal some interesting features of isothermal flow, the calculation of pressure drop is most easily accomplished by use of Eq. 11-70 whenever possible. A trial-and-error solution using Eq. 11-68 or Eq. 11-72 may be required in other cases. Once the downstream pressure is calculated, however, the density at section 2 can be calculated by Eq. 1-11 and the velocity by continuity.

EXAMPLE 11-12

At a reference section in an 8-in.-diameter commercial steel pipe, the velocity of helium is 300 ft/s. Further, its pressure is 200 psia and its temperature is 80°F. Determine the pressure and velocity at a section 200 ft downstream. Compare the resulting pressure with that based on the incompressible flow solution. What is the pressure 4000 ft downstream of the reference section?

SOLUTION:

For helium, $k = 1.66$ and $R = 386$ ft/°R. At section 1

$$\rho = \frac{p}{gRT} = \frac{(200)(144)}{(32.2)(386)(540)} = 0.00429 \text{ slugs/ft}^3$$

From Fig. A-1, $\mu = 4.2 \times 10^{-7}$ lb-s/ft². Hence, the Reynolds number, which is a constant, is given by

$$\mathrm{Re} = \frac{VD\rho}{\mu} = \frac{(300)(8/12)(0.00429)}{4.2 \times 10^{-7}} = 2.05 \times 10^6$$

In addition, the relative roughness is

$$\frac{k}{D} = \frac{0.00015}{\frac{8}{12}} = 0.000225$$

From Fig. 8-12, $f = 0.015$. Assuming a long pipe (and applicability of Eq. 11-70)

$$p_1^2 - p_2^2 = 2p_1 f \frac{L}{D} \frac{\rho_1 V_1^2}{2}$$

$$[(200)(144)]^2 - p_2^2 = \frac{(2)(200)(144)(0.015)(2000)(0.00429)(300)^2}{(\frac{8}{12})(2)}$$

Solving, we obtain

$$p_2 = 1.86 \times 10^4 \text{ psf(abs)} = 129 \text{ psia}$$

By comparison, the incompressible flow solution gives

$$p_1 - p_2 = f \frac{L}{D} \frac{\rho V^2}{2}$$

or

$$p_2 = (200)(144) - \frac{(0.015)(2000)}{\frac{8}{12}} \frac{(0.00429)(300)^2}{2}$$

$$= 2.04 \times 10^4 \text{ psf(abs)}$$

$$= 142 \text{ psia}$$

showing that the pressure drop occurs more rapidly in compressible flow. By Eq. 1-11,

$$\frac{p_1}{\rho_1} = \frac{p_2}{\rho_2}$$

Hence,

$$\rho_2 = \frac{(129)(0.00429)}{200} = 0.00277 \text{ slugs/ft}^3$$

and the velocity by continuity is

$$V_2 = \frac{\rho_1 V_1}{\rho_2} = \frac{(0.00429)(300)}{0.00277} = 465 \text{ ft/s}$$

Checking the validity of Eq. 11-70, which was used above,

$$f \frac{L}{D} = \frac{(0.015)(2000)}{\frac{8}{12}} = 45.0$$

and

$$2 \ln \left(\frac{p_1}{p_2} \right) = 2 \ln \left(\frac{200}{129} \right) = 1.55 \ll 45.0$$

Hence, Eq. 11-68 is not required.

For a pipe length of 4000 ft, Eq. 11-70 becomes

$$[(200)(144)]^2 - p_2^2 = \frac{(2)(200)(144)(0.015)(4000)(0.00429)(300)^2}{(\frac{8}{12})(2)}$$

Hence,

$$p_2^2 = -1.71 \times 10^8$$

The impossibility of extracting a negative square root indicates that under the given conditions, isothermal flow is not possible for a length of 4000 ft.

Example 11-12 demonstrates the effect of increasing length on isothermal pipe flow. It comes about because the pressure gradient dp/dx, rather than remaining constant as in incompressible flow, increases with increasing distance in the flow direction. To develop this point, first combine the isothermal relationship $p/\rho = $ constant, and continuity in the form of $\rho V = $ constant to yield $pV = $ constant. Upon differentiating with respect to x,

$$V\frac{dp}{dx} + p\frac{dV}{dx} = 0$$

Upon substituting into Eq. 11-63, we have

$$-\frac{dp}{dx} - \frac{f}{D}\frac{\rho V^2}{2} = \rho V\left(-\frac{V}{p}\frac{dp}{dx}\right)$$

Introducing $\text{Ma} = V/\sqrt{kp/\rho}$ and rearranging yields

$$\frac{dp}{dx}(k\text{Ma}^2 - 1) = \frac{f}{D}\frac{\rho V^2}{2} \tag{11-73}$$

As the pressure gradient increases, it approaches the limit $dp/dx \rightarrow \infty$, at which point $k\text{Ma}^2 \rightarrow 1$. Thus, the limiting value of the Mach number is

$$\text{Ma}_{\text{max}} = \sqrt{\frac{1}{k}} \tag{11-74}$$

At the other extreme, as $\text{Ma} \rightarrow 0$, note that Eq. 11-73 reverts to the incompressible Darcy–Weisbach equation.

In a similar manner, Eq. 11-67 requires that as $dp/dx \rightarrow \infty$:

$$p^2 = \rho_1 V_1^2 p_1$$

By introducing the upstream Mach number $\text{Ma}_1 = V_1/\sqrt{kp_1/\rho_1}$, this indicates that the pressure can only drop to a minimum, given in terms of upstream conditions as

$$p_{\text{min}} = p_1\sqrt{k}\,\text{Ma}_1 \tag{11-75}$$

If Eq. 11-72 is now solved for the length L, the resulting equation,

$$L = \frac{D}{f}\left[\frac{1}{k\text{Ma}_1^2}\left(1 - \frac{p_2^2}{p_1^2}\right) - 2\ln\left(\frac{p_1}{p_2}\right)\right] \tag{11-76}$$

is immediately applicable for determining the required length between the two sections in isothermal flow, where the pressures are given by p_1 and p_2. If we further let section 2 be the limiting section for isothermal flow, p_2 becomes p_{min}, as given by Eq. 11-75, and the corresponding length L becomes the maximum possible length for isothermal flow based on the specified conditions at section 1. Thus,

$$L_{\text{max}} = \frac{D}{f}\left[\frac{1}{k\text{Ma}_1^2}(1 - k\text{Ma}_1^2) - 2\ln\left(\frac{1}{\sqrt{k}\,\text{Ma}_1}\right)\right]$$

or

$$L_{\text{max}} = \frac{D}{f}\left[\frac{1}{k\text{Ma}_1^2} - 1 - \ln\left(\frac{1}{k\text{Ma}_1^2}\right)\right] \tag{11-77}$$

If this length is exceeded by a given pipe, the flow will adjust its upstream conditions until it is compatible with this equation (but not necessarily the design requirements).

EXAMPLE 11-13

Calculate the maximum length that permits isothermal flow for the conditions given in Example 11-12. What are the pressure, velocity, and Mach number at the downstream end?

SOLUTION:

In Example 11-12 the upstream Mach number is

$$\text{Ma}_1 = \frac{300 \text{ ft/s}}{\sqrt{(1.66)(32.2 \text{ ft/s}^2)(386 \text{ ft/}^\circ\text{R})(540^\circ\text{R})}} = 0.090$$

By Eq. 11-77 the maximum length is

$$L_{\max} = \frac{\frac{8}{12} \text{ ft}}{0.015}\left[\frac{1}{(1.66)(0.090)^2} - 1 - \ln\left(\frac{1}{(1.66)(0.090)^2}\right)\right]$$

$$= 3070 \text{ ft}$$

The pressure at the downstream end is given by Eq. 11-75,

$$p_2 = p_{\min} = (200 \text{ psia})\sqrt{1.66}(0.090) = 23.19 \text{ psia}$$

The corresponding density is

$$\rho_2 = \frac{(23.19)(0.00429)}{200} = 4.974 \times 10^{-4} \text{ slugs/ft}^3$$

and therefore the velocity is

$$V_2 = \frac{(4.29 \times 10^{-3} \text{ slugs/ft}^3)(300 \text{ ft/s})}{4.974 \times 10^{-4} \text{ slugs/ft}^3} = 2587 \text{ ft/s}$$

The Mach number at the downstream end is

$$\text{Ma}_2 = \frac{2587}{\sqrt{(1.66)(32.2)(386)(540)}} = 0.776$$

Checking against the maximum Mach number as given by Eq. 11-74, we get

$$\text{Ma}_2 = \sqrt{\frac{1}{k}} = \sqrt{\frac{1}{1.66}} = 0.776$$

11-4 DRAG AND COMPRESSIBILITY EFFECTS

From dimensional considerations we found in Section 9-2 that a drag force on a body moving relative to a fluid was a function of the geometry of the body and the Reynolds number of the flow (Eq. 9-19). Since fluid compressibility was ignored at that time, the original formulation will be in error to the extent that compressibility influences the results. We may anticipate at this point that the inclusion of the modulus of compressibility,

E, in the dimensional analysis would give rise to one additional term: some power of the quantity $V/\sqrt{E/\rho}$ or the Mach number. Thus, in general, Eq. 9-20 becomes

$$F_D = C_D A \frac{\rho V_0^2}{2} \tag{11-78a}$$

where

$$C_D = C_D(\text{geometry, Re, Ma}) \tag{11-78b}$$

When applying the drag equation to surface (or skin friction) drag, the coefficient of drag has been indicated by C_f. For compressible boundary layer flow we may therefore write (refer to Section 9-1)

$$F_s = C_f BL \frac{\rho V_0^2}{2} \tag{11-79a}$$

where

$$C_f = C_f(\text{Re}_x, \text{Ma}) \tag{11-79b}$$

Here the Mach number would be defined on the basis of free stream conditions and the Reynolds number, as before, by the free stream velocity and the length along the surface. Only limited information is available on the effects of compressibility on the surface drag coefficient. The trend, however, is for the drag coefficient to decrease as the Mach number increases. Figure 11-10 gives the results of theoretical calculations for both the adiabatic and

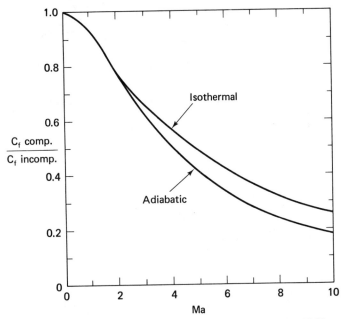

Fig. 11-10. Effects of compressibility on surface drag. [From F. K. Hill, "Boundary Layer Measurements in Hypersonic Flow," *J. Aer. Sci.*, Vol. 23 (1956), 35–42.]

isothermal cases. Although the curves of Fig. 11-10 are verified only in the vicinity of $Re_x \approx 10^7$, they presumably would give reasonably accurate results over a range of turbulent boundary layers.

Equations 11-78 can be applied to form drag, where for any specific body form we will have

$$C_D = C_D(\text{Re, Ma}) \tag{11-80}$$

An experimental study is required to provide actual drag coefficients. Such a study for the drag coefficient for a sphere is included in Fig. 11-11, where C_D is given as a function of both Re and Ma.

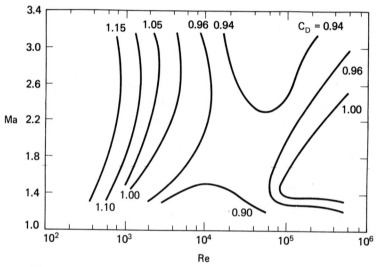

Fig. 11-11. Drag coefficient for a sphere. [From A. May "Supersonic Drag of Spheres at Low Reynolds Numbers in Free Flight," *J. Appl. Phys.*, Vol. 28 (1957), 910–912.]

Although the effects of Re and Ma are not mutually exclusive (as Fig. 11-11 clearly shows), generally at low and moderate values of Re, where viscous effects are important, the Mach number is sufficiently low that it can be ignored. Likewise, by the time the Mach number is large enough that compressibility is no longer negligible, the Reynolds number is usually so large that its effects may be ignored. In the remainder of this section only compressibility effects will be specifically considered.

The reinforced wave patterns of high-speed flow (Fig. 11-2) suggest that the actual causes of a resulting drag force will be due to different mechanisms. This is most vividly demonstrated in the various methods used to achieve streamlining. In the subsonic or low-velocity flows, much of the form drag is due to the low-pressure zone of separation at the rear of the body. Streamlining attempts to eliminate this by utilizing a rounded front portion followed by a long, tapered tail section. At high speeds, on the other hand, streamlining is concentrated on the reduction of the shock wave. This is best accomplished by a pointed nose section. Typical drag coefficients are given in Fig. 11-12 for bodies of various shapes. The reduction of the drag coefficient with the more pointed nose shapes is readily apparent.

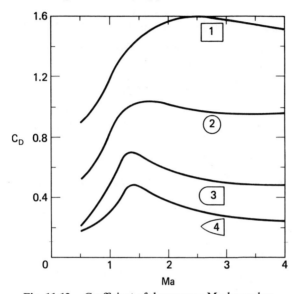

Fig. 11-12.   Coefficient of drag versus Mach number.

EXAMPLE 11-14

Determine the drag force on a 3-in.-diameter sphere passing at a velocity of 1500 ft/s through air at 70°F and 14.7 psia.

SOLUTION:

At 70°F, $\rho = 0.00233$ slugs/ft³. Thus,

$$\text{Ma} = \frac{V}{\sqrt{kgRT}} = \frac{1500}{\sqrt{(1.4)(32.2)(53.3)(530)}}$$

$$= 1.33$$

From Fig. 11-12 and curve 2,

$$C_D = 1.0$$

Hence, the drag force is

$$F_D = C_D A \frac{\rho V^2}{2}$$

$$= (1.0)\left(\frac{\pi}{4}\right)\left(\frac{3}{12}\right)^2 (0.00233)\frac{(1500)^2}{2}$$

$$= 129 \text{ lb}$$

EXAMPLE 11-15

Determine the terminal velocity of a 4-m-diameter sphere with a specific gravity =
9.5 falling through air that has a temperature of 0°C and pressure of 10^5 N/m²(abs).

SOLUTION:

The air has a density given by

$$\rho = \frac{p}{gRT} = \frac{10^5 \text{ N/m}^2}{(9.81 \text{ m/s}^2)(29.2 \text{ m/°K})(273°K)} = 1.28 \text{ kg/m}^3$$

Using curve 2 of Fig. 11-12, a value of $C_D = 1.0$ is assumed. Then, from Eq. 11-78a,
where the drag force equals the weight of the sphere,

$$F_D = C_D A \frac{\rho V_0^2}{2}$$

or

$$\left(\frac{\pi}{6}\right)(4 \text{ m})^3(9.5)(9800 \text{ N/m}^3) = \frac{(1.0)(\pi/4)(4 \text{ m})^2(1.28 \text{ kg/m}^3)(V_0 \text{ m/s})^2}{2}$$

Upon solving, $V_0 = 623$ m/s. The speed of sound is

$$c = \sqrt{kgRT} = \sqrt{(1.4)(9.81)(29.2)(273)} = 331 \text{ m/s}$$

and the Mach number

$$\text{Ma} = \frac{V}{c} = \frac{623}{331} = 1.88$$

From Fig. 11-12 this gives a new $C_D = 1.02$. Again using Eq. 11-78a,

$$\left(\frac{\pi}{6}\right)(4)^3(9.5)(9800) = \frac{(1.02)(\pi/4)(4)^2(1.28)(V_0)^2}{2}$$

for a new $V_0 = 617$ m/s. Checking, we obtain

$$\text{Ma} = \frac{617}{331} = 1.86$$

and C_D remains unchanged. Hence, the terminal velocity is 617 m/s.

PROBLEMS

Sec. 11-1

11-1. Determine the speed of sound in (a) water at 100°F; (b) air at 100°F and
120 psia.

11-2. Determine the speed of sound in (a) water at 30°C; (b) air at 30°C and
600 kN/m²(abs).

11-3. Derive Eq. 1-14.

11-4. A sonar signal bounced off of a submarine requires 30 s to reach the submarine and return. If the water temperature is 45°F, what is the distance to
the submarine?

11-5. How long will be required for a sonar signal bounced off a submerged object to return to the source if the distance is 4 km and the water temperature is 12°C?

11-6. If the Mach angle of a bullet is determined to be 30°, what is the speed of the bullet if the air temperature is 60°F and the pressure is 14.7 psia?

11-7. What will be the Mach angle associated with a bullet traveling at 900 m/s through air at 15°C and standard atmospheric pressure?

Sec. 11-2

11-8. What is the temperature change in the Example 11-4?

11-9. What is the pressure increase at a stagnation point if an airflow has a velocity of 500 ft/s with a temperature of 80°F and a pressure of 12 psia? What is the error if the flow is assumed to be incompressible?

11-10. If air with a velocity of 600 ft/s, pressure of 20 psia, and temperature of 70°F undergoes an adiabatic change so that the pressure becomes 10 psia, what are the resulting velocity and temperature?

11-11. Air in a tank at 200°F and 250 psia discharges isentropically through a convergent nozzle. If the ambient pressure is 14.7 psia, determine the exit pressure and temperature. If the flow rate at these conditions is 2.30 lb/s, what diameter of nozzle is required?

11-12. Helium at 100°F and 75 psia discharges isentropically from a large tank through a convergent nozzle ($d = 1$ in.). What ambient pressure is required to produce sonic velocity in the throat? Calculate the corresponding mass flow rate. If the ambient pressure is 50% and 150% of that required to produce sonic velocity, calculate the respective flow rates.

11-13. Air discharges isentropically from a pressure tank through a convergent nozzle. The air jet has a pressure of 100 kN/m²(abs), a temperature of $-30°C$, and a velocity of 250 m/s. Calculate the pressure and temperature in the tank.

11-14. Carbon dioxide in a large tank discharges isentropically through a convergent nozzle. The ambient pressure is 50 kN/m², the tank temperature is 150°C, and the nozzle has a diameter of 2 cm. What is the minimum tank pressure that will produce sonic velocity in the jet? What is the corresponding flow rate? Calculate the temperature and density of the jet.

11-15. Flow of air into a vacuum tank from the atmosphere, $p = 100$ kN/m²(abs) occurs isentropically through a convergent nozzle. What minimum vacuum (mm Hg) must be maintained in the tank if the sonic velocity is produced in the nozzle?

11-16. Air in a pressure tank ($T = 150°F$) discharges isentropically through a convergent nozzle with area 0.01 ft². If the tank is maintained at 120 psia, plot a graph of mass flow rate versus ambient pressure over the range 40 psia $\leq p_3 \leq 120$ psia. Mark the point $\text{Ma}_2 = 1$.

11-17. Oxygen discharges isentropically through a convergent nozzle with area 0.007 ft² into an ambient pressure of 14.7 psia. What tank pressure is required to just produce sonic velocity in the nozzle? Assuming that the temperature in the tank remains constant, what pressure would be required to double the mass flow rate?

11-18. Carbon dioxide in a large pressure tank discharges isentropically through a convergent nozzle into an ambient pressure of 20 psia. The temperature in the tank is 250°F. Calculate the nozzle diameter necessary for a discharge of 0.2 slugs/s if the pressure in the tank is 35 psia. Repeat for a tank pressure of 40 psia. What is the Mach number at the nozzle in each case? What is the temperature in the nozzle in each case?

11-19. Ammonia in a large pressure tank discharges isentropically through a convergent nozzle into an ambient pressure of 100 kN/m²(abs). The temperature in the tank is 200°C. Calculate the nozzle diameter necessary for a weight discharge of 20 N/s if the pressure in the tank is 180 kN/m²(abs). Repeat for a tank pressure of 190 kN/m²(abs).

11-20. A circular duct reduces in diameter from 1 ft to 0.8 ft. In the larger section the pressure is 40 psia and the temperature is 150°F. In the reduced section the pressure is 35 psia. What is the flow rate in slugs/s, assuming an isentropic flow of air through the reduction? Calculate the velocity in both sections.

11-21. A circular duct reduces in diameter from 20 cm to 15 cm. In the larger section the pressure is 400 kN/m² and the temperature is 120°C. In the reduced section the pressure is 300 kN/m². What is the flow rate in kg/s assuming an isentropic flow of air through the reduction? Calculate the Mach number in each section.

11-22. A normal shock occurs in an airflow in which the upstream conditions are $p_1 = 20$ psi (gage), $V_1 = 2000$ ft/s, and $T_1 = 80°F$. Determine the downstream pressure, velocity, and temperature.

11-23. A normal shock occurs in a flow of ammonia. The upstream velocity, pressure, and temperature are 2000 ft/s, 20 psi (gage), and 80°F, respectively. Determine the downstream pressure, velocity, and temperature.

11-24. If pressures on the upstream and downstream sides of a normal shock wave in air are 120 kN/m²(abs) and 600 kN/m²(abs), respectively, calculate the corresponding Mach numbers. If the upstream temperature is 20°C, what is the downstream temperature?

11-25. In the course of passing through a normal shock wave in nitrogen, the pressure increases from 150 kN/m²(abs) to 640 kN/m²(abs). The upstream velocity is 680 m/s. What must be the upstream and downstream temperatures of the nitrogen?

11-26. As the Mach number upstream of a normal shock increases without bound, determine the lower limit for the downstream Mach number (if such a limit exists).

11-27. A normal shock occurs in an airflow. Downstream of the shock wave the velocity is 855 ft/s, the pressure 100 psia, and the temperature 300°F. Calculate the upstream velocity, pressure, and temperature, and the upstream and downstream densities.

11-28. A normal shock occurs in a flow of carbon dioxide. Downstream of the shock wave the velocity is 250 m/s, the pressure 400 kN/m²(abs), and the temperature 200°C. Calculate the upstream velocity, pressure, and temperature, and the upstream and downstream densities.

11-29. A convergent–divergent nozzle with a throat diameter of 1 in. and an exit diameter of 1.2 in. is connected to an air tank. If the air jet is to discharge with full expansion and Ma = 3 into an ambient pressure of 14.7 psia, what tank pressure is required? If the tank temperature is 350°F, what are the flow rate in slugs/s and the exit velocity?

11-30. A convergent–divergent nozzle with a throat diameter of 3 cm and an exit diameter of 3.5 cm is connected to an air tank. If the air jet is to discharge with full expansion and Ma = 2 into an ambient pressure of 100 kN/m²(abs), what tank pressure is required? If the tank temperature is 150C°, what are the exit temperature and velocity?

11-31. A jet of nitrogen with Ma > 1 is to pass from a convergent–divergent nozzle connected to a pressure tank. If $p_1 = 600$ kN/m²(abs) and $T_1 = 150$°C, what exit diameter is required for an ambient pressure of 100 kN/m²(abs) if full expansion is to occur in the nozzle? The throat diameter is 2 cm. What is the exit temperature?

11-32. A supersonic jet of oxygen (Ma > 1) is to pass isentropically from a convergent–divergent nozzle connected to a pressure tank. The throat has a diameter of 1 in. and the tank pressure and temperature are 100 psia and 250°F, respectively. What exit diameter is required for an ambient pressure of 14.7 psia? What will be the exit Mach number and temperature?

11-33. Determine the alternative ambient pressure that will produce the identical isentropic flow rate as that of Prob. 11-32 for the same nozzle. What will be the exit Mach number and temperature now?

11-34. If a normal shock occurs just at the exit of the convergent–divergent nozzle of Prob. 11-30, what will be the subsequent presure, temperature, velocity, and Mach number?

Sec. 11-3

11-35. If the velocity at the reference section of Example 11-12 is 400 ft/s, what are the pressure and velocity (a) 1000 ft downstream; (b) 2000 ft downstream?

11-36. Air flows isothermally along a 4-in.-diameter smooth conduit at the rate of 40.0 lb/s with an initial pressure of 300 psia and temperature of 100°F. Plot a graph showing the actual pressure and the incompressible solution for pressure, for a length of 500 ft. Choose points at 100-ft intervals.

11-37. Air flows isothermally through a 20-cm-diameter smooth pipe. The initial pressure and temperature are 700 kN/m²(abs) and 100°C, respectively, when the mass flow rate is 20 kg/s. Plot the actual pressure distribution and that found by assuming incompressible flow, over a length of 200 m.

11-38. Assume an isothermal gas flow with initial conditions $p_1 = 500$ kN/m²(abs), $T_1 = 20°C$, and $V_1 = 100$ m/s, in a duct of 0.3 m diameter and $f = 0.03$. Calculate the maximum length and minimum pressure if the gas is (a) air; (b) carbon dioxide; (c) hydrogen.

11-39. Air is to discharge into the atmosphere ($p = 14.7$ psia) through 500 ft of smooth 1-ft-diameter pipe. If the air temperature is 90°F and the flow rate is 29 lb/s, what upstream pressure is required for isothermal flow? What is the maximum possible length based on the upstream conditions?

11-40. Air at 20°C flows isothermally through a 0.4-m-diameter duct with $f = 0.010$. Determine the flow rate in kg/s if over a length of 150 m the pressure drops from 300 kN/m²(abs) to 150 kN/m²(abs). What is the Mach number at each end?

11-41. Air at 20°C flows isothermally through a 0.4-m duct with an absolute roughness of 0.9 mm. Determine the flow rate in kg/s if over a length of 150 m the pressure drops from 300 kN/m²(abs) to 150 kN/m²(abs). What is the Mach number at each end?

11-42. If at a specified section in a 1-ft-diameter smooth duct the pressure is 100 psia when the flow rate is 75 lb/s, what is the pressure at a section 2000 ft downstream? Assume an isothermal air flow at 60°F. What is the percent error in using Eq. 11-70? What is the error in assuming incompressible flow?

Sec. 11-4

11-43. Determine the surface resistance on a wing that is 50 ft long and has an average chord length of 10 ft. The air speed is 550 mph and the airplane is at 30,000 ft in a standard atmosphere. Assume that the airflow past the wing is adiabatic.

11-44. Assume that the airflow past a wing is adiabatic and that the air has a pressure of 95 kN/m²(abs) and temperature of 0°C. The wing has an average chord length of 3 m and a span or length of 20 m. Plot a graph of surface resistance versus velocity over the range 0 to 3000 m/s. Include for comparison the surface resistance, assuming incompressible flow.

11-45. What is the terminal velocity of a bomb (body shape 4 in Fig. 11-12) falling through air at 0°F and 14.7 psia if it weighs 2000 lb and has a diameter of 18 in.?

11-46. What is the terminal velocity of a bomb (body shape 4 in Fig. 11-12) falling through air at 0°C and 100 kN/m²(abs) if it has a diameter of 1 m and weighs 30 kN?

11-47. Plot a graph of drag force versus Mach number for a body of shape 3 in Fig. 11-12 if its diameter is 1 m and the air has a pressure of 90 kN/m²(abs) and temperature of −20°C.

REFERENCES

CAMBEL, A. B., "Compressible Flow," Section 8 in *Handbook of Fluid Dynamics*, V. L. Streeter (ed.). New York: McGraw-Hill, 1961.

OLSON, R. M., *Essentials of Engineering Fluid Mechanics*, 3rd ed. New York: Intext, 1973.

OWCZAREK, J. A., *Fundamentals of Gas Dynamics*. New York: McGraw-Hill, 1971.

SHAPIRO, A. H., *Compressible Fluid Flow* (2 vols.). New York: Ronald Press, 1953.

THOMPSON, P. A., *Compressible Fluid Dynamics*. New York: McGraw-Hill, 1971.

12

Ideal Fluid Flow

We have previously considered, particularly in the early portion of the book, flows for which the viscosity is negligible. This situation will now be further examined, particularly in conjunction with an additional restriction known as irrotationality. Since no real fluid can exactly satisfy these constraints, the flows will be identified as those of an ideal fluid. In reality, many actual flows are reasonably well approximated by an ideal fluid.

In this chapter the conditions mentioned above will first be developed and described, and a more general Bernoulli equation obtained. The ideal flow fields will then be analyzed by a graphic technique utilizing a flow net. This will be followed by mathematical and finally finite-difference solutions to ideal flow problems. The various solutions will be related to real flows. This will be done most completely in the final section, which deals with lift forces on an air foil. In all cases a steady incompressible flow will be assumed.

12–1 IRROTATIONAL FLOW

The concept of irrotationality must first be defined. In simplest terms a flow is *irrotational* if the fluid, and more particularly, a fluid element, is not rotating. If, on the other hand, rotation of a fluid element occurs, the flow is *rotational*. We will define the rotation of an element by the net rotation of any two mutually perpendicular lines in the element. Consequently, irrotational flow can be defined as flow in which every fluid element has zero angular velocity as indicated by the average or net rotation of any two perpendicular lines.

Rotation and Circulation

A mathematical definition of rotation can be developed in the following fashion. A rectangular element in an arbitrary flow field is shown in Fig. 12-1.

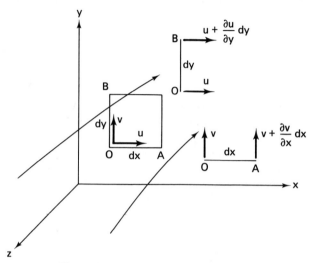

Fig. 12-1.   Definition sketch for rotation.

Two mutually perpendicular lines with lengths of dx and dy are labeled OA and OB, respectively. For clarity, the two line segments are also shown removed with vertical velocities identified at the end points of OA and horizontal velocities at either end of OB. The angular velocity of each line (ignoring translation) may be obtained by dividing the algebraic difference in the end velocities by the respective length. Accordingly,

$$\text{rotation of } OA = \frac{\left(v + \frac{\partial v}{\partial x}\,dx\right) - v}{dx}$$

$$= \frac{\partial v}{\partial x}$$

and

$$\text{rotation of } OB = \frac{u - \left(u + \frac{\partial u}{\partial y}\,dy\right)}{dy}$$

$$= -\frac{\partial u}{\partial y}$$

The rotation of the element ω_z (in the plane normal to the z axis) is the average angular velocity of the two lines, hence

$$\omega_z = \frac{1}{2}\left(\frac{\partial v}{\partial x} - \frac{\partial u}{\partial y}\right) \tag{12-1a}$$

In two-dimensional motion in the x-y plane this will be indicated simply by ω.[1] In a general three-dimensional motion, the additional components of rotation are obtained in a similar manner, with the following results:

$$\omega_x = \frac{1}{2}\left(\frac{\partial w}{\partial y} - \frac{\partial v}{\partial z}\right) \tag{12-1b}$$

and

$$\omega_y = \frac{1}{2}\left(\frac{\partial u}{\partial z} - \frac{\partial w}{\partial x}\right) \tag{12-1c}$$

Using the same technique, the rotation of a fluid element in the r–θ plane of polar-cylindrical coordinates (see Fig. 3-15) becomes

$$\omega_z = \frac{1}{2}\left(\frac{1}{r}\frac{\partial rv_\theta}{\partial r} - \frac{1}{r}\frac{\partial v_r}{\partial \theta}\right) \tag{12-2}$$

Other components of rotation in polar-cylindrical coordinates may be determined, but they will not be included here.

Finally, in the streamline coordinates of Fig. 3-16, an element with sides of length ds and dn would lead to a rotation given by

$$\omega = \frac{1}{2}\left(\frac{\partial v_n}{\partial s} - \frac{\partial v_s}{\partial n}\right) \tag{12-3}$$

For the significance of the subscripts, refer to Section 3-3. If a flow is specified in rectangular Cartesian coordinates, Eqs. 12-1 will give the rotation at any point. Likewise, Eq. 12-2 or 12-3 gives the rotation at any point in a flow specified in polar-cylindrical or streamline coordinates, respectively. In either of the three cases, if the rotation is found to be zero at every point throughout the flow field, the flow is irrotational.[2]

The following examples should help give some physical significance to the differences between rotational and irrotational two-dimensional flows. For each case, and in fact for the rest of the chapter, the streamlines will be selected so as to divide the flow into regions of equal discharge. Figure 12-2 shows a constant-velocity uniform flow between parallel boundaries. A typical element with mutually perpendicular lines (1 and 2) is selected at

---

[1] Frequently an additional quantity, the vorticity, is defined as well. The vorticity is simply twice the rotation, thereby eliminating the "$\frac{1}{2}$" from the various expressions.

[2] We will also find ideal flows which are everywhere irrotational with the exception of one or more specific points, known mathematically as *singular points*, where the flow is rotational. Figure 12-6 is such an example, since the only point that is rotational is the axis.

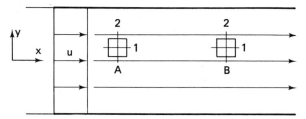

Fig. 12-2.   Irrotational flow between parallel boundaries.

point A. As the element moves to a point B, line 1, parallel to the streamline, translates as shown. Line 2 remains perpendicular to the streamline, since both ends of the line move with the same velocity. Consequently, the flow is irrotational and the element moves without rotation or distortion.

Consider next the typical real, perhaps laminar, flow between the same parallel boundaries in Fig. 12-3. The flow is still uniform and line 1 will

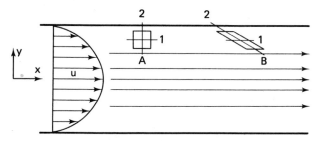

Fig. 12-3.   Rotational flow between parallel boundaries.

again follow a streamline as shown. Now, however, the end of line 2 farthest from the boundary moves with higher velocity than the near-wall end. Hence, line 2 will rotate as it moves from A to B and the element distorts as shown. This is an example of rotational flow. The rotation is usually greatest near the boundary. In fact, in flow involving a boundary layer the rotational character is confined to the boundary layer and the remainder of the flow may be treated as irrotational.

The converging flow of Fig. 12-4 is also irrotational if the frictional effects of the boundaries are ignored. Lines 1 and 2 are both seen to move without rotation, even though the streamline convergence distorts the shape of the element. Figures 12-5 and 12-6 give two examples of circular or vortex flow. In Fig. 12-5 the velocity varies directly with distance from the axis, the solid body rotation of Section 5-2. The velocity is largest at the outer boundary, as indicated by the closer spacing of the streamlines. Line 1 follows a streamline and consequently rotates through a clockwise angle. Additionally, the outer extremity of line 2 moves with greater velocity than the inner, so line 2 rotates through the same clockwise angle. Since the rotation of the element

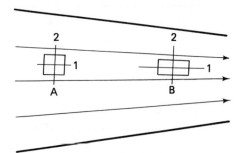

Fig. 12-4. Converging irrotational flow.

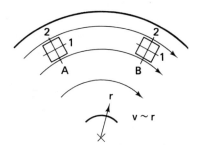

Fig. 12-5. Rotational vortex.

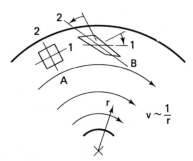

Fig. 12-6. Irrotational vortex.

is the average of the rotation of the two line segments, the element itself rotates identically with each of the two individual lines. Recalling from Section 5-2 that the entire flow has a constant angular velocity, it is to be expected that the element does not distort. Figure 12-6 introduces a new situation in which the velocity along the curved path varies inversely with radial distance. Consequently, the streamlines are grouped more closely to the axis. As in the rotational case, line 1 follows the streamline and rotates through a clockwise angle. Because of the inverse relationship of velocity with radial distance, the outer end of line 2 lags behind the inner end, causing the line to rotate through an angle of equal magnitude to line 1 but in the opposite direction. The average angular velocity, or net rotation, is therefore zero, and although the element has deformed, the flow is irrotational. This is somewhat analogous to the passenger on a Ferris wheel, who, although following a circular path, does not actually rotate!

EXAMPLE 12-1

Determine the components of the rotation for the flow field specified below. What is the magnitude of the rotation at the origin?

$$u = 2x^2 + 2y^2$$
$$v = -2yx - z$$
$$w = x(1 - 2z)$$

SOLUTION:

From Eqs. 12-1, we have

$$\omega_x = \tfrac{1}{2}\left(\frac{\partial w}{\partial y} - \frac{\partial v}{\partial z}\right) = \tfrac{1}{2}(0 + 1) = \tfrac{1}{2}$$

$$\omega_y = \tfrac{1}{2}\left(\frac{\partial u}{\partial z} - \frac{\partial w}{\partial x}\right) = \tfrac{1}{2}[0 - (1 - 2z)] = z - \tfrac{1}{2}$$

$$\omega_z = \tfrac{1}{2}\left(\frac{\partial v}{\partial x} - \frac{\partial u}{\partial y}\right) = \tfrac{1}{2}(-2y - 4y) = -3y$$

At the origin these components become

$$\omega_x = \tfrac{1}{2}, \qquad \omega_y = -\tfrac{1}{2}, \qquad \omega_z = 0$$

Hence, the magnitude of the rotation at the origin becomes

$$\omega = \sqrt{\omega_x^2 + \omega_y^2 + \omega_z^2} = \sqrt{(\tfrac{1}{2})^2 + (-\tfrac{1}{2})^2} = 0.707$$

It is convenient before continuing, to introduce the related concept of circulation, Γ (Greek capital gamma). The circulation of the flow is defined as the integration around a closed contour of the component of the velocity tangent to the contour. This is indicated on Fig. 12-7, which shows a closed contour C in the x–y plane which encloses an area A. The circulation may be expressed as

$$\Gamma = \int_C v \cos\theta \, ds \tag{12-4}$$

which in vector notation is simply

$$\Gamma = \int_C \mathbf{V} \cdot \mathbf{ds} \tag{12-5}$$

This may be immediately expanded in the two-dimensional flow field to

$$\Gamma = \int_C u \, dx + v \, dy \tag{12-6}$$

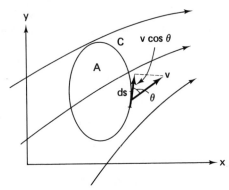

Fig. 12-7. Definition sketch for circulation.

where dx and dy are the x and y components of $\mathbf{ds}$, respectively. If use is now made of Stokes' theorem, which converts a line integral to a surface integral (refer to Appendix D), Eq. 12-6 can be written alternatively as

$$\Gamma = \int_A \left(\frac{\partial v}{\partial x} - \frac{\partial u}{\partial y}\right) dA \tag{12-7}$$

Since the integrand is twice the rotation normal to the x–y plane, the circulation around a contour may be considered to be twice the integral of the rotation over the area. Further, if the circulation is zero, so must be the rotation, and hence the flow must be irrotational.

Bernoulli's Equation in Irrotational Flow

Starting, for convenience, with streamline coordinates, the Euler equations in steady, incompressible, two-dimensional flow were previously written (Eqs. 5-5) as

$$\frac{\partial}{\partial s}\left(\frac{p}{\gamma} + y\right) = -\frac{1}{g}\frac{\partial}{\partial s}\left(\frac{v^2}{2}\right) \tag{12-8a}$$

and

$$\frac{\partial}{\partial n}\left(\frac{p}{\gamma} + y\right) = -\frac{1}{g}\frac{v^2}{r} \tag{12-8b}$$

The first equation was integrated in Chapter 5 to give the Bernoulli equation along a streamline:

$$\frac{p}{\gamma} + y + \frac{v^2}{2g} = \text{constant} \tag{12-9}$$

If we now recall that the normal acceleration of Eq. 12-8b was originally given in Section 3-3 as $v_s\,\partial v_n/\partial s$, we can rewrite Eq. 12-8b as

$$\frac{\partial}{\partial n}\left(\frac{p}{\gamma}+y\right) = -\frac{1}{g}\left(v_s\frac{\partial v_n}{\partial s}\right)$$

If the term

$$\frac{v_s}{g}\frac{\partial v_s}{\partial n} = \frac{1}{g}\frac{\partial}{\partial n}\left(\frac{v_s^2}{2}\right)$$

is now added to both sides, there results

$$\frac{\partial}{\partial n}\left(\frac{p}{\gamma}+y+\frac{v_s^2}{2g}\right) = \frac{v_s}{g}\left(\frac{\partial v_s}{\partial n}-\frac{\partial v_n}{\partial s}\right) \tag{12-10}$$

From Eq. 12-3, the quantity within the right-hand parentheses is twice the rotation (i.e., 2ω). The equation is not easily integrated in general; however, if the flow is irrotational so that the right-hand side of the equation is zero, the remainder is readily integrated in the normal direction. Thus, for steady, incompressible, two-dimensional, irrotational flow, the quantity

$$\frac{p}{\gamma}+y+\frac{v^2}{2g} = \text{constant} \tag{12-11}$$

in the n direction. Since the total head

$$H = \frac{p}{\gamma}+y+\frac{v^2}{2g} \tag{12-12}$$

was previously found to be constant along a streamline, and it has now been shown to be constant in the perpendicular direction as well, the total head must be a constant throughout the flow field. Thus, the Bernoulli equation may be written between any two points in the flow field as follows:

$$\frac{p_1}{\gamma}+y_1+\frac{v_1^2}{2g} = \frac{p_2}{\gamma}+y_2+\frac{v_2^2}{2g} \tag{12-13}$$

If the fluid is a gas, or if the elevation does not otherwise enter into the problem, Eq. 12-13 reduces to

$$p_1 + \rho\frac{v_1^2}{2} = p_2 + \rho\frac{v_2^2}{2} \tag{12-14}$$

between any two points in the flow field. The following examples will illustrate the use of these equations. They will be utilized further after additional procedures are introduced.

EXAMPLE 12-2

The whirlpool above an open drain is essentially an irrotational vortex (Fig. 12-8). If the velocity at a radius of 20 cm is 15 cm/s, what is the velocity at 5 cm? At 80 cm? What is the drawdown Δy at $r = 5$ cm? At $r = 80$ cm?

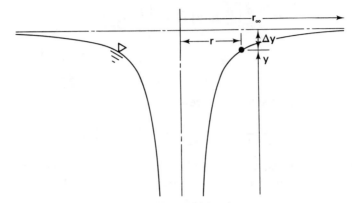

Fig. 12-8. Whirlpool.

SOLUTION:

Since the velocity in an irrotational vortex is given by $v \sim 1/r$, we may write

$$v = k/r$$

or

$$k = vr = (15 \text{ cm/s})(20 \text{ cm}) = 300 \text{ cm}^2/\text{s}$$

Hence at

$$r = 5 \text{ cm} \qquad v = \frac{300}{5} = 60 \text{ cm/s}$$

and at

$$r = 80 \text{ cm} \qquad v = \frac{300}{80} = 3.75 \text{ cm/s}$$

Since the flow is irrotational we may write the Bernoulli equation between a point at infinity and any other point even though the stream lines are approximately concentric circles. Along the free surface the pressure is zero so that between $r = \infty$ and $r = 5$ cm we have

$$y_\infty + \frac{v_\infty^2}{2g} = y_5 + \frac{v_5^2}{2g}$$

Thus

$$\Delta y_5 = y_\infty - y_5 = \frac{v_5^2}{2g} - \frac{v_\infty^2}{2g} = \frac{(60)^2}{(2)(981)} = 1.83 \text{ cm}$$

Likewise

$$\Delta y_{80} = \frac{(3.75)^2}{(2)(981)} = 0.007 \text{ cm}$$

EXAMPLE 12-3

Circular storms such as hurricanes are nearly irrotational outside of the center portion or eye. If the velocity at a radius of 20,000 ft is 100 ft/s, and the pressure is 14.7 psia, what is the pressure at a radius of 10,000 ft? Compare this solution with the solid body rotation of Section 5-2.

SOLUTION:

Since the flow is irrotational, Eq. 12-14 will apply between points at the two radial distances. Further, the velocity at the inner point can be obtained once again from $v \sim k/r$. Hence

$$k = v_2 r_2 = (100)(20,000) = 2 \times 10^6 \text{ ft}^2/\text{s}$$

and at $r_1 = 10,000$ ft

$$v_1 = \frac{2 \times 10^6}{10^4} = 200 \text{ ft/s}$$

Thus, the pressure at the inner point is given by

$$p_1 + \frac{\rho v_1^2}{2} = p_2 + \frac{\rho v_2^2}{2}$$

or for an assumed $\rho = 0.0024$ slugs/ft^3,

$$p_1 = (14.7)(144) + \frac{0.0024}{2}(100^2 - 200^2)$$

$$= 2081 \text{ psf(abs)} = 14.45 \text{ psia}$$

Recall that solid body rotation gives

$$V_1 = 50 \text{ ft/s} \quad \text{and} \quad \omega = \frac{V}{r} = \frac{50}{10,000} = 0.005 \text{ rad/s}$$

Then, by applying the final equation of Section 5-2,

$$p_2 - p_1 = \frac{\rho \omega^2}{2}(r_2^2 - r_1^2)$$

or

$$p_1 = (14.7)(144) - \frac{0.0024}{2}(0.005)^2(20,000^2 - 10,000^2)$$

$$= 2108 \text{ psf(abs)} = 14.6 \text{ psia}$$

Note that even though the velocity varied in an opposite manner in the two cases, both resulted in a pressure decrease toward the axis.

12–2 FLOW NET

Toward the end of the previous section a Bernoulli equation was developed for irrotational flow. The use of this equation will be considerably expanded as a result of the graphic technique to be introduced next. We will introduce without proof (the justification will follow later) that a two-dimensional flow field can be represented by a series of orthogonal lines. Streamlines, which we have now required to divide the flow into regions of equal discharge, will represent one set of lines. Lines normal to these streamlines, to be known as *potential lines*, form the second set. The most significant aspect of the pattern of lines, which together form a *flow net*, lies in their uniqueness. That is, one and only one flow net can be constructed for a given set of boundary conditions.

The construction technique consists of sketching, or roughing in, an approximate flow net and then making successive improvements using a pencil and eraser in about equal proportion. As the curvilinear grid is improved, all intersections between the two pairs of lines must be at 90° and the spacing of adjacent lines must be such that squares rather than rectangles are formed. The finite mesh is of course approximate, and the "squares" will generally consist of curved rather than straight elements. The requirements noted above may, nevertheless, be achieved. An additional test of accuracy is obtained by drawing diagonals through all the squares, as the resulting pattern must also be curvilinear. Free surface boundaries that do not change with time will also be streamlines, and hence the potential lines must intersect them orthogonally.

Typical examples of flow nets are given in Figs. 12-9 through 12-11. Flow nets will give a reasonable realization for those flows which are nearly irrotational. Accelerating flows are, as a group, most susceptible to flow net analysis, while deceleration, particularly near a boundary, and short radius turns lead to separation and a resulting flow that differs considerably from the predicted flow fields. Figure 12-9 is an example where the flow field is almost

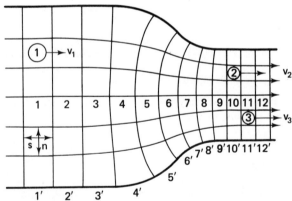

Fig. 12-9. Flow net for accelerating flow. Adapted from Hunter Rouse, *Elementary Mechanics of Fluids.* (New York, John Wiley and Sons Inc., 1946) p. 22, with permission of the author.

entirely accelerative, and hence the results of the flow net should be quite accurate. Figure 12-10, on the other hand, has regions of deceleration at both the outer corner (area *A*) and downstream of the sharp inner corner (area *B*). In both these regions separation will occur as approximated by the dashed lines. The flow net will clearly give erroneous results near these regions unless estimated zones of separation are taken as the boundary streamlines.

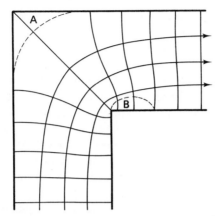

Fig. 12-10. Flow net for sharp conduit bend. Adapted from Hunter Rouse, *Elementary Mechanics of Fluids*. (New York, John Wiley and Sons Inc., 1946) p. 24, with permission of the author.

Flow in the upstream regions will still be quite similar to the flow net solution, in any case.

The final flow field (Fig. 12-11) involves a free surface. Since the flow field is largely accelerative, the results should be reasonably good. Considerably more effort is required, however, since the flow net must be combined with the basic flow principles (i.e., the Bernoulli equation) in order to locate the water surface. This theoretically can be accomplished by assuming a

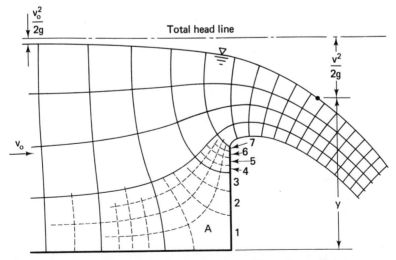

Fig. 12-11. Flow net for free surface flow. Adapted from Hunter Rouse, *Elementary Mechanics of Fluids*. (New York, John Wiley add Sons, Inc., 1946) p. 93, with permission of the author.

trajectory for the falling liquid and then testing whether the sum of elevation and velocity head at each point equals the total head. To the extent that they differ, the nappe must be adjusted and reevaluated until the required equality is achieved. The flow net can be drawn far more rapidly, however, if the free surfaces are obtained initially from observation of an actual flow.

In a region of the flow field where large spacing of the grid lines might adversely affect the accuracy of the flow net, the squares may be repeatedly subdivided as shown by the dashed streamlines in region A of Fig. 12-11. The use of this technique for increased resolution will be illustrated in Example 12-5. Care must be taken that the number of subdivisions is properly accounted for when using that portion of the flow net for subsequent calculations.

Up to this point the flow net has given only qualitative information concerning a two-dimensional flow. If the continuity and Bernoulli equations are applied to the resulting flow net, quantitative results will be available as well. With reference to Fig. 12-9, the flow rate per unit width is $q = vn$, where n is the distance between streamlines at the point at which the velocity is v. Thus, for points 1 and 2, which lie between the same pair of streamlines, continuity immediately requires that

$$v_1 n_1 = v_2 n_2 \qquad (12\text{-}15\text{a})$$

For computational purposes, note that since the spacing n is equal to the spacing s in each square, Eq. 12-15a may also be written as

$$v_1 s_1 = v_2 s_2 \qquad (12\text{-}15\text{b})$$

Further, since the flow rate between every pair of streamlines is identical, it also follows that

$$v_1 n_1 = v_3 n_3 \qquad (12\text{-}16\text{a})$$

or even

$$v_1 s_1 = v_3 n_3 \qquad (12\text{-}16\text{b})$$

Therefore, the velocity at any point in the flow field may be determined relative to a known or reference velocity by simply measuring the respective spacings on the flow net and applying the appropriate equation from the above. In highly curved portions of the flow net, one direction (either s or n) may be more convenient to use.

EXAMPLE 12-4

Determine and plot the velocity along an outside boundary and along the centerline of the contraction of Fig. 12-9. Take the uniform approach velocity as v_1.

SOLUTION:

By scaling, the reference spacing (s_1) is 8.20 units. By further scaling the various lengths $(s_1', s_2, s_2',$ etc.), the following table is established. The resulting velocity ratios are plotted on Fig. 12-12. The measured points are labeled with the respective

Section	Length, s (units)	$\dfrac{v}{v_1} = \dfrac{s_1}{s}$
1	8.20	1
2	8.20	1
3	8.02	1.02
4	7.23	1.13
5	6.68	1.23
6	5.82	1.41
7	5.25	1.56
8	4.61	1.78
9	4.32	1.90
10	4.17	1.97
11	4.11	2.00
12	4.11	2.00
1′	8.20	1
2′	8.48	0.97
3′	8.98	0.91
4′	10.83	0.76
5′	8.45	0.97
6′	4.50	1.82
7′	3.83	2.14
8′	3.53	2.32
9′	3.63	2.26
10′	3.97	2.07
11′	4.13	2.03
12′	4.13	2.03

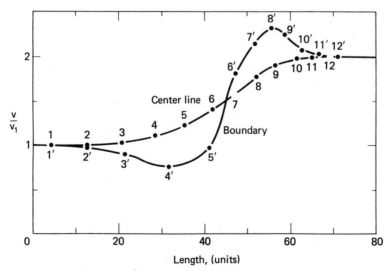

Fig. 12-12.   Velocity distributions for Fig. 12-9.

stationing. The stations themselves are taken along the centerline or boundary and halfway between vertical (potential) lines. This assumes that a given length s best represents conditions at the midpoint of that length. The scale along the abscissa of Fig. 12-12 is the distance along the appropriate streamline, with zero taken as the leftmost vertical line.

Consider next the use of the flow net in conjunction with the Bernoulli equation. If the fluid is a gas, or if we can otherwise ignore elevation effects, we may begin with

$$p_1 + \frac{\rho v_1^2}{2} = p_2 + \frac{\rho v_2^2}{2}$$

where the points 1 and 2 refer to any two points in the flow field, such as in Fig. 12-9 considered previously. Taking section 1 as the reference location, where both p_1 and v_1 are known, we get

$$p_2 - p_1 = \frac{\rho}{2}(v_1^2 - v_2^2)$$

or

$$\frac{p_2 - p_1}{\rho v_1^2/2} = 1 - \frac{v_2^2}{v_1^2} \tag{12-17}$$

But from Eq. 12-15,

$$\frac{v_2^2}{v_1^2} = \frac{n_1^2}{n_2^2}$$

and hence

$$\frac{p_2 - p_1}{\rho v_1^2/2} = 1 - \frac{n_1^2}{n_2^2} \tag{12-18}$$

This says that the pressure at point 2 (p_2) relative to the reference pressure (p_1) and made dimensionless by the reference dynamic pressure ($\rho v_1^2/2$) is a function of the streamline spacing only. Thus, the type of tabulation used in Example 12-4 is easily expanded to give the pressure distribution as well. Further, lines of constant pressure may now be visualized, as they must pass through squares of equal size. This is illustrated for the partial flow net in the vicinity of a corner (Fig. 12-13). Based on the square size, typical lines of constant pressure are shown (dashed). In order of decreasing pressure they are p_1, p_2, and p_3. The acceleration vectors, which must be perpendicular to lines of constant pressure, are shown by arrows at points A, B, C, and D. At point A symmetry of the flow field causes the acceleration to be purely radial. At point B the acceleration vector can be resolved into two components, a radial component due to the curvature and normal to the streamline, and a tangential component due to the convergence of the streamlines at that point. At points C and D the streamline is straight and consequently the acceleration is purely tangential. Since the acceleration is in the direction of decreasing pressure gradient, the flow is decelerating at D and accelerating at C.

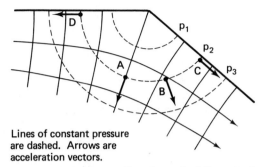

Lines of constant pressure
are dashed. Arrows are
acceleration vectors.

Fig. 12-13. Constant-pressure lines determined from the flow net.

If elevation effects must be included as well, the Bernoulli equation (Eq. 5-15) must be used. In terms of piezometric head h, this equation may be written

$$h_1 + \frac{v_1^2}{2g} = h_2 + \frac{v_2^2}{2g}$$

whereupon

$$\frac{h_2 - h_1}{v_1^2/2g} = 1 - \frac{v_2^2}{v_1^2} = 1 - \frac{n_1^2}{n_2^2} \tag{12-19}$$

Thus, the piezometric head variations, made dimensionless by the reference velocity head, may be determined directly from the flow net. In the uniform upstream region of Fig. 12-11 the piezometric head takes on a constant value equal to the depth of flow. Elsewhere, the acceleration, as discussed in Section 5-1, would now be perpendicular to lines of constant piezometric head. The acceleration is, of course, zero in the regions of uniform flow. If the piezometric head is determined by Eq. 12-19, the pressure head may subsequently be evaluated by subtracting the elevation head at each point from the respective piezometric head, as illustrated in the following example.

EXAMPLE 12-5

Determine and plot the pressure distribution on the upstream face of the weir of Fig. 12-11.

SOLUTION:

Seven sections have been identified on the upstream face of Fig. 12-11. As in Example 12-4, the numbers are located midway between the normal lines. Section 1 is not used in the calculations, since an appropriate length cannot readily be measured. It is not needed, however, as the bottom corner is a stagnation point and its pressure head must equal the total head. By direct scaling the following initial measurements may be determined:

Total head   = 69.6 (units)
Upstream depth or piezometric head, h_0 = 67.8
Upstream (reference) grid spacing s_0 = 4.24

Since the basic flow net has four flow regions,[3] the reference spacing $s_0 = n_0$ would normally be

$$s_0 = n_0 = \frac{67.8}{4} = 17.0$$

However, the flow net has twice been subdivided in the region of interest near the upstream face of the weir. Hence, for calculation purposes the flow net effectively has 16 flow regions, and the reference spacing must actually be

$$s_0 = \frac{h_0}{16} = \frac{67.8}{16} = 4.24$$

The calculations may now be made in the following table:

Section	Length, s	$\dfrac{h - h_0}{v_0^2/2g} = 1 - \dfrac{s_0^2}{s^2}$	h	y	$\dfrac{p}{\gamma} = h - y$
—	—	—	69.6	0	69.6 (corner)
2	7.95	0.716	67.9	15.4	52.5
3	6.26	0.541	67.9	22.5	45.4
4	2.66	−1.54	67.5	26.9	40.6
5	2.24	−2.58	67.3	29.4	37.9
6	1.92	−3.88	67.1	31.5	35.6
7	1.50	−6.99	66.5	33.2	33.3
—	—	—	—	33.9	0 (crest)

All values in the table are in units of length of the same scale. The third column is obtained by the equation that is the counterpart to Eq. 12-19, when the grid length in the streamline or s direction is used. The fourth column is obtained directly from the pre eding column and the pressure head may then be obtained by subtracting the elevation head at each point from the piezometric head. The initial value of pressure head equals the total head, and the final value, occurring at the weir crest, is the atmospheric pressure of the lower surface of the nappe. The pressure head is plotted on Fig. 12-14, where it is compared with the hydrostatic solution shown by the dashed line.

12–3   STREAM FUNCTION AND VELOCITY POTENTIAL

We have examined how streamlines and accompanying normal lines form a flow net and how the resulting flow net may be used to analyze the flow. Mathematical characteristics of these lines will now be considered, and this will lead to mathematical representation of the same types of flow fields.

---

[3] These are the spaces between the five streamlines shown, the three intermediate streamlines and the upper and lower boundaries.

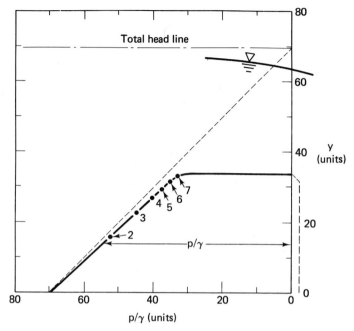

Fig. 12-14. Pressure distribution on weir face.

Stream Function

The stream function may be introduced by consideration of the steady two-dimensional flow field of Fig. 12-15. Points a and b are connected by two arbitrary paths, labeled (1) and (2). On each path a differential path length ds has been chosen and resolved into components dx and dy. Note that in passing from a to b on path (2) through the differential element, a $(-dx)$ is traversed. In both cases, velocity components in the positive directions have been indicated. The flow rate (per unit width) across the length ds on path (1) is

$$dq = u\,dy - v\,dx \qquad (12\text{-}20)$$

and hence the flow rate passing between points a and b, by integration along path (1), is

$$q = \int_{(1)} (u\,dy - v\,dx) \qquad (12\text{-}21a)$$

Likewise, the flow rate across the differential length ds on path (2) is

$$dq = u\,dy + v(-dx) \qquad (12\text{-}20)$$

and accordingly the flow between a and b based on integration along the

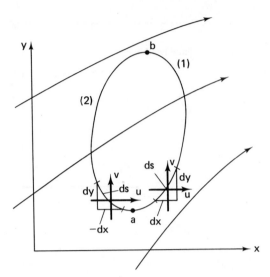

Fig. 12-15. Definition sketch for the stream function.

second path is

$$q = \int_{(2)} (u\,dy - v\,dx) \tag{12-21b}$$

Since, by continuity, the flow rate passing across both lines is identical, the integration of the quantity $(u\,dy - v\,dx)$ is dependent only on the end points and independent of the path taken. The integrand must therefore be a total differential, say $d\psi$. Thus, the flow rate may be written

$$q = \int (u\,dy - v\,dx) = \int d\psi \tag{12-22}$$

where the quantity ψ is defined as the stream function. In general, it will depend on position and hence be a function of x and y. Therefore,

$$d\psi = \frac{\partial \psi}{\partial x}\,dx + \frac{\partial \psi}{\partial y}\,dy$$

and by comparison with Eq. 12-22,

$$u = \frac{\partial \psi}{\partial y} \tag{12-23a}$$

and

$$v = -\frac{\partial \psi}{\partial x} \tag{12-23b}$$

Although the discussion above relates the velocity components to the stream function, it still remains to attach physical significance to the term. This may be achieved by consideration of a line of constant ψ. On such a line, $d\psi = 0$ and from Eq. 12-22,

$$u \, dy - v \, dx = 0$$

or

$$\frac{dx}{v} = \frac{dy}{v} \tag{12-24}$$

Recall now the definition of a streamline, namely, a line that is everywhere tangent to the velocity vectors. This implies that the cross product between the velocity $\mathbf{V}$ and a line segment $\mathbf{ds}$ must equal zero.[4] Expanding the cross product and setting the result equal to zero, we get

$$\mathbf{V} \times \mathbf{ds} = \begin{vmatrix} \mathbf{i} & \mathbf{j} & \mathbf{k} \\ u & v & w \\ dx & dy & dz \end{vmatrix} = \mathbf{k}(u \, dy - v \, dx) = 0$$

in the two-dimensional case where both w and dz do not exist. Thus, the equation of a streamline in two-dimensional flow is

$$\frac{dx}{u} = \frac{dy}{v}$$

which is identically Eq. 12-24, and lines of constant ψ are therefore streamlines. Additionally, as a consequence of Eqs. 12-20 and 12-22, the difference in magnitude of the stream function ($d\psi$) between any two streamlines is also the flow rate (dq) between the same pair. This will be demonstrated in the next section.

Stream Potential

The stream potential for a two-dimensional flow is obtained from the circulation around a closed contour as in Fig. 12-16. In this case the contour is divided into two portions on either side of the upper and lower extremities a and b. As indicated by Eq. 12-6, the circulation Γ around the contour is

$$\Gamma = \int_C (u \, dx + v \, dy)$$

$$= \int_{a\,(1)}^{b} (u \, dx + v \, dy) + \int_{b\,(2)}^{a} (u \, dx + v \, dy)$$

$$= \int_{a\,(1)}^{b} (u \, dx + v \, dy) - \int_{a\,(2)}^{b} (u \, dx + v \, dy)$$

If the flow is irrotational with zero circulation, $\Gamma = 0$, then

$$\int_{a\,(1)}^{b} (u \, dx + v \, dy) = \int_{a\,(2)}^{b} (u \, dx + v \, dy) \tag{12-25}$$

[4]See Appendix D.

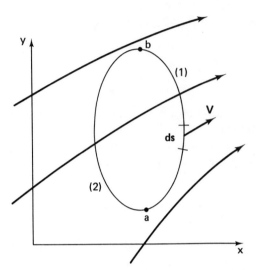

Fig. 12-16. Definition sketch for stream potential.

Once again the integration is independent of the path and the integrand a total differential, this time denoted as $d\varphi$. The quantity φ is defined as the stream potential and, in general, it will be a function of both x and y. Writing

$$\int_a^b (u \, dx + v \, dy) = \int_a^b d\varphi$$

where

$$d\varphi = \frac{\partial \varphi}{\partial x} \, dx + \frac{\partial \varphi}{\partial y} \, dy$$

we have by comparison

$$u = \frac{\partial \varphi}{\partial x} \tag{12-26a}$$

and

$$v = \frac{\partial \varphi}{\partial y} \tag{12-26b}$$

Although the stream function, which has been shown to represent streamlines, has been found to exist for any two-dimensional flow, the stream potential has meaning only for an irrotational flow. On a line of constant φ, where $d\varphi = 0$, we have

$$u \, dx + v \, dy = 0$$

or

$$\frac{dy}{dx} = -\frac{u}{v} \tag{12-27}$$

Since the equation for a line of constant ψ (see Eq. 12-24) may be written

$$\frac{dy}{dx} = \frac{v}{u}$$

we see that slopes of lines of constant φ and lines of constant ψ are negative reciprocals of each other and the lines must be orthogonal. Hence, lines of constant φ are the potential lines introduced in the preceding section and together the ψ–φ lines form the flow net.

Knowing the equation for either ψ or φ will permit calculation of the other, as will be demonstrated in Example 12-6. Of course, the flow net may also be plotted from these same equations. The velocity field may then be determined using Eq. 12-23 or 12-26.

EXAMPLE 12-6

If the stream potential φ is given by

$$\varphi = x^2 - y^2$$

determine:
(a) The velocity field.
(b) If the flow satisfies continuity.
(c) The stream function.
and plot:
(d) The flow net for $x, y > 0$.

SOLUTION:

(a) The velocity components are

$$u = \frac{\partial \varphi}{\partial x} = 2x$$

and

$$v = \frac{\partial \varphi}{\partial y} = -2y$$

Attempt at this point to visualize the magnitude and direction of the velocity vectors.
(b) Checking continuity,

$$\frac{\partial u}{\partial x} + \frac{\partial v}{\partial y} = 2 - 2 = 0$$

and continuity is satisfied.
(c) From Eq. 12-23a,

$$\psi = \int u \, dy + f(x)$$

That is, the integration with respect to y of the partial derivative cannot exclude an additional term or terms which are either functions of x or a constant. Since velocity determination involves only derivatives of ψ or φ, the magnitude of the constant is generally unimportant and in fact usually arbitrary. Continuing,

$$\psi = \int 2x \, dy + f(x)$$

or

$$\psi = 2xy + f(x)$$

Similarly, from Eq. 12-23b,

$$\psi = -\int v\,dx + f(y)$$
$$= -\int (-2y)\,dx + f(y)$$
$$= 2xy + f(y)$$

By comparison of the two equations for ψ the functions of x and y must be equal $[f(x) = f(y)]$ and therefore be at most constant. Thus, upon dropping the constant,

$$\psi = 2xy$$

(d) In order to plot the flow net, specific values of ψ and φ are tabulated below and plotted in Fig. 12-17. Consider the streamlines first. For $\psi = 0$, $xy = 0$, which represents the x and y axes. Next consider

$$\psi = 16, \qquad xy = 8$$

Typical Values

x	y
1	8
2	4
3	2.67
2.83	2.83
2.67	3
4	2
8	1

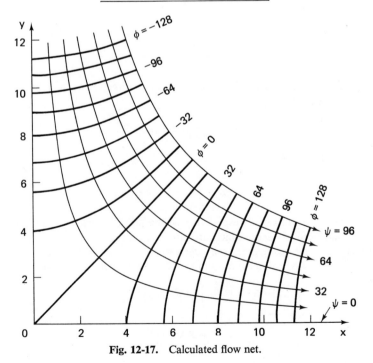

Fig. 12-17.   Calculated flow net.

In the first quadrant of Fig. 12-17, these values are plotted together with $\psi = 32$, 48, 64, 80, and 96. The potential lines are treated identically.

For $\varphi = 0$, $x^2 = y^2$, or a 45° line in the first quadrant. Continuing, we obtain

$$\varphi = 16, \quad x^2 = 16 + y^2 \qquad \varphi = -16, \quad y^2 = 16 + x^2$$

Typical Values			Typical Values	
x	y		x	y
4	0		0	4
4.12	1		1	4.12
4.47	2		2	4.47
5	3		3	5
5.66	4		4	5.60
6.40	5		5	6.44
7.21	6		6	7.21

These are also plotted in Fig. 12-17 together with $\varphi = \pm32, \pm48, \pm64, \pm80, \pm96$, ±112, and ±128. This completes the flow net. We can see that it represents irrotational flow in the vicinity of a corner. If both the first and second quadrants had been plotted, this would be a two-dimensional flow striking a flat surface.

Example 12-6 relates the flow field to specific equations for φ and ψ. It is more often necessary to determine the equations for φ and ψ themselves. This is frequently possible, as the following development will show. Taking Eqs. 12-23 and substituting into the equation for rotation of a two-dimensional flow (Eq. 12-1a), we get

$$\omega = \frac{1}{2}\left(\frac{\partial v}{\partial x} - \frac{\partial u}{\partial y}\right)$$

$$= \frac{1}{2}\left[\frac{\partial}{\partial x}\left(-\frac{\partial \psi}{\partial x}\right) - \frac{\partial}{\partial y}\left(\frac{\partial \psi}{\partial y}\right)\right] \qquad (12\text{-}28)$$

$$= -\frac{1}{2}\left(\frac{\partial^2 \psi}{\partial x^2} + \frac{\partial^2 \psi}{\partial y^2}\right)$$

For irrotational flow with $\omega = 0$, this becomes

$$\frac{\partial^2 \psi}{\partial x^2} + \frac{\partial^2 \psi}{\partial y^2} = 0 \qquad (12\text{-}29)$$

which is the well-known *Laplace equation*. Similarly, substituting Eqs. 12-26 into the continuity equation (Eq. 4-4) yields

$$\frac{\partial}{\partial x}\left(\frac{\partial \varphi}{\partial x}\right) + \frac{\partial}{\partial y}\left(\frac{\partial \varphi}{\partial y}\right) = 0$$

or

$$\frac{\partial^2 \varphi}{\partial x^2} + \frac{\partial^2 \varphi}{\partial y^2} = 0 \qquad (12\text{-}30)$$

Thus, for an irrotational flow, both ψ and φ satisfy Laplace's equation. Boundary conditions for many flows can be imposed on known solutions to these equations, but as this is more properly in the realm of more advanced fluid mechanics, it will not be pursued further here.

12–4 FLOW FIELDS

After developing the stream function and stream potential in the previous section, we found that they may be used mathematically to determine and subsequently analyze a flow net and the associated flow characteristics. Equations for the stream function and stream potential will now be considered for some basic steady irrotational flow fields and then, by superposition, more complex flows as well.

Uniform Flow

Consider first, flow with constant velocity, U, parallel to the x axis and in the positive direction (Fig. 12-18a). We must have at all points $u = U$, $v = 0$. Then, from Eqs. 12-23 and 12-26,

$$u = \frac{\partial \varphi}{\partial x} = \frac{\partial \psi}{\partial y}$$

and

$$v = \frac{\partial \varphi}{\partial y} = -\frac{\partial \psi}{\partial x}$$

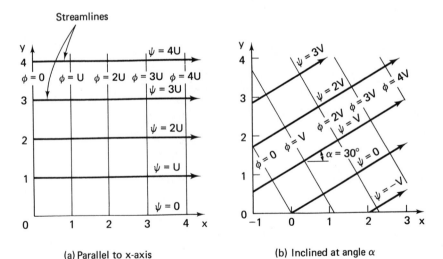

(a) Parallel to x-axis   (b) Inclined at angle α

Fig. 12-18. Uniform flow.

From the former,

$$\varphi = \int u \, dx + f(y)$$
$$= \int U \, dx + f(y)$$
$$= Ux + f(y)$$

and from the latter,

$$\varphi = \int v \, dy + f(x)$$
$$= f(x)$$

By comparison of the two equations for φ, we conclude that

$$\varphi = Ux \qquad (12\text{-}31)$$

Repeating the integration process for ψ similarly yields

$$\psi = Uy \qquad (12\text{-}32)$$

Curves of φ and ψ are plotted on Fig. 12-18a for values of 0, U, $2U$, $3U$, and $4U$ in each case. Note at this point that the difference in magnitude between any pair of streamlines is U, which for the unit spacing of the streamlines is also the discharge between them.

If a uniform flow of velocity V is inclined at an angle α to the x axis as in Fig. 12-18b, then

$$u = V \cos \alpha \qquad (12\text{-}33a)$$
$$v = V \sin \alpha \qquad (12\text{-}33b)$$

and in the same fashion as before,

$$\varphi = \int V \cos \alpha \, dx + f(y)$$
$$= Vx \cos \alpha + f(y)$$

and

$$\varphi = \int V \sin \alpha \, dy + f(x)$$
$$= Vy \sin \alpha + f(x)$$

The $f(y)$ of the first equation for φ must be $Vy \sin \alpha$ from the second, and $f(x)$ from the second is apparently $Vx \cos \alpha$; thus,

$$\varphi = V(x \cos \alpha + y \sin \alpha) \qquad (12\text{-}34)$$

Similarly,

$$\psi = V(y \cos \alpha - x \sin \alpha) \qquad (12\text{-}35)$$

Using Eqs. 12-33, these two equations may also be expressed by

$$\varphi = ux + vy \qquad (12\text{-}36)$$

and

$$\psi = uy - vx \qquad (12\text{-}37)$$

The flow field based on Eqs. 12-34 and 12-35 is plotted in Fig. 12-18b for an angle of inclination $\alpha = 30°$. Values plotted for the stream function are $-V, 0, V, 2V$, and $3V$, while values of the stream potential are $0, V, 2V, 3V$, and $4V$.

Source (or Sink)

A *source* flow is a steady radially outward flow from a point, as shown in Fig. 12-19. The velocity is at all points radial and at any radial distance r

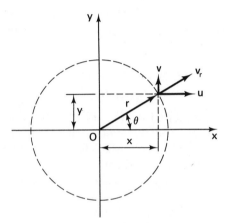

Fig. 12-19. Definition sketch for a source.

it will be a constant v_r for all values of the angle θ. Clearly, polar cylindrical coordinates will be advantageous, although the velocity may be related to its components u and v at any time. The flow is two-dimensional, occurring in the x–y plane, and the flow rate per unit of length perpendicular to this plane will be the velocity v_r times the circumference of the dashed circle of radius r. That is,

$$q = 2\pi r v_r \qquad (12\text{-}38)$$

As the flow is steady, q will be constant and hence at the origin where $r = 0$ the velocity becomes infinite. As such, the source has no exact physical counterpoint in nature, although it is often well approximated except at $r = 0$, which is known in mathematics as a *singular point*. A *sink* is simply a negative source with radially inward flow (to a point). Its flow rate would be given by

$$q = -2\pi r v_r \qquad (12\text{-}39)$$

To obtain the equations for ψ and φ for a source or sink, we first need companion equations to Eqs. 12-23 and Eqs. 12-26 in polar-cylindrical coordinates. These are as follows:

$$v_r = \frac{1}{r}\frac{\partial \psi}{\partial \theta} \qquad (12\text{-}40a)$$

$$v_\theta = -\frac{\partial \psi}{\partial r} \qquad (12\text{-}40b)$$

and

$$v_r = \frac{\partial \varphi}{\partial r} \qquad (12\text{-}41a)$$

$$v_\theta = \frac{1}{r}\frac{\partial \varphi}{\partial \theta} \qquad (12\text{-}41b)$$

By integration of Eq. 12-40a, we get

$$\psi = \int v_r r\, d\theta + f(r)$$

$$= \int \frac{q}{2\pi}\, d\theta + f(r)$$

$$= \frac{q\theta}{2\pi} + f(r)$$

but from Eq. 12-40b, $f(r) = 0$, so

$$\psi = \frac{q\theta}{2\pi} \qquad (12\text{-}42)$$

Similarly, we can obtain

$$\varphi = \frac{q}{2\pi}\ln r \qquad (12\text{-}43)$$

Thus, lines of constant ψ are radial lines emanating from the origin of the source and the potential lines are concentric circles. The resulting flow net is shown on Fig. 12-20.

Once again, note that the difference in magnitude between adjacent stream-lines is $q/8$. As the flow field is divided into eight equal sectors, this is also the flow rate between each pair of streamlines.

Since $\tan \theta = y/x$ and $r^2 = x^2 + y^2$, we may convert Eqs. 12-42 and 12-43 into rectangular Cartesian coordinates, with the results

$$\psi = \frac{q}{2\pi}\tan^{-1}\left(\frac{y}{x}\right) \qquad (12\text{-}44)$$

and

$$\varphi = \frac{q}{4\pi}\ln (x^2 + y^2) \qquad (12\text{-}45)$$

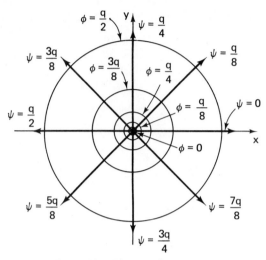

Fig. 12-20. Flow net for a source.

Further, if the source is located elsewhere than at the origin (say at the point x_1, y_1), the equations for ψ and ϕ become

$$\psi = \frac{q}{2\pi} \tan^{-1} \left(\frac{y - y_1}{x - x_1} \right) \tag{12-46}$$

and

$$\varphi = \frac{q}{4\pi} \ln [(x - x_1)^2 + (y - y_1)^2] \tag{12-47}$$

Doublet

We will see shortly that the basic flow fields may be combined in an infinite number of ways. One particular combination, a source and a sink of equal discharge, is treated as one of the basic flows when the distance between the source and sink is reduced to zero. A source and sink of equal discharge located on the x axis at points $-a$ and $+a$, respectively, are shown in Fig. 12-21. With radii and angles locating an arbitrary point P in the flow field, the stream function and stream potential may be obtained upon addition of the appropriate equations for a source and a sink:

$$\psi = \frac{q\theta_1}{2\pi} - \frac{q\theta_2}{2\pi} \tag{12-48}$$

or

$$\psi = \frac{q}{2\pi} (\theta_1 - \theta_2) \tag{12-48}$$

and

$$\varphi = \frac{q}{2\pi} \ln r_1 - \frac{q}{2\pi} \ln r_2$$

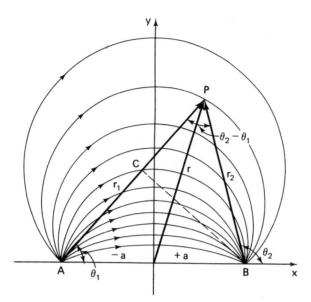

Fig. 12-21.   Source–sink combination.

or

$$\varphi = \frac{q}{2\pi} \ln \left(\frac{r_1}{r_2} \right) \qquad (12\text{-}49)$$

The resulting streamlines for the upper half of the flow field have been plotted by a technique which will be considered later in the section. If we now let the length a shrink to zero, then both θ_1 and θ_2 will approach θ and r_1 and r_2 will similarly approach r. In order to get a significant relation, we must impose an additional constraint—that the product qa remains at a constant value (here called μ) as a goes to zero. (Otherwise, the source and sink will simply cancel each other.)

At this point, noting that the interior angle at point P must be $\theta_2 - \theta_1$, we may write

$$r_2 \sin (\theta_2 - \theta_1) = 2a \sin \theta_1$$

the equality being justified since both sides of the expression are equal to the length BC. Then as the length a approaches zero,

$$\sin (\theta_2 - \theta_1) \approx \theta_2 - \theta_1$$

and Eq. 12-48 becomes

$$\psi = -\frac{q}{2\pi} \left(\frac{2a}{r} \sin \theta \right)$$

or

$$\psi = -\frac{\mu \sin \theta}{\pi r} \qquad (12\text{-}50)$$

Since r_1 is composed of the lengths AC and CP, we may further write

$$r_1 = 2a \cos \theta_1 + r_2 \cos (\theta_2 - \theta_1)$$

whereupon Eq. 12-49 may be written as

$$\varphi = \frac{q}{2\pi} \ln \left[\frac{2a \cos \theta_1}{r_2} + \cos (\theta_2 - \theta_1) \right]$$

Again, as the length a tends to zero,

$$\cos (\theta_2 - \theta_1) \approx 1$$

and

$$\varphi = \frac{q}{2\pi} \ln \left(\frac{2a \cos \theta}{r} + 1 \right)$$

But for any quantity $\epsilon \ll 1$,

$$\ln (\epsilon + 1) \approx \epsilon$$

and therefore

$$\varphi = \frac{q}{2\pi} \frac{2a \cos \theta}{r}$$

or finally

$$\varphi = \frac{\mu}{\pi} \frac{\cos \theta}{r} \qquad (12\text{-}51)$$

The streamline pattern is sketched in Fig. 12-22.

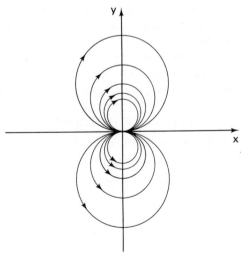

Fig. 12-22. Streamlines for a doublet.

Irrotational Vortex

The irrotational vortex was introduced in Section 12-1. A counterclockwise vortex is characterized by

$$v_r = 0 \tag{12-52a}$$

$$v_\theta = \frac{C}{r} \qquad C = \text{constant} \tag{12-52b}$$

Upon integration of Eqs. 12-40 and 12-41 with the vortex velocities given by
Eqs. 12-52, we get

$$\psi = -C \ln r \tag{12-53}$$

$$\varphi = C\theta \tag{12-54}$$

The flow field is graphed in Fig. 12-23, where C has been replaced according
to the following argument. Although the flow field is irrotational in general,

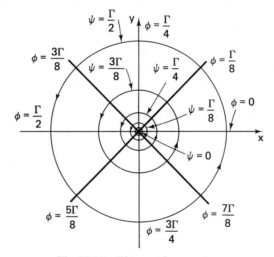

Fig. 12-23.   Flow net for a vortex.

integration of the velocity according to Eq. 12-4, around any closed contour
that includes the axis, gives a constant magnitude for the circulation. Taking
the simplest contour, a circle of radius r, and integrating, we obtain

$$\Gamma = \int_{\text{circle}} v_\theta \, ds$$

$$= \int_0^{2\pi} v_\theta r \, d\theta$$

$$= \int_0^{2\pi} \left(\frac{C}{r}\right) r \, d\theta = 2\pi C$$

Thus, the constant of Eqs. 12-53 and 12-54 is the circulation of the vortex divided by 2π. The constant circulation of the irrotational vortex is a non-zero constant of integration of Eq. 12-7. Note that the flow nets for a source and a vortex are identical in form. The streamlines and potential lines are merely interchanged between the two. Further, the origin of the vortex is also a singular point.

Combined Flow Fields

An important characteristic of the Laplace equation is that for a specified set of boundary conditions, there can be only one solution, hence the success of the flow net previously. Another important aspect, boundary conditions aside, is that if two equations for ψ (or φ) satisfy the Laplace equation, their sum or difference must satisfy the Laplace equation as well. In other words, any number of equations, each of which is a solution to the Laplace equation, may be added together. Therefore, all the basic flow fields considered thus far in this section can be combined by superposition. Not only can different types be put together, but they may be used repeatedly. For example, any number of sources and sinks, each even with a different discharge, may be arranged throughout the flow field and their effects added algebraically. The following will illustrate the technique as well as the application to practical problems.

Consider the combination of a uniform flow of velocity U from left to right and a source at the origin of discharge q. This is shown in the initial sketch of Fig. 12-24. In the resulting flow field of Fig. 12-25, which follows, the magnitude of q has been taken as equal to $2\pi U$ for plotting purposes.

The equation for ψ will be the sum of the stream functions for the two basic flows, namely,

$$\psi = Uy + \frac{q\theta}{2\pi}$$

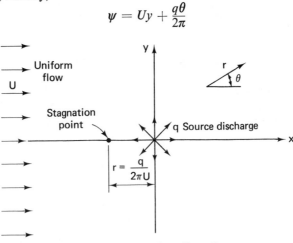

Fig. 12-24. Source in uniform flow.

Converting to a consistent coordinate system, this becomes

$$\psi = Ur \sin \theta + \frac{q\theta}{2\pi} \qquad (12\text{-}55)$$

The components of the velocity, in polar-cylindrical coordinates, may now be obtained by differentiation of Eq. 12-55 according to Eqs. 12-40. They are

$$v_r = \frac{1}{r}\frac{\partial \psi}{\partial \theta} = U \cos \theta + \frac{q}{2\pi r} \qquad (12\text{-}56a)$$

and

$$v_\theta = -\frac{\partial \psi}{\partial r} = -U \sin \theta \qquad (12\text{-}56b)$$

Consider next that along the negative x axis the velocity due to both basic flow fields is parallel to that axis. From the left the velocity is a constant, U, while from the right the velocity is decreasing from an infinite velocity at the source to a zero velocity infinitely far along the negative x axis. Hence, there must be some point along this axis where the two velocities exactly cancel. This point may be located from Eq. 12-56a by setting the velocity equal to zero; thus,

$$0 = U \cos \theta + \frac{q}{2\pi r}$$

and since $\theta = \pi$ along the negative x axis, the point of zero velocity is

$$r = \frac{q}{2\pi U} \qquad (12\text{-}57)$$

as identified and labeled on Fig. 12-24. This point is by definition a stagnation point of the flow. Further, although it will be taken without proof here, the streamline along the x axis must turn 90° at the stagnation point. The value of the stream function passing through the stagnation point must next be determined so that this streamline may be plotted. Since the stagnation point has coordinates $r = q/(2\pi U)$ and $\theta = \pi$, we have

$$\psi_{\text{st. pt.}} = Ur \sin \theta + \frac{q\theta}{2\pi}$$

or

$$\psi_{\text{st. pt.}} = q/2$$

and the equation of this streamline becomes

$$\frac{q}{2} = Ur \sin \theta + \frac{q\theta}{2\pi}$$

Solving for r, this rearranges to

$$r = \frac{q(\pi - \theta)}{2\pi U \sin \theta} \qquad (12\text{-}58)$$

This line is plotted as the heavy line on the completed flow field of Fig. 12-25.

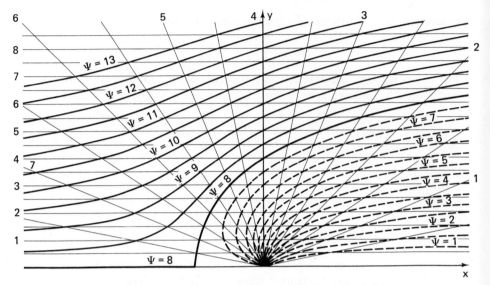

Fig. 12-25. Resulting flow field for a source in uniform flow.

Note that only the positive y axis has been included. Other values of ψ have been chosen and plotted on Fig. 12-25 as well. Each of these values can be substituted in Eq. 12-55 and various values of r versus θ obtained. However, a more rapid graphic technique may also be used, as indicated by the following example.

EXAMPLE 12-7

Consider the source of Fig. 12-24 to have a discharge $q = 16$ (units), and the uniform flow to have a velocity U given by $q = 2\pi U$. By graphic addition of the two basic flow fields, determine the combined flow field previously indicated as Fig. 12-25.

SOLUTION:

The streamlines of the source are shown as light lines radiating from the origin in Fig. 12-25. As a convenient number they are spaced every $11\frac{1}{4}°$ or $\pi/16$ radians. From Eq. 12-42, with $q = 16$, we have

$$\psi = \frac{8\theta}{\pi}$$

Thus, $\psi = 0$ is the positive x axis and moving counterclockwise around the origin, the streamlines successively increase in value by an amount

$$\Delta\psi = \frac{8}{\pi} \Delta\theta = \frac{8}{\pi} \frac{\pi}{16} = \frac{1}{2}$$

The alternate lines have been labeled at their end points by their respective magnitudes, $\psi = 0, 1, 2, 3, \ldots$, up to $\theta = \pi$, where $\psi = 8$. The stream function for the uniform flow was found previously as $\psi = Uy$. Since the problem specified that $q = 2\pi U$, we therefore have

$$\psi = \frac{qy}{2\pi} = \frac{8y}{\pi}$$

Thus, the horizontal streamlines, starting with $\psi = 0$ at $y = 0$, are plotted at values of y according to the equation above and labeled at the extreme left. They y values are as follows for those lines having integer values of ψ:

ψ	y
0	0
1	0.39
2	0.79
3	1.18
4	1.57
5	1.96
6	2.36
7	2.75
8	3.14
9	3.53
10	3.93

Refer to the two basic flow fields shown on Fig. 12-25 with their streamlines appropriately labeled. Now, the streamlines of the combined flow field must pass through intersections of the two basic flow fields, which have values of the individual streamlines which sum to the magnitude of the specific combined streamlines. For example, the resulting streamline $\psi = 9$ must pass through the following intersections:

Source Stream Function: $\psi =$	Uniform Flow Stream Function: $\psi =$
7	2
6	3
5	4
4	5
3	6
2	7
1	8

The streamline $\psi = 9$ may then be drawn by connecting the intersections as shown. The procedure may be repeated for all the other streamlines as well, but note that the procedure is very systematic and after one line is drawn, the remainder may be located very rapidly. The resulting flow field is labeled with the appropriate values of ψ. Streamlines with a stream function less than 8 are shown dashed.

We have developed the equation that will yield the flow field of Fig. 12-25. We have also, in the foregoing example, considered a relatively simple means of constructing the flow field. Let us now consider the significance of a flow field such as this. Any streamline may be treated as a fixed boundary. If the heavy line is chosen and both the plus and minus y axes are included, this could very well represent the two-dimensional flow past a blunt body such as the leading edge of a wing, or considering the figure to be a plane view, it could be the flow past the upstream end of a bridge pier or even an island! If only the positive y axis is considered, it could represent a contraction in the side of a channel. If one of the other streamlines were considered as the boundary, say $\psi = 9$ or 10, it might easily be considered as wind past a hillside. Those streamlines with $\psi < 8$ would be of no interest to the problems above. However, if both positive and negative y axes were included, the heavy streamline ($\psi = 8$) could represent the limits of an estuary. The source could then represent a waste treatment plant outflow and the dashed streamlines the spreading of the effluent. Note in all these physical interpretations, that as in all ideal flows, slip occurs at the boundaries and a finite, non-zero velocity is assumed.

To further illustrate the combining of basic flow fields, consider the superposition of a uniform flow and a doublet. In polar-cylindrical coordinates, the stream function is

$$\psi = Ur \sin \theta - \frac{\mu \sin \theta}{\pi r} \tag{12-59}$$

which is plotted on Fig. 12-26. Setting $\psi = 0$ and solving for r, we get the constant

$$r_{\psi=0} = \sqrt{\frac{\mu}{\pi U}} = R$$

Thus, the streamline $\psi = 0$ is, in part, a circle of radius R as given above,

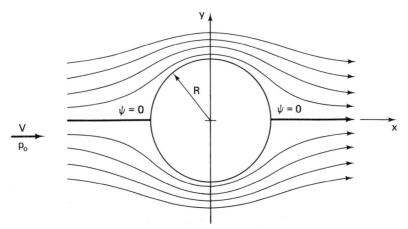

Fig. 12-26. Doublet in uniform flow.

and the flow pattern for $r > R$ is the irrotational flow past a cylinder. The streamlines inside the cylinder have not been plotted. Rewriting Eq. 12-59 in terms of R from above gives

$$\psi = U\left(r - \frac{R^2}{r}\right) \sin \theta \qquad (12\text{-}60)$$

Differentiating, according to Eqs. 12-40, the velocity components throughout the flow field are found to be

$$v_r = \frac{1}{r}\frac{\partial \psi}{\partial \theta} = U\left(1 - \frac{R^2}{r^2}\right) \cos \theta \qquad (12\text{-}61a)$$

and

$$v_\theta = -\frac{\partial \psi}{\partial r} = -U\left(1 + \frac{R^2}{r^2}\right) \sin \theta \qquad (12\text{-}61b)$$

On the cylinder itself $v_r = 0$ and the velocity is given by

$$v_\theta = -2U \sin \theta \qquad (12\text{-}62)$$

By Eq. 12-14 the pressure on the cylinder, relative to the ambient pressure of the approach flow, is

$$p - p_0 = \frac{\rho}{2}(U^2 - v_\theta^2)$$

or

$$p - p_0 = \frac{\rho U^2}{2}(1 - 4 \sin^2 \theta) \qquad (12\text{-}63)$$

This expression may be integrated over any portion of the cylinder to get the corresponding force. If integrated over the entire cylinder, the symmetry of the equation results in a net force of zero. It remains to include the effects of surface drag and separation, as previously considered in Chapter 9, in order to obtain the actual drag force.

12–5 NUMERICAL SOLUTIONS TO FLOW PROBLEMS

There are a variety of other techniques to obtain the irrotational solution of a relatively complicated flow. These include experimental approaches such as the membrane analogy, electrical analogy, and the viscous flow analogy. The latter leads to the well-known *Hele–Shaw technique*. The references at the end of the chapter develop and apply the various procedures. Various numerical methods are available which replace a differential equation by a difference equation and then solve the latter by finite-difference calculus. These have become very popular because of their relative ease in programming on a digital computer. One of the simplest of these procedures will be pursued at this point.

The differential equation that we wish to solve is the Laplace equation. Since both ψ and φ have been shown to satisfy this equation (see Eqs. 12-29 and 12-30), we could just as readily work with either; however, only the stream function ψ will be considered here. In order to illustrate the procedure as it is developed, the flow around the corner of Fig. 12-27 will be considered.

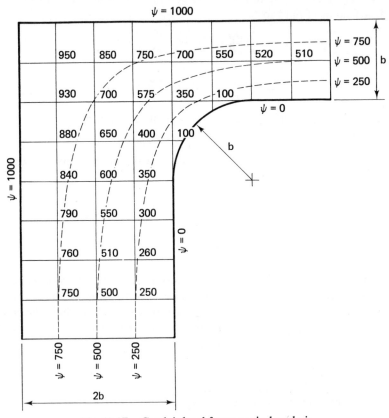

Fig. 12-27. Conduit bend for numerical analysis.

The inner boundary, which will be a streamline, is picked as $\psi = 0$. If the flow rate is taken as 1000 (units), the outer streamline will differ from the inner by this amount, and is so labeled. All boundary conditions must be completely specified. This has now been done for those boundaries paralleling the flow. At the entrance and exit sections, the velocity will be assumed constant across the section and the streamlines will therefore be evenly spaced. If three interior streamlines are desired, their magnitudes and entrance and exit locations are immediately known, as is also shown in Fig. 12-27. An estimate of the complete streamlines is shown dashed, as this will serve as a guide for the numerical analysis that follows. A square grid is now superimposed on the flow field and an estimate (using the dashed streamlines as a guide) of the stream function is made at each intersection or node. These values are also entered at the appropriate points in Fig. 12-27.

The problem is now to adjust these assumed values of ψ so that they will satisfy the Laplace equation. To develop the technique, refer to the definition sketch of Fig. 12-28a. A nodal point 0 has been identified surrounded by

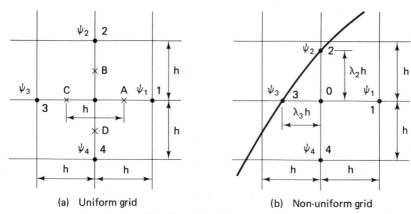

(a)   Uniform grid   (b)   Non-uniform grid

Fig. 12-28.   Definition sketch for numerical analysis.

points 1, 2, 3, and 4. The corresponding values of the stream function will be $\psi_0, \psi_1, \psi_2, \psi_3$, and ψ_4, and the grid spacing is h. If the grid is sufficiently fine, variations in ψ and its derivatives may be treated as linear. Then $\partial\psi/\partial x$ may be approximated at the midpoints A and C by

$$\left(\frac{\partial\psi}{\partial x}\right)_A = \frac{\psi_1 - \psi_0}{h}$$

and

$$\left(\frac{\partial\psi}{\partial x}\right)_C = \frac{\psi_0 - \psi_3}{h}$$

respectively. The second derivative at point 0 may be approached in the same manner,

$$\left(\frac{\partial^2\psi}{\partial x^2}\right)_0 = \frac{(\partial\psi/\partial x)_A - (\partial\psi/\partial x)_C}{h} = \frac{\psi_1 + \psi_3 - 2\psi_0}{h^2}$$

Similarly,

$$\left(\frac{\partial\psi}{\partial y}\right)_B = \frac{\psi_2 - \psi_0}{h}$$

and

$$\left(\frac{\partial\psi}{\partial y}\right)_D = \frac{\psi_0 - \psi_4}{h}$$

leading to

$$\left(\frac{\partial^2 \psi}{\partial y^2}\right)_0 = \frac{\psi_2 + \psi_4 - 2\psi_0}{h^2}$$

Thus, at point 0, the Laplace equation becomes

$$\left(\frac{\partial^2 \psi}{\partial x^2} + \frac{\partial^2 \psi}{\partial y^2}\right)_0 = \frac{\psi_1 + \psi_2 + \psi_3 + \psi_4 - 4\psi_0}{h^2} = 0$$

Therefore, the stream function at point 0 must satisfy

$$\psi_0 = \tfrac{1}{4}(\psi_1 + \psi_2 + \psi_3 + \psi_4) \tag{12-64}$$

The numerical analysis procedure is an iterative process which continually improves the value of ψ at each point by averaging the values at the four surrounding points according to Eq. 12-64.

If one or more of the grid lengths is intersected by a boundary as shown on Fig. 12-28b, where legs 2 and 3 are shortened, the shorter lengths may be represented by λh, where $\lambda < 1$. Those nodes which are physically closer to point 0 should have a more pronounced influence on ψ_0. This effect is obtained by the following weighting equation:

$$\psi_0 = \frac{\psi_1 + \psi_2/\lambda_2 + \psi_3/\lambda_3 + \psi_4}{1 + 1/\lambda_2 + 1/\lambda_3 + 1} \tag{12-65}$$

The equation is easily modified for any number of nonuniform grid lengths.

For clarity, Fig. 12-27 has been reprinted as Fig. 12-29, and the previous estimates of ψ at each node may be found immediately to the right of the nodal point. Also note that only the points labeled (a) and (b) have shortened grid lengths and that the estimated value of λ in both cases is $\tfrac{1}{4}$. Referring now to Fig. 12-29, start at the upper left-hand interior node labeled with an initial value of 950. This value may be improved, according to Eq. 12-64, as follows:

$$\psi = \tfrac{1}{4}(850 + 1000 + 1000 + 930) = 944$$

The value of 950 is thus replaced by 944, which is written immediately above the original number. Moving to the second point, the value of 850 is similarly replaced by

$$\psi = \tfrac{1}{4}(750 + 1000 + 944 + 700) = 849$$

and so entered. Note that the best estimate of ψ is always used, as demonstrated by the value of 944 in the equation above, rather than the initial 950. The procedure is continued systematically through all the nodes and then repeated until the values of ψ become essentially unchanged. The results of several passes are shown in Fig. 12-29. The check marks indicate values that remained unchanged through successive iterations.

Those points with uneven grid lengths were evaluated using an equation

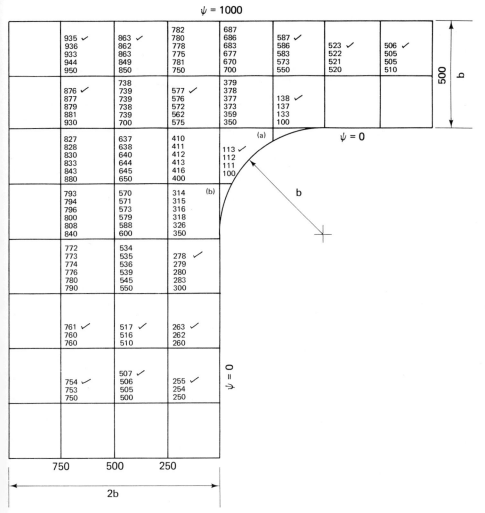

Fig. 12-29.   Numerical analysis for Fig. 12-27.

in the form of Eq. 12-65. For point (a) the equation becomes

$$\psi_a = \frac{\psi_1 + \psi_2 + \psi_3 + 4\psi_4}{1 + 1 + 1 + 4}$$

which for the first pass gives

$$\psi_a = \frac{0 + 573 + 359 + 0}{7} = 133$$

as shown.

Final numerical values of ψ are given on Fig. 12-30, and the streamlines are drawn by interpolation between the nodal values. A higher degree of

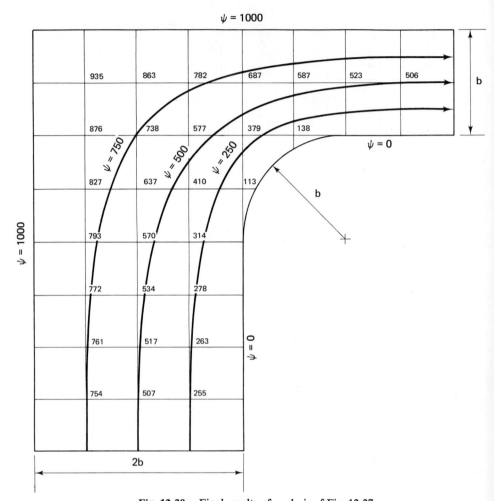

Fig. 12-30. Final results of analysis of Fig. 12-27.

accuracy may be obtained by starting with a coarse grid, as was used here, and then after a few iterations dividing the grid into a finer mesh. The results of the coarse grid may then be used as starting values for the fine grid.

12–6 CIRCULATION AND LIFT

The subject of lift was introduced in Chapter 9. We will now pursue this analysis in the light of irrotational flow. As the entire concept is tied up with circulation (see Section 12-1), we will first examine circulation with respect to basic flow fields. The irrotational doublet was defined in Section 12-4 and then combined with a uniform flow. The resulting pattern (Eq. 12-60 and Fig. 12-26) was found to be the irrotational solution to streaming flow past a cylinder of radius R. If a clockwise irrotational vortex is now superposed on the field of Eq. 12-60, the stream function will immediately become

$$\psi = U\left(r - \frac{R^2}{r}\right) \sin \theta + C \ln r \tag{12-66}$$

which represents uniform flow past a cylinder with circulation. Note that the stream function for the vortex was found in Eq. 12-53; however, for a clockwise direction the sign becomes positive. The velocity components at any point are

$$v_r = \frac{1}{r}\frac{\partial \psi}{\partial \theta} = U\left(1 - \frac{R^2}{r^2}\right) \cos \theta \tag{12-67a}$$

and

$$v_\theta = -\frac{\partial \psi}{\partial r} = -U\left(1 + \frac{R^2}{r^2}\right) \sin \theta - \frac{C}{r} \tag{12-67b}$$

On the cylinder itself the velocity reduces to the tangential component

$$v_\theta = v_c = -2U \sin \theta - \frac{C}{R} = -2U \sin \theta - \frac{\Gamma}{2\pi R} \tag{12-68}$$

since the irrotational vortex was previously found to have a constant circulation equal to $2\pi C$.

The flow field of Eq. 12-66 varies significantly, depending on the relative magnitude of the circulation and approach velocity, but for relatively low circulation the resulting flow field will appear similar to Fig. 12-31. The effect of the clockwise vortex is to shift the streamlines so as to compress the streamlines above the cylinder while correspondingly expanding those

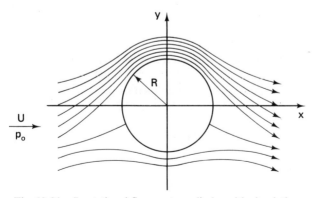

Fig. 12-31.   Irrotational flow past a cylinder with circulation.

below. Reflecting the streamline adjustment, the velocity must be increased over the cylinder and decreased below it, whereas the pressure will be greater below the cylinder than it is above. This pressure distribution must cause a net force, or lift, in the positive y direction. Specifically, for an approach velocity U and an ambient pressure p_0, the pressure at any point on the cylinder is

$$p = p_0 + \frac{\rho}{2}(U^2 - v_c^2)$$

$$= p_0 + \frac{\rho U^2}{2}\left[1 - \left(-2\sin\theta - \frac{C}{RU}\right)^2\right]$$

$$= p_0 + \frac{\rho U^2}{2}\left(1 - 4\sin^2\theta - \frac{4C\sin\theta}{RU} - \frac{C^2}{R^2U^2}\right) \qquad (12\text{-}69)$$

Referring to Fig. 12-32, the pressure on an element of length $R\,d\theta$ gives rise to the incremental force $pR\,d\theta$, which may be resolved into two com-

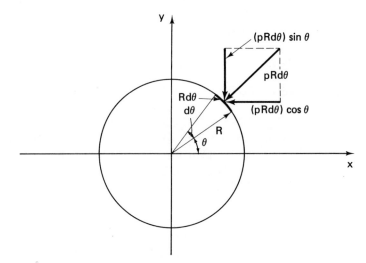

Fig. 12-32. Definition sketch for force on cylinder.

ponents as shown. Thus, for forces defined as positive in the positive coordinate directions and for a unit length of cylinder, we get

$$F_x = -\int_0^{2\pi} pR\cos\theta\,d\theta = 0 \qquad (12\text{-}70a)$$

and

$$F_y = -\int_0^{2\pi} pR\sin\theta\,d\theta = 2\pi\rho UC = \rho U\Gamma \qquad (12\text{-}70b)$$

Again, an irrotational flow causes no drag; however, a lateral force, or lift, exists in the positive y direction. The magnitude of the force depends on the approach velocity and the circulation but is independent of the size of the cylinder. By comparison with the lift equation of Chapter 9 (Eq. 9-24), the coefficient of lift becomes

$$C_L = \frac{F_y}{\rho(2R)U^2/2} = \frac{\rho U \Gamma}{\rho R U^2} = \frac{\Gamma}{RU} \qquad (12\text{-}71a)$$

In terms of the tangential velocity of the cylinder v_c, the lift coefficient may also be expressed as

$$C_L = \frac{2\pi R v_c}{RU} = \frac{2\pi v_c}{U} \qquad (12\text{-}71b)$$

Dwelling on these results briefly, the zero force in the flow direction should again be anticipated on account of the symmetry of the pressure distribution with respect to the y axis. As mentioned previously, either shear stress or flow separation, or both, account for the drag force in a real fluid. Nevertheless, the irrotational flow solution does establish not only a mathematical expression for, but also an explanation of, the lift process.

This type of lift may be achieved as a real fluid passes a cylinder by simply rotating the cylinder. In this case the circulation is established by the transmittal of shear stress from the boundary of the cylinder to and through the fluid. The lateral force, known as the *Magnus effect*, is found to be only about half as great as that due to irrotational circulation, however.

The significance of the foregoing lies in the application of conformal transformations in the complex plane as discovered by N. Joukowski. Specifically, a circle may be mapped into the shape of a foil similar to Fig. 9-11, with no change in circulation. Thus, Eq. 12-70b is appropriate for an airfoil as well. It has been found that the circulation for the airfoil is given by

$$\Gamma = \pi c U \sin \alpha \qquad (12\text{-}72)$$

Since the chord length c is twice the radius R in the transformation process, the coefficient of lift becomes

$$C_L = \frac{\Gamma}{RU} = 2\pi \sin \alpha \qquad (12\text{-}73)$$

This equation is plotted on Fig. 12-33, which is for the most part a reprint of Fig. 9-12. There is a significant difference between the angle of attack of Fig. 9-11 and the angle α as expressed here. The angle α_0 was measured as the angle from a straight line connecting the lower foil extremities to a horizontal line, whereas α, again coming out of the transformation of a circle, is the angle measured from a line connecting the end points (see the insert on Fig. 12-33). The angle α is about 8° greater than α_0, and this has been taken into account in plotting C_L.

It is clear from this figure that the irrotational flow solution is a much better approximation of flow past an airfoil than it is for the flow past the rotating cylinder discussed previously. This is due in part to the far more

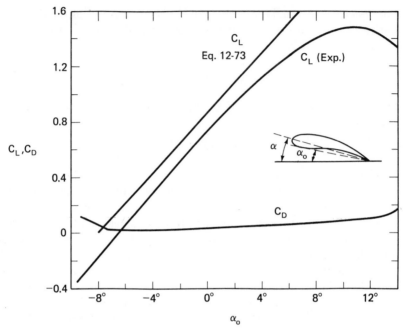

Fig. 12-33. Comparison of theoretical and experimental lift coefficients.

severe separation that forms behind the cylinder and in part to the fact that the circulation generated by the rotating cylinder is not as similar to the irrotational circulation as that which occurs around the airfoil. It now remains to show how and why circulation is established around an actual airfoil.

As a foil starts to move through a fluid at rest, a vortex forms at the trailing edge of the foil. This was previously mentioned in conjunction with Fig. 9-13. This was first identified photographically by Prandtl and is readily observed when moving a canoe paddle through the water. Its explanation is as follows. The initial flow pattern is nearly irrotational and results in a rear stagnation point as shown in Fig. 12-34a. This implies that the flow must turn the impossibly sharp corner at the trailing edge. In attempting to do so, the flow separates and the starting vortex forms (Fig. 12-34b). As the relative velocity of the flow increases the vortex continues to intensify. Now, according to theorems discovered by Helmholtz and Kelvin, if an ideal flow has a given circulation around any defined contour, that circulation must remain constant. Therefore, if the flow has zero circulation, that circulation must continue to be zero as the flow progresses. Although the starting vortex is due to the viscous or real fluid characteristics, the nearly irrotational flow

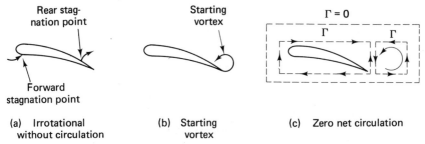

Fig. 12-34.   Circulation around an air foil.

must still have zero circulation in general. This is achieved, as shown in Fig. 12-34c, by the establishment of a clockwise vortex around the airfoil of equal strength to that of the starting vortex. The overall circulation is still zero, as shown by the outer contour of Fig. 12-34c, but nevertheless a circulation is now created around the airfoil. This therefore gives a circulation around the airfoil which is nearly equivalent to that obtained by the previously discussed transformation of irrotational flow around a cylinder with circulation. It might also be noted that the circulation shifts the rear stagnation point back to the trailing edge. This solves the separation problem in that region and the starting vortex is swept downstream from the foil. In the case of an airplane moving down the runway, the starting vortex is left, as it were, at the airport. Theoretically, it would always be possible to draw an ever-enlarging contour around both the wing and the starting vortex and thus maintain the zero net circulation. In fact, of course, the starting vortex is shortly dissipated by viscous shear.

PROBLEMS

Sec. 12-1

12-1. What is the rotation at the point $x = 3, y = 3, z = 0$ of the flow in Prob. 4-1?

12-2. Is the flow in Example 3-6 rotational or irrotational?

12-3. Determine the rotation of the flow in Prob. 4-8.

12-4. Determine the rotation of the flow in Prob. 3-14.

12-5. Determine the rotation in the r–θ plane of the flow in Prob. 3-17.

12-6. Determine the rotation of the flow in Prob. 3-15 at the point $x = 5$ mm, $y = 3$ mm, $z = 1$ mm after 10 s.

12-7. Why can a real flow never be entirely irrotational?

12-8. A two-dimensional flow is specified by

$$u = x^2 + y^2$$
$$v = -2xy$$

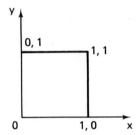

What is the circulation around the square contour formed by the linear segments shown?

12-9. If a whirlpool has a drawdown of 1 in. at a distance of 2 in. from the axis, what is the velocity at that point? What is the velocity at a distance of 1 ft from the axis?

12-10. If a whirlpool has a drawdown of 0.5 cm at a distance of 10 cm from its axis, plot the drawdown curve from the axis out to 50 cm.

Sec. 12-2

12-11. Sketch a flow net for irrotational flow between the boundaries shown. Indicate regions where separation would invalidate the irrotational solution.

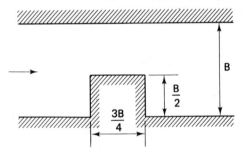

12-12. Draw a flow net for the boundaries shown.

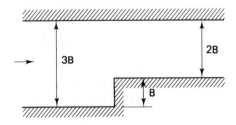

12-13. Draw the flow net for the two-dimensional airflow over a 6-ft-high wall.

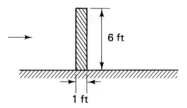

12-14. Draw the flow net for flow around the cylinder centered between two parallel boundaries.

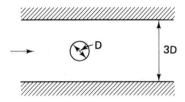

12-15. Draw the flow net for flow around the cylinder placed between two parallel boundaries as shown.

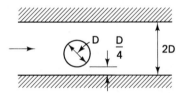

12-16. Determine and plot the velocity variation along the free surface of Fig. 12-11.

12-17. Determine and plot the velocity along the two boundaries of Fig. 12-10.

12-18. Determine and plot the velocity along the top boundary of Prob. 12-11.

12-19. Determine and plot the velocity along the top and bottom boundaries of Prob. 12-14.

12-20. Determine and plot the velocity along the top and bottom boundaries of Prob. 12-15.

12-21. From the flow net of Fig. 12-11, evaluate the pressure at representative points inside the nappe.

12-22. From the flow net of Fig. 12-11, plot the pressure variation along the lower boundary up to the corner. To what extent does it differ from hydrostatic?

12-23. Determine the force on the upstream face of the wall in Prob. 12-13 from the pressure distribution indicated by the flow net.

Sec. 12-3

12-24. If the stream function is given by $\psi = 16xy$, determine the stream potential, the rotation, and sketch the flow field.

12-25. If $\psi = 4x - 2y$, determine u and v. Does the flow satisfy continuity? Plot the flow net.

12-26. Does $\psi = x^2 + y^2$ satisfy continuity?

12-27. Does $\varphi = 2x^2 + 4y^2$ satisfy continuity?

12-28. Determine the flow rate between streamlines $\psi = 4$ and $\psi = 8$ in Prob. 12-25.

12-29. If $\varphi = x^3y - xy^3$, is continuity satisfied? What are u and v? What is ψ? Sketch the flow field.

Sec. 12-4

12-30. Determine the expression for ψ and φ if the flow is in the positive y direction with magnitude V.

12-31. If $u = 2x - 2y$ and $v = -2x - 2y$, determine ψ and φ and plot representative streamlines.

12-32. Show that ψ and φ (Eqs. 12-42 and 12-43) for a source satisfy the continuity equation.

12-33. Determine the velocity at the origin if a source with strength $q = 30$ cfs/ft is located at the point $x = 2$ ft, $y = 2$ ft.

12-34. If a source and sink with strengths ± 30 cfs/ft are located at points $x = -2$ ft and $x = +2$ ft, respectively, what are the values of ψ and φ at the point $y = +2$ on the vertical axis? What is the velocity at this point?

12-35. Derive Eqs. 12-53 and 12-54.

12-36. Determine the velocity at points $x = 0, 2, 4$, and 8 m on the x axis if an irrotational vortex at the origin has a constant $C = 16$ m²/s. What is the discharge passing between the points $x = 4$ m and $x = 8$ m?

12-37. Determine the stagnation point and sketch the dividing streamline for the combined flow field consisting of a uniform flow from left to right of velocity $U = 10$ fps and two sources each of strength $2\pi U$ located at the points $x = 0$ and $x = 2$ ft on the x axis.

12-38. Determine the pressure distribution along the body (heavy streamline) of Fig. 12-25.

Sec. 12-5

Use numerical analysis to determine the streamline pattern for each of the following:

12-39. (Prob. 12-11).

12-40. (Prob. 12-12).

12-41. (Prob. 12-13).

12-42. (Prob. 12-14).

12-43. (Prob. 12-15).

12-44. (Fig. 12-10).

12-45. (Fig. 12-11).

Sec. 12-6

12-46. Assume when measured in degrees that $\alpha = \alpha_0 + 8$. Determine the error in C_L as calculated by Eq. 12-73, and plot it as a function of α_0 over the range $-8 < \alpha_0 < 14°$.

12-47. Show that Eqs. 12-67 satisfy continuity and determine the rotation of the flow.

12-48. Consider the spinning cylinder rotating counterclockwise with an angular velocity ω and moving to the left with velocity V_0. From the foregoing discussion, will the cylinder tend to move up or down in the plane of the figure? Why?

REFERENCES

MILNE-THOMSON, L. M., *Theoretical Hydrodynamics*, 5th ed. New York: Macmillan, 1968.

VALLENTINE, H. R., *Applied Hydrodynamics*, 2nd ed. New York: Plenum Press, 1967.

YIH, CHIA-SHUN, "Ideal Fluid Flow," Section 4 in *Handbook of Fluid Dynamics*, V. L. Streeter (ed.). New York: McGraw-Hill, 1961.

Fluid Machinery

Fluid machinery includes those devices that transmit energy either to or away from a fluid. Machines falling into the first group are collectively called *pumps*, while the second group consists of *turbines*. Although other machines will receive some mention, the emphasis will be on turbomachinery, those types of pumps and turbines that transmit energy by means of a rotating shaft. Since the chapter deals with subject matter heavily dependent on industrial practice, complete with its own terminology, the first section will provide an overview of the subject and a general discussion of pumps and turbines. This will be followed by modeling laws and their significance. Finally, the different kinds of pumps and turbines will be analyzed in detail.

13–1 INTRODUCTION

Only three basic types of turbines are in common use. These are the Pelton wheel,[1] and two types of reaction turbines, the Francis turbine[2] and the propeller turbine.

[1]Named after Lester A. Pelton (1829–1908), the American engineer who perfected this efficient waterwheel at Camptonville, California, during the Gold Rush days.
[2]Named after the American engineer James B. Francis (1815–1892).

Fig. 13-1. Pelton wheels; Runners destined for the SHARAVATHI Power House, India (104,410 kW), IDIKKI Power House, India (134,410 kW), and LOTRU Power House, Romania (187,500 kW) in grinding shop of NEYRPIC. Note flow splitter in each bucket. (*Courtesy of NEYRPIC, Grenoble, France*)

A *Pelton wheel*, often called an impulse turbine, is shown in Figs. 13-1 and 13-2. It consists of a circular ring of split buckets. The development of the splitter by Pelton is largely responsible for its excellent performance and consequent high popularity. A jet (or multiple jets on large units) of water is directed against a given bucket and upon striking the splitter is thrown back and out to each side, thereby imparting a thrust to the bucket. As the wheel rotates, each succeeding bucket comes into line with the jet.

A typical *Francis turbine* is shown in Figs. 13-3 and 13-4. Water enters the outer circumference with a tangential component imparted by guide vanes. The runner design is such that as the water passes radially through the turbine blades, it loses its angular momentum, consequently exerting a torque on the runner. Although originally a radial flow turbine, present Francis turbines are generally a combination of radial and axial flow, as the blades usually turn the direction of the water from a radial to an axial course.

The second type of reaction turbine is shown in Figs. 13-5 and 13-6. The *propeller turbine* is essentially an axial flow machine, which, like the Francis turbine, reduces the angular momentum of the flow, thereby creating a torque

Fig. 13-2. Pelton wheel of one of the MONT CENIS, France, power house units and its 6 nozzles. Output 200,000 kW, head 869 m. Note the hydraulically operated jet deflectors. (*Courtesy of NEYRPIC, Grenoble, France*)

Fig 13-3. Francis turbine. Handling of one runner of the 6 units of AGUA VERMELHA Power House, Brazil. Output 250,000 kW, head 57 m, speed 94.7 rpm. (*Courtesy of NEYRPIC, Grenoble, France*)

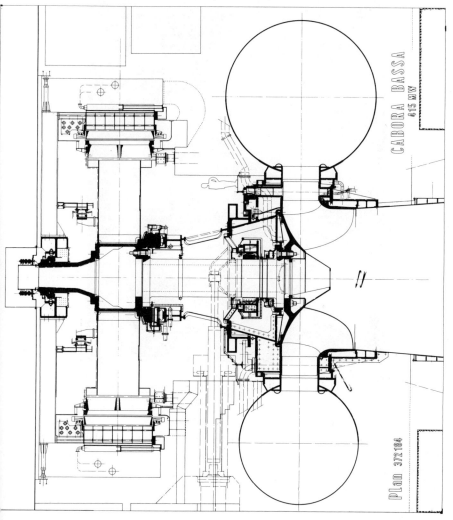

Fig. 13-4. Francis turbine. Schematic of the CABORA BASSA Power House machine, Mozambique. Five units: Output 485,300 kW, head 127 m, speed 107 rpm. (*Courtesy of NEYRPIC, Grenoble, France*)

451

Fig. 13-5. Propellor turbine. Machining of one of the 4 runners of MARCKOLSHEIM Power House, France. Output 40,810 kW, head 15.4 m, speed 75 rpm. (*Courtesy of NEYRPIC, Grenoble, France*)

on the propeller blades. Most modern propeller turbines have blades with an adjustable pitch so as to maintain a high efficiency over a range of discharges. Such a unit is called a *Kaplan turbine.*[3]

Almost all turbines are directly connected to an electrical generating unit and as a consequence must be kept at a nearly constant rotational speed, known as the *syncronous speed.* This speed, which is maintained by a governor, is determined by the number of poles in the generator and the frequency of the electrical current generated. For 60-hertz (cycles per second) current, the speed N, in revolutions per minute (rpm), is given by

$$N = \frac{7200}{n_p} \tag{13-1}$$

[3] Again named after the inventor, an Austrian engineer, Viktor Kaplan (1876–1934).

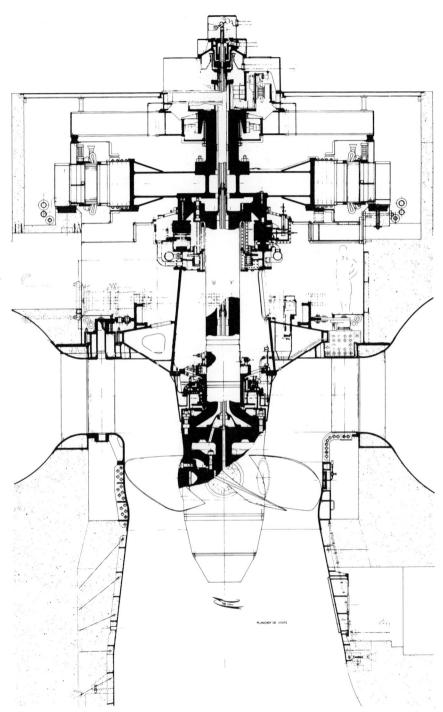

Fig. 13-6. Propeller turbine. Schematic of the SALIGNAC Power House Kaplan turbine, France. Output 43,600 kW, head 28 m, speed 150 rpm. (*Courtesy of NEYRPIC, Grenoble, France*)

453

where n_p is the number of poles in the generator, of necessity an even integer.[4]

Typical arrangements for impulse and reaction turbines are shown in Figs. 13-7 and 13-8. An essential difference between the impulse and reaction turbine is that the reaction turbine is completely surrounded by liquid, whereas the impulse turbine is not. As can be seen, the Pelton wheel must obtain its energy from a jet that has no pressure change. Thus, the energy can be obtained only from the kinetic energy of the fluid.

The water is delivered from the forebay or headwork to the turbine by a

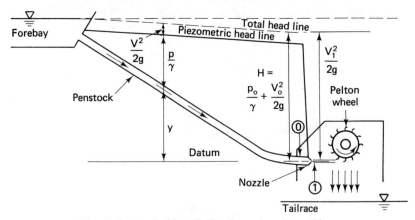

Fig. 13-7. Typical installation for an impulse turbine.

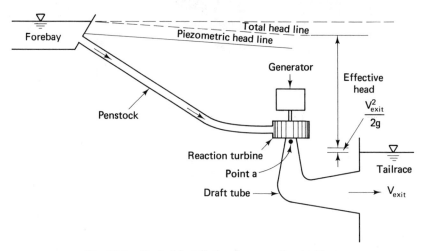

Fig. 13-8. Typical installation for a reaction turbine.

[4] The general expression is $N = 120f/n_p$ where f is the frequency of the current in hertz.

conduit known as a *penstock*. A carefully designed nozzle is required to increase the jet velocity and maximize the available energy. The discharge is controlled by a needle valve, and a bypass valve or jet deflector is usually used to protect the system from rapid reductions in load. Alternatively, a surge tank may be used to reduce the effect of pressure surges or water hammer if the needle valve must be closed rapidly. The passage of spent water into the *tailrace*, or tail water below, has little effect on the performance of a Pelton wheel, since it cannot recover any of the remaining energy of the flow. The wheel is usually mounted on a horizontal axis and directly connected to a generator. Often two wheels are balanced on opposite sides of the generating unit driving a common shaft.

As with the impulse turbine, a penstock delivers the water from a forebay to either type of reaction turbine. The flow then passes through a spiral or volute scroll case designed to distribute the flow evenly around the circumference of the turbine. At this point the water passes through wicket gates, which not only regulate the discharge but also serve to direct the flow in a rotational course. As the flow passes through the runner the passage remains full, allowing for a greater discharge than can be handled by an impulse-type turbine. The runner is usually mounted on a vertical axis. There is also a continual change in the pressure so that power is developed from the reduction in both total kinetic energy and pressure. Consequently, the design of the passage from the runner to the tailrace (known as the *draft tube*) becomes an important consideration. The draft tube is usually designed with a gradually expanding cross section so that the exit velocity (and hence the exit loss) into the tailrace is minimized. The vertical distance from the reaction turbine to the tailrace also contributes to the power developed, since, as indicated by Eq. 5-42b, it is the difference in total head between the forebay and tailrace which primarily determines the effective head. In this regard, note that the draft tube cannot enlarge so rapidly that separation occurs, nor can it extend over a vertical distance that will severely reduce the pressure in the vicinity of the runner and possibly create cavitation problems.

Although a turbine will occasionally be employed to drive a small piece of machinery, they are almost exclusively used for commercial generation of electricity in large and expensive installations. Thus it is that the industry has centered on only the three basic types of units. We will see that, in fact, the three types are necessary to completely cover the required range of operating conditions. Pumps, on the other hand, range in size from those which supply a liquid at the rate of only a few drops a minute to enormous units pumping 300 cfs against heads of several hundred feet. In everyday life we can hardly avoid involvement with pumps, whether it be the pressurized domestic water supply; fuel, lubricant, or coolant pumps in an automobile; or household appliances such as clothes washers, dishwashers, and refrigerators. Thus, there is much more variation in the types and styles of pumps. We will concentrate on only the most important types.[5]

Like turbines, most pumps are turbomachines, but there is no counterpart to the impulse turbine. We will divide the pumps into three groups, based on the primary flow direction; these are radial (or centrifugal) pumps, axial-flow (or propeller) pumps, and mixed-flow pumps. Consistent with the many applications, sizes, and types of pumps, there is no set arrangement or typical installation, as with turbines. The inlet or low-pressure side of the pump is known as the *suction side* and the outlet or high-pressure side is called the *discharge side*. If liquid is pumped from a reservoir situated so that its water surface elevation is below the pump housing, most types of pumps will require priming. *Priming* is the prefilling of the pump chamber with liquid so that the pump can initially draw the liquid and subsequently pump efficiently. This requires also that the vertical elevation change on the suction line be sufficiently small that pressure in the vicinity of the pump does not drop near to the vapor pressure and make lifting of the liquid impossible. Care must further be taken to ensure that under flow conditions low pressures do not lead to cavitation. Whereas turbines are used almost exclusively with water, pumps are used with virtually every kind of liquid, and even liquid–solid mixtures. Many aspects of such design are beyond the intentions of this introductory chapter. The "pumping" of gases is done by either blowers or compressors.

The basic operational principle of centrifugal, axial-flow, and mixed-flow pumps is opposite to that of reaction turbines. That is, the pump, driven by a motor or machine, exerts a torque on the fluid which thereby increases the angular momentum of the fluid as it passes through. The pump housing then recoups this increased angular momentum as an increase in the energy or head.

A typical radial flow or centrifugal pump is shown in Figs. 13-9 and 13-10. The flow enters at the axis and is forced radially outward by the impeller action. The vanes may have plates or shrouds on both sides to increase the efficiency or the vanes may be open, which reduces the efficiency but makes the impeller less susceptible to clogging. The pump usually has a volute casing with or without stationary diffusing or guide waves. If flow enters from both sides of the impeller, it is called a *double-suction impeller*.

An axial flow or propeller pump is shown in Fig. 13-11. It is an obvious counterpart of the propeller turbine. Indeed, many hydroelectric power installations make use of a Kaplan propeller to serve alternately, depending on the adjustable pitch, as a turbine and a pump. The water may then be

---

[5]A further class of pumps, called *positive displacement pumps*, will not be treated herein. These include such types as cam and piston pumps, external gear pumps, internal gear pumps, and screw pumps.

Fig. 13-9. Radial flow pump turbine. Shop assembly of rotor of one of the two pump turbines in LA COCHE Power House, France. Power 79,412 kW, head as a pump 928 m, head as a turbine 930 m, speed 600 rpm. This rotor, which is designed to be operated both as a pump and a turbine, is also a multiple-stage unit as the housing will direct the flow of water through each unit in turn. (*Courtesy of NEYRPIC, Grenoble, France*)

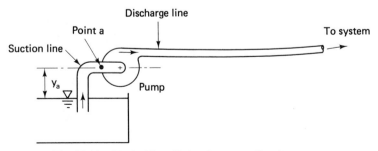

Fig. 13-10. Typical installation for a centrifugal pump.

Fig. 13-11.   Axial flow pump. The rotor (not visible in photograph) is a propeller. (*Courtesy of Worthington Pump Inc.*)

continuously run back and forth between upper and lower reservoirs, the losses due to inefficiency being more than offset by the ability to provide "peaking power," as needed. A typical mixed-flow impeller is shown in Fig. 13-12. They represent a transition between the other two types of impellers and, as we will see, have a middle range of operating conditions.

13–2 MODELING LAWS

The purpose of this section is to first determine the important dimensional and dimensionless parameters associated with pumps and turbines. This knowledge will be useful not only in the modeling and selection of fluid machinery but also in analyzing machine characteristics and their operating ranges. Specifically, the modeling laws will permit the determination of the performance characteristics of a particular type of pump or turbine based on the tests of a geometrically similar model. In addition, the parameters may further be used to determine which type of pump or turbine will be required to handle a given job.

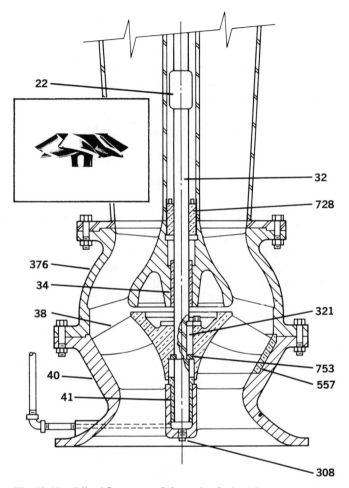

Fig. 13-12.   Mixed flow pump. Schematic of mixed flow pump with rotor shown in insert. (*Courtesy of Peerless Pump*)

A dimensional analysis may be performed which is general enough for both pumps and turbines. Without selecting a dependent variable for the present, the following variables may be taken as significant and expressed in equation form as

$$f(Q, D, N, \gamma H, \rho, \mu, P) = 0 \tag{13-2}$$

where Q is the discharge passing through the unit, D is the runner diameter,[6] N is the runner speed in rpm, γH is the energy per unit volume of fluid added

---

[6]For purposes of similitude, all lengths will be scaled in the same proportion as the diameter. Similarly, all areas will be proportional to D^2.

to or removed from the system, ρ and μ are the fluid density and viscosity, and P is the power exchange between fluid and runner. The quantity γH is chosen rather than the head H because it permits the dimensional analysis process to differentiate between the head and the diameter (a convenient but not absolutely necessary technique). If Q, D, and ρ are chosen as repeating variables, the four pi terms become

$$\varphi\left(\frac{Q}{ND^3}, \frac{Q\rho^{1/2}}{\gamma^{1/2}H^{1/2}D^2}, \frac{Q\rho}{D\mu}, \frac{PD^4}{\rho Q^3}\right) = 0 \qquad (13\text{-}3)$$

The third pi form may be rewritten as

$$\frac{(Q/D^2)D\rho}{\mu}$$

The quantity Q/D^2 will have dimensions of velocity and may be defined as the reference fluid velocity. If proper similitude is achieved, all other fluid velocities must be proportional to it. From its appearance, the third pi term must be a type of Reynolds number. For almost all turbines and most pumps, the velocities and dimensions will be sufficiently large that a fully turbulent flow will occur throughout. Because of the number of parameters involved in Eq. 13-3, further simplification is desirable. Thus, it is usually assumed that the viscous effects play only a minor role and can be ignored, thus dropping the third pi term. Since the viscous effects are not completely negligible, this introduces a small error known as a scale effect in the resulting modeling relationships. Finally, if g replaces the ratio γ/ρ in the second term, Eq. 13-3 becomes,

$$\varphi_1\left(\frac{Q}{ND^3}, \frac{Q}{D^2\sqrt{gH}}, \frac{PD^4}{\rho Q^3}\right) = 0 \qquad (13\text{-}4)$$

Alternatively, the last term in Eq. 13-4 is often replaced by the product of the cube of the first pi term and the third term[7]:

$$\left(\frac{Q}{ND^3}\right)^3 \frac{PD^4}{PQ^3} = \frac{P}{\rho N^3 D^5}$$

in which case Eq. 13-4 may be replaced by

$$\varphi_2\left(\frac{Q}{ND^3}, \frac{Q}{D^2\sqrt{gH}}, \frac{P}{\rho N^3 D^5}\right) = 0 \qquad (13\text{-}5)$$

A third set of useful pi terms may be generated if the second term is replaced by the square of the ratio of the first to the second term,

$$\left[\frac{(Q/ND^3)}{(Q/D^2\sqrt{gH})}\right]^2 = \frac{gH}{N^2 D^2}$$

---

[7]Recall from dimensional analysis that this type of operation is permissible provided that the number of pi terms is not reduced in the process.

The resulting functional equation is

$$\varphi_3\left(\frac{Q}{ND^3}, \frac{gH}{N^2D^2}, \frac{P}{\rho N^3 D^5}\right) = 0 \tag{13-6}$$

The significance of the individual terms and the different relationships will now be treated. Although each equation is just as "correct," the functional relationship must be different because of the different parameters involved. This difference is recognized by the different subscripts on φ. The alternative forms will prove advantageous because of specific variables the pi terms do or do not include. The first term in each of the equations is

$$\frac{Q}{ND^3} = \frac{Q/D^2}{ND}$$

The numerator, as discussed previously, is the reference fluid velocity (and proportional to all other fluid velocities), while the denominator ND is proportional to the runner velocity. Henceforth, the peripheral runner velocity will be indicated by u (where specifically $u = D\omega/2 \sim ND$). As a parameter it represents the ratio of fluid velocity to runner velocity, its relative magnitude being indicative of the type of machine. As applied to turbines, for example, high values are associated with the Pelton wheel, intermediate values with the Francis turbine, and lowest values with a propeller turbine.[8] As a modeling law, a constant value of Q/ND^3 between two geometrically similar (or homologous) units[9] indicates that all velocity ratios between the two units are equal. This is, therefore, the necessary condition for kinematic similitude. To expand further, if this ratio is a constant between two homologous units (pump or turbine), the actual velocity ratio (i.e., the ratio of the velocity at a specific point in one unit to the velocity at the corresponding point in the second unit) will be the same for every point throughout the flow. This also means that the direction of the velocity vector must be identical at every common point between the two units.

The second term of Eq. 13-5 is, in effect, a flow coefficient. Compare the quantity $Q/D^2\sqrt{gH}$ with an orifice equation (see Eq. 14-9) such as

$$Q = CA\sqrt{2gH}$$

Alternatively, the second term of Eq. 13-6 may be treated as a head parameter. In either case it should be pointed out that in the light of fluid mechanics relationships, the second term is not independent of the first. That is, on the basis of the energy equation, the first and second terms of either equation are related. In a turbine the discharge Q is determined by the head,

---

[8] More specific values will be quoted in the course of discussing the next parameter.

[9] Recall from Section 6-2 that the first requirement for complete similitude is geometric similitude. Hence, homologous machines provide a set of different size but geometrically similar units.

whereas the reverse is true for a pump. Because the relationship is dependent on losses, complex geometry, etc., it is not possible to express this relation explicitly. Both terms will be retained in both equations since they will be found helpful in the analyzing and sizing of pumps and turbines.

To illustrate this aforementioned dependence, consider the first two terms of Eq. 13-6 as applied to a Pelton wheel. If friction and other losses are ignored, the total head H (relative to a datum at the elevation of the nozzle) is all converted into kinetic energy (see Fig. 13-7). As expressed by the energy equation, this becomes

$$V = \sqrt{2gH}$$

The peripheral speed of the wheel is

$$u = \frac{D}{2}\omega = \frac{D}{2}\frac{2\pi N}{60}$$

where ω is in rad/s and N is in rpm. Ignoring the various numerical constants,

$$\frac{gH}{N^2 D^2} \sim \frac{V^2}{u^2}$$

Thus, the second term is the square of the ratio of the reference fluid velocity to the runner velocity. Since the first term was previously established as the ratio V/u, an obvious dependence of the two parameters results in this case. Purely from the point of view of similitude, if either of the two parameters is held constant, the other will be constant as well, a result that will greatly simplify the modeling process.

For turbines the ratio of peripheral speed u to reference velocity defined by $V = \sqrt{2gH}$ is called the *relative speed* of the unit, φ. Therefore,

$$\varphi = \frac{u}{V} = \frac{(D/2)\omega}{\sqrt{2gH}} = \frac{(D/2)(2\pi N/60)}{\sqrt{2gH}} = \frac{1}{27.0}\frac{ND}{\sqrt{gH}} \qquad (13\text{-}7)$$

As both the relative speed and the numerical constant are dimensionless, the equation is valid in any consistent units; optimum values of φ are roughly as follows:

> Pelton wheel: $0.43 < \varphi < 0.48$
>
> Francis turbine: $0.6 < \varphi < 0.9$
>
> Propeller turbine: $1.4 < \varphi < 2$

Turning our attention to the final term in Eqs. 13-5 and 13-6, the quantity $P/\rho N^3 D^5$ is a dimensionless power parameter. As a modeling tool, a constant value of this parameter will permit proper scaling of the power in homologous units. Before considering this dimensionless parameter further, it is necessary to discuss the related subjects of power and efficiency in some detail. In Chapter 5 the power was equated to the quantity $Q\gamma H$, where the head H was subscripted by P or T for pump and turbine, respectively. Specifically, $Q\gamma H_P$ is the power added to the fluid by a pump and $Q\gamma H_T$ is the power removed from the fluid by a turbine. The power P was defined in Eq. 13-2 as the power exchanged between fluid and runner. Differences between P and $Q\gamma H$ will occur because of fluid friction and eddy losses in the unit and possibly because some of the water bypasses the runner through small clearance spaces. These factors combined represent a loss in hydraulic efficiency, a quantity that may be defined for a pump by

$$\eta_h = \frac{Q\gamma H}{P} \qquad (13\text{-}8a)$$

and for a turbine by

$$\eta_h = \frac{P}{Q\gamma H} \qquad (13\text{-}8b)$$

In addition to the losses that reduce the hydraulic efficiency, there are mechanical losses due to bearing friction and drag on the runner. If these are all lumped in the mechanical efficiency η_m, the total pump or turbine efficiency is

$$\eta = \eta_m \eta_h \qquad (13\text{-}9)$$

If the mechanical efficiency may be treated as constant, the power P may represent the shaft power and the total efficiency of a pump or turbine[10] will be given by Eqs. 13-8 when η_h is replaced by η.

Noting now that if the last term of Eq. 13-6 is divided by the product of the first two, there results

$$\frac{P}{\rho N^3 D^5} \frac{ND^3}{Q} \frac{N^2 D^2}{gH} = \frac{P}{\gamma Q H}$$

the ratio of shaft power to hydraulic power. With reference to the foregoing, this new parameter is the machine efficiency η. Since it involves each of the terms of Eq. 13-6, it may be used to replace any of the three as desired.

Summarizing the above and at the same time identifying dependent parameters, we find the following results. Since the first two parameters of Eqs. 13-4, 13-5, and 13-6 are not independent, only one parameter must be held constant to ensure similitude among homologous units. This parameter could be any of the dimensionless variables Q/ND^3, $Q/D^2\sqrt{gH}$, $gH/N^2 D^2$, $P/\rho N^3 D^5$, or even η. Immediately the other parameters, which become dependent

---

[10]In the normal course of operation a pump will be driven by an electric motor or other engine and a turbine will be connected to an electrical power generator, each of which will have an efficiency of its own which is not included here. The shaft power specifically represents the power into a pump or out of a turbine.

variables, will be constant as well. Thus, we may write

$$\frac{P}{\rho N^3 D^5} = f_1\left(\frac{Q}{ND^3}\right) \tag{13-10a}$$

$$\frac{gH}{N^2 D^2} = f_2\left(\frac{Q}{ND^3}\right) \tag{13-10b}$$

$$\frac{Q}{D^2\sqrt{gH}} = f_3\left(\frac{Q}{ND^3}\right) \tag{13-10c}$$

$$\eta = f_4\left(\frac{Q}{ND^3}\right) \tag{13-10d}$$

$$\frac{P}{\rho N^3 D^5} = f_5(\eta) \tag{13-10e}$$

$$\frac{gH}{N^2 D^2} = f_6(\eta) \tag{13-10f}$$

etc.

In each of the relations independent and dependent parameters may be reversed at will. Applications of these relationships will be illustrated by the examples that follow.

The foregoing argument, and consequently Eqs. 13-10 as well, ignore possible scaling effects. For example, the Reynolds number has not been held constant, and smaller machines will have a smaller Reynolds number than homologous larger machines. This will generally give rise to some (usually small) scale effects. In addition, clearances and relative roughness of the housing, runner, and so on, will not be properly scaled, thereby providing further sources of scale effects. Various equations have been developed to estimate the change in efficiency due to some of these scale effects, which occur under supposedly dynamically similar conditions. Typical of these are the pump equation by Wislicenus[11]:

$$\frac{0.95 - \eta_1}{0.95 - \eta_2} = \left(\frac{\ln Q_2}{\ln Q_1}\right)^2 \tag{13-11}$$

where Q must be in gal/min, and the reaction turbine equation, by Moody:

$$\frac{1 - \eta_1}{1 - \eta_2} = \left(\frac{D_2}{D_1}\right)^{1/5} \tag{13-12}$$

The former requires that the absolute roughness and the size of the clearances be identical for the two units, while the latter is based on a constant absolute roughness only. Both equations result in a (usually) slightly lower efficiency in the smaller unit.

---

[11] Both equations are discussed in the reference to Wislicenus at the end of the chapter.

EXAMPLE 13-1

A centrifugal pump will discharge 0.080 m³/s of water against a head of 35 m at a rotational speed of 1400 rpm. The power requirement is 38 kW. If the pumping head is increased to 45 m, what speed would be required if the efficiency is to remain constant? What would be the resulting discharge and power requirement? What is the efficiency of the pump?

SOLUTION:

By Eq. 13-10f for constant g and D,

$$\frac{H_1}{N_1^2} = \frac{H_2}{N_2^2}$$

or

$$N_2 = N_1 \left(\frac{H_2}{H_1}\right)^{1/2} = (1400)\left(\frac{45}{35}\right)^{1/2} = 1587 \text{ rpm}$$

By Eq. 13-10b or Eq. 13-10d,

$$Q_2 = Q_1 \frac{N_2}{N_1} = (0.080)\left(\frac{1587}{1400}\right) = 0.0907 \text{ m}^3/\text{s}$$

By Eq. 13-10a,

$$P_2 = P_1 \left(\frac{N_2}{N_1}\right)^3 = (38)\left(\frac{1587}{1400}\right)^3 = 55.35 \text{ kW}$$

The efficiency is given by

$$\eta = \frac{Q\gamma H}{P} = \frac{(0.080 \text{ m}^3/\text{s})(9800 \text{ N/m}^2)(35 \text{ m})}{38,000 \text{ W or N} \cdot \text{m/s}} = 0.722$$

Thus, $\eta = 72.2\%$.

EXAMPLE 13-2

A model pump with a 12-in. impeller and speed of 750 rpm discharges 2000 gpm of water against a 25-ft head at optimum efficiency. The power requirement is 16 hp. Determine the characteristics of a homologous pump to deliver 10,000 gpm against a 50-ft head at dynamically similar conditions. What are the model and prototype efficiencies?

SOLUTION:

By Eq. 13-10c, assuming similitude,

$$\frac{Q_p}{D_p^2\sqrt{H_p}} = \frac{Q_m}{D_m^2\sqrt{H_m}}$$

or

$$D_p = D_m \left(\frac{Q_p}{Q_m}\right)^{1/2}\left(\frac{H_m}{H_p}\right)^{1/4}$$

$$= (12 \text{ in.})\left(\frac{10,000 \text{ gpm}}{2000 \text{ gpm}}\right)^{1/2}\left(\frac{25 \text{ ft}}{50 \text{ ft}}\right)^{1/4} = 22.56 \text{ in.} = 1.88 \text{ ft}$$

For this impeller diameter, similitude will be attained when N is given by $Q/ND^3 =$ constant. Thus,

$$N_p = N_m \frac{Q_p}{Q_m}\left(\frac{D_m}{D_p}\right)^3$$

$$= (750 \text{ rpm})\left(\frac{10,000}{2000}\right)\left(\frac{12}{22.56}\right)^3 = 564 \text{ rpm}$$

The power required will be

$$P_p = P_m\left(\frac{N_p}{N_m}\right)^3\left(\frac{D_p}{D_m}\right)^5$$

$$= (16)\left(\frac{564}{750}\right)^3\left(\frac{22.56}{12}\right)^5 = 159.8 \text{ hp}$$

If perfect similitude, then $\eta_m = \eta_p$, where η_m is given by

$$\eta_m = \frac{Q\gamma H/550}{P}$$

$$= \frac{(2000 \text{ gpm})(62.4 \text{ lb/ft}^3)(25 \text{ ft})}{(449.1 \text{ gpm/cfs})[550 \text{ (ft-lb/s)/hp}](16 \text{ hp})}$$

$$= 0.79 \text{ or } 79\%$$

A better estimate of the prototype efficiency may be obtained from Eq. 13-11,

$$\frac{0.95 - 0.79}{0.95 - \eta_p} = \left(\frac{\ln 10,000}{\ln 2000}\right)^2$$

which gives $\eta_p = 84\%$.

EXAMPLE 13-3

A model test with a 30-in.-diameter model turbine shows that at maximum efficiency this turbine delivers 49 hp when the head is 45 ft and the discharge is 11.0 cfs. The turbine speed is 700 rpm.

Determine the size, speed, and shaft horsepower of a homologous unit which is to be connected to a 60-Hz generator if the available head is 150 ft and the discharge is 120 cfs.

SOLUTION:

Using the parameter $Q/D^2H^{1/2}$ for similitude, the best diameter for the flow and head conditions is

$$D_p = D_m\left(\frac{Q_p}{Q_m}\right)^{1/2}\left(\frac{H_m}{H_p}\right)^{1/4}$$

$$= (30)\left(\frac{120}{11.0}\right)^{1/2}\left(\frac{45}{150}\right)^{1/4} = 73.33 \text{ in.}$$

Using this diameter, the corresponding "best" speed is

$$N_p = N_m\frac{Q_p}{Q_m}\left(\frac{D_m}{D_p}\right)^3$$

$$= (700)\left(\frac{120}{11.0}\right)\left(\frac{30}{73.33}\right)^3 = 522.9 \text{ rpm}$$

Checking to determine whether this turbine speed is compatible with the generator equation (Eq. 13-1), we find that

$$n_p = \frac{7200}{522.9} = 13.77 \text{ poles}$$

The generator must have an even number of poles, and hence $n_p = 14$ will be best. Thus, the speed of 522.9 rpm cannot be used, and instead the speed will be

$$N = \frac{7200}{n_p} = \frac{7200}{14} = 514.3 \text{ rpm}$$

From Eq. 13-10a the power delivered by the prototype will be

$$P_p = P_m \left(\frac{N_p}{N_m}\right)^3 \left(\frac{D_p}{D_m}\right)^5$$

$$= (49)\left(\frac{514.3}{700}\right)^3 \left(\frac{73.33}{30}\right)^5 = 1696 \text{ hp}$$

Complete similitude is no longer achieved, but reasonably accurate results have been determined. A 73.3-in wheel operated at 514.3 rpm under discharge and head specified will produce about 1700 hp.

Specific Speed

Although the usefulness of the dimensionless parameters has been demonstrated, the one drawback up to this point is that the type of pump or turbine has been assumed. What is needed is a parameter, independent of runner size, which will immediately indicate the most suitable type of unit for the given conditions. The necessary parameter, which will be called the *specific speed* N_s, is based on the following considerations.

For purposes of pump selection a suitable combination of the speed, head, and discharge can be obtained from the dimensionless parameters Q/ND^3 and gH/N^2D^2 by elimination of the diameter. Accordingly,

$$\left(\frac{Q}{ND^3}\right)^{1/2} \bigg/ \left(\frac{gH}{N^2D^2}\right)^{3/4} = \frac{NQ^{1/2}}{(gH)^{3/4}}$$

Although this term is dimensionless (except that N involves revolutions rather than radians), it is the normal industry practice to drop the constant acceleration of gravity g, leaving the dimensional specific speed for a pump defined as

$$N_{s_{\text{pump}}} = \frac{NQ^{1/2}}{H^{3/4}} \tag{13-13}$$

For N in rpm, Q in gpm, and H in ft (the typical English units, although the discharge for larger pumps is sometimes expressed in cfs), the approximate range of N_s for different types of pumps is given below:

Pump Type	Specific Speed (English Units): $N_s = \dfrac{NQ^{1/2}}{H^{3/4}} = \dfrac{(rpm)(gpm)^{1/2}}{(ft)^{3/4}}$
Radial flow	500–5,000
Mixed flow	3,600–10,000
Axial flow	9,000–15,000

Similarly, in S.I. units where N remains in rpm, Q is given in ℓ/s and H in m the corresponding range of specific speeds is

Pump Type	Specific Speed (SI units): $N_s = \dfrac{NQ^{1/2}}{H^{3/4}} = \dfrac{(rpm)(\ell/s)^{1/2}}{m^{3/4}}$
Radial flow	300–3,000
Mixed flow	2,200–6,100
Axial flow	5,500–9,200

Turbine selection involves the power developed and the conventional specific speed comes about by elimination of D between gH/N^2D^2 and $P/\rho N^3 D^5$ with the result

$$\left(\frac{P}{\rho N^3 D^5}\right)^{1/2} \Big/ \left(\frac{gH}{N^2D^2}\right)^{5/4} = \frac{NP^{1/2}}{\rho^{1/2}(gH)^{5/4}}$$

Since turbines involve only a single fluid, namely water, it is normal to drop both p and g, so that the turbine specific speed is given by

$$N_{s_{turbine}} = \frac{NP^{1/2}}{H^{5/4}} \tag{13-14}$$

In English units N is in rpm, P in horsepower, and H in ft. The range of N_s for the major types of turbines, is as follows:

Turbine Type	Specific Speed (English Units): $N_s = \dfrac{NP^{1/2}}{H^{5/4}} = \dfrac{(rpm)(hp)^{1/2}}{(ft)^{5/4}}$
Pelton wheel	3–7
Francis turbine	10–110
Propeller turbine	110–300

Alternatively, using N in rpm, P in kW, and H in m, we have:

Turbine Type	Specific Speed (SI Units): $N_s = \dfrac{NP^{1/2}}{H^{5/4}} = \dfrac{(rpm)(kW)^{1/2}}{(m)^{5/4}}$
Pelton wheel	11–27
Francis turbine	38–420
Propeller turbine	420–1100

Since the specific speed can be used alternately with any of the parameters from which it is composed, the efficiency of a given type of turbine (or pump) must be a function of N_s. Figure 13-13 is an example of this relationship. It further shows the limits in English units, given in tabular form above. Study of Eqs. 13-13 and 13-14 shows that for given values of Q and H, or P and H,

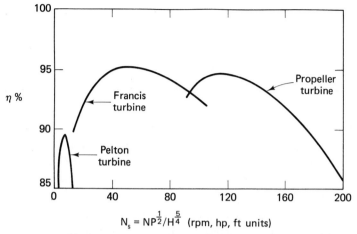

$$N_s = NP^{\frac{1}{2}}/H^{\frac{5}{4}} \text{ (rpm, hp, ft units)}$$

Fig. 13-13. Turbine efficiency versus specific speed.

the specific speed depends only on the actual speed, N. Holding the parameter Q/ND^3 constant further shows that the higher the speed, the lower will be the diameter of the unit. Hence, economic design suggests that as high a value of specific speed be selected as possible.

In addition to the usefulness of specific speed as a selection parameter, it may be used in conjunction with the relationships of Eqs. 13-10. Note that through use of Eq. 13-14 as a modeling law, the speed N could have been determined directly in Example 13-3, even before determining the wheel diameter.

EXAMPLE 13-4

Is the specific speed identical for both model and prototype in Example 13-2? What type of pump is indicated thereby?

SOLUTION:

In the model (by Eq. 13-13),

$$N_s = \frac{(750)(2000)^{1/2}}{(25)^{3/4}} = 3000$$

while in the prototype

$$N_s = \frac{(564)(10,000)^{1/2}}{(50)^{3/4}} = 3000$$

the specific speeds are identical. The value of 3000 in English units indicates that the pump type lies in the transition between purely centrifugal and mixed flow pumps.

EXAMPLE 13-5

Determine the specific speed of both the model and the prototype turbines in Example 13-3 and discuss the significance of the results.

SOLUTION:

The model turbine has a specific speed

$$N_s = \frac{NP^{1/2}}{H^{5/4}} = \frac{(700)(49)^{1/2}}{(45)^{5/4}} = 42.04$$

while the specific speed of the prototype is found to be

$$N_s = \frac{(514.3)(1696)^{1/2}}{(150)^{5/4}} = 40.35$$

The different specific speeds in this case result from the adjustment that was made in the prototype speed (see Example 13-3) in order to generate 60-Hz current.

Performance Curves

The dimensionless parameters for pumps and turbines also lead to dimensional performance or characteristic curves. Although designed to operate at optimum efficiency, the operating conditions often vary and hence information over the range of operation must be available. The efficiency, of course, will decrease as the operating conditions differ from the design conditions. To illustrate, consider Eq. 13-10d. If a pump is operated at constant speed (as is the usual case), Q/ND^3 will vary directly with the discharge. Now Eq. 13-10d shows that η will also change and as the change is away from optimum conditions, η can only decrease. Similarly, for constant N and D, Eqs. 13-10a and 13-10b show that P and H, respectively, will vary with Q. Representative pump performance curves for the major types of pumps are shown on Fig. 13-14.

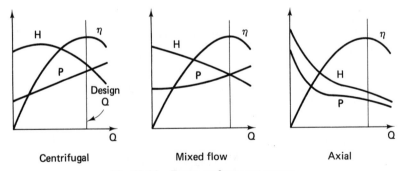

Fig. 13-14.   Pump performance curves.

The relationships are intended only to indicate the typical form of the curves, as the variation in design details of any given type of pump will cause marked changes in the characteristics. A couple of general comments may be made, however. The power requirement for a centrifugal pump increases with discharge, a condition known as "self-regulating." Since the pump speed is constant (if connected to a synchronous motor), the discharge might be regulated by a valve. As it opens, permitting a greater discharge, the pump draws more power. This may be contrasted with an axial-flow pump, in which the greatest shaft power is required at low discharge to maintain the constant pump and motor speed. This leads to potential problems, as care must be taken either in design or operation to avoid overloading the motor. A second potential problem arises when the head curve has a peak, as in the case of a centrifugal pump. Operation in that range may be unstable, as more than one discharge is possible for a given head. Not only is the resulting discharge uncertain, but it is also quite likely to be variable. When faced with a head characteristic of this type, the best solution is to ensure that the normal operating range is some distance from the unstable portion of the curve.

A turbine will generally operate under conditions of constant head and speed. Typical performance curves are shown in Fig. 13-15 for a Francis turbine operating at constant speed.

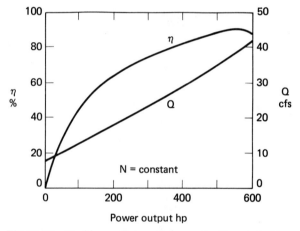

Fig. 13-15. Turbine performance curves for Francis turbine.

13–3 ANALYSIS OF TURBOMACHINERY

Various important aspects of pumps and turbines will be developed in this section. The emphasis will be on those design features which apply the basic fluid mechanics principles, and no attempt is made to cover all the many facets of turbomachine design. The relationship of the machines to the overall fluid system will be treated in more detail than the introductory material in Section 5-5, particularly as regards cavitation.

Pelton Wheel

The Pelton wheel will be considered first because of its somewhat simpler analysis. The relation between the jet and a single bucket is shown on Fig. 13-16. Although the bucket follows a circular path, the portion of the time

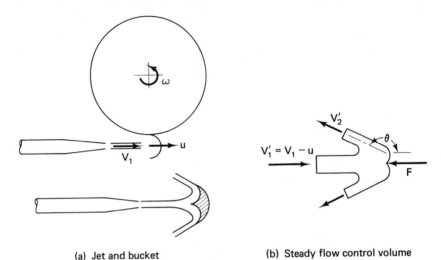

(a) Jet and bucket   (b) Steady flow control volume

Fig. 13-16. Pelton wheel analysis.

that it is in the line of the jet may be approximated as a translational motion. The momentum principle, as applied to vanes in Section 5-7, is therefore appropriate. The actual jet velocity is V_1 and the vane velocity is u. By halting the translation (i.e., by superimposing a constant velocity u to the left) the steady-state control volume shown in Fig. 13-16b is obtained. Applying the momentum equation to this control volume,

$$-F = \rho Q(V'_2 \cos \theta - V'_1)$$

Unlike the single vane analyzed in Section 5-7, the discharge relative to the vane is in this case identical to the jet discharge. This is because the continuous progression of buckets (or vanes) uses all the water.[12] There is some energy loss due to friction and some due to the jet striking the splitter, so V'_2 is slightly less than V'_1. This may be reflected by the equation

$$V'_2 = kV'_1$$

where it is understood that k is usually close to unity. Then

$$F = \rho Q V'_1(1 - k \cos \theta) \qquad (13\text{-}15)$$

---

[12]Compare with Example 5-13b. In the interaction between jet and buckets, there is no water placed into or removed from storage as was the case with a translating single vane.

which in terms of the actual jet and wheel velocities becomes

$$F = \rho Q(V_1 - u)(1 - k \cos \theta) \qquad (13\text{-}16)$$

As this is also the force applied to the bucket, the power transferred from the jet to the wheel is

$$P = Fu = \rho Q(V_1 - u)(1 - k \cos \theta)u \qquad (13\text{-}17)$$

Ignoring, in this analysis, the mechanical friction of the wheel, this is also the shaft power from the turbine. The maximum power may be obtained when $dP/du = 0$; hence, assuming that k is a constant,

$$\frac{dP}{du} = \rho Q(1 - k \cos \theta)(V_1 - 2u) = 0$$

Accordingly, the maximum power is obtained when $u = V_1/2$, at which speed

$$P_{max} = \frac{\rho Q V_1^2 (1 - k \cos \theta)}{4} \qquad (13\text{-}18)$$

If $k = 1$ and $\theta = 180°$, a theoretical maximum power

$$P_{max} = \frac{\rho Q V_1^2}{2} \qquad (13\text{-}19)$$

results corresponding to 100% efficiency. The theoretical power curve (Eq. 13-17) with $k = 1$ and $\theta = 180°$) is shown in Fig. 13-17. In an actual Pelton

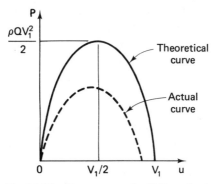

Fig. 13-17. Power curves for Pelton wheel.

wheel, an angle $\theta = 180°$ would leave the spent water in the way of the following bucket. Consequently, an angle of 165° is usually used, which reduces the power output. The efficiency also drops since k will be less than unity, because of mechanical friction, and because of air drag (or windage) on the wheel. The windage, like any fluid drag, increases rapidly with runner speed. The effect of these several factors is not only to lower the power output, but also to reduce the optimum speed to about 46% of the jet velocity (compare with the relative speed in Eq. 13-7). The resulting actual power curve is shown on Fig. 13-17 along with the theoretical curve.

In addition to the foregoing factors there is some hydraulic loss in passing through the nozzle. This factor may be treated by considering the flow between sections 0 and 1 of Fig. 13-7. The available head at section 0 is $H = p/\gamma + y + V^2/2g$. This quantity is less than the initial total head because of entrance loss, penstock friction, and possibly other losses, all of which can be treated separately by the procedures of Chapter 8. Introducing a nozzle coefficient C_v to account for the loss of energy in the nozzle, we may write

$$V_1 = C_v\sqrt{2gH} \qquad (13\text{-}20)$$

By comparison, the conventional loss coefficient C_L introduced in Section 8-6 gives

$$H = \frac{V_1^2}{2g} + C_L\frac{V_1^2}{2g}$$

and hence C_v is related to C_L by

$$C_v = (1 + C_L)^{-1/2} \qquad (13\text{-}21)$$

The nozzle coefficient will approach unity in a well-designed nozzle.

The ratio of nozzle diameter to wheel diameter must also be considered. A ratio of 1/14 to 1/16 is most common, although considerable variance from the range is sometimes allowed. The diameter of a Pelton wheel is defined as the diameter of the circle passing through the midpoints of the buckets. When all the factors are considered, the resulting efficiency of a Pelton wheel is usually 85 to 90%, the larger values being associated with the larger units.

EXAMPLE 13-6

Determine the size, speed, expected power, and efficiency of a Pelton wheel if the available head is 215 m and the flow rate is 0.15 m³/s. Assume that $C_v = 0.98$, bucket angle $\theta = 165°$, $k = 0.99$, and the mechanical efficiency is 95%. Make reasonable assumptions of turbine parameters as needed. The turbine is to be connected to a 60-Hz generator.

SOLUTION:

The jet velocity is given by Eq. 13-20.

$$V_1 = (0.98)\sqrt{(2)(9.81 \text{ m/s}^2)(215 \text{ m})} = 63.65 \text{ m/s}$$

Assuming that the relative speed $\varphi = 0.46$, the peripheral wheel speed is

$$u = (0.46)(63.65) = 29.28 \text{ m/s}$$

The power developed from V_1 is given by Eq. 13-17

$$P = (1000 \text{ kg/m}^3)(0.15 \text{ m}^3/\text{s})[(63.65 \text{ m/s})$$
$$- (29.28 \text{ m/s})][1 - (0.99) \cos 165°](29.28 \text{ m/s})$$
$$= 295,300 \text{ W} = 295.3 \text{ kW}$$

Since the mechanical efficiency is 95%, the shaft power is

$$P_{\text{shaft}} = (0.95)(295.3) = 280.5 \text{ kW}$$

Assuming a specific speed $N_s = 15$ in rpm-kW-m units, the corresponding speed can be obtained from

$$15 = \frac{(N \text{ rpm})(280.5 \text{ kW})^{1/2}}{(215 \text{ m})^{5/4}}$$

Upon solving, $N = 737$ rpm. The number of poles on a 60-Hz generator required for this speed is

$$P_N = \frac{7200}{N} = \frac{7200}{737} = 9.77$$

Selecting a generator with 10 poles, the speed becomes

$$N = \frac{7200}{P_N} = \frac{7200}{10} = 720 \text{ rpm}$$

Checking the specific speed,

$$N_s = \frac{(720)(280.5)^{1/2}}{(215)^{5/4}} = 14.65$$

Comparing with the acceptable range, this is satisfactory. The wheel diameter may now be determined from the values of u and N. Since the angular velocity ω in rad/s is related to N in rpm by $\omega = 2\pi N/60$ and u is related to ω by $u = \omega D/2$, we have $u = \pi N D/60$, whereupon

$$D = \frac{60u}{\pi N} = \frac{(60)(29.28)}{\pi(720)} = 0.777 \text{ m}$$

We must check whether the wheel diameter is compatible with the jet diameter. The area of the jet is given by

$$A = \frac{\pi d^2}{4} = \frac{Q}{V_1} = \frac{0.15}{63.65}$$

Solving, the jet diameter $d = 0.0548$ m and hence

$$\frac{D}{d} = \frac{0.777}{0.0548} = 14.18$$

which falls within the recommended range $14 < D/d < 16$. The overall efficiency η is given by the ratio of shaft power to available power.

$$\eta = \frac{P_{\text{shaft}}}{Q\gamma H} = \frac{(280.5 \text{ kW})(1000 \text{ W/kW})}{(0.15 \text{ m}^3/\text{s})(9800 \text{ N/m}^3)(215 \text{ m})}$$
$$= 0.888 \quad \text{or} \quad 88.8\%$$

Thus, $D = 0.777$ m, $N = 720$ rpm, $P_{\text{shaft}} = 280.5$ kW, and the efficiency $\eta = 88.8\%$.

Radial Flow Machines: Francis Turbine and Centrifugal Pump

Because of the similarities in their flow patterns and consequently in their analysis, these two radial flow machines will be treated together. For the sake of clarity the Francis turbine will be considered first. As with the Pelton wheel, certain idealized assumptions must be made. The extent to which these assumptions fit the actual flow will be reflected in the various efficiencies. We may begin with the sets of rotating and fixed vanes, a portion of which is shown in Fig. 13-18.

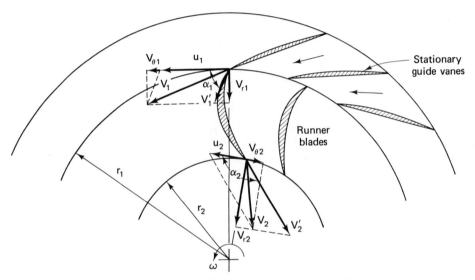

Fig. 13-18. Flow diagram for Francis turbine.

The function of the fixed vanes is to guide the flow so that at the design speed the fluid is directed smoothly into the rotating vanes. The velocity leaving the guide vane has magnitude and direction V_1, which can be resolved into tangential and radial components $V_{\theta 1}$ and V_{r1}, respectively. The velocity relative to the moving runner vane is V_1'. This velocity must be tangent to the initial runner angle, which is α_1. The runner velocity at the point of entrance is $u_1 = r_1 \omega$, where ω is the angular velocity of the runner in radians per second. The various velocities must be related by the concept of relative motion (Section 3-1), which states that the actual velocity V_1 must equal the vector sum of the runner velocity u_1 and the relative velocity V_1'. With reference to the vector diagram of Fig. 13-18, this requires that

$$V_{\theta 1} = \omega r_1 + V_1' \cos \alpha_1$$

or, in terms of the normal component $V_{r1} = V_1' \sin \alpha_1$,

$$V_{\theta 1} = \omega r_1 + V_{r1} \cot \alpha_1, \tag{13-22}$$

The fluid exits the runner with absolute velocity V_2 and relative velocity V_2'. Since the runner velocity is $u_2 = r_2\omega$, the significant velocity relationship corresponding to Eq. 13-22 is

$$V_{\theta 2} = \omega r_2 + V_{r2} \cot \alpha_2 \qquad (13\text{-}23)$$

If it is assumed that these vector diagrams and accompanying equations are valid for all of the fluid,[13] the moment of momentum equation may be applied to the control volume between the concentric rings of radii r_1 and r_2. The only forces acting on the control volume are those which the moving vanes exert on the fluid. The summation of the moments of these forces, as required by the left-hand side of Eq. 5-58, is the net torque T of the vanes on the fluid. As the flow is steady (under the assumption that all fluid follows the same general flow pattern), the first term on the right-hand side of the moment of momentum equation equals zero. The last term of Eq. 5-58 becomes

$$\int_{\substack{\text{control}\\ \text{volume}}} (\mathbf{r} \times \rho\mathbf{V})(\mathbf{V} \cdot \mathbf{dA}) = \int_{A_1} r_1 \rho V_{\theta 1}(-V_{r1}\, dA_1) + \int_{A_2} r_2 \rho V_{\theta 2}(V_{r2}\, dA_2)$$

$$= -\rho r_1 V_{\theta 1} V_{r1} A_1 + \rho r_2 V_{\theta 2} V_{r2} A_2$$

The quantities A_1 and A_2 are the respective areas of the regions of the control volume through which the flow enters and exits. By continuity,

$$Q = V_{r1}A_1 = V_{r2}A_2$$

Thus, the torque the fluid exerts on the runner (opposite in sign to the foregoing) is

$$T = \rho Q(V_{\theta 1}r_1 - V_{\theta 2}r_2) \qquad (13\text{-}24)$$

Use of Eqs. 13-22, 13-23, and 13-24, along with continuity, permits the calculation of the theoretical torque and hence the power (since $P = T\omega$) developed by a Francis turbine based on the discharge, the blade angles, and the runner size and speed. As usual, the various efficiencies must be taken into account to obtain the shaft power.

The corresponding pump relationship may be obtained from Fig. 13-19, which gives the vector diagrams for a centrifugal pump. Study of the diagram will reveal that for blade angles α_1 and α_2 defined as shown, the tangential components of the velocity are again given by Eqs. 13-22 and 13-23. The torque that is applied by the vanes to the fluid is

$$T = \rho Q(V_{\theta 2}r_2 - V_{\theta 1}r_1) \qquad (13\text{-}25)$$

which differs only in sign from Eq. 13-24.[14]

---

[13]This is tantamount to assuming that the runner consists of an infinite number of zero-thickness vanes.

[14]Note that the sign difference is due only to the fact that it is the torque delivered to a turbine runner which is of interest, whereas it is the torque the pump vane applies to fluid that is significant.

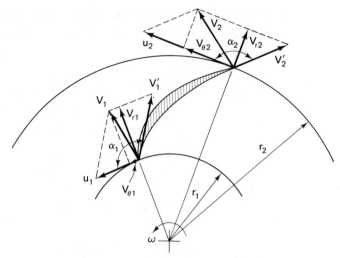

Fig. 13-19. Flow diagram for a centrifugal pump.

Although analysis is more important than design detail in this section, it is worth mentioning that the turbine runner is usually designed so that the exit velocity V_2 is nearly radial, thus eliminating the swirl component $V_{\theta 2}$. Similarly, the entrance velocity to the pump blade V_1 is usually radial.

Since $P = T\omega$, we may express the power supplied to a turbine as

$$P = \rho Q(V_{\theta 1} r_1 \omega - V_{\theta 2} r_2 \omega) \qquad (13\text{-}26)$$

or

$$P = \rho Q(V_{\theta 1} u_1 - V_{\theta 2} u_2) \qquad (13\text{-}27)$$

The corresponding equation for centrifugal pumps is

$$P = \rho Q(V_{\theta 2} u_2 - V_{\theta 1} u_1) \qquad (13\text{-}28)$$

The available power for a turbine is $P = Q\gamma H_T$; thus, the hydraulic efficiency is given by

$$\eta_{\text{turbine}} = \frac{\rho Q(V_{\theta 1} u_1 - V_{\theta 2} u_2)}{\gamma Q H_T} = \frac{V_{\theta 1} u_1 - V_{\theta 2} u_2}{g H_T} \qquad (13\text{-}29)$$

The quantity $(V_{\theta 1} u_1 - V_{\theta 2} u_2)/g$ is the theoretical head (i.e., energy/unit weight) removed by the turbine. Because the idealized conditions are not completely met, it is less than the actual head removed, H_T.

Likewise, the power added to the fluid by a centrifugal pump is $P = Q\gamma H_P$ and the hydraulic efficiency is

$$\eta_{\text{pump}} = \frac{g H_P}{V_{\theta 2} u_2 - V_{\theta 1} u_1} \qquad (13\text{-}30)$$

Here $(V_{\theta 2}u_2 - V_{\theta 1}u_1)/g$ is the theoretical head added to the fluid. It will always be greater than H_p.

If, as is usually the case, the incoming fluid to a pump impeller has no tangential component, $V_{\theta 1} = 0$, and Eq. 13-28 becomes

$$P = \rho Q V_{\theta 2} u_2 \tag{13-31}$$

with inlet conditions no longer affecting the theoretical result. Correspondingly, the theoretical head H_{theor} then becomes (with use of Eq. 13-23)

$$H_{\text{theor}} = \frac{V_{\theta 2} u_2}{g} = \frac{u_2^2}{g} + \frac{u_2 V_{r2} \cot \alpha_2}{g}$$

whence by continuity

$$H_{\text{theor}} = \frac{u_2^2}{g} + \frac{u_2 Q \cot \alpha_2}{A_2 g} \tag{13-32}$$

This equation permits the determination of the theoretical head-discharge characteristics for a pump. If the impeller speed is held constant, it is apparent that the head is going to vary linearly with the discharge at a rate that is dependent only on the exit blade angle α_2. Specifically, if the blade curves backward (i.e., $\alpha_2 > 90°$ as per Fig. 13-19), then $\cot \alpha_2 < 0$ and the head decreases linearly with increasing discharge. Conversely, the less common forward-facing blade ($\alpha_2 < 90°$) results in a characteristic in which the head increases with discharge. These, as well as the limiting case where the blade is radial at the exit, are shown in Fig. 13-20.

Again, the results of Fig. 13-20 are ideal and several factors combine to alter them in an actual pump. The presence of a limited number of blades means that the fluid is not all going to follow the same path, as has been assumed. As the discharge drops below or rises above the optimum discharge,

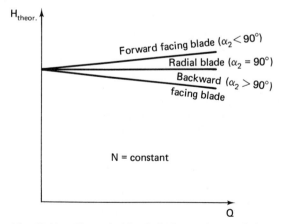

Fig. 13-20. Theoretical head-discharge characteristics.

the flow angle varies from that required for smooth entry, and turbulent eddies causing additional head loss will occur. When the effects of the foregoing, as well as that of friction are included, the curves shift to the more realistic curves shown in Fig. 13-21.

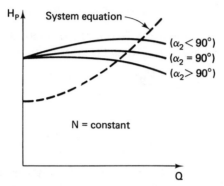

Fig. 13-21. Actual head-discharge characteristics.

Pumps are usually significantly less efficient than turbines. This is partly due to scale as pumps are generally smaller. A second important factor, however, is the diverging pump housing, which converts velocity to pressure head, but also encourages flow separation and subsequent head loss. Conversely, the housing or scroll case of a reaction turbine is converging in the flow direction, which reduces the tendency toward separation.

A final aspect of the problem requires some discussion. A curve such as one of the characteristic curves of Fig. 13-21 is not sufficient, since the physical system of which the pump forms a part must also be considered. Between upstream and downstream points we customarily write

$$H_1 + H_P = H_2 + H_L$$

This may generally be arranged to

$$H_P = h_2 - h_1 + \frac{V_2^2}{2g} - \frac{V_1^2}{2g} + C\frac{V^2}{2g} \qquad (13\text{-}33)$$

where the coefficient C includes both friction and minor losses and h is the piezometric head. Since the velocities may all be expressed in terms of the discharge, the pump head H_P is equal to the increase in piezometric head plus a function of Q^2:

$$H_P = \Delta h + f(Q^2) \qquad (13\text{-}34)$$

This type of relationship, which the system must satisfy, is represented by the dashed line on Fig. 13-21. The solution to a given problem lies at the intersection of this curve and the appropriate characteristic curve.

EXAMPLE 13-7

A centrifugal pump with the following dimensions is designed to pump 0.3 m³/s of water when rotating at 1800 rpm: $r_1 = 10$ cm, $r_2 = 20$ cm, $\alpha_1 = 150°$, $\alpha_2 = 135°$, and impeller width $b = 5$ cm. Determine the theoretical power developed by the pump. If the mechanical efficiency is 91 % and the hydraulic efficiency is 92 %, also determine the shaft power required and the actual pump head added to the fluid. What discharge would be required if the flow is to enter the impeller radially?

SOLUTION:

By continuity,

$$V_{r_1} = \frac{Q}{A} = \frac{Q}{2\pi r_1 b}$$

$$= \frac{0.31 \text{ m}^3/\text{s}}{(2\pi)(0.1 \text{ m})(0.05 \text{ m})} = 9.55 \text{ m/s}$$

and

$$V_{r_2} = \frac{0.31 \text{ m}^3/\text{s}}{(2\pi)(0.2 \text{ m})(0.05 \text{ m})} = 4.77 \text{ m/s}$$

while the angular velocity ω is

$$\omega = \frac{2\pi N}{60} = \frac{(2\pi)(1800)}{60} = 188.5 \text{ rad/s}$$

By Eqs. 13-22 and 13-23, the tangential velocity components are

$$V_{\theta 1} = (188.5 \text{ rad/s})(0.1 \text{ m}) + (9.55 \text{ m/s})(\cot 150°) = 2.31 \text{ m/s}$$

and

$$V_{\theta 2} = (188.5 \text{ rad/s})(0.2 \text{ m}) + (4.77 \text{ m/s})(\cot 135°) = 32.93 \text{ m/s}$$

By Eq. 13-25 the torque is

$$T = (1000 \text{ kg/m}^3)(0.3 \text{ m}^3/\text{s})[(32.93 \text{ m/s})(0.2 \text{ m}) - (2.31)(0.1)] = 1906 \text{ m} \cdot \text{N}$$

The resulting power is

$$P = T\omega = (1906 \text{ m} \cdot \text{N})(188.5 \text{ rad/s})$$
$$= 359,400 \text{ m} \cdot \text{N/s}$$

Thus, $P = 359,400$ W or 359.4 kW. Since $\eta_m = 0.91$,

$$P_{\text{shaft}} = \frac{P}{\eta_m} = \frac{359.4 \text{ kW}}{0.91} = 394.9 \text{ kW}$$

For $\eta_H = 0.92$, Eq. 13-30 gives

$$H_P = \frac{[(32.93 \text{ m/s})(188.5 \text{ rad/s})(0.2 \text{ m}) - (2.31)(188.5)(0.1)](0.92)}{9.81 \text{ m/s}^2} = 112.3 \text{ m}$$

Finally, if the flow is to enter radially (the most usual case), then $V_{\theta 1} = 0$. The corresponding radial velocity V_{r1} is obtained from Eq. 13-22:

$$0 = (188.5 \text{ rad/s})(0.1 \text{ m}) + (V_{r1} \text{ m/s})(\cot 150°)$$

Solving $V_{r_1} = 10.88$ m/s, the necessary discharge is

$$Q = 2\pi r_1 b V_{r1} = (2\pi)(0.1 \text{ m})(0.05 \text{ m})(10.88 \text{ m/s})$$
$$= 0.34 \text{ m}^3/\text{s}$$

EXAMPLE 13-8

A centrifugal pump has the characteristic head-discharge curve shown in Fig. 13-22. If it is to be used to pump water from a lower reservoir to an upper reservoir situated some 60 ft above the lower, what discharge will result? The connecting pipe has a diameter of 6 in. and an overall length of 200 ft. The pipe entrance is square-edged and the valves have a combined loss coefficient of 3.0. Assume that $f = 0.02$.

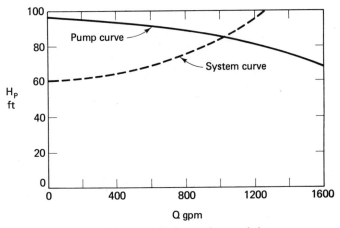

Fig. 13-22. Head-discharge characteristics.

SOLUTION:

Writing the energy equation between the lower and the upper reservoir surfaces using the customary subscripts,

$$y_1 + H_P = y_2 + \underset{\substack{\text{friction} \\ \text{loss}}}{\frac{fL}{D}\frac{V^2}{2g}} + \underset{\substack{\text{entrance} \\ \text{loss}}}{0.5\frac{V^2}{2g}} + \underset{\substack{\text{valve} \\ \text{loss}}}{3.0\frac{V^2}{2g}} + \underset{\substack{\text{exit} \\ \text{loss}}}{\frac{V^2}{2g}}$$

Therefore,

$$H_P = 60 \text{ ft} + \left[\frac{(0.02)(200 \text{ ft})}{(0.5 \text{ ft})} + 0.5 + 3.0 + 1.0\right]\frac{(Q \text{ cfs})^2}{(\pi/4)^2(0.5)^4(2)(32.2 \text{ ft/s}^2)}$$

or

$$H_P = 60 + 5.03Q^2 \qquad (Q \text{ in cfs})$$

This is the head-discharge relation required by the system in consistent units. Since the typical pump discharge is expressed in gpm, this must be modified to

$$H_P = 60 + (5.03)\left(\frac{Q \text{ gpm}}{448.8 \text{ gpm/cfs}}\right)^2$$

or

$$H_P = 60 + \frac{Q^2}{40,000} \qquad (Q \text{ in gpm})$$

This equation has been plotted as the dashed line on Fig. 13-22. Its intersection with the pump characteristic curve indicates that the pump will deliver 1000 gpm to the upper reservoir.

Axial-Flow Machines:
Propeller Turbine and Pump

The theoretical considerations developed for radial-flow machines may be applied to axial-flow and mixed-flow machines as well. This is because all these machines operate on the principle that a change in angular momentum is either due to or causes a change in the torque. The analysis suffers somewhat as the necessary assumption made in the development of the theory are not met as well by axial-flow machines as they were for radial-flow machines Most critical perhaps is the assumption that the flow enters (and also leaves) the blades with a symmetrical flow pattern. A more accurate approach is to treat each blade as an air foil. Since the blade velocity varies according to $r\omega$, each section of the blade has a different velocity and hence angle of attack. The analysis becomes fairly complex and beyond the scope of this text.

Cavitation in Turbo Machinery

The phenomenon of cavitation has been described previously as the formation and subsequent rapid collapse of vapor pockets in a region of liquid where the pressure has been reduced to that of the vapor pressure of the liquid. With the exception of the Pelton wheel, which is rarely susceptible to cavitation problems, the avoidance of cavitation is an important design factor. Cavitation may readily occur because of the placement of the runner (for both pumps and turbines) in a region of low pressure. The inlet or suction side of a pump tends to have a low pressure (point a of Fig. 13-10 is typical), since the pressure usually drops in the flow direction and the pump is often placed above the source reservoir. Likewise, the outlet of a turbine is situated above the tailrace (point a of Fig. 13-8) and hence at a lower pressure. The foregoing identifies the region of low pressure in both pumps and turbines. The problem is further intensified because the local velocity in the vicinity of the runner blade is likely to be still higher and hence the pressure lower than that at the inlet or outlet sections previously identified. In choosing and locating a turbomachine, both the inherent low pressure at the unit and the subsequent pressure drop between that point and the critical point on the runner must be considered.

Cavitation is most likely to occur on the convex side of the blade or runner. On an axial-flow machine the blade speed is greatest at the outer end; consequently, the cavitation will tend to occur toward the blade end as well. Axial-flow or propeller machines are more susceptible to cavitation than are radial-flow machines, because they operate with greater relative velocities,[15] and hence the fluid has higher local velocities. As this corresponds to higher specific speeds as well, we may anticipate that this parameter is of some importance with respect to cavitation.

To proceed with the analysis we will first examine pumps. As previously mentioned, we must consider not only the pressure at the suction side, which can be determined from the energy equation, but also the pressure drop from the pump inlet to the "critical" point. The latter can only be determined from pump tests, but results have been generalized to provide a guide. Writing the energy equation between the lower reservoir surface (which is chosen as the datum) and the pump inlet (point a of Fig. 13-10), we have

$$\frac{p_{\text{atmos}}}{\gamma} = y_a + \frac{p_a}{\gamma} + \frac{V_a^2}{2g} + H_L \tag{13-35}$$

where the pressures are all in absolute units, y_a, is the elevation of the inlet (it is positive as shown in Fig. 13-10 but may be negative) and H_L includes all head losses between the reservoir and the inlet section. The pressure at point a is readily determined and hence provides a reference point even though it is not the location most likely to cavitate. It must be ensured that the pressure head p_a/γ remains sufficiently greater than the vapor pressure head p_v/γ, so that the pressure does not drop to p_v as the velocity increases from that at the inlet to that near the critical point on the impeller. This difference in pressure heads is conventionally called the *net positive suction head* (NPSH). By definition,

$$\text{NPSH} = \frac{p_a}{\gamma} - \frac{p_v}{\gamma} \tag{13-36}$$

In other words, the NPSH represents the head necessary to accelerate the fluid from the inlet to the impeller. Combining Eqs. 13-35 and 13-36 and rearranging,

$$y_a = \frac{p_{\text{atmos}}}{\gamma} - \text{NPSH} - \left(\frac{p_v}{\gamma} + \frac{V_a^2}{2g} + H_L\right) \tag{13-37}$$

With some further explanation, this equation will allow calculation of the maximum value of y_a and hence the maximum suction lift that can occur before cavitation will result. An immediate conclusion may now be drawn from Eq. 13-37: namely, the greater the magnitude of the NPSH, the smaller must be the value of y_a. To completely avoid cavitation, the pump may have to be located below the level of the reservoir surface (i.e., $y_a < 0$).

[15]Refer back to the acceptable ranges of the relative speed ϕ given previously in Section 13-2.

The NPSH is independent of the pump position. It must be determined experimentally; however, once determined it may be readily used with Eq. 13-37 to determine the placing of the pump relative to the reservoir surface. The ratio of NPSH to the total head added by the pump H_P is

$$\frac{\text{NPSH}}{H_P} = \frac{(p_a - p_v)/\gamma}{H_P} \qquad (13\text{-}38)$$

Recall the two dimensionless turbomachine parameters Q/ND^3 and gH/N^2D^2. Since $Q \sim VD^2$, the first may be replaced by V/ND and then squared to give V^2/N^2D^2. For given conditions both gH and V^2 are proportional to N^2D^2 and hence to each other. Thus, the pump head H_P in Eq. 13-38 may be replaced by the velocity head $V^2/2g$ and Eq. 13-38 becomes

$$\frac{\text{NPSH}}{H_P} = \frac{p_a - p_v}{\rho V^2/2} = \sigma \qquad (13\text{-}39)$$

This ratio is now seen to be the cavitation parameter defined in Section 6-2. We may designate the experimentally determined[16] value of σ at which cavitation begins as the critical value σ_c. Consequently,

$$\text{NPSH} = \sigma_c H_P \qquad (13\text{-}40)$$

at critical conditions. The magnitude of the critical value σ_c depends heavily on both specific speed and pump design. As a rough guide,

$$\sigma_c = \frac{N_s^{1.44}}{421,000} \qquad (13\text{-}41)$$

Here N_s is in gpm, ft, and rpm units. A comparison of Eqs. 13-40 and 13-41 indicates that the higher the specific speed, the lower the pump head must be to operate without cavitation. If cavitation is to be avoided, a high pumping head can only be achieved by a pump with a low specific speed. Propeller pumps, for example, are restricted to relatively low heads.

The theoretical developments for dealing with turbine cavitation are similar to the foregoing. If point a is now chosen at the outlet of the turbine unit, the energy equation differs from Eq. 13-35 only by the sign of the head losses.

$$y_a + \frac{p_a}{\gamma} + \frac{V_a^2}{2g} = \frac{p_{\text{atmos}}}{\gamma} + H_L \qquad (13\text{-}42)$$

Using the same notation of NPSH for the difference between the pressure head at point a and that of the vapor pressure head at the critical point in the turbine gives Eq. 13-36, as before, whence the equation for setting the turbine

---

[16] The test procedure is to vary the inlet elevation y_a while holding all other variables constant during pumping tests. The onset of cavitation will be indicated by an abrupt drop in pump efficiency.

height (the counterpart of Eq. 13-37) becomes

$$y_a = \frac{p_{atmos}}{\gamma} - \text{NPSH} - \left(\frac{p_v}{\gamma} + \frac{V_a^2}{2g} - H_L\right) \qquad (13\text{-}43)$$

If head losses are ignored, Eqs. 13-36 and 13-43 become identical. Replacing the pump head H_P by the turbine head H_T, Eqs. 13-38, 13-39, and 13-40 can be applied directly. For turbine specific speeds based on horsepower, cfs, and rpm units, experimental critical values of the cavitation parameter are very approximately given by the following:

$$\sigma_c = \frac{N_s^2}{16,000} \qquad \begin{array}{c} \text{for Francis turbine} \\ 15 < N_s < 100 \end{array} \qquad (13\text{-}44)$$

and

$$\sigma_c = \frac{N_s^{1.8}}{10,000} \qquad \begin{array}{c} \text{for propeller turbine} \\ 100 < N_s < 200 \end{array} \qquad (13\text{-}45)$$

EXAMPLE 13-9

A pump is to be installed to pump water from a reservoir at a rate of 300 gpm through a 3-in. pipe. The pump has an overall efficiency of 79%, a speed of 1750 rpm, and requires 7 hp. The reservoir is approximately at sea level and has a water temperature of 50°F. The total loss between the pipe inlet and the pump, including pipe friction, is 13 ft. Determine the maximum elevation of the pump relative to the reservoir level.

SOLUTION:

The power delivered by the pump to the water is

$$(7 \text{ hp})(0.79) = 5.53 \text{ hp}$$

The pump head can be determined from

$$P = \frac{Q\gamma H_P}{550}$$

For $Q = 300$ gpm $= 0.668$ cfs, H_P is given by

$$H_P = \frac{[550(\text{ft-lb/s})/\text{hp}](5.53 \text{ hp})}{(0.668 \text{ ft}^3/\text{s})(62.4 \text{ lb/ft}^3)} = 72.97 \text{ ft}$$

The average velocity in the pipe is

$$V = \frac{Q}{(\pi/4)D^2} = \frac{0.668}{(\pi/4)(3/12)^2} = 13.61 \text{ ft/s}$$

The specific speed in the usual English units is

$$N_s = \frac{NQ^{1/2}}{H^{3/4}} = \frac{(1750 \text{ rpm})(300 \text{ gpm})}{(72.97)^{3/4}} = 1210$$

By Eq. 13-41 an estimate of the critical value of the cavitation parameter is

$$\sigma_c = \frac{(1210)^{1.44}}{421,000} = 0.065$$

By Eq. 13-40,

$$\text{NPSH} = \sigma_c H_P = (0.065)(72.97 \text{ ft}) = 4.7 \text{ ft}$$

Finally, Eq. 13-37 may be solved for the pump height y_a (at 50°F, $p_v = 0.18$ psia)

$$y_a = \frac{(14.7)(144)}{62.4} - 4.7 - \left[\frac{(0.18)(144)}{62.4} + \frac{(13.61)^2}{64.4} + 13 \right]$$

$$= 12.9 \text{ ft}$$

Consequently, the pump should be placed some distance less than 12.9 ft above the reservoir.

Blowers and Compressors

The "pumping" of gasses is based on the same principle as that of liquids. The most common turbomachines are classified as either blowers or compressors. *Blowers* may be either radial, as for example, a squirrel cage blower, or axial, using a propeller. As the flow is essentially incompressible, the preceding analyses are immediately applicable. Of course, the elevation head is no longer important and cavitation no longer a concern.

Compressors, as the name implies, involve considerable compression of the gas. Consequently, the basic principle of torque/moment of momentum, previously used, must be combined with the appropriate thermodynamic relationship. This subject will not be pursued further in this text.

Propellers and Windmills

Propellers and windmills represent another important type of fluid machine. As with propeller pumps and turbines, the complexity of the flow leads to a rather complicated analysis. However, some understanding of their performance may be gleaned from the following approximate approach.

The propeller will be considered first, using Fig. 13-23 as a definition sketch. A one-dimensional analysis may be used, applying only the several average quantities at selected cross sections. The appropriate control volume is delineated on the figure. For a propeller or windmill the outer streamlines are customarily called the *slipstream*. Ignored in the process will be the actual pressure and velocity distributions across the section; the rotation of the slipstream as a whole, which is imparted by the rotating blades; and the helical pattern of the tip vortices, which are shed from the propeller as they must be from any finite-length foil section.

Assuming that the propeller advances to the left with constant velocity V_1 through otherwise stationary fluid, the steady-state problem will result if this same velocity is superimposed in the opposite direction. Thus, the velocity V_1 is shown at the approach section in Fig. 13-23. (If, in fact, a stationary propeller or fan is analyzed, the present development changes only in that $V_1 = 0$.) Sections 1 and 2 are selected far enough upstream and downstream

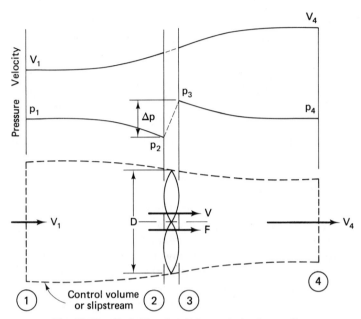

Fig. 13-23. Definitive sketch for analysis of propeller.

of the propeller that the ambient pressure prevails at both and hence $p_1 = p_4$. The fluid is accelerated as it passes the propeller, and correspondingly the diameter of the slipstream diminishes. The thrust from the propeller, which is responsible for the fluid acceleration, is applied to the fluid as a net pressure $\Delta p = p_3 - p_2$ acting over the area of the slipstream or nominally that area $A = (\pi/4)D^2$ swept by the propeller.

$$F = \Delta p A = (p_3 - p_2)A \qquad (13\text{-}46)$$

To be compatible with the ambient pressure and $p_1 = p_4$, the pressure must decrease between sections 1 and 2 consistent with the increasing velocity and decrease further from section 3 to 4 as the slipstream shrinks still further. The longitudinal distribution of the average velocity and pressure are shown on Fig. 13-23. From the foregoing and the energy equation,

$$p_1 + \frac{\rho V_1^2}{2} = p_2 + \frac{\rho V_2^2}{2} \qquad (13\text{-}47)$$

$$p_3 + \frac{\rho V_3^2}{2} = p_4 + \frac{\rho V_4^2}{2} \qquad (13\text{-}48)$$

Taking $V_2 = V_3 = V$, the momentum equation, as applied to the control volume (or slipstream) gives

$$F = \rho Q(V_4 - V_1) = \rho A V(V_4 - V_1) \qquad (13\text{-}49)$$

which relates the propeller thrust to the various velocities. Combining Eqs.

13-46 through 13-49 leads to the important relationship

$$V = (\tfrac{1}{2})(V_1 + V_4) \tag{13-50}$$

Thus, the average velocity of the fluid as it passes the propeller is the mean of the upstream and downstream velocities. In other words, half of the increase in velocity occurs before the propeller and half following the propeller.

The propeller advances with velocity V_1; hence, the useful power developed is the product of the thrust and V_1, or

$$P_{out} = \rho Q(V_4 - V_1)V_1 \tag{13-51}$$

The initial (i.e. at section 1) energy flux or power of the flow is $\rho Q V_1^2/2$. The input power is that required to bring the velocity of the slipstream up to V_4, at which point the total power of the flow is $\rho Q V_4^2/2$. Therefore, the input power (with the use of Eq. 13-50) is

$$P_{in} = \rho Q\left(\frac{V_4^2}{2} - \frac{V_1^2}{2}\right) = \rho Q(V_4 - V_1)V \tag{13-52}$$

The theoretical efficiency may be defined as the ratio of power output to power input. Thus,

$$\eta_{theor} = \frac{P_{in}}{P_{out}} = \frac{V_1}{V} \tag{13-53}$$

which indicates that the less the velocity of the slipstream increases, the greater will be the efficiency. Of course, the actual efficiency will be less than that indicated by Eq. 13-53.

A windmill may be analyzed using the same principles as were used for a propeller. The windmill, of course, operates in the opposite sense from the propeller. If upwind and downwind sections of the control volume are labeled (1) and (4), respectively (compare with Fig. 13-23), then since the windmill removes energy from the air flow, V_4 will be less than V_1, and the cross section of the slipstream will expand. Repetition of the analysis used for the propeller will also show that the air, as it passes the propeller, will have a velocity V which is again the average of V_1 and V_4.

The theoretical efficiency is defined as the ratio of power removed from the wind (and hence used by the windmill) to the total available power of the undisturbed air (i.e., air with velocity V_1) passing through the area $A = (\pi/4)D^2$ swept by the windmill blades. The former is

$$P_{out} = \rho Q\left(\frac{V_1^2}{2} - \frac{V_4^2}{2}\right) \tag{13-54}$$

while the total available power by the definition above is

$$P_{total} = \rho V_1 A\left(\frac{V_1^2}{2}\right) \tag{13-55}$$

Noting that $Q = AV$ in Eq. 13-54, the theoretical efficiency becomes

$$\eta_{\text{theor}} = \frac{V(V_1^2 - V_4^2)}{V_1^3} = \frac{(V_1 + V_4)(V_1^2 - V_4^2)}{2V_1^3} \tag{13-56}$$

This may be rewritten as

$$\eta_{\text{theor}} = \frac{1}{2}\left[1 + \left(\frac{V_4}{V_1}\right)\right]\left[1 - \left(\frac{V_4}{V_1}\right)^2\right] \tag{13-57}$$

The maximum theoretical efficiency may be obtained by differentiating η with respect to (V_4/V_1) and setting the result equal to zero. Upon solving $V_4/V_1 = \frac{1}{3}$ and hence the maximum efficiency (by Eq. 13-57) is $\frac{16}{27}$, or 59%. Again, the actual efficiency may be very much lower than this theoretical value, particularly for a poorly designed unit.

EXAMPLE 13-10

A windmill with a blade diameter of 10 m reduces the wind velocity from 20 m/s to 9 m/s. Calculate the upwind and downwind slipstream diameters and the theoretical efficiency. Assuming an air density of 1.20 kg/m³, calculate the thrust on the windmill and the theoretical power output from the machine. If the actual power output is 150 kW, what is the overall efficiency of the windmill?

SOLUTION:

The velocity passing the windmill is

$$V = \frac{V_1 + V_2}{2} = \frac{20 + 9}{2} = 14.5 \text{ m/s}$$

The slipstream diameters may be obtained from continuity relations,

$$\left(\frac{\pi}{4}\right)D_1^2(20 \text{ m/s}) = \left(\frac{\pi}{4}\right)D_4^2(9 \text{ m/s}) = \left(\frac{\pi}{4}\right)(10 \text{ m})^2(14.5 \text{ m/s})$$

Upon solving $D_1 = 8.5$ m and $D_2 = 12.7$ m. By Eq. 13-57 the theoretical efficiency is

$$\eta_{\text{theor}} = \frac{1}{2}\left[1 + \left(\frac{9}{20}\right)\right]\left[1 - \left(\frac{9}{20}\right)^2\right] = 0.58$$

or 58%. The thrust on the windmill may be obtained from the propeller relationship, Eq. 13-49,

$$F = (1.20 \text{ kg/m}^3)\left(\frac{\pi}{4}\right)(10 \text{ m})^2(14.5 \text{ m/s})(9 \text{ m/s} - 20 \text{ m/s})$$

$$= -15{,}000 \text{ N}$$

The negative sign merely indicates that the thrust on the windmill is in the opposite direction to the thrust on a propeller. The theoretical power is obtained from Eq. 13-54.

$$P_{\text{out}} = (1.20 \text{ kg/m}^3)(14.5 \text{ m/s})\left(\frac{\pi}{4}\right)(10 \text{ m})^2\left[\frac{(20 \text{ m/s})^2}{2} - \frac{(9 \text{ m/s})^2}{2}\right]$$

$$= 218{,}000 \text{ W} = 218 \text{ kW}$$

Since the actual power output is 150 kW, the additional efficiency factor (combining mechanical and hydraulic efficiencies) is

$$\eta_{additional} = \frac{150 \text{ kW}}{218 \text{ kW}} = 0.69$$

and the overall efficiency is

$$\eta = (0.58)(0.69) = 0.40 \quad \text{or} \quad 40\%$$

PROBLEMS

Sec. 13-2

13-1. A given type of pump with a diameter of 12 in. delivers water at the rate of 1000 gpm against a head of 80 ft when operated at 1800 rpm. What discharge and head could be expected for the same speed if a similar pump is used with a diameter of (a) 8 in.; (b) 16 in. ?

13-2. If the 12-in. pump in Prob. 13-1 has an efficiency of 75%, what is the power requirement for each of the three pump sizes, assuming a constant efficiency? Assuming that the efficiency is given by Eq. 13-11 ?

13-3. A given type of pump with a diameter of 20 cm is to pump 0.30 m³/s of water at a pump speed of 1400 rpm against a head of 40 m. If the power required is 140 kW, determine the pump efficiency. If a 15-cm-diameter pump is to run at the same speed, what will be its discharge?

13-4. If a 30-cm-diameter pump of the type of Prob. 13-3 is run at 1200 rpm, what will be its discharge, head, and power requirement assuming the same efficiency as Prob. 13-3 ?

13-5. A pump with a diameter of 20 cm delivers water at the rate of 0.05 m³/s against a head of 12 m when driven at the rate of 1400 rpm. For constant efficiency determine the flow rate and head if the speed (a) is reduced to 900 rpm; (b) increased to 1800 rpm.

13-6. If the pump of Prob. 13-5 requires 7.5 kW to operate at 1400 rpm, what will be the power consumption at (a) 900 rpm; (b) 1800 rpm?

13-7. Assuming constant efficiency, determine the required speed and head for the 20-cm-diameter pump of Prob. 13-5 if the discharge is (a) 0.10 m³/s; (b) 0.02 m³/s.

13-8. Determine the diameter and speed required for a model pump if the 8-ft-diameter prototype pump is to operate at 180 rpm and deliver 300 cfs against a head of 600 ft. The laboratory discharge and head must not exceed 1.5 cfs and 50 ft, respectively.

13-9. What is the efficiency of the model turbine in Example 13-3 ? Estimate the efficiency of the prototype turbine.

13-10. A 50-in.-diameter turbine, geometrically similar to the model of Example 13-3, is connected to a 16-pole generator. Determine the ideal head and discharge for this setup. What power will be delivered by this unit under these conditions?

13-11. Determine the size, speed, and shaft horsepower of a turbine which is geometrically similar to that of the model turbine in Example 13-3 if it is to be connected to a 50-Hz generator. The head and discharge are 100 ft and 300 cfs, respectively.

13-12. At maximum efficiency a model turbine 75 cm in diameter develops 35 kW when the head is 15 m and the flow rate 0.3 m³/s. Its speed is 1000 rpm. Determine the power developed under dynamically similar conditions by a homologous unit 2.5 m in diameter when the discharge is 5.5 m³/s. What must be the prototype speed?

13-13. Determine optimum head and discharge for the model turbine of Prob. 13-12 if its speed is 500 rpm. What will be the corresponding power?

13-14. What is the relative speed of the model turbine of Prob. 13-12?

13-15. A prototype turbine is to have a diameter of 4.5 ft and develop 5000 hp when the head is 150 ft. What size of model turbine will be necessary if the model power and head are 18 hp and 30 ft?

13-16. What is the specific speed of the turbine in Prob. 13-12?

13-17. What is the specific speed of the prototype turbine in Prob. 13-15 if it has a speed of 450 rpm? What type of turbine is this?

13-18. A turbine with a specific speed of 80 is to generate 4900 hp with a head of 150 ft. At what speed must it run, and what efficiency may be expected? Assuming this efficiency, what discharge is required?

13-19. What pump type is indicated in Prob. 13-1?

13-20. What is the specific speed of the pump in Prob. 13-3?

13-21. What pump type is required for the data of Prob. 13-8?

13-22. A water pump has a specific speed of 6500 and an efficiency of 85% in English units. If a speed of 1450 rpm delivers 2500 gpm, what power is required?

13-23. Determine the conversion factor between pump specific speed in English and SI units.

13-24. Determine the conversion factor between turbine specific speed in English and SI units.

13-25. A Pelton wheel with a specific speed of 5 has a speed of 400 rpm and is designed for a head of 2000 ft. If it has an optimum efficiency of 88%, what is the design discharge? If the relative speed $\varphi = 0.46$, what is the wheel diameter?

13-26. A Pelton wheel with a specific speed of 20 (SI units) has a speed of 600 rpm. It delivers 630 kW with an optimum efficiency of 87%. What is the design discharge? If the relative speed $\varphi = 0.47$, what is the wheel diameter?

Sec. 13-3

13-27. Assume a hydraulic efficiency of 92% and a mechanical efficiency of 94%. The available head and discharge are 450 ft and 600 cfs, respectively. Determine the number and size of Pelton wheels if a speed of 300 rpm is required. Make assumptions as needed. How many nozzles are required for each wheel?

13-28. Redo Example 13-6 for a discharge of 4 m³/s, making the necessary assumptions, and use multiple wheels or jets as necessary.

13-29. Redo Example 13-6 as in Prob. 13-28 except that the available discharge is 10 m³/s and the head is 300 m.

13-30. Redo Prob. 13-29 using four wheels.

13-31. Determine the power developed by a Pelton wheel if the blade angle $\theta = 160°$, $k = 0.97$, the relative speed $\varphi = 0.45$, $C_v = 0.97$, the available head is 500 ft, and the discharge is 30 cfs. Will a speed of 360 rpm be possible? What diameter is required?

13-32. If a Pelton turbine has a diameter of 8 ft, a jet/wheel ratio of 1/15, $Q = 55$ cfs, $\theta = 165°$, and $k = 0.97$, determine and plot a graph of power in hp versus relative speed for the range $0 < \varphi < 1$.

13-33. An impulse turbine with four jets has a jet to wheel diameter ratio of 1/15, a wheel diameter of 8 ft, and a jet velocity of 200 ft/s. The buckets have $\theta = 165°$ and $k = 0.97$. If the wheel operates at 225 rpm, determine the theoretical power developed. Determine the diameter of a homologous wheel for the same jet velocity (i.e., same head) and power if a single jet is used. At what speed must it run?

13-34. A Francis turbine with runner blade angles $\alpha_1 = 80°$ and $\alpha_2 = 130°$ at radii of 3 ft and 2 ft, respectively, has a blade height of 1 ft. At a discharge of 1000 cfs, the speed is 128.6 rpm. What are the theoretical torque and power developed by the runner?

13-35. Repeat Prob. 13-34 for runner angles of $\alpha_1 = 70°$ and $\alpha_2 = 145°$.

13-36. Determine the actual magnitudes and directions of the water as it enters and leaves the blades of Prob. 13-34.

13-37. Repeat Prob. 13-36 for the blades of Prob. 13-35.

13-38. Determine the theoretical head removed by the turbine of Prob. 13-34. If the hydraulic efficiency is 95% and the mechanical efficiency is 94%, determine the available water power and the shaft power delivered by the turbine.

13-39. A Francis turbine develops 2000 hp from 650 cfs when run at 30 rpm. The blade height is 2 ft, the outer radius is 7 ft, and the inner radius is 4.5 ft. The guide vanes make an angle of 30° to the tangent to the outer circumference of the runner. For smooth entry, what is the blade angle α_1? What is α_2? What should be the value of α_2 for no swirl?

13-40. A Francis turbine has runner blade angles of $\alpha_1 = 140°$ and $\alpha_2 = 150°$. The blades have a height of 0.4 m and radii $r_1 = 0.7$ m and $r_2 = 0.4$ m. What speed is required for no swirl in the exiting water at $Q = 10$ m³/s? What torque and power are developed at this speed and discharge? If the available head is 77 m, what is the hydraulic efficiency?

13-41. A centrifugal pump has runner blade angles of $\alpha_1 = 130°$ and $\alpha_2 = 145°$. The impeller has a thickness of 2 in. and radii $r_1 = 3$ in. and $r_2 = 5$ in. The pump speed is 1750 rpm. What power is required to deliver 6 cfs? Assume smooth entry to the impeller.

13-42. What speed is required for the pump of Prob. 13-41 if for a discharge of 6 cfs, smooth entry occurs with $V_{\theta 1} = 0$? What power is required?

13-43. What entry angle α_1 is required for the pump of Prob. 13-41 so that for a discharge of 6 cfs and a speed of 1750 rpm, smooth entry occurs with $V_{\theta 1} = 0$? What power is required?

13-44. A centrifugal blower with a blade width of 1 m has radii of $r_1 = 0.7$ m and $r_2 = 1$ m. The blower delivers 1600 m³/min of air (25°C) when the rotational speed is 400 rpm. The air enters smoothly in the radial direction and exits with an absolute angle (relative to the tangent to the outer circumference) of 18°. What must be the blade angles α_1 and α_2? What power is required?

13-45. Assume that the pump characteristic curve of Fig. 13-22 is appropriate for a given centrifugal pump. If a 1500-ft-long, smooth, 6-in. pipe is used with this pump to lift water from a reservoir, what maximum lift can be achieved if the discharge must equal 500 gpm? (Ignore minor losses.) If the required lift is increased 10% above this value, what is the maximum discharge? (Assume that f does not change.)

13-46. What discharge can be obtained from the pump in Example 13-8 if an 8-in. pipe is substituted for the 6-in. pipe in the example? (Assume that $f = 0.019$.) What power is required for the 6-in. pipe of Example 13-8? What power is now required for the 8-in. pipe?

13-47. Repeat Prob. 13-46 if a 4-in. pipe is used. (Assume that $f = 0.022$.)

13-48. Express Eq. 13-41 in SI units.

13-49. Express Eqs. 13-44 and 13-45 in SI units.

13-50. A pump with specific speed of 10,000 lifts water at 60°F from a reservoir. The pump head is 40 ft and the flow rate is 40 cfs. Determine the maximum elevation of the pump relative to the reservoir surface that will avoid cavitation if the total head loss between reservoir and pump is 4 ft and the pipe has a diameter of 18 in.

13-51. Repeat Example 13-9 if the water temperature is 200°F.

13-52. Determine the maximum elevation of a Francis turbine above the lower water level that will ensure no cavitation. The water temperature is 60°F. The head removed by the turbine is 80 ft, the discharge is 250 cfs, the specific speed is 65, the velocity at the start of the draft tube is 15 ft/s, and the head loss through the draft tube is 1.5 ft.

13-53. How far may the pump of Example 13-8 be placed above the lower reservoir and still avoid cavitation? Assume that $T = 60°F$, $N = 1750$ rpm and the loss up to the pump is four times the velocity head.

13-54. Redo Prob. 13-53 if $N = 750$ rpm.

13-55. Develop Eq. 13-50 for a propeller.

13-56. A plane flies at 220 ft/s through air at standard atmospheric pressure and 70°F. The 8-ft-diameter propeller is powered by 1000 hp. Determine the slipstream diameter and velocities.

13-57. What is the thrust delivered by the propeller of Prob. 13-56? What is its ideal efficiency? What is the actual velocity of the air past the propeller?

13-58. An engine delivers 750 kW to a 2.5-m-diameter propeller. If the thrust is 10 kN, determine the plane speed and the theoretical efficiency of the propeller. Assume that $\rho = 1.2$ kg/m³.

13-59. What are the slipstream diameters for the propeller of Prob. 13-58? What is the pressure difference across the propeller?

13-60. What is the maximum power that could theoretically be extracted from the windmill of Example 13-10 in a wind of 20 m/s? What must be the downwind velocity and the slipstream diameter? Use $\rho = 1.2$ kg/m³.

13-61. Determine the maximum power and thrust available from a windmill with a span of 40 ft if the wind velocity is 80 ft/s. Use $\rho = 0.0023$ slug/ft³.

13-62. Determine the efficiency of the windmill of Prob. 13-61 if the downwind velocity is 50 ft/s.

13-63. Plot a graph of efficiency versus V_4/V_1 over the range $0 \leq V_4/V_1 \leq 1$.

REFERENCES

DAILY, J. W., "Hydraulic Machinery," Chapter 13 in *Engineering Hydraulics*, H. Rouse (ed.). New York: Wiley, 1950.

NORRIE, D. H., *An Introduction to Incompressible Flow Machines*, New York: American Elsevier, 1963.

PARNA, P. S., *Fluid Mechanics for Engineers*. London: Butterworth, 1957.

SHEPHERD, D. G., *Principles of Turbomachinery*. New York: Macmillan, 1956.

WISLICENUS, G. F., *Fluid Mechanics of Turbomachinery*. New York: McGraw-Hill, 1947.

14

Flow Measurements

The emphasis throughout the book has been on the development and application of the basic principles of fluid mechanics. The implementation of these principles, both in scientific research and engineering practice, generally requires one or more types of fluid measurement. The intent of this chapter is to provide an introduction to the more common types of measurements. Although many of the techniques are examined in some detail, this chapter does not pretend to replace an instruction manual or even to consider all the fine points of any given type of flow measurement. The reader who wishes a more in-depth analysis should consult the references at the end of the chapter. On several occasions flow-measuring devices have been previously introduced because they offered a particularly instructive application of the subject matter at hand. These devices will be repeated here in abbreviated form with a footnote reference to the previous material.

14–1 MEASUREMENT OF SURFACE ELEVATION AND DEPTH

The only common type of length measurement requiring special consideration is that involving depths, thickness of a liquid layer, or water surface elevation. The most common laboratory device is the point or hook gage, shown in Fig. 14-1. Either type can be used to measure the water surface

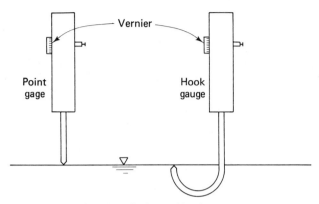

Fig. 14-1.   Point and hook gages.

elevation. However, if the liquid is wavy or swift, the hook gage may be more difficult to read. The point is lowered or raised until it just touches the surface. If the operator is positioned so that an image of the point is also visible, a very accurate reading can be obtained as the image and real points are brought together.

The actual reading is made where the large scale connected to the point (or hook) passes through a vernier. With use of the vernier, the reading may be made to the nearest 0.001 ft or 0.2 mm. The scale is arranged so that the reading increases in magnitude as the gage is raised. To determine the liquid depth the point gage may be read at both the channel bottom and at the water surface. The difference in readings will be the depth.

A manometer[1] may be used to determine the depth of a liquid as in Fig. 14-2. In the measurements of flowing liquids,[2] care must be taken that the measurement is made in a region of uniform flow. Otherwise, the manometer, which actually reflects the piezometric head rather than the depth, will give erroneous depth measurements.

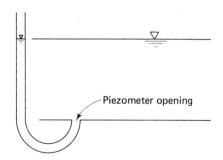

Fig. 14-2.   Measurement of depth with a manometer.

[1]See Section 2-2.
[2]See Sections 5-1 and 10-1.

A float is often used to measure the water surface elevation of bodies of water. In fact, a float placed in a stilling basin and connected to a continuously recording chart, is the most common method employed by the U.S. Geological Survey in their measurements of river elevation or "stage."

A number of electrical devices have been developed. These are generally based on resistance or capacitance schemes in which the resistance or capacitance varies as the depth changes.

14–2 MEASUREMENT OF PRESSURE

Pressure measurements are quite significant since the pressure is often necessary in order to calculate (or indirectly measure) other fluid mechanics quantities (e.g., depth, velocity, or discharge). As pressure measurements have been treated rather completely in previous chapters, the different types of pressure measurement will be summarized at this point along with some additional measurement details.

Static Pressure

Static pressure measurements[3] are those measurements which are so obtained that they do not directly measure any dynamic effect of the flow. A static pressure measurement is usually obtained by a small opening known as a *piezometer opening* (see Fig. 14-2), which is connected to either a manometer or pressure gage. If the fluid is at rest, there is no dynamic effect, and consequently the static pressure is immediately measured. The result will be correct subject only to a leak in a connection, an inaccurate gage, or surface tension error in a manometer column. If flow occurs, the pressure tap (or piezometer opening) must be mounted flush with the surface and perpendicular to the velocity of the fluid in the vicinity of the tap. Any burrs or projections near the top will disturb the local flow pattern altering the velocity and hence the pressure at the tap. If the tap is inclined toward the flow direction, a component of the velocity will be sensed by the piezometer and the pressure measurement will also include a component of the dynamic pressure.

To improve the accuracy of static pressure measurements in a pipe, a ring of interconnected pressure taps is sometimes placed around the circumference of the pipe. This tends to average out the effects of imperfections in the pipe wall. If a pipe carrying a liquid has much air carried with the flow, a pressure tap should not be placed at the top of the pipe. Likewise, if the flow carries any settleable material, it is ill advised to place a piezometer tap near the bottom of the pipe cross section.

[3]See Section 2-2.

The calculation of pressure from a manometer reading was covered in Section 2-2 and will not be repeated here.

Stagnation Pressure

Any point in the flow field at which the velocity is brought to zero is a *stagnation point*.[4] In incompressible flow a pressure rise equal to the dynamic pressure of the flow, $\rho V^2/2$, occurs at the stagnation point. A piezometer opening placed at the stagnation point, as in Fig. 5-10, will sense this additional pressure, and hence the gage or manometer connected to the piezometer opening will indicate the static pressure plus the dynamic pressure, or, in other words, the stagnation pressure.

A slender tube, such as that shown in Fig. 5-10 but with only the single stagnation pressure tap, is known as a *stagnation tube* (or sometimes a *Pitot tube* or *impact tube*). If the static pressure is known, the velocity may be readily calculated. The more complete Pitot-static tube shown in Fig. 5-10 and mentioned in the next section obviously accomplishes this directly. The main advantage of the single stagnation tube is that it can have a very small diameter. Thus, it disturbs the flow field to a smaller degree and, more important, permits a more precise location of the "point" of measurement. The resulting stagnation pressure in compressible flow is given by Eqs. 11-35.

14–3 MEASUREMENT OF VELOCITY

Only selected velocity measurements will be discussed here. Many other important procedures such as photographic methods and relatively new techniques such as the laser Doppler anemometer will be found in the references.

Pitot Tubes

There are two basic types of Pitot tubes. The type previously introduced in Section 14-2 has a single piezometer opening at the stagnation point. The second basic type, which was introduced in Section 5-3, has both the stagnation and static pressure tubes combined on a single probe, as shown on Fig. 5-10. Properly called a *Pitot-static tube*, it is often called simply a Pitot tube. Regardless of the type of Pitot tube, the equations developed in Section 5-3 give

$$V = \sqrt{\frac{2(p_2 - p_1)}{\rho}} = \sqrt{\frac{2\Delta p}{\rho}} \qquad (14\text{-}1)$$

[4]See, for example, Fig. 5-9 or 5-10 in Section 5-3.

Here, p_2 and p_1 represent the stagnation and static pressure, respectively; V is the velocity of the flow at the point where the probe is placed; and ρ is the density of the fluid. The piezometric openings may be connected directly to separate pressure gages or to a differential pressure gage. Alternatively, a manometer may be used. For example, if a manometer using water as the manometer fluid is used with a Pitot tube in an airflow, the velocity is given by

$$V = \sqrt{\frac{2\gamma_{H_2O}(h_2 - h_1)}{\rho_{air}}} = \sqrt{\frac{2\gamma_{H_2O}\,\Delta h}{\rho_{air}}} \qquad (14\text{-}2)$$

where $h_2 - h_1 = \Delta h$ is the difference in water levels in the manometer columns.

The physical presence of a probe in the flow causes some disturbance to the flow field, particularly to the static pressure at the probe. For precise work Eq. 14-1 may be replaced by

$$V = C\sqrt{\frac{2(p_2 - p_1)}{\rho}} \qquad (14\text{-}3)$$

where the coefficient C would generally be experimentally determined.

A variety of Pitot tubes have been developed and endorsed by different organizations. They differ slightly in their geometric shape, need for calibration, and sensitivity to the alignment of the probe with the flow.

The Pitot tube is regularly used for velocity measurements in laboratory work as well as in such diversified areas as hydroelectric power and airplanes in flight. The Pitot tube may be used in compressible flow, whereupon the velocity may be obtained from the equations of Section 11-2.

Current Meters and Anemometers

The measurement of river discharge covered in the next section requires velocity measurements. These velocities are usually measured with a commercial device known as a *current meter*. Although there are several types of current meters in use, the most common type used in the United States is the *Price meter*, shown in Fig. 14-3. This device consists of a series of conical cups which rotate about a vertical axis. Since the cups have a higher drag coefficient when their open side is facing the flow than when facing downstream, the cups rotate with an angular velocity proportional to the velocity of the flow. Standard operation is to place the Price current meter into the flow and count the revolutions of the cups during a period of time. The velocity is then obtained from a previous calibration.

The assembly includes a vane, as shown on Fig. 14-3, to hold the unit steady toward the flow. In shallow streams the meter is supported rigidly on a rod while a wire support is used for deeper flows. In the latter case a weight is fastened below the meter to offset the drag of the flow on the probe.

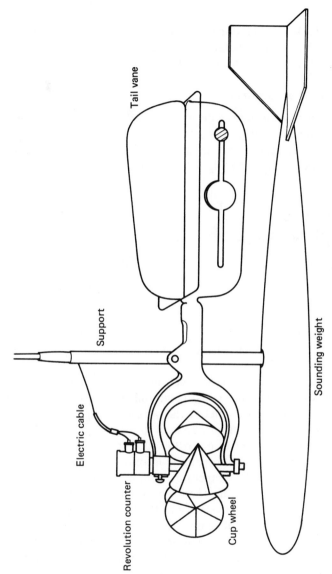

Tail vane

Support

Electric cable

Revolution counter

Cup wheel

Sounding weight

Fig. 14-3. Price current meter.

501

A variety of propeller current meters that rotate about a horizontal axis are also in use. Although current meters are primarily a field tool, they are available in different sizes, and the very small sizes also find some use in the laboratory.

Similar to the basic operation of the Price current meter is the cup anemometer, which is the standard device for measuring wind velocity. The cup anemometer, which uses hemispherical cups, also requires calibration.

Hot-Wire Anemometer

The *hot-wire anemometer* is a device that measures both the mean velocity and the instantaneous velocity at a "point." The probe usually consists of a platinum-coated tungsten wire about 0.00015 in. in diameter and 0.05 in. long, supported as shown in Fig. 14-4a. The wire is heated to a relatively

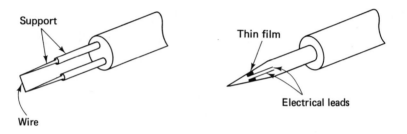

(a) Hot-wire probe   (b) Conical hot-film probe

Fig. 14-4.   Hot-wire and hot-film probes.

high temperature by passing an electrical current through it. The fluid passing the wire tends to cool it and consequently change its electrical resistance. Because of its very small diameter, the wire can respond very rapidly to velocity changes, and hence it may be used to measure the turbulent fluctuations in a flow with frequencies up to 100,000 Hz.

The most common mode of operation is known as a *constant-temperature anemometer*. In this case the temperature and hence resistance of the wire is maintained at a constant value. The sensor forms one leg of a balanced Wheatstone bridge. When the velocity of the flow changes, this changes the resistance of the wire and unbalances the bridge. This unbalance is sensed by a feedback amplifier, which then adjusts the current to rebalance the bridge and thereby maintains the constant temperature. The current flowing through the wire is monitored and related to the mean and fluctuating components of the velocity. The second type is known as a *constant-current anemometer*. In this anemometer a constant current is applied to the wire, which again forms a leg of a bridge circuit. As the wire resistance varies with changing velocity, the voltage unbalance of the bridge is monitored and analyzed.

The analysis of the hot-wire anemometer involves a consideration of heat transfer as well as fluid mechanics and is beyond the intent of this book. The probe does require a calibration of the current passing through the sensor to the time-averaged velocity $\bar{u}$.[5] A typical calibration curve for a constant-temperature anemometer is shown on Fig. 14-5. The voltage, which is proportioned to the current for constant resistance, has been chosen as the ordinate of the calibration curve. Here, E is the anemometer voltage corresponding to the velocity $\bar{u}$, and E_0 is the voltage at zero velocity. The various turbulent components can be obtained from the current or voltage fluctuations. For example, the turbulent intensity[6] $\sqrt{\overline{u'^2}}$ is related to E', the root mean square of the voltage fluctuations, by

$$\frac{\sqrt{\overline{u'^2}}}{\bar{u}} = \frac{E'/E}{(dE/E)/(d\bar{u}/\bar{u})} \qquad (14\text{-}4)$$

where $dE/d\bar{u}$ is obtained from the slope of Fig. 14-5.

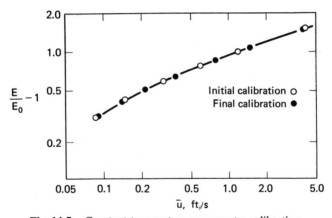

Fig. 14-5.   Constant-temperature anemometer calibration.

The fine wire is very fragile and usually restricted to gas flow. A number of film probes, such as the conical probe shown on Fig. 14-4b and a cylindrical probe in which a small diameter cylinder is arranged essentially as the fine wire in Fig. 14-4a, have been developed for use in liquids. The conducting surface consists of a thin metal film, which may in turn be covered by a protective coating. At the sacrifice of some frequency loss, the hot-film probe

[5] See Eq. 3-22.
[6] See Sections 3-4 and 7-3.

gives good results in water. The calibration curve in Fig. 14-5 was obtained using such a conical probe in water. Typical profiles of $\bar{u}$ and $\sqrt{\overline{u'^2}}$ versus depth are shown in Fig. 14-6. The conical probe was used and the data were obtained from water flow over a movable sand bed.[7] Here, y/y_0 represents the relative elevation above the sand bed for a depth y_0, and $\sqrt{\overline{u'^2}}$ and $\bar{u}$ are referenced to the average velocity V.

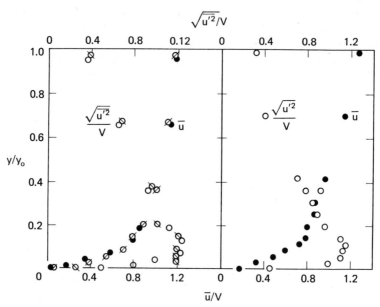

Fig. 14-6. Typical turbulent and mean velocity profiles over a sand bed.

14–4 MEASUREMENT OF DISCHARGE

Discharge measurements are perhaps the most frequent type of fluid measurement. Because of its importance, many of the common methods will be covered. As has been the case throughout the book, the term "discharge" will imply the volumetric discharge unless stated to the contrary. Of course, for incompressible flow the volumetric discharge is proportional to the mass discharge and weight discharge, the constants of proportionality being ρ and γ, respectively.

[7]A. L. Prasuhn, "Turbulence Measurements Over Sand Beds," *Proceedings, International Symposium of River Mechanics, International Association for Hydraulic Research,* January 1973.

Direct Integration

By definition the discharge is the integration of the velocity over the cross-sectional area. Thus, if the velocity distribution is known, the discharge may be obtained by direct integration. If the velocity distribution can be expressed mathematically, it may be possible to perform the integration in closed form. This procedure was previously developed in Section 3-2 and illustrated by Example 3-4. It is also applied in Sections 7-1 and 8-3. If the velocity distribution has been obtained experimentally, say with a Pitot tube or hot-wire anemometer, a graphic integration will usually be required. This procedure has been demonstrated in Example 3-5.

Stream Discharge

The determination of discharge in streams and rivers poses special problems because of the irregular geometry and often large quantities of water involved. The usual procedure is a modification of the integration method using a current meter for the velocity measurements. The cross section is divided into vertical sections extending from the water surface to the stream bed. Generally, enough vertical sections are selected so that no one section contains more than 10% of the total flow. The discharge in each vertical is the product of the average velocity in that section and the cross-sectional area. The total discharge is obtained by summing the individual sectional discharges.

Vertical velocity profiles are sufficiently similar (and approximately logarithmic) so that the average velocity for a profile, and hence a section, can be found by just two velocity measurements. Specifically, the average of velocity measurements at two-tenths and eight-tenths of the depth is taken as the average for the section. In shallow sections a single measurement at six-tenths of the depth usually suffices. The computational scheme is shown in Example 14-1.

EXAMPLE 14-1

A stream has been divided into sections as shown on Fig. 14-7. Velocity measurements have been obtained at 2/10 and 8/10 of the depth at all sections except the bank sections, where only a single measurement at 6/10 of the depth was made. Each section is 4 ft wide. The velocity measurements and the elevation of the bed at each section are given in the table that follows. Section 6 has been taken as typical in Fig. 14-7 to illustrate the various measurements.

SOLUTION:

Typical calculations: section 6

$$\text{Depth} = 100 - 92.8 = 7.2 \text{ ft}$$
$$\text{Average velocity} = \tfrac{1}{2}(6.5 + 4.3) = 5.40 \text{ ft/s}$$
$$\text{Discharge} = (4)(7.2)(5.4) = 155.5 \text{ cfs}$$

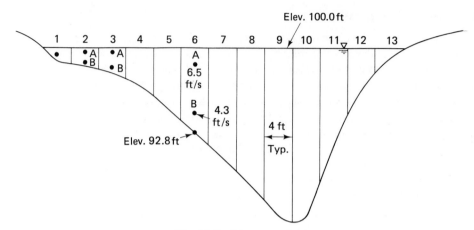

Fig. 14-7. River cross section.

		Given Information		Required Calculations		
Section		Elevation of Bed (ft)	Velocity (ft/s)	Depth (ft)	Average Velocity (ft/s)	Discharge (cfs)
1		98.9	2.6	1.1	2.6	11.4
2	A	98.3	3.6	1.7	2.85	19.4
	B		2.1			
3	A	97.8	4.7	2.2	3.85	33.9
	B		3.0			
4	A	96.9	5.7	3.1	4.60	57.0
	B		3.5			
5	A	94.9	6.1	5.1	5.05	103.0
	B		4.0			
6	A	92.8	6.5	7.2	5.40	155.5
	B		4.3			
7	A	90.9	6.8	9.1	5.70	207.5
	B		4.6			
8	A	88.6	7.1	11.4	5.95	271.3
	B		4.8			
9	A	85.8	7.4	14.2	6.35	360.7
	B		5.3			
10	A	85.4	7.7	14.6	6.30	367.9
	B		4.9			
11	A	91.9	6.8	8.1	5.60	181.4
	B		4.4			
12	A	96.4	5.8	3.6	4.10	66.2
	B		3.4			
13		99.2	3.7	0.8	3.70	11.8
					Total discharge	1847

Volumetric Discharge

An accurate procedure for determining liquid discharge under suitable conditions is to direct a steady flow into a tank for a measured period of time. Upon measuring the portion of tank volume containing liquid, the discharge is obtained by dividing the volume by the filling time.

This method is obviously restricted to relatively small flow rates. If 40 s is taken as the minimum time interval (to reduce timing error to 0.5% or less), a fairly large volume tank may be required. Even for small discharges the procedure is not suitable for most stream or open-channel flows and many industrial applications. It is, however, well suited for many laboratory applications and in this context is often the standard for calibration of meters and other flow-measuring devices.

The usual procedure is to begin with an empty (or nearly empty) tank, and after establishing a steady flow in the system quickly direct the liquid into the tank. After a satisfactory time interval the flow is again rapidly directed away from the tank. The volume should then be determined after giving the liquid sufficient time for any waves to be damped out. For additional details the reader is referred to *Engineering Hydraulics* (see the references at the end of the chapter).

Gravimetric Discharge

If a tank similar to that used for volumetric discharge is placed on a scale, the volume of liquid entering the tank during a time interval can be determined by dividing the increase in weight by the specific weight of the liquid. The discharge is then found as before. This is often more convenient than measuring the volume change, since the geometry of the tank does not have to be carefully determined.

This method is also restricted to relatively small discharges, usually under laboratory conditions. Either of two operating techniques may be followed. The more accurate is probably to use the same procedure as with the volumetric discharge. That is, divert the flow into and then out of the tank, making the initial and final weight measurement, respectively, before and after the filling period. Alternatively, the initial and final weights may be obtained "on the run." After a steady flow into the tank has been established, the timing process commences as the scale indicator passes a predetermined weight. Timing then ends as the scale indicator passes some upper limit. Dividing the difference in weights by the time interval now yields the weight discharge. Further details may again be found in *Engineering Hydraulics*.

Closed-Conduit Meters

Many different meters have been developed for measurement of the flow rate through closed conduits. This subsection examines a few of the most commonly used devices. In addition to their similar application, they share a similar theoretical basis. They each create a region of nonuniform flow and hence a pressure difference. As the pressure difference is dependent on the discharge, once this relationship is determined manometers or pressure gages may be used to obtain the pressure difference and in turn the discharge. In some cases the pressure difference/discharge relationship can be developed theoretically with a small experimental correction necessary only for precise work. In other cases the relationship can only be obtained by experiment.

Almost anything that is done to create a local nonuniform region in a closed-conduit flow can be instrumented and used as a flow meter. An experimental calibration would always be required under these circumstances, however. If a meter, either standardized or "homemade," is to be calibrated, it is preferable if an in-place calibration can be done. Otherwise, care must be taken so that the conduit flow both upstream and downstream of the unit is similar during calibration to that which the meter will experience during actual use. If at all possible the meter should be isolated from other regions of nonuniform flow, such as valves or bends. This is best accomplished by straight sections of conduit on both sides of the unit.[8] Flow straighteners (see Fig. 14-9) are sometimes placed in the conduit to help achieve this goal.

To assist with the following analyses, certain coefficients need to be introduced; the first of these is the contraction coefficient C_c. This is purely a geometric factor which accounts for the inability of the flow to follow an abrupt boundary change. As illustrated in Fig. 14-8, the contraction coeffi-

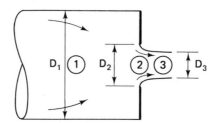

Fig. 14-8.   Contraction coefficient definition.

cient is defined for a flow meter as the ratio of the area of the contracted section to the area of the opening A_3/A_2 or D_3^2/D_2^2. The second coefficient is the velocity coefficient C_v, defined as the ratio of the actual average velocity to the ideal velocity. This coefficient reflects the difference between the actual average velocity at say section 3 of Fig. 14-8, and the ideal or theoretical velocity at that section obtained by ignoring friction. Denoting the actual velocity at 3 by V and the ideal velocity by V_i, the ideal (ignoring both friction and contraction) discharge is $Q_i = V_i A_2$. Taking the actual discharge as Q, a third

---

[8]A straight length of 25 to 30 diameters upstream and 10 diameters downstream is usually adequate, but even more is preferred.

coefficient, the discharge coefficient C_d, may be introduced, defined so that the actual discharge is given by $Q = C_d Q_i$. Note that upon combining the above, the actual discharge also becomes $Q = V A_3 = (C_v V_i)(C_c A_2) = C_v C_c V_i A_2$ and hence $C_d = C_v C_c$.

Orifice Meter

An *orifice meter* consists of a machined plate that is inserted into a usually circular conduit or pipe. A typical plate with orifice diameter D_2 is shown in a pipe of diameter D_1 in Fig. 14-9. Manometer columns are shown at an

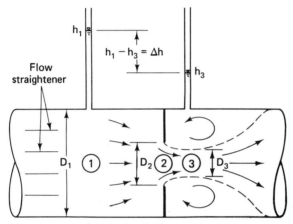

Fig. 14-9. Orifice meter.

upstream section (section 1) and in the contracted section or vena contracta (section 3). The manometer columns indicate the piezometric heads at the respective sections. Relative to the pipe and orifice center line of a horizontal pipe the level in the columns indicates the pressure heads as well. In terms of piezometric heads, the frictionless energy equation may be written between sections 1 and 3 as

$$h_1 + \frac{V_1^2}{2g} = h_3 + \frac{V_3^2}{2g}$$

where V_1 is the average velocity at the approach section and V_3 is the average velocity across the contracted section A_3. Combining this equation with continuity in the form

$$Q = V_1 A_1 = V_3 A_3$$

we get

$$h_1 - h_2 = \frac{V_3^2}{2g} - \frac{V_3^2}{2g}\left(\frac{A_3}{A_1}\right)^2$$

and hence

$$V_3 = \frac{1}{[1 - (A_3/A_1)^2]^{1/2}} \sqrt{2g(h_1 - h_3)} \qquad (14\text{-}5)$$

Introducing the contraction coefficient $C_c = A_3/A_2$, and indicating the velocity as ideal since friction and other losses have been ignored, Eq. 14-5 becomes

$$V_{3\,(\text{ideal})} = \frac{1}{[1 - C_c^2(A_2/A_1)^2]^{1/2}} \sqrt{2g(h_1 - h_3)} \qquad (14\text{-}6)$$

The unknown area A_3 has been eliminated from the area ratio, which now contains only the usually known areas of the orifice and pipe. The contraction effects are now contained in C_c. Although C_c may be easily determined for an orifice when a liquid flow through the orifice discharges into the atmosphere,[9] it is not possible to physically measure the contraction when within the orifice meter.

Introducing the ideal discharge,

$$Q_{(\text{ideal})} = V_{3\,(\text{ideal})}A_2$$

and the actual discharge

$$Q = C_d Q_{\text{ideal}} = C_v C_c Q_{\text{ideal}}$$

we have

$$Q = \frac{C_v C_c A_2}{[1 - C_c^2(A_2/A_1)^2]^{1/2}} \sqrt{2g(h_1 - h_3)} \qquad (14\text{-}7)$$

A meter coefficient defined by

$$C = \frac{C_v C_c}{[1 - C_c^2(A_2/A_1)^2]^{1/2}} \qquad (14\text{-}8)$$

is often introduced, whereupon

$$Q = CA_2\sqrt{2g(h_1 - h_3)} \qquad (14\text{-}9)$$

Recalling that $C_d = C_v C_c$, we see that C is different than a discharge coefficient since C includes geometric terms as well. In spite of not being a "pure" coefficient, the meter coefficient C is the most conveniently determined coefficient. Once the magnitudes of any two of the four coefficients (C_c, C_v, C_d, and C) are found, the other two can immediately be calculated. At low to moderate values of the Reynolds number, the coefficients depend on both orifice geometry and Reynolds number, whereas at higher Reynolds numbers the coefficients depend only on the geometry. For an orifice in which the liquid discharges as a jet the contraction coefficient ranges from a minimum $C_c = 0.61$ up to 1.0 as the ratio A_2/A_1 varies from zero to unity. The C_c for an orifice meter should be roughly similar. The velocity coefficient C_v is usually about 0.98. Typical meter coefficients for high Reynolds numbers are given in Table 14-1. These can only be considered as approximate, as any small change in the geometry of the orifice meter will alter the value of C. For example, even a slight rounding of the otherwise sharp edge at the orifice

---

[9] For example, with a pair of calipers.

Table 14-1   Orifice Meter Coefficient C^a

Orifice/Pipe Diameter Ratio, D_2/D_1	C
0.2	0.6
0.3	0.605
0.4	0.61
0.5	0.62
0.6	0.65
0.7	0.70
0.8	0.77

[a]Data are from various sources included in the references at end of chapter.

will cause an increase in C_c and hence C. Furthermore, in practice the piezometer taps are often not placed as in Fig. 14-9, since the location of the vena contracta will change with the Reynolds number.

Frequently, the piezometer taps are placed immediately before and after the orifice plate. Equation 14-9 remains appropriate, but for a given Q different values of h_1 and h_2 will be observed and the coefficient C will have to be obtained by calibration tests. The Reynolds number for an orifice meter is usually defined in terms of the orifice diameter and velocity. Thus,

$$\text{Re} = \frac{(Q/A_2)D_2}{\nu} = \frac{4Q}{\pi D_2 \nu} \tag{14-10}$$

On this basis, C becomes a constant above $\text{Re} = 10^5$.

The orifice meter is a very reliable flow meter, particularly if well calibrated. It is inexpensive to make and install. It is often, in fact, slid in between two pipe flanges with the piezometer taps placed in the flanges immediately next to the plate. The largest drawback to the orifice meter is its large head loss.

EXAMPLE 14-2

The flow rate of air ($\rho = 0.0023$ slugs/ft³) through an 8-in. pipe is to be measured using an orifice plate with a diameter of 4 in. The piezometer taps are connected to a U-tube manometer, which has a manometer fluid with sp. gr. $= 0.85$. What is the flow rate in ft³/min (cfm) corresponding to a manometer differential of 45 in.? Assuming that $C_v = 0.98$, what is C_c?

SOLUTION:

For $D_2/D_1 = \frac{4}{8} = 0.5$, we get $C = 0.62$ from Table 14-1. Thus, from Eq. 14-9,

$$Q = (0.62)\left(\frac{\pi}{4}\right)\left(\frac{4}{12}\right)^2 \sqrt{(2)(32.2)\left(\frac{45}{12}\right)\left(\frac{1.94}{0.0023}\right)} = 24.4 \text{ cfs}$$

or

$$Q = (24.6)(60) = 1465 \text{ cfm}$$

Note in this case that the differential reading in inches of water must be converted into feet of air. Using Eq. 14-8,

$$0.62 = \frac{0.98C_c}{[1 - C_c^2(\frac{1}{4})^2]^{1/2}}$$

Solving, $C_c = 0.625$.

Flow Nozzle

A *flow nozzle* is shown in Fig. 14-10. Because of the nozzle shape the flow is directed toward the opening in such a way that there is no further contrac-

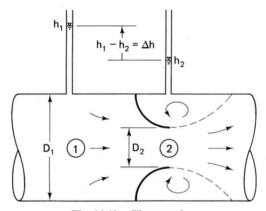

Fig. 14-10. Flow nozzle.

tion downstream of section 2. The analysis of the flow nozzle between sections 1 and 2 is essentially similar to that between sections 1 and 3 of the orifice meter except that now $C_c = 1$. Thus, Eq. 14-7 becomes

$$Q = \frac{C_v A_2}{[1 - (A_2/A_1)^2]^{1/2}} \sqrt{2g(h_i - h_2)} \tag{14-11}$$

Further, we now have $C_d = C_v$, where C_v remains about 0.98, and the meter coefficient becomes

$$C = \frac{C_v}{[1 - (A_2/A_1)^2]^{1/2}} \tag{14-12}$$

Equation 14-9 is also appropriate for the flow nozzle, and it should be noted that if the velocity coefficient is ignored (i.e., $C_v \approx 1.0$), then Eq. 14-9 is wholly theoretical and Eq. 14-12 for the meter coefficient becomes

$$C = \frac{1}{[1 - (A_2/A_1)^2]^{1/2}} \tag{14-13}$$

For values of $\text{Re} = 4Q/\pi D_2 v$ above 10^5, approximate values of C are given in Table 14-2.

Table 14-2   Flow Nozzle Coefficient C

Nozzle Diameter/Pipe Diameter Ratio, D_2/D_1	C (Eq. 14-13)	C Experimental (Typical)
0.3	1.004	0.988
0.4	1.013	0.993
0.5	1.033	1.006
0.6	1.072	1.030
0.7	1.147	1.077

Like the orifice meter, the flow nozzle is relatively inexpensive. It may also be placed between flanges at a pipe joint. The flow nozzle has less head loss than the orifice meter (although there remains a zone of separation and eddy losses behind the nozzle). Unless a high degree of accuracy is required, the flow nozzle may be used without calibration. This is not true for the orifice meter unless a very standard unit is used.

Venturi Meter

The *venturi meter* (Fig. 14-11) has an approach section somewhat similar to that of the flow nozzle, but the nozzle portion now forms a throat that is

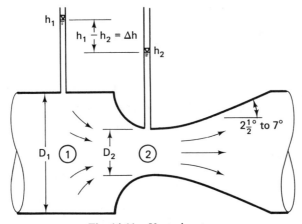

Fig. 14-11.   Venturi meter.

followed by a long diffusing section. The analysis of the venturi meter is identical to that of the flow nozzle. The contraction coefficient is again unity, and Eqs. 14-9, 14-11, and 14-12 are immediately applicable. If C_v is assumed equal to 1, Eq. 14-13 also gives the meter coefficient C. For throat Reynolds numbers $Re = V_2 D_2/v$ above 10^5, the error in assuming $C_v = 1$ is usually less than 2%. In fact, fair accuracy may be obtained by assuming C_v values of 0.99 for large meters and 0.98 for moderate-size units. The main advantage of the venturi meter over the flow nozzle is that head loss through the meter is nearly eliminated. This can only be achieved by keeping the flare of the diffuser section quite low, as indicated by the half-angle of $2\frac{1}{2}°$ to $7°$ in Fig. 14-11. This requires a lengthy and hence relatively expensive meter.

EXAMPLE 14-3

A commercial venturi meter is placed in a vertical pipe as shown in Fig. 14-12. Pressure gages are located at sections 1 and 2 and the pipe and throat diameters are as indicated. Assume that $C_v = 0.98$ and calculate the downward discharge of water corresponding to pressures $p_1 = 65$ kN/m² and $p_2 = 40$ kN/m².

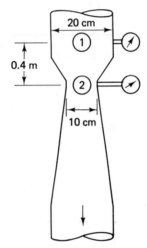

Fig. 14-12. Venturi meter in vertical line.

SOLUTION:

The discharge as given by Eq. 14-9 is

$$Q = CA_2\left[2g\left(y_1 + \frac{p_1}{\gamma} - y_2 - \frac{p_2}{\gamma}\right)\right]^{1/2}$$

where

$$C = \frac{0.98}{[1 - (0.1/0.2)^4]^{1/2}} = 1.012$$

according to Eq. 14-12. Since $y_1 - y_2 = 0.4$ m and $p_1 - p_2 = 25$ kN/m², we have

$$Q = (1.012)\left(\frac{\pi}{4}\right)(0.1)^2\left[(2)(9.81)\left(0.4 + \frac{25,000}{9800}\right)\right]^{1/2}$$

$$= 0.0605 \text{ m}^3/\text{s}$$

Elbow Meter

Flow passing through a bend or elbow experiences a centrifugal effect as its direction is changed. This results in an increase in piezometric head at the outside of the bend and a decrease at the inside. Piezometer taps at these two points (see Fig. 14-13) may be instrumented to measure the difference in

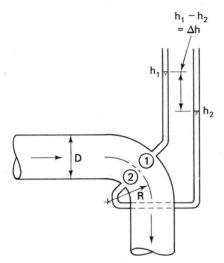

Fig. 14-13. Elbow meter.

piezometric head, $h_1 - h_2$. Replacing A_2 by the cross-sectional area A of the pipe, Eq. 14-9 again gives the relationship between the discharge and the manometer (or pressure gage) differential:

$$Q = CA\sqrt{2g(h_1 - h_2)} \qquad (14\text{-}14)$$

The meter coefficient C is best obtained by calibration. If this is not possible, Lansford[10] offered the following equation as accurate to within 10% at moderate to high Reynolds numbers provided the elbow is preceded by a straight length of 25 diameters and followed by a 10-diameter straight section:

$$C = \sqrt{\frac{R}{2D}} \qquad (14\text{-}15)$$

Here R is the centerline radius of the elbow and D is the pipe diameter.

Once calibrated, the elbow meter is very accurate. It is easily installed on an elbow in an existing system. It has the additional advantage that it causes no additional head loss beyond that of the elbow itself.

[10]W. M. Lansford, "The Use of an Elbow on a Pipe Line for Determining the Flow in the Pipe," *Univ. Illinois Eng. Exp. Sta. Bull. 289*, December 1936.

Open-Channel Measurement: Weirs

It is often very difficult to obtain an accurate measurement of the discharge in an open channel. In the laboratory the flow rate is often measured in a closed conduit before it is released into an open channel or flume. If this is not possible, a weir, usually one of the types described in this section, is employed. In large open channels and rivers, stream gaging is most commonly used as described previously. However, a very quick, but rough estimate may be obtained by timing an object floating on the surface as it traverses a given distance. The average velocity will be about 0.8 of this surface velocity. If the cross-sectional area can be estimated, the product of this area and the average velocity will be the discharge.

A weir is a device placed across an open channel such that as the liquid (usually water) passes over it (or occasionally through it), there is a rapid change in the surface elevation. Although there are occasions where the difference in water level is related to the discharge and hence used, most frequently the discharge is related to the depth upstream of the weir. This involves the matter of "control" introduced in Chapter 10. Essentially, if in passing the weir, the water surface drops sufficiently that the critical depth is reached, the discharge is dependent only on the upstream depth. If the downstream depth is too great, this will not occur and the weir is said to be "drowned" or "submerged." It is still possible to use a drowned weir to determine the discharge, but this case will not be pursued further here.

To obtain an accurate measurement of the upstream depth, care should be taken that the approach flow is as straight and uniform as possible with no waves or other disturbances. Sometimes screens or straighteners will be required upstream. The upstream depth is often measured directly with a point or hook gage. Sometimes, particularly if the surface is subject to waves, a stilling well is connected to the main channel and the depth determined from measurements in it. The point of measurement should be immediately upstream of the nonuniform region created by the weir. If the measurement is obtained too far upstream, the depth will be overestimated because of channel friction between the point of measurement and the weir.

Various types of gates which are used to regulate the discharge in an open channel may also be used to measure the discharge. Although the flow is usually under the gate rather than over it, their basic behavior is similar to that of a weir. The references at the ends of both Chapters 10 and 14 should be consulted for further details.

It should be mentioned that the term "weir" often implies a sharp edge or crest. This will usually be the case, but not always. Note also that weirs were introduced previously, in Chapters 5, 6, and 12, through examples or problems.

Rectangular Weir

A *rectangular weir* that extends across the entire width of the channel is shown in Fig. 14-14.[11] The flow is nearly two-dimensional except for occasional vortexes which form near the upstream face of the weir in the corners. The flow details are shown in Fig. 14-14. The region below the nappe must be maintained at atmospheric pressure by providing ventilation of the region.

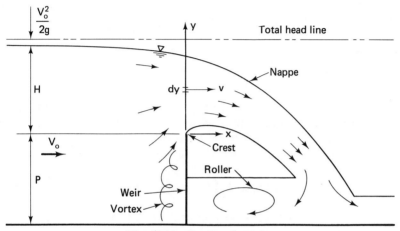

Fig. 14-14. Rectangular weir.

Unventilated, the air will be removed by the flow and the region will fill (or nearly fill) with water at reduced pressure. This, in effect, pulls the head down so that a significantly lower head will be observed for the same discharge.

A weir equation may be derived using Fig. 14-14. For a crest length L a differential area $L\,dy$ may be identified. Indicating the velocity through this area as v, the differential discharge is $dQ = vL\,dy$. The frictionless energy equation may be written between the uniform region and the differential area. For a datum at the crest elevation, we have

$$H + \frac{V_0^2}{2g} = y + \frac{v^2}{2g}$$

whereupon

$$v = \sqrt{2g\left[(H - y) + \frac{V_0^2}{2g}\right]} \tag{14-16}$$

In addition to the assumption of frictionless, two-dimensional flow, it has

---

[11] This section should be compared with the ideal solution given in Section 12-2.

also been assumed that the pressure is zero across the nappe. We may substitute this velocity into the differential discharge and integrate over the nappe (i.e., from $y = 0$ to $y = H$). This will further assume that the velocity is everywhere horizontal and that there is no contraction of the flow (contrary to the actual situation as depicted in Fig. 14-14). Proceeding, the discharge is

$$Q = L \int_0^H v \, dy$$

$$= L\sqrt{2g} \int_0^H \sqrt{(H - y) + \frac{V_0^2}{2g}} \, dy$$

and hence

$$Q = \tfrac{2}{3}L\sqrt{2g}\left[\left(H + \frac{V_0^2}{2g}\right)^{3/2} - \left(\frac{V_0^2}{2g}\right)^{3/2}\right] \tag{14-17}$$

It is now necessary to add a contraction coefficient C_c to account for the reduced cross-sectional area and a velocity coefficient C_v to allow for the reduction in velocity due to friction. Combining these coefficients as before into a discharge coefficient $C_d = C_c C_v$, the weir discharge equation becomes

$$Q = C_d(\tfrac{2}{3})\sqrt{2g}L\left[\left(H + \frac{V_0^2}{2g}\right)^{3/2} - \left(\frac{V_0^2}{2g}\right)^{3/2}\right] \tag{14-18}$$

This is cumbersome to use, as the approach velocity V_0 is dependent on the unknown discharge requiring a trial-and-error solution. Often, however, the approach velocity is sufficiently small that it may be neglected[12] and Eq. 14-18 reduces to the much simpler

$$Q = C_d(\tfrac{2}{3})\sqrt{2g}LH^{3/2} \tag{14-19}$$

A dimensional analysis of the weir problem[13] indicates that C_d must also be dependent on other variables. These would include the additional geometric parameter H/P, the Reynolds number, and the Weber number,

$$C_d = C_d\left(\frac{H}{P}, \text{Re}, \text{We}\right) \tag{14-20}$$

In general, H/P would be the most significant, as it will directly affect the shape of the nappe and hence the contraction coefficient. The Reynolds number will generally have a significant effect only if a viscous liquid is being measured, whereas the Weber number will become important only at very low heads, where surface tension may determine whether the nappe will adhere to the crest or spring free as it does under larger heads.

Attempts have been made to incorporate the factors in Eq. 14-20, but the

[12]This becomes the case for $P \gg H$.
[13]See Probs. 6-8 through 6-10.

most widely used expression is the purely empirical equation developed by Rehbock:[14]

$$C_d = 0.605 + \frac{1}{305H} + 0.08\frac{H}{P} \tag{14-21}$$

If $H/P < 0.4$, an approximate constant $C_d = 0.62$ is often assumed. This value is sometimes combined with the numerical values and acceleration of gravity in Eqs. 14-18 and 14-19 to give a weir coefficient $C_w = (0.62)(\frac{2}{3})\sqrt{2g}$. Then Eq. 14-18 becomes

$$Q = C_w L\left[\left(H + \frac{V_0^2}{2g}\right)^{3/2} - \left(\frac{V_0^2}{2g}\right)^{3/2}\right] \tag{14-22}$$

while Eq. 14-19 reduces to

$$Q = C_w LH^{3/2} \tag{14-23}$$

For $C_d = 0.62$, $C_w = 3.33$ in English units, and $C_w = 1.84$ in SI units.

If the crest of the rectangular weir does not extend the full width of the channel, the flow will not be completely two-dimensional. Although the side view will continue to look much as in Fig. 14-14, an end view would appear as in Fig. 14-15. In addition to the vertical contraction apparent in Fig.

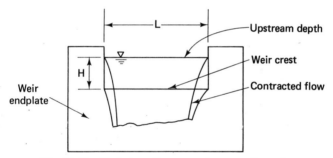

Fig. 14-15.   End view of contracted rectangular weir.

14-14, we now have horizontal contraction as well due to the end plate.[15] A method was developed experimentally by Francis[16] to account for the side contractions. This procedure consists of replacing the crest length L in Eqs. 14-18, 14-19, 14-22, and 14-23 by an effective crest length L' defined by

$$L' = L - (0.1)nH \tag{14-24}$$

[14]Theodor Rehbock, Discussion of "Precise Measurements" by E.W. Schoder and K.B. Turner, trans. Am. Soc. Civil Engrs., vol. 93 (1929), p. 1143.

[15]In the early work this was considered to be the standard weir. The previous two-dimensional weir was treated as a special case in which the side contractions had been "suppressed"; hence, it was referred to as a suppressed weir.

[16]James Francis, *Lowell Hydraulic Experiments*, 5th ed. (Princeton, N.J.: Van Nostrand, 1909).

where L and H are as shown on Fig. 14-15 and n is the number of side contractions, two as shown on Fig. 14-15, but occasionally one. Only a limited range of the geometric parameters was involved in the experimental study, and some care must be exercised in the use of Eq. 14-24. As with all weirs, the best results will be obtained if an individual calibration test is performed.

Triangular or V-Notch Weir

The weir plate for a *triangular weir* is shown in Fig. 14-16. Although a vertex angle of 90° is most often used, a general notch angle θ is shown. The

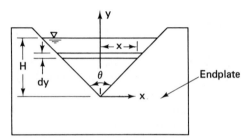

Fig. 14-16.   Triangular weir.

primary advantage of this weir occurs at very low flow rates, where an accurate head H may still be measured. This is in contrast to the very small and hence hard-to-measure H that would occur above the crest of the rectangular weir at low discharges.

Ignoring the approach velocity, but otherwise using the same approach as that used for the rectangular weir, the discharge through the differential area $2x\,dy$ is

$$dQ = \sqrt{2g(H - y)}\,2x\,dy$$

The distance x may be expressed by $x = y \tan(\theta/2)$. Thus, the discharge will be given by

$$Q = C_d 2\sqrt{2g} \tan\left(\frac{\theta}{2}\right) \int_0^H \sqrt{H - y}\, y\, dy$$

where C_d has again been included to account for the contraction and friction. Integrating, we obtain

$$Q = C_d\left(\tfrac{8}{15}\right)\sqrt{2g} \tan\left(\frac{\theta}{2}\right) H^{5/2} \qquad (14\text{-}25)$$

For a given triangular weir (with given value of θ) a dimensional weir coefficient can be introduced such that $C_w = C_d\left(\tfrac{8}{15}\right)\sqrt{2g} \tan(\theta/2)$, and hence

$$Q = C_w H^{5/2} \qquad (14\text{-}26)$$

Numerous tests have been run to evaluate C_d. However, for $\theta = 90°$, C_d is usually about 0.585, which leads to $C_w = 2.50$ in English units and 1.38

in SI units. If a calibration test is performed on an individual weir, Eq. 14-26 will be the more convenient equation.

There are many other weir shapes that have been extensively studied. In addition, virtually any shape weir suited to a particular purpose may be used if properly calibrated. For example, the modified V-notch shown in Fig. 14-17 is well suited (after calibration) to the measurement of both very small and relatively large discharges.

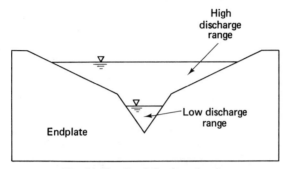

Fig. 14-17. Specially shaped weir.

EXAMPLE 14-4

A triangular weir with a notch angle of 70° has a head $H = 0.2$ m when the discharge is $Q = 0.018$ m³/s. Determine the discharge coefficient C_d and the weir coefficient C_w.

SOLUTION:

Using Eq. 14-26, we obtain

$$C_w = \frac{Q}{H^{5/2}} = \frac{0.018}{(0.2)^{5/2}} = 1.006$$

Thus,

$$C_d = \frac{C_w}{(8/15)\sqrt{2g}\,\tan{(\theta/2)}} = \frac{1.006}{(8/15)\sqrt{(2)(9.81)}\,\tan 35°}$$
$$= 0.608$$

PROBLEMS

Sec. 14-1

14-1. If a point gage reads 1.171 ft when the point rests on the bed of an open-channel flow, what will it read at the surface if the depth is 0.251 ft?

14-2. A common device for measuring the diameter of a jet of liquid is the combined point and hook gage. The one shown has a gap of 0.2 ft between the points. When the upper point is lowered until it makes contact with the top of the jet, the vernier is found to read 1.742 ft. When the lower point is raised until it touches the bottom of the jet, the vernier reads 1.805 ft. What is the diameter of the jet?

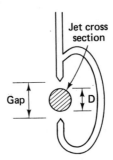

14-3. The combined point and hook gage illustrated in Prob. 14-2 has a gap of 0.08 m. If the vernier reading at the upper surface of a jet is 0.8644 m and the reading at the lower surface is 0.8978 m, determine the jet diameter.

14-4. If a point gage reads 0.6922 m when the pointer touches the surface of an open-channel flow and 0.5468 m when the pointer touches the bottom of the channel, what is the depth?

Sec. 14-2

Problems appropriate to this section may be found in Chapters 2, 4, and elsewhere.

Sec. 14-3

14-5. A Pitot tube placed into a stream of water indicates a pressure difference of 18 psi. What is the velocity?

14-6. What is the velocity if the Pitot tube of Prob. 14-5 reads 50 kN/m²?

14-7. A Pitot tube used to measure the velocity of water is connected to two manometer columns which indicate a differential head of 6 ft of water. What is the velocity?

14-8. What pressure difference in psi would be indicated by an air velocity of 85 ft/s? Assume air at 80°F and 14.2 psia.

14-9. If pressure gages connected to a Pitot tube read −1.31 and 15.2 psi, respectively, what velocity of water do they indicate?

14-10. A differential manometer indicates a differential of 5 in. of water when connected to a Pitot tube. What is the air velocity? Assume that $\rho_{air} = 0.0023$ slugs/ft³.

14-11. A differential manometer uses an indicator fluid with sp. gr = 2.4. If the manometer has a reading of 2.74 cm when connected to a Pitot tube in an air flow, what is the air velocity? Assume air at 20°C and 90 kN/m²(abs).

14-12. A Pitot tube placed in an airflow with a known velocity of 35 m/s is connected to a differential manometer which indicates a differential of 79 mm of water. Assume air at 98 kN/m²(abs) and 10°C. What is the coefficient of the Pitot tube?

14-13. If a stopwatch can be used with a precision of ± 0.2 s, determine the time period required if the timing error is to be less than (a) 1%; (b) 0.5%.

14-14. The relationship between water velocity and rate of rotation of a current meter may be expressed approximately by $V = a + bN$. For V in ft/s and N in rev/s, a Price meter has constants $a = 0.1$ and $b = 2.2$. Determine the values of the constants in SI units with V in m/s and N in rev/s.

14-15. Using the data of Fig. 14-5, develop and plot a graph of $(dE/E)/(d\bar{u}/\bar{u})$ versus the velocity $\bar{u}$. What is the mean velocity and turbulence intensity corresponding to a voltage $E = 8.68$ V and rms voltage $E' = 0.20$ V if $E_0 = 3.78$ V?

Sec. 14-4

14-16. A Price current meter is used to determine the discharge in a river with cross section given in Fig. 14-7. The meter equation is $V = 2.2N + 0.15$ with V in ft/s and N in rev/s. At each position of the current meter the number of revolutions during a 40-s interval was counted. This information is tabulated below. What is the discharge?

Section	Revolutions	Section	Revolutions
1	24	8A	137
2A	39	B	105
B	18	9A	150
3A	48	B	121
B	27	10A	152
4A	66	B	122
B	37	11A	140
5A	88	B	110
B	51	12A	92
6A	110	B	47
B	71	13	63
7A	125		
B	90		

14-17. A circular tank used for a volumetric discharge measurement is 1.5 m in diameter. During a time interval of 26.2 s the depth increases by 2.74 m. What is the flow rate? If the timing device has an accuracy of ± 0.2 s, what is the magnitude of the possible error in discharge?

14-18. A rectangular tank used for a volumetric discharge measurement is 6 ft by 10 ft in plan view. What discharge is indicated if the depth increases from 0.75 ft to 7.36 ft during a time interval of 40 s?

14-19. What depth circular tank with diameter of 1 m is required to permit a timing interval of 40 s when filling at the rate of 0.071 m³/s?

14-20. A tank is placed on a scale to gravimetrically determine the discharge of water into it. If a weight of 20 kN enters the tank during 40 s, what is the discharge in ℓ/min? What volume of water is measured?

14-21. In obtaining the discharge gravimetrically, the timing interval commences as the scale reads 570 lb and terminates 29.8 s later when the scale reads 4000 lb. What is the discharge in lb/s? cfs?

14-22. Water discharges into the atmosphere from an orifice such as shown in Fig. 14-8 with $D_1 = 4$ in. and $D_2 = 2$ in. The pressure at section 1 is 1.50 psi. Measurement of the jet at the vena contracta gives $D_3 = 0.131$ ft. Determine C_c. Determine the discharge assuming $C_v = 1.00$. If $C_v = 0.98$, what is the value of (a) C_d; (b) of Q?

14-23. An orifice meter with a 5-cm-diameter orifice is placed in a 7-cm pipe. If manometer columns are connected as in Fig. 14-9, what differential will be indicated for a water discharge of 0.025 m³/s?

14-24. The meter of Prob. 14-23 is connected to a U-tube manometer in which the manometer fluid is mercury. All connecting tubing is filled with water. What mercury differential will indicate the water discharge of 0.025 m³/s?

14-25. A 2-in. pipe has an orifice plate with a $\frac{3}{4}$-in.-diameter orifice. What is the water discharge if pressure gages upstream and downstream of the orifice read 60 psi and 20 psi, respectively?

14-26. A calibration test of an orifice meter plots as a straight line on log-log graph paper. The equation of this line is $Q = 0.28\Delta h^{0.5}$. If the pipe diameter is 4 in. and the orifice diameter is 3 in., what is the meter coefficient C?

14-27. A flow nozzle with a diameter of 4 cm is placed in a 10-cm pipe. For a differential head of 1 m, what is the water discharge if (a) $C_v = 1.0$; (b) the experimental value of C is used?

14-28. What is the magnitude of C_v for each of the flow nozzle/diameter ratios in Table 14-2?

14-29. If the venturi meter of Example 14-3 is inverted to measure an upward flow of water, determine the discharge associated with $p_1 = 65$ kN/m² and $p_2 = 40$ kN/m². Point 2 is now 0.4 m above point 1.

14-30. Calculate the velocity coefficient C_v for the venturi meter of Fig. 14-12 if a differential of 14 in. occurs when $Q = 3.3$ cfs. $D_1 = 12$ in and $D_2 = 8$ in.

14-31. Determine the relationship between Q and Δh in an elbow meter such as Fig. 14-13 if the pipe diameter is 4 in. and the bend radius is 6 in.

14-32. Determine the meter coefficient C for an elbow meter in an 8-in.-diameter pipe if a discharge of 5.2 cfs corresponds to a meter differential of 6.3 ft. If the pipe bend has a radius of 10 in., what is the error in using Eq. 14-15?

14-33. Calculate the discharge per unit width over a 2-ft-high rectangular weir if the head is (a) 0.02 ft; (b) 0.2 ft; (c) 2 ft. Use the velocity of approach and Eq. 14-21.

14-34. What is the error in each part of Prob. 14-33 if you assume that $C_d = 0.62$?

14-35. What is the error in each part of Prob. 14-33 if the velocity of approach is ignored?

14-36. Assuming that the value of 0.605 in Eq. 14-21 is a pure constant, convert Eq. 14-21 into SI units.

14-37. What is the discharge past a 0.8-m-high by 2-m-long rectangular weir if the upstream depth is 1.4 m?

14-38. If the weir in Prob. 14-33 is a contracted weir with a crest length of 1 ft, calculate the discharge in parts (a) and (b).

14-39. If a triangular weir has a weir coefficient $C_w = 2.5$, what head will be expected for a discharge of 0.4 cfs?

14-40. Calculate the discharge past a 90° V-notch weir if the head is 0.08 m.

14-41. If a V-notch weir has a discharge of 0.0036 m³/s at a head of 0.1 m, what discharge will be expected at a head of 0.3 m?

REFERENCES

BINDER, R. C., "Flow Measurement," Section 14 in *Handbook of Fluid Dynamics*, V. L. Streeter (ed.), New York: McGraw-Hill, 1961.

BRADSHAW, P., *Experimental Fluid Mechanics*. New York: Macmillan, 1964.

BRATER, E. F., and H. W. KING, *Handbook of Hydraulics*, 6th ed. New York: McGraw-Hill, 1976.

CHOW, VEN TE, *Open Channel Hydraulics*. New York: McGraw-Hill, 1959.

HENDERSON, F. M., *Open Channel Flow*. New York: Macmillan, 1966.

HOWE, J. W., "Flow Measurement," Chapter 3 in *Engineering Hydraulics*, H. Rouse (ed.). New York: Wiley, 1950.

Appendices

APPENDIX A NOTATION, DIMENSIONS, AND FLUID PROPERTIES

Table A-1 Partial List of Symbols

Symbol	Quantity	Usual Units		Dimensions	
		English	SI	F-L-T	M-L-T
a	Acceleration, acceleration component	ft/s^2	m/s^2	LT^{-2}	LT^{-2}
A	Area	ft^2	m^2	L^2	L^2
B	Distance	ft	m	L	L
C	Constant, cavitation number				
C	Chezy coefficient	ft$^{1/2}$/s	m$^{1/2}$/s	$L^{1/2}T^{-1}$	$L^{1/2}T^{-1}$
C	Meter coefficient				
C_c	Contraction coefficient				
C_d	Coefficient of discharge				
C_D	Coefficient of drag				
C_f	Coefficient of surface drag				
c_f	Local coefficient of drag				
C_H	Hazen–William coefficient				
C_L	Loss coefficient, coefficient of lift				
C_v	Velocity coefficient				

| Symbol | Quantity | Usual Units | | Dimensions | |
		English	SI	F-L-T	M-L-T
C_w	Weir coefficient				
D, d	Diameter	ft	m	L	L
E	Modulus of compressibility	psi	N/m^2	FL^{-2}	$ML^{-1}T^{-2}$
Eu	Euler number				
F	Force, force dimension	lb	N	F	MLT^{-2}
f	Frequency	cycles/s	cycles/s	T^{-1}	T^{-1}
f	Resistance coefficient				
Fr	Froude number				
G	Mass discharge	slugs/s	kg/s	FTL^{-1}	MT^{-1}
g	Acceleration of gravity	ft/s^2	m/s^2	LT^{-2}	LT^{-2}
H	Head, total head	ft	m	L	L
h	Distance, piezometric head	ft	m	L	L
h	Enthalpy	ft	m	L	L
$\bar{h}$	Vertical distance to centroid	ft	m	L	L
h_ℓ	Head loss due to friction	ft	m	L	L
I	Moment of inertia	ft^4	m^4	L^4	L^4
k	Specific heat ratio				
k	Absolute roughness	ft	m	L	L
L	Length, length dimension	ft	m	L	L
l	Mixing length	ft	m	L	L
M	Mass, mass dimension	slug	kg	FT^2L^{-1}	M
Ma	Mach number				
N	Rotational speed	rev/s or rpm	rev/s or rpm	T^{-1}	T^{-1}
n	Manning coefficient	$ft^{1/6}$	$m^{1/6}$	$L^{1/6}$	$L^{1/6}$
P	Power	ft-lb/s	m·N/s	FLT^{-1}	ML^2T^{-3}
P	Wetted perimeter	ft	m	L	L
p	Pressure	psi or psf	N/m^2	FL^{-2}	$ML^{-1}T^{-2}$
p_v	Vapor pressure	psi	N/m^2	FL^{-2}	$ML^{-1}T^{-2}$
Q	Discharge	cfs	m^3/s	L^3T^{-1}	L^3T^{-1}
q	Discharge per unit width	cfs/ft	$m^3/s/m$	L^2T^{-1}	L^2T^{-1}
R	Gas constant	$ft/^\circ R$	$m/^\circ K$		
R	Radius, hydraulic radius	ft	m	L	L
r	Radius	ft	m	L	L
Re	Reynolds number				
S	Slope				
T	Time, time dimension	s	s	T	T
T	Temperature	$^\circ F$ or $^\circ R$	$^\circ C$ or $^\circ K$		
t	Time	s	s	T	T
u	Velocity, velocity component	ft/s	m/s	LT^{-1}	LT^{-1}
u_*	Shear velocity	ft/s	m/s	LT^{-1}	LT^{-1}
V	Velocity, average velocity	ft/s	m/s	LT^{-1}	LT^{-1}
v	Velocity, velocity component	ft/s	m/s	LT^{-1}	LT^{-1}

		Usual Units		Dimensions	
Symbol	Quantity	English	SI	F-L-T	M-L-T
Ψ	Volume	ft³	m³	L^3	L^3
W	Weight	lb	N	F	MLT^{-2}
w	Velocity component	ft/s	m/s	LT^{-1}	LT^{-1}
We	Weber number				
x	Distance	ft	m	L	L
y	Distance, depth	ft	m	L	L
$\bar{y}$	Distance to centroid	ft	m	L	L
y_n	Normal depth	ft	m	L	L
y_p	Distance to center of pressure	ft	m	L	L
α (alpha)	Angle, angle of attack	degrees	degrees		
α	Kinetic-energy correction factor				
α	Angle of heel	degrees	degrees		
β (beta)	Angle	degrees	degrees		
β	Momentum correction factor				
γ (gamma)	Angle	degrees	degrees		
γ	Specific weight	lb/ft³	N/m³	FL^{-3}	$ML^{-2}T^{-2}$
δ (delta)	Boundary layer thickness	ft	m	L	L
δ'	Laminar sublayer thickness	ft	m	L	L
ϵ (epsilon)	Kinematic eddy viscosity	ft²/s	m²/s	L^2T^{-1}	L^2T^{-1}
η (eta)	Vertical direction	ft	m	L	L
η	Eddy viscosity	lb-s/ft²	N·s/m²	FTL^{-2}	$ML^{-1}T^{-1}$
θ (theta)	Angle	degrees	degrees		
κ (kappa)	von Kármán universal constant				
μ (mu)	Dynamic viscosity	lb-s/ft²	N·s/m²	FTL^{-2}	$ML^{-1}T^{-1}$
ν (nu)	Kinematic viscosity	ft²/s	m²/s	L^2T^{-1}	L^2T^{-1}
π (pi)	Dimensionless term, constant				
ρ (rho)	Density	slugs/ft³	kg/m³	FT^2L^{-4}	ML^{-3}
σ (sigma)	Surface tension	lb/ft	N/m	FL^{-1}	MT^{-2}
τ (tau)	Shear stress	lb/ft²	N/m²	FL^{-2}	$ML^{-1}T^{-2}$
ω (omega)	Angular velocity	rad/s	rad/s	T^{-1}	T^{-1}

Table A-II Properties of Common Liquids at Atmospheric Pressure and Approximately 60 to 70°F (16 to 21°C)

Liquid	Specific Weight, γ		Density, ρ		Surface Tension,[a] σ		Vapor Pressure, p_v	
	lb/ft³	N/m³	slugs/ft³	kg/m³	lb/ft	N/m	psia	kN/m²
Alcohol, ethyl	49.3	7,744	1.53	789	0.0015	0.022	—	—
Benzene	56.2	8,828	1.75	902	0.0020	0.029	1.50	10.3
Carbon tetrachloride	99.5	15,629	3.09	1,593	0.0018	0.026	12.50	86.2
Gasoline	42.4	6,660	1.32	680	—	—	—	—
Glycerin	78.6	12,346	2.44	1,258	0.0043	0.063	2×10^{-6}	1.4×10^{-5}
Kerosene	50.5	7,933	1.57	809	0.0017	0.025	—	—
Mercury	845.5	132,800	26.29	13,550	0.032	0.467	2.31×10^{-5}	1.59×10^{-4}
SAE 10 oil	57.4	9,016	1.78	917	0.0025	0.036	—	—
SAE 30 oil	57.4	9,016	1.78	917	0.0024	0.035	—	—
Turpentine	54.3	8,529	1.69	871	0.0018	0.026	7.7×10^{-3}	5.31×10^{-2}
Water	62.4	9,790	1.94	998	0.0050	0.073	0.34	2.34

[a]In contact with air.

Table A-III Properties of Common Gases at Atmospheric Pressure and 68°F (20°C)

Gas	Chemical Formula	Specific Weight, γ		Density, ρ		Gas Constant, R		Adiabatic Constant, k
		lb/ft³	N/m³	slugs/ft³	kg/m³	ft/°R	m/°K	
Air	—	0.0753	11.8	0.00234	1.206	53.3	29.2	1.40
Ammonia	NH_3	0.0448	7.04	0.00139	0.716	89.5	49.1	1.32
Carbon dioxide	CO_2	0.115	18.1	0.00357	1.840	34.9	19.1	1.29
Helium	He	0.0104	1.63	0.000323	0.166	386.	212.	1.66
Hydrogen	H_2	0.00522	0.820	0.000162	0.0835	767.	421.	1.40
Methane	CH_4	0.0416	6.53	0.00129	0.665	96.4	52.9	1.32
Nitrogen	N_2	0.0726	11.4	0.00225	1.160	55.2	30.3	1.40
Oxygen	O_2	0.0830	13.0	0.00258	1.330	48.3	26.5	1.40
Sulfur dioxide	SO_2	0.170	26.7	0.00528	2.721	23.6	12.9	1.26

Table A-IV Properties of Air at Atmospheric Pressure

Tempera-ture (°F)	Specific Weight, $\gamma \times 10^2$ (lb/ft³)	Density, $\rho \times 10^3$ (slugs/ft³)	Dynamic Viscosity, $\mu \times 10^7$ (lb-s/ft²)	Kinematic Viscosity, $\nu \times 10^4$ (ft²/s)	Tempera-ture (°C)	Specific Weight, γ (N/m³)	Density, ρ (kg/m³)
0	8.62	2.68	3.38	1.26	0	12.68	1.293
10	8.46	2.63	3.45	1.31	5	12.46	1.270
20	8.27	2.57	3.50	1.36	10	12.24	1.247
30	8.11	2.52	3.58	1.42	15	12.02	1.226
40	7.94	2.47	3.62	1.46	20	11.82	1.205
50	7.79	2.42	3.68	1.52	25	11.62	1.184
60	7.63	2.37	3.74	1.58	30	11.43	1.165
70	7.50	2.33	3.82	1.64	35	11.24	1.146
80	7.35	2.28	3.85	1.69	40	11.06	1.128
90	7.23	2.24	3.90	1.74	50	10.72	1.093
100	7.09	2.20	3.96	1.80	60	10.40	1.060
120	6.84	2.15	4.07	1.89	70	10.10	1.029
140	6.63	2.06	4.14	2.01	80	9.81	1.000
160	6.41	1.99	4.22	2.12	90	9.54	0.972
180	6.21	1.93	4.34	2.25	100	9.28	0.946
200	6.02	1.87	4.49	2.40			

Temperature (°F)	Specific Weight, γ (lb/ft³)	Density, ρ (slugs/ft³)	Dynamic Viscosity, $\mu \times 10^5$ (lb-s/ft²)	Kinematic Viscosity, $\nu \times 10^5$ (ft²/s)	Surface Tension, $\sigma \times 10^2$ (lb/ft)	Vapor Pressure, p_v (psia)	Modulus of Compressibility, $E \times 10^{-5}$ (psi)
32	62.42	1.940	3.746	1.931	0.518	0.087	2.93
40	62.43	1.940	3.229	1.664	0.514	0.12	2.94
50	62.41	1.940	2.735	1.410	0.509	0.18	3.05
60	62.37	1.938	2.359	1.217	0.504	0.26	3.11
70	62.30	1.936	2.050	1.059	0.500	0.36	3.20
80	62.22	1.934	1.799	0.930	0.492	0.51	3.22
90	62.11	1.931	1.595	0.826	0.486	0.70	3.23
100	62.00	1.927	1.424	0.739	0.480	0.96	3.27
110	61.86	1.923	1.284	0.667	0.473	1.28	3.31
120	61.71	1.918	1.168	0.609	0.465	1.69	3.33
130	61.55	1.913	1.069	0.558	0.460	2.22	3.34
140	61.38	1.908	0.981	0.514	0.454	2.89	3.30
150	61.20	1.902	0.905	0.476	0.447	3.72	3.28
160	61.00	1.896	0.838	0.442	0.441	4.75	3.26
170	60.80	1.890	0.780	0.413	0.433	5.99	3.22
180	60.58	1.883	0.726	0.385	0.426	7.51	3.18
190	60.36	1.876	0.678	0.362	0.419	9.34	3.13
200	60.12	1.868	0.637	0.341	0.412	11.52	3.08
212	59.83	1.860	0.593	0.319	0.404	14.69	3.00

Table A-V (Continued)   Properties of Water at Atmospheric Pressure (SI units)

Temperature ($°C$)	Specific Weight, γ (N/m^3)	Density, ρ (kg/m^3)	Dynamic Viscosity, $\mu \times 10^3$ ($N \cdot s/m^2$)	Kinematic Viscosity, $\nu \times 10^6$ (m^2/s)	Surface Tension, $\sigma \times 10^2$ (N/m)	Vapor Pressure, p_v (kN/m^2)	Modulus of Compressibility, $E \times 10^{-9}$ (N/m^2)
0	9805	999.8	1.794	1.794	7.62	0.61	2.02
5	9806	1000.0	1.519	1.519	7.54	0.87	2.06
10	9802	999.7	1.308	1.308	7.48	1.23	2.11
15	9797	999.1	1.140	1.141	7.41	1.70	2.14
20	9786	998.2	1.005	1.007	7.36	2.34	2.20
25	9777	997.1	0.894	0.897	7.26	3.17	2.22
30	9762	995.7	0.801	0.804	7.18	4.24	2.23
35	9747	994.1	0.723	0.727	7.10	5.61	2.24
40	9730	992.2	0.656	0.661	7.01	7.38	2.27
45	9711	990.2	0.599	0.605	6.92	9.55	2.29
50	9689	988.1	0.549	0.556	6.82	12.33	2.30
55	9665	985.7	0.506	0.513	6.74	15.78	2.31
60	9642	983.2	0.469	0.477	6.68	19.92	2.28
65	9616	980.6	0.436	0.444	6.58	25.02	2.26
70	9588	977.8	0.406	0.415	6.50	31.16	2.25
75	9560	974.9	0.380	0.390	6.40	38.57	2.23
80	9528	971.8	0.357	0.367	6.30	47.34	2.21
85	9497	968.6	0.336	0.347	6.20	57.83	2.17
90	9473	965.3	0.317	0.328	6.12	70.10	2.16
95	9431	961.9	0.299	0.311	6.02	84.36	2.11
100	9398	958.4	0.284	0.296	5.94	101.33	2.07

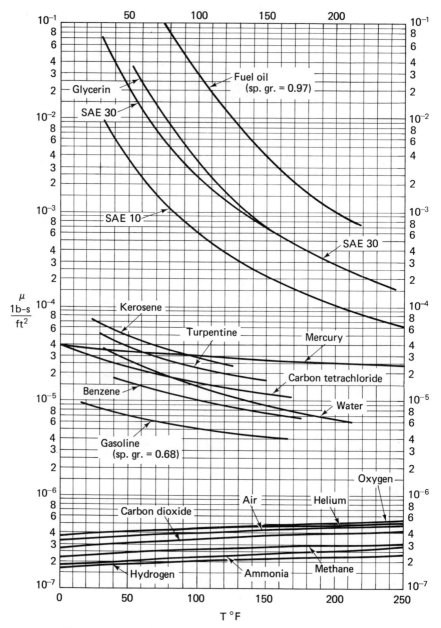

Fig. A-1. Dynamic viscosity of common Newtonian fluids. To get viscosity in units of N·s/m², multiply chart values by 47.88.

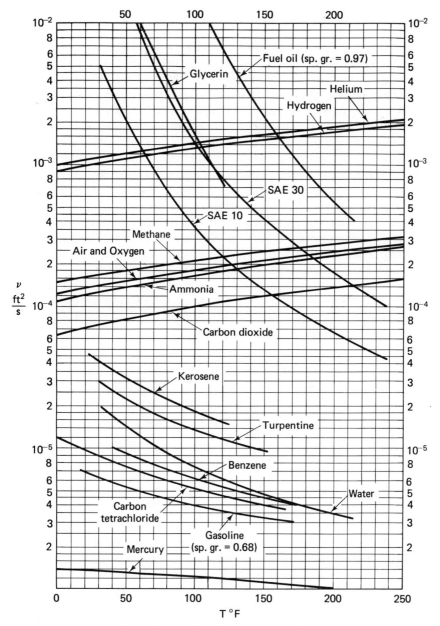

Fig. A-2. Kinematic viscosity of common Newtonian fluids. Gases are at atmospheric pressure. To get viscosity in units of m²/s, multiply chart values by 0.0929.

APPENDIX B SI UNITS

In addition to English units, this textbook employs SI or Système International units. Application of this system is relatively new; thus, the rules and abbreviations included herein are possibly subject to further modifications. This will be illustrated by the consideration of pressure units below.

The basic or primary units of the SI system used herein are the newton for force, the kilogram for mass and the meter for length, along with the kelvin absolute temperature scale. The secondary or derived units are composed from the primary units (e.g., work with dimensions of force times distance become the newton meter). Lowercase letters are used for all the units, whether or not the unit is named after a person. However, the abbreviation is an uppercase letter when the units bear a person's name. Thus, a force of 10 newtons will be written 10 N, a length of 3 meters is 3 m, and work equivalent to 30 newton meters is 30 N·m. Note that neither plurals nor periods are used in conjunction with the abbreviation, but when basic units are combined, a center dot should occur between the abbreviations.

For compactness, multiples and submultiples of the units are used in powers of 10. These generally follow a 10^{3n} rule, where n is a positive or negative integer. The prefixes used to express the multiples and the accepted abbreviations are given in Table B-1.

Table B-1 Prefixes for SI Units

Prefix	Symbol	Multiplying Factor
tera	T	10^{12}
giga	G	10^{9}
mega	M	10^{6}
kilo	k	10^{3}
milli	m	10^{-3}
micro	μ	10^{-6}
nano	n	10^{-9}
pico	p	10^{-12}

A force of 1,500,000 newtons may be written 1.5 meganewtons or 1.5 MN and a length of 0.0015 meters is 1.5 mm. According to the 10^{3n} rule the centimeter (10^{-2} m) is excluded from the SI system. Conceivably the centimeter will disappear with time, but because of its common usage, it is used in this text where convenient.

The following rules should also be kept in mind; only one prefix may be applied to a unit at a time, and it should be immediately adjacent to the unit, as shown in the example above. When the combination of basic units forms a quotient, such as for pressure (N/m^2), the prefix must be applied to the numerator. Thus, $150,000 \text{ N/m}^2$ becomes $150 \times 10^3 \text{ N/m}^3$ and hence 150 kN/m².

Certain of the derived units have been assigned specific names. Those which occur in this book include the following. The unit of work or energy is called the joule and is abbreviated J; $1 \text{ J} = 1 \text{ N·m}$. The unit of work equivalent to 1 J/s (or 1 N·m/s) is the watt (abbreviated W). The pascal (abbreviated Pa) is sometimes used as the unit of pressure. Then $1 \text{ Pa} = 1$ N/m². Another unit of pressure in common usage at present is the bar. Since $1 \text{ bar} = 10^5 \text{ N/m}^2$, it breaks the 10^{3n} rule and may disappear with time. Note that $150,000 \text{ N/m}^2 = 150 \text{ kN/n}^2 = 150 \text{ kPa} = 1.5$ bars.

Table B-2   Conversion Factors

To convert a quantity having dimensions of that in the left-hand column to that of the right-hand column, multiply by the conversion factor in the center column. To convert from the right-hand to the left-hand column, divide by the factor.

Quantity	English Units	Conversion Factor	SI Units
Length	ft	0.3048	m
Length	in.	25.4	mm
Length	mile (U.S. statute)	1609.3	m
Length	mile (nautical)	1852.	m
Area	ft²	0.0929	m²
Area	in.²	645.2	mm²
Volume	ft³	0.02832	m³
Volume	in.³	16,387	mm³
Velocity	ft/s	0.3048	m/s
Velocity	miles/hour	0.44704	m/s
Velocity	knot (nautical mile/hr)	0.51444	m/s
Acceleration	ft/s²	0.3048	m/s²
Mass	slug	14.594	kg
Density	slugs/ft³	515.38	kg/m³
Weight	lb	4.4482	N
Specific weight	lb/ft³	157.09	N/m³
Pressure	lb/ft²	47.88	N/m²
Pressure	psi	6894.8	N/m²
Energy, work	ft-lb	1.3558	joule (N·m)
Energy, work	Btu	1055.1	joule (N·m)
Power	ft-lb/s	1.3558	watt (N·m/s)
Power	horsepower	745.69	watt (N·m/s)
Absolute viscosity	lb-s/ft²	47.88	N·s/m²
Kinematic viscosity	ft²/s	0.0929	m²/s

APPENDIX C GEOMETRIC PROPERTIES

Table C-1   Geometric Properties of Plane Surfaces

Surface	Definition sketch	Area A	Location of centroid $\bar{y}$ or $\bar{x}$	Moment of inertia about centroidal axis $\bar{I}$
Rectangle		$A = ab$	$\bar{y} = \dfrac{a}{2}$	$\bar{I} = \dfrac{ba^3}{12}$
Triangle		$A = \dfrac{ab}{2}$	$\bar{y} = \dfrac{a}{3}$	$\bar{I} = \dfrac{ba^3}{36}$
Circle		$A = \dfrac{\pi D^2}{4}$	$\bar{y} = \dfrac{D}{2}$	$\bar{I} = \dfrac{\pi D^4}{64}$
Semicircle		$A = \dfrac{\pi D^2}{8}$	$\bar{y} = \dfrac{4r}{3\pi}$	$\bar{I} = \left(\dfrac{1}{4} - \dfrac{16}{9\pi^2}\right)\dfrac{\pi r^4}{2}$
Quarter circle		$A = \dfrac{\pi D^2}{16}$	$\bar{x} = \bar{y} = \dfrac{4r}{3\pi}$	$\bar{I} = \left(\dfrac{1}{4} - \dfrac{16}{9\pi^2}\right)\dfrac{\pi r^4}{4}$

Table C-1 (Continued)

Surface	Definition sketch	Area A	Location of centroid $\bar{y}$ or $\bar{x}$	Moment of inertia about centroidal axis $\bar{I}$
Ellipse		$A = \pi ab$	$\bar{y} = a$	$\bar{I} = \dfrac{\pi a^3 b}{4}$
Semi-ellipse		$A = \dfrac{\pi ab}{2}$	$\bar{y} = \dfrac{4a}{3\pi}$	$\bar{I} = \left(\dfrac{1}{4} - \dfrac{16}{9\pi^2}\right)\dfrac{\pi ba^3}{2}$
Quarter ellipse		$A = \dfrac{\pi ab}{4}$	$\bar{y} = \dfrac{4a}{3\pi}$ $\bar{x} = \dfrac{4b}{3\pi}$	$\bar{I} = \left(\dfrac{1}{4} - \dfrac{16}{9\pi^2}\right)\dfrac{\pi ba^3}{4}$
Parabola		$A = \dfrac{2ab}{3}$	$\bar{y} = \dfrac{3a}{5}$ $\bar{x} = \dfrac{3b}{8}$	$\bar{I} = \left(\dfrac{3}{7} - \dfrac{9}{25}\right)\dfrac{2ba^3}{3}$

Table C-2 Geometric Properties of Volumes

Volume	Definition sketch	Volume V	Location of centroid $\bar{y}$
Cylinder		$V = \dfrac{\pi D^2 a}{4}$	$\bar{y} = \dfrac{a}{2}$
Cone		$V = \dfrac{\pi D^2 a}{12}$	$\bar{y} = \dfrac{a}{4}$
Sphere		$V = \dfrac{\pi D^3}{6}$	$\bar{y} = \dfrac{D}{2}$
Hemi-sphere		$V = \dfrac{\pi D^3}{12}$	$\bar{y} = \dfrac{3r}{8}$
Paraboloid of revolution		$V = \dfrac{\pi D^2 a}{8}$	$\bar{y} = \dfrac{a}{3}$

APPENDIX D VECTOR OPERATIONS

The vector equations and operators used at various points in the book are summarized herein. A brief description is also included. For more information on the proofs of any of the equations, refer to any reference on vectors or vector calculus.[1]

A *vector* is a quantity that has both magnitude and direction. It may be expressed in terms of its components in any coordinate system (although only rectangular Cartesian coordinates will be used in this appendix). A *unit vector* is a vector with magnitude of unity.

Unit vectors in the x, y, and z directions of rectangular Cartesian coordinates are $\mathbf{i}, \mathbf{j}$, and $\mathbf{k}$, respectively, as shown in Fig. D-1. A vector $\mathbf{A}$ can be

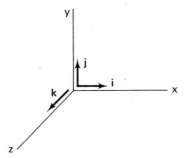

Fig. D-1. Unit vectors.

expressed in terms of its three components, A_x, A_y, and A_z[2] according to Eq. D-1 as

$$\mathbf{A} = A_x\mathbf{i} + A_y\mathbf{j} + A_z\mathbf{k} \tag{D-1}$$

The magnitude of $\mathbf{A}$ is

$$A = |\mathbf{A}| = \sqrt{A_x^2 + A_y^2 + A_z^2} \tag{D-2}$$

If $\mathbf{A}$ and $\mathbf{B}$ are two vectors, the quantity $\mathbf{A} \cdot \mathbf{B}$ is called the *scalar* or *dot product*. It is defined as the product of the magnitudes of the two vectors and the cosine of the smaller angle between them (Fig. D-2):

$$\mathbf{A} \cdot \mathbf{B} = AB \cos \theta \qquad 0 \le \theta \le \pi \tag{D-3}$$

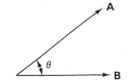

Fig. D-2. Scalar product definition sketch.

[1] Selected references are included at the end of this appendix.
[2] Here A_x, A_y, and A_z are the projections of $\mathbf{A}$ onto the x, y, and z axes, respectively.

The scalar product (so called because the result is a scalar rather than a vector quantity) may be determined from

$$\mathbf{A} \cdot \mathbf{B} = (A_x \mathbf{i} + A_y \mathbf{j} + A_z \mathbf{k}) \cdot (B_x \mathbf{i} + B_y \mathbf{j} + B_z \mathbf{k})$$

Upon multiplying each term in $\mathbf{A}$ by each of the terms in $\mathbf{B}$ and noting that $\mathbf{i} \cdot \mathbf{i} = 1, \mathbf{i} \cdot \mathbf{j} = 0$, and so on, according to Eq. D-3, we get

$$\mathbf{A} \cdot \mathbf{B} = A_x B_x + A_y B_y + A_z B_z \qquad \text{(D-4)}$$

Hence, the magnitude of $\mathbf{A}$ is $A = (\mathbf{A} \cdot \mathbf{A})^{1/2}$. Also, the scalar product of $\mathbf{A}$ and a unit vector in an arbitrary direction $\mathbf{n}$ is $\mathbf{A} \cdot \mathbf{n} = A \cos \theta$, which is the component of $\mathbf{A}$ in the $\mathbf{n}$ direction.

A second type of vector "multiplication" is the *vector* or *cross product*, written $\mathbf{A} \times \mathbf{B}$. This product is a vector quantity defined as the product of the magnitudes of the two vectors and the sine of the smaller angle between them. The direction of $\mathbf{A} \times \mathbf{B}$ is perpendicular to the plane of $\mathbf{A}$ and $\mathbf{B}$ such that if $\mathbf{C} = \mathbf{A} \times \mathbf{B}$, the vectors A, B, and C form a right-handed system (see Fig. D-3). Also, if

$$\mathbf{C} = \mathbf{A} \times \mathbf{B} \quad \text{then} \quad C = AB \sin \theta \qquad 0 < \theta < \pi \qquad \text{(D-5)}$$

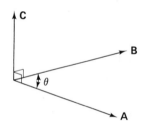

Fig. D-3.   Vector product definition sketch.

The cross product may be evaluated from the following determinant:

$$\mathbf{C} = \mathbf{A} \times \mathbf{B} = \begin{vmatrix} \mathbf{i} & \mathbf{j} & \mathbf{k} \\ A_x & A_y & A_z \\ B_x & B_y & B_z \end{vmatrix}$$

$$= \mathbf{i}(A_y B_z - A_z B_y) + \mathbf{j}(A_z B_x - A_x B_z) + \mathbf{k}(A_x B_y - A_y B_x)$$

It should be noted that $\mathbf{i} \times \mathbf{i} = 0, \mathbf{i} \times \mathbf{j} = \mathbf{k}$, and so on, and $\mathbf{A} \times \mathbf{B} = -\mathbf{B} \times \mathbf{A}$.

A single total or partial derivative of a vector quantity is essentially similar to the derivative of a scalar quantity. For example,

$$\frac{\partial \mathbf{A}}{\partial x} = \frac{\partial}{\partial x}(A_x \mathbf{i} + A_y \mathbf{j} + A_z \mathbf{k}) = \frac{\partial A_x}{\partial x}\mathbf{i} + \frac{\partial A_y}{\partial x}\mathbf{j} + \frac{\partial A_z}{\partial x}\mathbf{k}$$

The last step follows since the unit vectors in rectangular Cartesian coordinates do not change in either direction or magnitude.[3] Other derivatives can be introduced through the concept of the del operator. Written as ∇, it is defined as

$$\nabla(\ \ ) = \frac{\partial(\ \ )}{\partial x}\mathbf{i} + \frac{\partial(\ \ )}{\partial y}\mathbf{j} + \frac{\partial(\ \ )}{\partial z}\mathbf{k} \qquad \text{(D-6)}$$

It is incomplete as it stands and must, as its name implies, operate or act on some other quantity.

If the del operator acts upon a scalar T, it is written ∇T and read the *gradient* of T.[4] The gradient, which is a vector quantity, is obtained in rectangular Cartesian coordinates by insertion of the scalar quantity into Eq. D-6,

$$\nabla T = \frac{\partial T}{\partial x}\mathbf{i} + \frac{\partial T}{\partial y}\mathbf{j} + \frac{\partial T}{\partial z}\mathbf{k} \qquad \text{(D-7)}$$

The del operator may act on a vector to give a scalar quantity known as the *divergence*. The divergence is written $\nabla \cdot \mathbf{V}$ and read the divergence of $\mathbf{V}$.[5] It is defined somewhat similarly to the scalar product as follows:

$$\nabla \cdot \mathbf{V} = \left(\frac{\partial(\ \ )}{\partial x}\mathbf{i} + \frac{\partial(\ \ )}{\partial y}\mathbf{j} + \frac{\partial(\ \ )}{\partial z}\mathbf{k}\right) \cdot (A_x\mathbf{i} + A_y\mathbf{j} + A_z\mathbf{k})$$
$$= \frac{\partial A_x}{\partial x} + \frac{\partial A_y}{\partial y} + \frac{\partial A_z}{\partial z} \qquad \text{(D-8)}$$

The del operator may also act on a vector to yield a vector quantity. This result, called the *curl* of a vector, is written $\nabla \times \mathbf{A}$ and read the curl of $\mathbf{A}$.[6] Obtained similar to the vector product, it is defined by

$$\nabla \times \mathbf{A} = \left(\frac{\partial(\ \ )}{\partial x}\mathbf{i} + \frac{\partial(\ \ )}{\partial y}\mathbf{j} + \frac{\partial(\ \ )}{\partial z}\mathbf{k}\right) \times (A_x\mathbf{i} + A_y\mathbf{j} + A_z\mathbf{k})$$

$$= \begin{vmatrix} \mathbf{i} & \mathbf{j} & \mathbf{k} \\ \dfrac{\partial}{\partial x} & \dfrac{\partial}{\partial y} & \dfrac{\partial}{\partial z} \\ A_x & A_y & A_z \end{vmatrix} \qquad \text{(D-9)}$$

$$= \left(\frac{\partial A_z}{\partial y} - \frac{\partial A_y}{\partial z}\right)\mathbf{i} + \left(\frac{\partial A_x}{\partial z} - \frac{\partial A_z}{\partial x}\right)\mathbf{j} + \left(\frac{\partial A_y}{\partial x} - \frac{\partial A_x}{\partial y}\right)\mathbf{k}$$

Although no attempt is made here to list all the formulas involving the del operator, it should be noted that the divergence of the gradient of a scalar

---

[3]This does not follow for all coordinate systems. In cylindrical or spherical coordinate systems the unit vectors do change in direction, and the derivatives that take this into account are correspondingly more complicated.

[4]In lieu of ∇T, the gradient is sometimes written grad T.

[5]Alternatively, $\nabla \cdot \mathbf{V}$ is sometimes written Div V.

[6]The quantity $\nabla \times \mathbf{A}$ is also known as the *rotation* of **A**. It is also written as curl **A** or rot **A** in lieu of $\nabla \times \mathbf{A}$.

leads to

$$\nabla \cdot (\nabla T) = \left(\frac{\partial(\ )}{\partial x}\mathbf{i} + \frac{\partial(\ )}{\partial y}\mathbf{j} + \frac{\partial(\ )}{\partial z}\mathbf{k}\right) \cdot \left(\frac{\partial T}{\partial x}\mathbf{i} + \frac{\partial T}{\partial y}\mathbf{j} + \frac{\partial T}{\partial z}\mathbf{k}\right)$$

$$= \frac{\partial^2 T}{\partial x^2} + \frac{\partial^2 T}{\partial y^2} + \frac{\partial^2 T}{\partial z^2} = \nabla^2 T$$

(D-10)

The result is defined as the Laplacian of T and written $\nabla^2 T$. Alternatively, the Laplace operator is

$$\nabla^2(\ ) = \frac{\partial^2(\ )}{\partial x^2} + \frac{\partial^2(\ )}{\partial y^2} + \frac{\partial^2(\ )}{\partial z^2}$$

(D-11)

When the Laplacian is equal to zero, the result (e.g., $\nabla^2 T = 0$) is the important Laplacian equation.

Two vector theorems are particularly important in fluid mechanics. The first is the *theorem of Gauss*, which changes surface integrals into volume integrals, and vice versa. If V is a volume bounded by a surface S and $\mathbf{B}$ is a vector quantity, the theorem of Gauss states that

$$\iint_S \mathbf{B} \cdot d\mathbf{A} = \iiint_V \nabla \cdot \mathbf{B} \, dV$$

(D-12)

where $d\mathbf{A}$ is a differential area on the surface S having a magnitude dA and a direction outward from and normal to the surface.

The second theorem, known as *Stokes' theorem*, changes line integrals into surface integrals, and vice versa. If C is a closed contour around a surface S,

$$\oint_C \mathbf{B} \cdot d\mathbf{x} = \iint_S (\nabla \times \mathbf{B}) \cdot d\mathbf{A}$$

(D-13)

The vectors $\mathbf{B}$ and $d\mathbf{A}$ are as defined for Eq D-12 while $d\mathbf{x}$ is a differential length along the contour C having length of dx and a positive direction along the contour such that in passing around the contour the surface S is always on the left.

REFERENCES

MOON, P., and D. E. SPENCER, *Field Theory for Engineers*. New York: Van Nostrand, 1961.

SPIEGEL, M. R., *Theory and Problems of Vector Analysis*. New York: Schaum, 1959.

WYLIE, C. R., *Advanced Engineering Mathematics*, 4th ed. New York: McGraw-Hill, 1975.

Answers To Odd-Numbered Problems

CHAPTER 1

1-1	(a) L; (b) 1; (c) F/L^2, M/LT^2; (d) F/L^2, M/LT^2
1-3	All dimensionless
1-5	$C \sim L^{1/2}/T$
1-7	d, e, f
1-9	1.88 slugs/ft^3
1-11	968 kg/m^3
1-13	1.201 kg/m^3; 1.201 $\times$ 10^{-3} g/cm^3
1-15	196.5 psia
1-17	3.64 $\times$ 10^{-5} ft^2/s
1-19	1.33 $\times$ 10^{-5} ft^2/s; 1.24 $\times$ 10^{-6} m^2/s
1-21	0.00050 lb·s/ft^2 (106°F)
1-23	9160 N
1-25	(a) 5.99 $\times$ 10^{-3} N·m; (b) 0.331 N·m; (c) 1.26 $\times$ 10^5 n·m
1-27	(a) 47.34 kN/m^2; (b) 19.92 kN/m^2
1-29	0.0198 m
1-33	7.0 $\times$ 10^6 N/m^2

CHAPTER 2

2-3	(a) 1.69 MN/m^2 (abs); (b) -100 kN/m^2; (c) -50 kN/m^2; (d) 1.0 bar (abs)
2-5	(a) 124.8 psf; (b) 1691 psf
2-7	1.52 m
2-9	Plot, 586 psf at 10 ft
2-11	(a) 5.85 $\times$ 10^5 N/m^2, 84.9 psi; (b) 5.54 $\times$ 10^5 N/m^2, 80.4 psi; (c) 6.70 $\times$ 10^5 N/m^2, 97.1 psi
2-13	12.04 psia; 12.23 psia
2-15	3.40 psia
2-17	Plot, 1.11 kN/m^2 (abs) at 30,000 m
2-19	5.63 psi
2-21	-2.60 psi
2.23	(a) 0.361 psi; (b) 0.292 psi
2-25	(a) 5.89 psi; (b) -0.0885 psi
2-27	(a) 0.432 psi (b) -0.508 psi
2-29	(a) 2.31 psi; (b) 3.90 psi
2-31	4.46 psi
2-33	37.39 ft; 32.77 ft
2-35	31.26 ft
2-37	0.638 m by 6.38 m
2-39	245 MN
2-41	11,230 lb
2-43	3.80 m
2-45	49.0 MN; 13.33 m (along slope)
2-47	10.36 ft
2-49	14,040 lb; 20 ft (along slope)
2-51	5616 lb
2-53	134,800 lb at 4.67 ft above bottom; 211,700 lb at 0.85 ft left of center
2-55	249,600 lb; 187,200 lb; 285,200 lb; 98,000 lb
2-57	4170 N
2-59	29,300 N
2-61	154,100 ft^3
2-63	249 m^3
2-65	513 N up; 7537 N down
2-67	328 N
2-69	0.646 ft
2-71	Submerged: A 0.515 N, B 18 N; Half-submerged: A 0.686 N, B 18 N
2-73	Not stable
2-77	0.256 ft. below G; Not stable

CHAPTER 3

3-1	4.47; 10.25
3-3	24.05 ft/s at 32.3°
3-5	9.58 m/s at 8.46°
3-7	33.5 cfs; 16.8 ft/s
3-9	0.618 m
3-11	(4/3) $B u_{max}$
3-13	$a_x = 20$ ft/s^2; $a_y = 1$ ft/s^2; $a_z = 4$ ft/s^2; $a = 20.42$ ft/s^2
3-15	55.9 m/s^2

3-17 -33 ft/s^2; 8 ft/s^2; 0
3-19 0; -1.13 m/s^2
3-21 24.5 m/s
3-25 1.54 m/s; 0; 0.075 m/s

CHAPTER 4

4-3 Yes
4-5 Yes
4-11 0.281
4-13 24 m/s; 54 m/s
4-17 1.07 mm

CHAPTER 5

5-5 y_0 at all points
5-9 46.6 ft^3; 1.51 psi; 0.92 psi
5-11 12.9 ft/s^2; 1.51 psi; 0
5-13 6.41 m/s^2
5-15 29.9 kN
5-17 0.433 psi
5-19 13,500 N/m^2
5-21 8720 N/m^2; 39,900 N/m^2
5-23 0.117 psi
5-25 251 ft/s
5-27 20.02 psi
5-29 80.1 ft/s both cases
5-31 1.73 psi
5-33 0.0407 m^3/s
5-35 0.606 m^3/s
5-37 41.3 ft; 61.4 ft/s; 196.8 ft.
5-39 14.08 m
5-41 1.83 cfs
5-43 15.34 m/s; 9.59 cm
5-45 26.35 m; 125.6 m; 35.37 m/s at 40°
5-47 $y_1 = y_2 = 2.68$ m
5-49 11.13 psi
5-51 0.560 cfs; 102.6 ft/s
5-57 $y_1 = 3.127$ m; $y_2 = 1.564$ m; $V_1 = 3.20$ m/s; $V_2 = 6.40$ m/s
5-59 17.26 cfs; 40.1 psi

5-61 0.984 m^3/s; 5.89 $\times$ 10^5 N/m^2; 3.87 $\times$ 10^5 N/m^2; 0
5-63 0.787m^3/s
5-65 At A if $\geqslant$ 2033 ft; At B if $\geqslant$ 33.3 ft
5-67 41.9 cfs
5-69 24.9 kW; 43.1 kW; 48.1 kW
5-71 1.20
5-73 902 lb ; 73.7 ft/s at 7.8°
5-75 3142 N, 20 m/s (vertical); 4909 N, 25.5 m/s at 11.3°
5-77 $\rho q\, V_0 \sin\theta$
5-79 154.3 lb ; 20 ft/s
5-81 223.5 lb
5-83 4977 N; 7090 N
5-85 147,000 lb/ft
5-87 474 lb; 338 lb
5-89 $V_1 = 5.68$ m/s; $y_2 = 1.05$ m; 1.14 m^3/s
5-91 1595 N/s
5-93 11.18 m
5-95 15.59 N•m; 16.36 N•m

CHAPTER 6

6-1 $Q = d^2\sqrt{\Delta p/\rho}\,\phi\,(d/D)$
6-3 $Q = d^2\sqrt{\Delta p/\rho}\,\phi\,(d/D,\ E/\Delta p)$
6-5 $F = \rho a^2\,V^2\phi\,(a/L,\ \theta,\ Va\rho/\mu,\ V^2/E/\rho)$
6-7 $F = \rho\,a^2\,V^2\,\phi\,(a/L,\ \theta,\ Va\rho/\mu)$
6-9 $q = g^{1/2}H^{3/2}\phi\,(H/P,\ q\,\rho/\mu)$
6-11 $P = \rho L^2 V^3\phi\,(VL\rho/\mu,\ V^2\rho/L\,\gamma)$
6-13 $F_{L,\,D} = \rho\,L^2\,V^2\,\phi_{1,2}\,(E/\rho V^2)$
6-15 2.5 m/s
6-17 57.9 ft/s
6-19 1.50 cfs
6-21 2 ft/s; 308,000 lb ; 11,200 hp
6-23 3790 ft/s
6-25 (a) L_p/L_m; (b) $(L_m/L_p)^{1/2}$; (c) $(L_m/L_p)_{1/2}$; (d) $(L_m/L_p)^2$
6-27 3.76 min

CHAPTER 7

7-1	12.47 gpm/ft; 0.60 psf
7-3	0.289 B
7-5	2.94 cfs
7-7	0.188 m³/s; 0.714 m³/s
7-9	7840 psi; 91.5 hp
7-11	166 kN/m²; 20.7 N/m²
7-13	54.2 psi
7-15	25.41 ft/s, B to A
7-17	3.41×10^{-7} cfs = 0.22 gpd
7-19	$p = 0$ throughout
7-21	$u = V_1 y/B + V_1/2; \mu V_1/B$
7-25	46.3 kN/m²
7-31	Plot, $l = 0.141$ ft at $y = 0.5$ ft

CHAPTER 8

8-1	3.26×10^5
8-3	$10^5; 3.5 \times 10^5$
8-5	8.06×10^{-7} m²/s
8-7	15.96 m/s
8-9	0.59 m
8-11	0.0053 ft
8-13	6.65 ft
8-15	$\tau_0 = 8.35 \times 10^{-4}$ psf; $\nu = 2.56 \times 10^{-5}$ ft²/s; 2.2×10^{-4} ft; 3.1×10^{-3} ft.
8-17	$\tau_0 = 0.986 \rho; \delta' = 3.55 \times 10^{-3}$ ft.; $u = 11.54$ ft/s
8-19	0.05 mm; 0.70 mm
8-23	0.00023 m; 3.43 m/s
8-25	206.8 ft
8-29	80.11 ft water
8-31	29.43 N/m²
8-33	0.330 cfs
8-37	9.46 to 7.89 cfs
8-45	4.56 m
8-49	630 ft
8-51	0.0635 m³/s; 0.1865 m³/s
8-55	2.35 psf
8-59	229 cfs
8-63	307 cfs

8-65	20.6 m³/s
8-71	$n = 0.008$
8-73	1.12 cfs
8-75	10.87 cfs; 9.10 cfs; 8.30 cfs
8-77	0.216 m³/s

CHAPTER 9

9-1	(c) 0.0104 psf; 0.0366 psf
9-5	0.111 m/s
9-7	2.14 ft; 0.28 ft
9-9	0.664 m; 0.065 m
9-11	3824 N
9-13	65.9 lb
9-15	625 N
9-17	1.26 lb
9-19	0.252 ft/s or 0.0768 m/s
9-21	43.6 ft/s
9-23	19.9 ft/s
9-25	70.0 ft
9-27	206 N
9-29	Plot, $C_L/C_D = 19$ at $= 4°$
9-33	2705 N

CHAPTER 10

10-1	0.026
10-3	9.32 ft
10-5	18.46 ft
10-7	7.35 kN/m²
10-9	61,200 cfs; 79%
10-11	11,300 m³/s
10-29	1.06 m/s; 1.04 m/s; 0.99 m/s
10-31	2.3%; 6.9%
10-33	12.40 ft/s
10-35	21.9 ft/s
10-37	$y_2 = 24.4$ ft; $L = 139$ ft; $\Delta P = 59,600$ hp
10-39	2.98; 0.41
10-41	$Fr_1 = 6.0$; 18.79 m³/s/m; $Fr_2 = 0.27$
10-43	$V_S = 2.76$ m/s; $y_2 = 2.69$ m

CHAPTER 11

11-1   (a) 4943 ft/s; (b) 1160 ft/s
11-5   5.49 s
11-7   22.2°
11-9   244.3 psf; 4.8%
11-11   0.0627 ft
11-13   152.6 kN/m² (abs); 1 °C
11-15   355 mm Hg (Vac.)
11-17   27.84 psia; 55.68 psia
11-19   0.101 m; 0.0986 m
11-21 $G = 14.34$ kg/s; $Ma_1 = 0.324$; $Ma_2 = 0.736$
11-23   72.05 psia; 1162 ft/s; 191 °F
11-25 $T_1 = 20$ °C; $T_2 = 209$ °C
11-27 $\rho_2 = 0.0110$ slugs/ft³; $\rho_1 = 0.00491$ slugs/ft³; $V_1 = 1921$ ft/s; $p_1 = 30.1$ psia; $T_1 = 54$ °F
11-29   540 psia; 0.246 slugs/s; 7352 ft/s
11-31   24.3 mm; − 19 °C
11-33 $P_2 = 89.05$ psia; $Ma_2 = 0.411$; $T_2 = 227$ °F
11-35   (a) 140 psia, 571 ft/s; (b) No solution
11-39   23.7 psia; 639.4 m
11-41 $G = 34.96$ kg/s; $Ma_1 = 0.227$; $Ma_2 = 0.454$
11-43   724 lb
11-47   Plot, $F_D = 372,000$ N at Ma = 4

CHAPTER 12

12-1   0
12-3   Irrotational
12-5 $4 + 4/r^4$
12-9   2.32 ft/s; 0.39 ft/s
12-25   Yes
12-27   No
12-29   Yes; $u = 3x^2y − y^3$; $v = x^3 − 3xy^2$; x (psi) $= 3x^2y^2/2 − (x^4 + y^4)/4$
12-31 $\phi = x^2 − 2xy − y^2$; x (psi) $= x^2 + 2xy − y^2$

12-33   1.69 ft/s
12-37   − 1.41 ft.

CHAPTER 13

13-1   (a) 296 gpm, 35.6 ft; (b) 2370 gpm, 142.2 ft
13-3   84.0%; 0.127 m³/s
13-5   (a) 0.032 m³/s, 4.96 m; (b) 0.064 m³/s, 19.84m
13-7   (a) 2800 rpm, 48m; (b) 560 rpm, 1.92 m
13-9   87.3%; 89.4%
13-11   128.3 in.; 250 rpm; 3193 hp
13-13   3.75 m; 0.15 m³/s; 4.38 kW
13-15   10.8 in.
13-17   60.6; Francis turbine
13-19   2128; radial flow pump
13-21   545; radial flow pump
13-25   140 cfs; 7.88 ft
13-27   5 wheels; 4.88 ft; 8 jets
13-29   26,100 kW; 116.1 rpm; 5.69 m; 88.8%
13-31   4.16 ft
13-33   12,155 hp; 112.6 rpm
13-35 6.84×10^5 ft-lb; 16,750 hp
13-37 $V_1 = 79.88$ ft/s; $\theta_1 = 41.6°$; $V_2 = 117.7$ ft/s; $\theta_2 = 137.5°$
13-39   141.2°; 168.4°; 140.9°
13-41   65.9 hp
13-43   153.4°; 91.7 hp
13-47   440 gpm; 10.53 hp
13-51   − 13.24 ft
13-53   12.12 ft
13-57   2159 lb; 86.4%; 36 ft/s
13-59 $D_1 = 2.71$m; $D_4 = 2.33$m; Δp $= 2037$ N/m²
13-61   797 hp; 8220 lb

CHAPTER 14

14-1   1.422 ft
14-3   0.0466 m
14-5   51.7 ft/s

14-7 19.66 ft/s

14-9 49.5 ft/s

14-11 34.67 m/s

14-13 (a) 20 s; (b) 40 s

14-15 $u = 2.7$ ft/s; $u = 0.33$ ft/s

14-17 0.185 m³/s; ± 1.4 ℓ/s

14-19 3.616 m

14-21 115.1 lb/s; 1.84 cfs

14-23 16.39 m

14-25 0.144 cfs

14-27 (a) 5.64 × 10⁻³ m³/s; (b) 5.53 × 10⁻³ m³/s

14-29 0.0516 m³/s

14-31 $Q = 0.606 \Delta h^{0.5}$

14-33 (a) 0.0117 cfs/ft; (b) 0.301 cfs/ft (c) 11.19 cfs/ft

14-35 (a) 0; (b) 0; (c) 7.1%

14.39 0.48 ft

14-41 0.0561 m³/s

Index

Gas constant, 8, 530
Gases:
  adiabatic flow of, 358-80
  equation of state for, 8
  isentropic flow of, 360-71, 376-80
  isothermal flow of, 380-86
  properties of, 530-31, 534-35
Gas laws, 8, 16, 359
Gate valve, loss due to, 273
Gauss's theorem, 102, 594
Generator, number of poles, 452
Geometric properties, 538-40
Geometric similitude, 191-92
Globe valve, loss due to, 273
Gradient, 543
Gradually varied flow, 337-47
  step method, 343
Gravitational acceleration, 7-8
Guide vanes, 449, 476

H

Hammitt, F., 20
Hardy Cross method, 263
Hazen-Williams equation, 266
Head:
  change in, 144-46
  developed by pump, 144-46, 479
  elevation, 115
  loss, 141, 246, 255
  piezometric, 113, 115
  pressure, 115
  total, 121
  on turbine, 144-46, 474
  utilized, 478
  velocity, 121
Heat transfer, 141
Heel angle, 50-51
Hele-Shaw technique, 433
Henderson, F. M., 352, 525
Hickox, G. H., 201
Hinze, J. O., 230
Holt, M., 201
Homologous machines, 461
Hook gage, 496-97
Hot-film anemometer, 502-4

Hot-wire anemometer, 502-3
Howe, J. W., 525
Hump, effect of, 322-23
Hydraulically rough, 242
Hydraulically smooth, 242
Hydraulic efficiency, 463, 478
Hydraulic jump, 158-60, 194-95, 333-35
  head loss in 334-35
  length of, 334
  location of, 346-47
Hydraulic models, 194-98
Hydraulic radius, 263-64
Hydraulics, 2
Hydrostatics, 21-51

I

Ideal fluid, 396
Ideal fluid flow, 396-43
Ideal velocity, 508-9
Impact tube, 399
Impeller, 456-59
Impulse turbine (*see* Turbine, impulse)
Ince, S., 20, 181
Inclined manometer, 34
Induced angle of attack, 308-9
Induced drag, 307-9
Inertia, moment of, 38-39 50-51, 538-39
Instantaneous velocity, 87, 220
Internal energy, 133
International system (SI) of units,
      526-28, 536-37
Irrotational flow, 396-402
Irrotational vortex, 400-1, 403-5, 427-28
Isentropic flow, 360-71, 376-80
Isentropic process, 360
Isothermal flow, 380-86
Isothermal process, 16

J

Jet, 128-130
  definition of, 128
  force of, 153-55, 160-61, 472-73
  power of, 473